MY SCHOOLS AND

Hugh Miller was born in Cromarty in 1802. He originally worked as a stonemason, and later as an accountant, journalist and editor of *The Witness*. His pioneering work in the field of geology was recognised throughout the world, while in Britain his writing on many subjects made him one of the best known of Victorian literary figures. He committed suicide in 1856, only two years after completing *My Schools and Schoolmasters*.

James Robertson studied history at Edinburgh University, later returning to complete a doctorate on the works of Sir Walter Scott. His critically acclaimed first collection of short stories, *Close*, was published in 1991 and his second collection, *The Ragged Man's Complaint*, will be published in 1993. James Robertson is the first holder of the Brownsbank Writing Fellowship based at the former home of Hugh MacDiarmid near Biggar.

MY SCHOOLS AND SCHOOLMASTERS

OR THE STORY OF MY EDUCATION

HUGH MILLER

Edited and Introduced by
Dr James Robertson

EDINBURGH
B&W PUBLISHING
1993

First published 1854
This edition published 1993
by B&W Publishing
Edinburgh
Introduction © James Robertson 1993
ISBN 1 873631 18 9

The publisher acknowledges subsidy
from the Scottish Arts Council towards
the publication of this volume.

British Library Cataloguing in Publication Data:
A catalogue record for this book is available from
the British Library

Cover design by Harry Palmer
Cover photograph: Hugh Miller by Hill & Adamson
by kind permission of the Scottish National Portrait Gallery.

Printed by Werner Söderström

INTRODUCTION
by Dr James Robertson

Hugh Miller must rate as one of the most extraordinary of the many extraordinary minds Scotland has produced. He rose, if not from absolute poverty, certainly from a modest background, to become both a specialist in the field of geology and a generalist in the wider literary world, covering, as writer and editor, subjects as diverse as poetry, folklore, science, education, religion, history and travel; while in his working life he was a stonemason, banking accountant, journalist, editor, lecturer and defender of Christianity against the evolutionists. His prodigious output made him among the best-known of Victorian literary figures, admired by the likes of Thomas Carlyle, Charles Dickens and John Ruskin. By the latter part of the 19th century, his reputation extended across the world: his books were widely translated, and in America, according to the geologist Sir Archibald Geikie, "they were to be found in the remotest log huts of the Far West". Certainly they were known to the great environmentalist John Muir, who emigrated from Dunbar to Wisconsin at the age of eleven, and whose self-taught genius in so many ways resembles that of Miller. In 1879 Muir named one of the glaciers of Glacier Bay, Alaska, after the Cromarty stonemason.

Throughout his life and writings Miller demonstrated a strong belief in his own capabilities, tempered with a certain humility and a reluctance to expose himself to criticism. He was, in fact, the practical example of his own philosophy that the working man could and should have pride in his own trade and station, and that he should put faith in education rather than revolution as a means of improving his lot. For Miller, the idea of revolution was destructive and harmful. Far better to rely on self-help and hard work in spite of the obvious injustices of society. This—as the opening lines of *The Old Red Sandstone* attest—was the guiding principle of his life: do not, he advised others, let the upper classes get ahead of you in intelligence, for there is no reason why a working man should not be the moral and intellectual equal—or superior—of any gentleman.

So assured was he of this that he remained politically as well as religiously conservative throughout his life, relying on a sense of justice and decency for measuring the state of society. On matters such as the emancipation of slaves, the tolerance of Catholicism, electoral and political reform, and the social and economic conditions of the poor and oppressed, he was not a liberal by political inclination but rather a radical by the principle of humanity. He became the scourge of landowners who cleared the population of the Highlands for sheep, and of unscrupulous employers who practised cruelties such as the use of children for chimney-sweeping. He seemed completely confident in what he wrote both about himself and the times in which he lived, and yet, at the height of his success, at the age of fifty-four (suffering from brain disease and weakened lungs, and certainly under great emotional and intellectual stress) Miller took his own life with a revolver, to widespread public horror and dismay.

To offer a biographical sketch of him here would be merely to pre-empt his own delightful account, which is the best authority on his life, at least as far as December 1839 when he took up the editorship of *The Witness*. A succinct and thought-provoking biographical essay appeared in George Rosie's introduction to a selection of Miller's writings, published as *Hugh Miller: Outrage and Order* (Mainstream, Edinburgh, 1981; now out of print). Rosie skilfully describes the various facets of Miller's personality, the apparent contradictions of which might seem not untypical of the characteristics of the wider community of early 19th-century Scotland:

He was . . . a romantic Scottish nationalist who deeply approved of the Union with England, a trained and highly-skilled bank officer who penned fanciful stories and sentimental verse, a fierce Presby-

terian who was in favour of Catholic emancipation, a devout
Christian who argued for secular education. Miller was a radically-
inclined journalist who savaged the gentry, but who despised the
Chartists and Socialists, a man of the people who saved some of his
bleakest words for the unruly Scottish working class. Miller was a
hard-working scientist with a powerful undertow of mysticism in his
make-up, a level-headed researcher who saw ghosts and phantoms.
Even Miller's physique was a paradox; he was a big burly, well set-
up man, proud of his physical strength, whose lungs were rotting
from silicosis, and whose brain was diseased, either from cerebral
syphilis or tumour.[1]

One could elaborate on this portrait by contrasting the "Celtic"
and "Saxon" elements of his background. Cromarty, his birth-
place, was a prosperous and important manufacturing town with
a fine deep anchorage protected from the open sea by the North
and South Sutors, a natural gateway to both the rich lowland
farming country of the Black Isle and the Gaelic-speaking
Highlands on the north side of the Cromarty Firth. Miller was
himself the product of a union between, as he termed it, the Saxon
blood of his father's family and the Celtic blood of his mother's.
Much of his adult personality seems the very antithesis of the
feyness and superstition so often stereotyped as the mark of the
Highlander, yet in truth his fascination with folklore and the
supernatural was complementary to his perception that belief
systems were commonly devised to explain mysteries beyond the
understanding of uninformed minds. His first major book, *Scenes
and Legends of the North of Scotland; or, The Traditional History
of Cromarty* (1835), was, as its title suggests, a cunning mix of the
fantastic and fanciful with the historical, and showed a shrewd yet
artistic mind at work. In Chapter IX of *My Schools and
Schoolmasters* Miller relates his strange encounter with one Isabel
"Mad Bell" Mackenzie, who in the lucid periods between her
bursts of wildness identified something attractive to her in the

---

[1] *Hugh Miller: Outrage and Order*, p16

young apprentice:

> For some little time she stood beside me without speaking, and then somewhat abruptly asked—"What makes *you* work as a mason?" I made some commonplace reply; but it failed to satisfy her. "All your fellows are real masons," she said; "but you are merely in the disguise of a mason; and I have come to consult you about the deep matters of your soul."

This seemingly random remark gives a wonderful insight into Miller, not least because of the importance he clearly attached to it. It reminds us that, after all, "Saxon" and "Celtic" are only convenient but misleading bits of shorthand, and that the combination of pragmatism and science with imagination and philosophy is hardly unusual in human behaviour.

His suicide[1] brought to a close the career of a man who had made advances in geological knowledge through his own self-education that contemporary "experts" in the field could only applaud. Neal Ascherson has described him as "a tragic intellectual hero" who "volunteered to cover God's retreat, to hold off as

---

[1] The circumstances of Miller's death have their own morbid fascination, especially since, as a writer, he himself would have seized upon them as curious in the extreme. He had latterly become paranoid about his own and his family's safety, and kept an arsenal of weapons in the house. He had also been suffering from terrible dreams, fevers, and fits of dizziness and nausea. The day before he killed himself he told his doctor of the previous night's visitation: "I felt as if I had been ridden by a witch for fifty miles, and rose more weary in mind and body than when I lay down." Early next morning, on Christmas Eve, 1856, he woke in anguish, scribbled a farewell note to his wife which spoke of horror and a burning agony in his brain, and shot himself with the revolver which, in his paranoia, he carried with him at all times. Far to the north in Cromarty, as she afterwards recounted, his mother sat up in bed and saw a ball of bright light suspended in the air, which, after moving round the room as if seeking a place to rest, stopped and faded into nothing, leaving the old woman in utter darkness and convinced of the occurrence of "a sudden and awful calamity."

A crowd of some 4000 turned out on a bleak 29th December for the funeral procession, which led from the Miller home in Portobello to the Grange Cemetery in Edinburgh. Shops along the route were closed to mark the passing of a man of national stature. A little earlier in the same cemetery, the burial had taken place of Thomas Leslie, an Edinburgh gunsmith. The six-shot revolver which Miller had fired into his chest had afterwards fallen from his hand into the bath, and was not removed until it had lain for several hours rusting in the

long as he was able the encroaching armies of scientific materialism."[1] Indeed it is natural to see him in this light—as Stewart Conn did in his play *Hugh Miller*, first performed in Edinburgh in 1988—as a vast intellect tortured by the evidence of its own discoveries, struggling until the end to reconcile the irreconcilable—his belief in God's creation with the proof of evolution apparently contained in the rocks he examined. The posthumously published *Testimony of the Rocks* was his most sustained attempt at this task, but, as George Rosie has pointed out, he had already identified the weak link in the evolutionists' armour in *Footprints of the Creator* (1849). Miller found no paelaeontological proof that lower species graduated slowly over vast amounts of time to higher species. One class of fossils from one geological age, he maintained, bore absolutely distinctive characteristics from another class from another age. If change occurred, he could only conclude, it changed very fast indeed—and, for him, this simply reaffirmed his belief that God at different stages created entirely or substantially different creatures. He was not a "fundamentalist" in the current sense of that misapplied word: he did not believe in the literal truth of Genesis, but saw the Creation story as an allegory, with each day representing aeons. What he did believe was that God, at the end of a chain of manufacturing, had created mammals and, last of all, man. The precise "moment" of evolution, or the pace of such change, is a problem unresolved to this day.

Miller's most popular and successful works, *My Schools and Schoolmasters* and *The Old Red Sandstone*, ran to many editions,

[1] *Hugh Miller: Outrage and Order*, p10

water. Miller's friend, Professor James Miller, one of four doctors who performed a post-mortem and found evidence of brain disease, with great care took the weapon back to Alexander Thomson & Son, the gunsmith's where Miller had bought it, on 26th December. It was the lunch hour, and Thomas Leslie, a foreman who had worked there twenty-five years, was in charge. The Professor wanted to know how many shots had been fired. "Mind it is loaded," he said, handing the gun to Leslie. In raising the hammer, and turning the gun away from the Professor in order to count the bullets in the chamber, the gun went off, sending a bullet straight through Leslie's right eye, killing him instantly.

and the latter was still being reprinted in J.M. Dent's Everyman Classics series as late as 1922. It was an early example of science written for (and of course, coincidentally, *by*) the layman, and was as successful in its time as books today by the likes of Stephen Jay Gould or Richard Dawkins. Again, stereotypes are confounded by the fact that the first third of *The Old Red Sandstone* appeared in serialised form in *The Witness*, a theological paper and the mouthpiece of the anti-patronage party (which later went on to form the Free Church after the Disruption of 1843). Whatever the Free Church has since come to represent to those outwith it, in Miller's day it stood for freedom for Presbyterians to choose their own Ministers without the interference of landowners, for rigorous social and political debate, and for a profound defence of the rights of Scotland within the Union. In all of these areas Miller was well able to mount an articulate and intelligent argument.

My Schools and Schoolmasters is not simply an autobiography, but, as he explains in the preface, "a sort of educational treatise, thrown into the narrative form, and addressed more especially to working men." The first twenty chapters appeared in instalments every Saturday in *The Witness* from June 1853, and the following year the whole book was published. Miller was fifty, and looking back on a life of great change and achievement. He was too much a man of application merely to have recorded the incidents of his life, as if they in themselves were of the slightest significance in the scheme of things. As an earlier editor of the book, W.M. Mackenzie, wrote, Miller was "a literary man writing with a purpose."

It is no mere summary of leading events, or series of unimpassioned jottings directed by psychological interest, but a carefully planned, consecutive, skilfully fashioned and charmingly written narrative, scarcely ever tending to diffusiveness save in some passages of inevitable moralising. Fully aware of the peculiar perils of this form of composition—such as that expressed by Hume in his own case: "It is difficult for a man to speak long of himself without vanity"—Hugh Miller, in spirit, for all his self-consciousness, avoids this besetting danger by his frankness and essential simplicity of mind; and formally, by giving his autobiography an impersonal note, presenting it as primarily an account not of himself, but of his "schools and schoolmasters." Its further intention is to help in a cause always dear to his heart—"that of rousing the humble classes to the important work of self-culture and self-government"—and incidentally to throw light, for those above them, on their conditions of living. His pictures of humble life, north and south, are invaluable documents. For all that, he cannot help that he himself is at once the real theme of his book and the most enduring and effective part of its teaching.[1]

Some of Miller's work has a religiosity, even a pomposity about it, which is a little hard to take. There are occasions in the autobiography (for instance in the passages in Chapter XV, about his time at Niddry) when he comes across as rather stuffy and pedagogic, but the quality of the prose carries him through, revealing at the same time something of his own vulnerability. By and large, however, the book is quite free of tediousness. Its weakest parts are the reproductions of his verse, which can be glided over without much loss: as a whole, it reads easily both as a personal narrative and as a fascinating picture of 19th-century Scottish life. Throughout, Miller demonstrates a great wit and sense of humour, and above all humanity. He never forgot that his origins were, if not of the humblest, certainly far below those of most of the men and women of science and learning with whom his writings brought him into contact. He may have been flattered by these attentions, but he did not altogether trust them. As the bicentenary of his birth approaches, Miller deserves to be recognised once more, and there is no better place to begin than with this classic account of his life, of which Thomas Carlyle wrote: "it is really a long while since I have read a book worthy of so much recognition from me, or likely to be so interesting to sound-hearted men of every degree."

[1] *My Schools and Schoolmasters*, (Edinburgh, 1907), pp.viii-ix. Introduction and Notes by W.M. Mackenzie.

A Note on the Text

This edition of *My Schools and Schoolmasters* has been reset and revised from earlier editions, retaining all of Miller's own footnotes and most of the footnotes from W.M. Mackenzie's 1906 edition. I have added extra notes to explain references to names less well-known now than they were eighty years ago, but have kept these to a minimum in order to avoid over-burdening Miller's text.

James Robertson
Biggar, September 1993

TO THE READER

IT is now nearly a hundred years since Goldsmith remarked, in his little educational treatise, that "few subjects have been more frequently written upon than the education of youth." And during the century which has well-nigh elapsed since he said so, there have been so many more additional works given to the world on this fertile topic, that their number has been at least doubled. Almost all the men who ever taught a few pupils, with a great many more who never taught any, deem themselves qualified to say something original on education; and perhaps few books of the kind have yet appeared, however mediocre their general tone, in which something worthy of being attended to has not actually been said. And yet, though I have read not a few volumes on the subject, and have dipped into a great many more, I never yet found in them the sort of direction or encouragement which, in working out my own education, I most needed. They insisted much on the various modes of teaching others but said nothing—or, what amounted to the same thing, nothing to the purpose—on the best mode of teaching one's-self. And as my circumstances and position, at the time when I had most occasion to consult them, were those of by much the largest class of the people of this and every other civilized country—for I was one of the many millions who need to learn, and yet have no one to teach them—I could not help deeming the omission a serious one. I have since come to think, however, that a formal treatise on self-culture might fail to supply the want. Curiosity must be awakened ere it can be satisfied; nay, once awakened, it never fails in the end fully to satisfy itself; and it has occurred to me, that, by simply laying before the working men of the country the "Story of my Education," I may succeed in first exciting their curiosity, and next, occasionally at least, in gratifying it also. They will find that by far the best schools I ever attended are schools open to them all—that the best teachers I ever had are (though severe in their discipline) always easy of access—and that the special *form* at which I was, if I may say so, most successful as a pupil, was a form to which I was drawn by a strong inclination, but at which I had less assistance from my brother men, or even from books, than at any of the others. There are few of the natural sciences which do not lie quite as open to the working men of Britain and America as Geology did to me.

My work, then, if I have not wholly failed in it, may be regarded as a sort of educational treatise, thrown into the narrative form, and addressed more especially to working men. They will find that a considerable portion of the scenes and incidents which it records read their lesson, whether of encouragement or warning, or throw their occasional lights on peculiarities of character or curious natural phenomena, to which their attention might be not unprofitably directed. Should it be found to possess an interest to any other class, it will be an interest chiefly derivable from the glimpses which it furnishes of the inner life of the Scottish people, and its bearing on what has been somewhat clumsily termed "the condition-of-the-country question." My sketches will, I trust, be recognised as true to fact and nature. And as I have never perused the autobiography of a working man of the more observant type, without being indebted to it for new facts and ideas respecting the circumstances and character of some portion of the people with which I had been less perfectly acquainted before, I can hope that, regarded simply as the memoir of a protracted journey through *districts* of society not yet very sedulously explored, and scenes which few readers have had an opportunity of observing for themselves, my story may be found to possess some of the interest which attaches to the narratives of travellers who see what is not often seen, and know, in consequence, what is not generally known. In a work cast into the autobiographic form, the writer has always much to apologize for. With himself for his subject, he usually tells not only more than he ought, but also, in not a few instances, more than he intends. For, as has been well remarked, whatever may be the character which a writer of his own Memoirs is desirous of assuming, he rarely fails to betray the real one. He has almost always his unintentional revelations, that exhibit peculiarities of which he is not conscious, and weaknesses which he has failed to recognise as such; and it will no doubt be seen that what is so generally done in works similar to mine, I have not escaped doing. But I cast myself full on the good-nature of the reader. My aims have, I trust, been honest ones; and should I in any degree succeed in rousing the humbler classes to the important work of self-culture and self-government, and in convincing the higher that there are instances in which working men have at least as legitimate a claim to their respect as to their pity, I shall not deem the ordinary penalties of the autobiographer a price too high for the accomplishment of ends so important.

CONTENTS

CHAPTER I

A sailor's early career—First Marriage—Escape from shipwreck
—Second Love—Traits of character   1

CHAPTER II

Childhood and childish visions—A Father's death—Favourite books
—Sketch of two maternal uncles   19

CHAPTER III

Dawn of patriotism—Cromarty Grammar School—Prevalent
amusements—Old Francie—Earliest geological researches   38

CHAPTER IV

Uncle Sandy as a naturalist—Important discovery—Cromarty Sutors and
their caves—Expedition to the "Doocot"—Difficulties and dangers
—Sensation produced   59

CHAPTER V

A would-be patroness—Boyish games—First friendship—Visit to the
Highlands—Geologing in the Gruids—Ossian-worship   80

CHAPTER VI

Cousin George and Cousin William—Excursion with Cousin Walter
—Painful accident—Family bereavements—Links between
the present and the past   101

CHAPTER VII

Subscription school—Vacation delights—Forays and fears—Quarrel
with the schoolmaster—Poetical revenge—Johnstone the forester   122

CHAPTER VIII

Choice of a calling—Disappointment to relatives—Old Red Sandstone
quarry—Depression and walking-sleep—Temptations of toil
—Friendship with William Ross   144

CHAPTER IX

Life in the bothy—Mad Bell—Mournful history—Singular intimacy
—Manners and Customs of North-Country Mansions   165

CHAPTER X

Evening walks—Lines on a sun-dial—A haunted stream—Insect
transformations—Jock Mo-ghoal—Musings   185

CHAPTER XI

An antiquary in humble life—Poor Danie—Proficiency in
porridge-making—Depressed health—A good omen—Close
of apprenticeship   209

CHAPTER XII

Swimming the Conon—Click-Clack the carter—Loch Maree—Fitting
up a barrack—Highland characteristics   233

CHAPTER XIII

The Brothers Fraser—Flora of the Northern Hebrides—Diving in
the Gareloch—Sabbaths in Flowerdale woods—Causes of
Highland distress   255

CHAPTER XIV

A cragsman's death—Providential escape—Property in Leith—First
sight of Edinburgh—Peter M'Craw—Niddry Woods—Researches
among the Coal Measures   281

CHAPTER XV

A worthy Seceder—The hero of the squad—Apology for fanaticism
—Strikes—Recollections of the theatre   305

CHAPTER XVI

Great fires in Edinburgh—Dr. Colquhoun—Dr. M'Crie—Return to
the North—Stanzas written at sea—Geological dreams   330

CHAPTER XVII

Religious phases—True centre of Christianity—Bearing of geology
upon theological belief—Delicate health—A gipsy wedding   354

CHAPTER XVIII

Convalescence—Pursuit of algeology—Jock Gordon—Theory of idiocy
—Mr. Stewart of Cromarty   375

CHAPTER XIX

Stone-cutting at Inverness—A jilted lover—The *Osars*—Death of
Uncle James—Farewell letter from William Ross   395

CHAPTER XX

Publication of poems—Newspaper criticisms—Walsh the lecturer
—Enlarged circle of friends—Miss Dunbar of Boath   414

CHAPTER XXI

Arenaceous formations—Antiquity of the earth—Tremendous hurricane
—*Loligo Vulgare*—Researches amid the Lias—Interesting discoveries   435

CHAPTER XXII

Religious controversies—Ecclesiastical dispute—Cholera—Preventative
measures—Reform Bill   451

CHAPTER XXIII

Visitors in the churchyard—The Ladies' Walk—First interview
—Friendship—Love—Second visit to Edinburgh—Linlithgow Bank
—Favourable reception of "Scenes and Legends"— Marriage   473

CHAPTER XXIV

Married life at Cromarty—Ichthyolitic deposit of Old Red Sandstone
—Correspondence with Agassiz and Murchison—Happy evenings
—Death of eldest child   497

CHAPTER XXV

Voluntary principle—Position of the Establishment—Letter to Lord
Brougham—Invitation to Edinburgh—Editorship of the *Witness*
—Introduction to Dr. Chalmers—Visit from an old friend—Removal
to Edinburgh   516

MY SCHOOLS AND SCHOOLMASTERS

OR

THE STORY OF MY EDUCATION

CHAPTER I

"Ye gentlemen of England,
Who live at home at ease,
Oh, little do ye think upon
The dangers of the seas."—OLD SONG

RATHER more than eighty years ago, a stout little boy, in his sixth or seventh year, was despatched from an old-fashioned farm-house in the upper part of the parish of Cromarty, to drown a litter of puppies in an adjacent pond. The commission seemed to be not in the least congenial. He sat down beside the pool, and began to cry over his charge; and finally, after wasting much time in a paroxysm of indecision and sorrow, instead of committing the puppies to the water, he tucked them up in his little kilt, and set out by a blind pathway which went winding through the stunted heath of the dreary Maolbuie Common, in a direction opposite to that of the farm-house—his home for the two previous twelve months. After some doubtful wandering on the waste, he succeeded in reaching, before nightfall, the neighbouring seaport town,[1] and presented himself, laden with his charge, at his mother's door. The poor woman—a sailor's widow, in very humble circumstances—raised her hands in astonishment: "Oh, my unlucky boy," she exclaimed, "what's this?—what brings you here?" "The little doggies, mither," said the boy; "I couldna drown the little doggies and I took them to you." What afterwards befell the "little doggies," I know not; but trivial as the incident

[1] Cromarty.

1

may seem, it exercised a marked influence on the circumstances and destiny of at least two generations of creatures higher in the scale than themselves. The boy, as he stubbornly refused to return to the farm-house, had to be sent on shipboard, agreeably to his wish, as a cabin-boy; and the writer of these chapters was born, in consequence, a sailor's son, and was rendered, as early as his fifth year, mainly dependent for his support on the sedulously plied but indifferently remunerated labours of his only surviving parent, at the time a sailor's widow.

The little boy of the farm-house was descended from a long line of seafaring men—skilful and adventurous sailors—some of whom had coasted along the Scottish shores as early as the times of Sir Andrew Wood and the "bold Bartons," and, mayhap, helped to man that "verrie monstrous schippe the Great Michael," that "cumbered all Scotland to get her to sea." They had taken as naturally to the water as the Newfoundland dog or the duckling. That waste of life which is always so great in the naval profession had been more than usually so in the generation just passed away. Of the boy's two uncles, one had sailed round the world with Anson, and assisted in burning Paita, and in boarding the Manilla galleon; but on reaching the English Coast he mysteriously disappeared, and was never more heard of. The other uncle, a remarkably handsome and powerful man—or, to borrow the homely but not inexpressive language in which I have heard him described, "as *pretty* a fellow as ever stepped in shoe-leather,"—perished at sea in a storm; and several years after, the boy's father, when entering the Firth of Cromarty, was struck overboard, during a sudden gust, by the boom of his vessel, and, apparently stunned by the blow, never rose again. Shortly after, in the hope of screening her son from what seemed to be the hereditary fate, his mother had committed the boy to the charge of a sister, married to a farmer of the parish, and now the mistress of the farm-house of Ardavell; but the family death was not to be so avoided; and the arrangement terminated, as has been seen, in the transaction beside the pond.

In course of time the sailor boy, despite of hardship and rough usage, grew up into a singularly robust and active man, not above the middle size—for his height never exceeded five feet eight inches—but broad-shouldered, deep-chested, strong-limbed, and so compact of bone and muscle, that in a ship of the line, in which he afterwards sailed, there was not, among five hundred able-bodied seamen, a man who could lift so great a weight, or grapple with him on equal terms. His education had been but indifferently cared for at home: he had, however, been taught to read by a female cousin, a niece of his mother's, who, like her too, was both the daughter and the widow of a sailor; and for his cousin's only child, a girl somewhat younger than himself, he had contracted a boyish affection, which in a stronger form continued to retain possession of him after he grew up. In the leisure thrown on his hands in long Indian and Chinese voyages, he learned to write; and profited so much by the instructions of a comrade, an intelligent and warm-hearted though reckless Irishman, that he became skilful enough to keep a log-book, and to take a reckoning with the necessary correctness—accomplishments far from common at the time among ordinary sailors. He formed, too, a taste for reading. The recollection of his cousin's daughter may have influenced him, but he commenced life with a determination to rise in it—made his first money by storing up instead of drinking his grog—and, as was common in those times, drove a little trade with the natives of foreign parts in articles of curiosity and vertu, for which, I suspect, the custom-house dues were not always paid. With all his Scotch prudence, however, and with much kindliness of heart and placidity of temper, there was some wild blood in his veins, derived, mayhap, from one or two buccaneering ancestors, that, when excited beyond the endurance point, became sufficiently formidable; and which, on at least one occasion, interfered very considerably with his plans and prospects.

On a protracted and tedious voyage in a large East Indiaman, he had, with the rest of the crew, been subjected to harsh usage by a stern, capricious captain; but, secure of relief on reaching port, he had borne uncomplainingly with it all. His comrade and quondam teacher, the Irishman, was, however, less patient; and for remonstrating with the tyrant, as one of a deputation of the seamen, in what was deemed a mutinous spirit, he was laid hold of, and was in the course of being ironed down to the deck under a tropical sun, when his quieter comrade, with his blood now heated to the boiling point, stepped aft, and with apparent calmness re-stated the grievance. The captain drew a loaded pistol from his belt; the sailor struck up his hand; and, as the bullet whistled through the rigging above, he grappled with him, and disarmed him in a trice. The crew rose, and in a few minutes the ship was all their own. But having failed to calculate on such a result, they knew not what to do with their charge; and, acting under the advice of their new leader, who felt to the full the embarrassing nature of the position, they were content simply to demand the redress of their grievances as their terms of surrender; when, untowardly for their claims, a ship of war hove in sight, much in want of men, and, bearing down on the Indiaman, the mutiny was at once suppressed, and the leading mutineers sent aboard the armed vessel, accompanied by a grave charge, and the worst possible of characters. Luckily for them, however, and especially luckily for the Irishman and his friend, the warship was so weakened by scurvy, at that time the untamed pest of the navy, that scarce two dozen of her crew could do duty aloft. A fierce tropical tempest, too, which broke out not long after, pleaded powerfully in their favour; and the affair terminated in the ultimate promotion of the Irishman to the office of ship-schoolmaster, and of his Scotch comrade to the captaincy of the foretop.

My narrative abides with the latter. He remained for several years aboard a man-of-war, and, though not much in love with the service, did his duty in both storm and battle. He served in the action off the Dogger Bank—one of the last naval engagements fought ere the manoeuvre of breaking the line gave to British valour its due superiority, by rendering all our great sea-battles decisive; and a comrade who sailed in the same vessel, and from whom, when a boy, I have received kindness for my father's sake, has told me that, their ship being but indifferently manned at the time, and the extraordinary personal strength and activity of his friend well known, he had a station assigned him at his gun against two of the crew, and that during the action he actually outwrought them both. At length, however, the enemy drifted to leeward to refit; and when set to repair the gashed and severed rigging, such was his state of exhaustion, in consequence of the previous overstrain on every nerve and muscle, that he had scarce vigour enough left to raise the marlingspike employed in the work to the level of his face. Suddenly, when in this condition, a signal passed along the line, that the Dutch fleet, already refitted, was bearing down to renew the engagement. A thrill like that of an electric shock passed through the frame of the exhausted sailor; his fatigue at once left him; and, vigorous and strong as when the action first began, he found himself able, as before, to run out against his two comrades the one side of a four-and-twenty pounder. The instance is a curious one of the influence of that "spirit" which, according to the Wise King, enables a man to "sustain his infirmity."

It may be well not to inquire too curiously regarding the mode in which this effective sailor quitted the navy. The country had borrowed his services without consulting his will; and he, I suspect, reclaimed them on his own behalf without first asking leave. I have been told by my mother that he found the navy very intolerable;—the mutiny at the Nore had not yet meliorated the service to the common sailor. Among other hardships, he had been oftener than once under not only very harsh, but also very incompetent officers; and on one occasion, after toiling on the foreyard in a violent night-squall, with some of the best seamen aboard, in fruitless attempts to furl up the sail, he had to descend, cap in hand, at the risk of a flogging, and humbly implore the boy-lieutenant in charge that he should order the vessel's head to be laid in a certain direction. Luckily for him, the advice was taken by the young gentleman, and in a few minutes the sail was furled. He left his ship one fine morning, attired in his best, and having on his head a three-cornered hat, with tufts of lace at the corners, which I well remember, from the circumstance that it had long after to perform an important part in certain boyish masquerades at Christmas and the New Year; and as he had taken effective precautions for being reported missing in the evening, he got clear off.

Of some of the after-events of his life I retain such mere fragmentary recollections, dissociated from date and locality, as might be most readily seized on by the imagination of a child. At one time, when engaged in one of his Indian voyages, he was stationed during the night, accompanied by but a single comrade, in a small open boat, near one of the minor mouths of the Ganges; and he had just fallen asleep on the beams, when he was suddenly awakened by a violent motion, as if his skiff were capsizing. Starting up, he saw in the imperfect light a huge tiger, that had swam, apparently, from the neighbouring jungle, in the act of boarding the boat. So much was he taken aback, that though a loaded musket lay beside him, it was one of the loose beams, or *foot-spars*, used as fulcrums for the feet in rowing, that he laid hold of as a weapon; but such was the blow he dealt to the paws of the creature, as they rested on the gunwale, that it dropped off with a tremendous snarl, and he saw it no more. On another occasion, he was one of three men sent with despatches to some Indian port in a boat, which, oversetting in the open sea in a squall, left them for the greater part of three days only its upturned bottom for their resting-place. And so thickly during that time did the sharks congregate around them, that though a keg of rum, part of the boat's stores, floated for the first two days within a few yards of them, and they had neither meat nor drink, none of them, though they all swam well, dared attempt regaining it. They were at length relieved by a Spanish vessel, and treated with such kindness, that the subject of my narrative used ever after to speak well of the Spaniards, as a generous people, destined ultimately

6

to rise. He was at one time so reduced by scurvy, in a vessel half of whose crew had been carried off by the disease, that, though still able to do duty on the tops, the pressure of his finger left for several seconds a dent in his thigh, as if the muscular flesh had become of the consistency of dough. At another time, when overtaken in a small vessel by a protracted tempest, in which "for many days neither sun nor moon appeared," he continued to retain his hold of the helm for twelve hours after every other man aboard was utterly prostrated and down, and succeeded, in consequence, in weathering the storm for them all. And after his death, a nephew of my mother's, a young man who had served his apprenticeship under him, was treated with great kindness on the Spanish Main for his sake, by a West Indian captain, whose ship and crew he had saved, as the captain told the lad, by boarding them in a storm, at imminent risk to himself, and working their vessel into port, when, in circumstances of similar exhaustion, they were drifting full upon an iron-bound shore. Many of my other recollections of this manly sailor are equally fragmentary in their character; but there is a distinct bit of picture in them all, that strongly impressed the boyish fancy.

When not much turned of thirty, the sailor returned to his native town, with money enough, hardly earned, and carefully kept, to buy a fine large sloop, with which he engaged in the coasting trade: and shortly after he married his cousin's daughter. He found his cousin, who had supported herself in her widowhood by teaching a school, residing in a dingy, old-fashioned house, three rooms in length, but with the windows of its second storey half-buried in the eaves, that had been left her by their mutual grandfather, old John Feddes, one of the last of the buccaneers. It had been built, I have every reason to believe, with Spanish gold; not, however, with a great deal of it, for, notwithstanding its six rooms, it was a rather humble erection, and had now fallen greatly into disrepair. It was fitted up with some of the sailor's money, and, after his marriage, became his home—a home rendered all the happier by the presence of his cousin, now rising in years, and

who, during her long widowhood, had sought and found conso-
lation, amid her troubles and privations, where it was surest to be
found. She was a meek-spirited, sincerely pious woman; and the
sailor, during his more distant voyages—for he sometimes traded
with ports of the Baltic on the one hand, and with those of Ireland
and the south of England on the other—had the comfort of
knowing that his wife, who had fallen into a state of health
chronically delicate, was sedulously tended and cared for by a
devoted mother. The happiness which he would have otherwise
enjoyed was, however, marred in some degree by his wife's great
delicacy of constitution, and ultimately blighted by two unhappy
accidents.

He had not lost the nature which had been evinced at an early
age beside the pond: for a man who had often looked death in the
face, he had remained nicely tender of human life, and had often
hazarded his own in preserving that of others; and when
accompanied, on one occasion, by his wife and her mother to his
vessel, just previous to sailing, he had unfortunately to exert
himself in her presence, in behalf of one of his seamen, in a way
that gave her constitution a shock from which it never recovered.
A clear frosty moonlight evening had set in; the pier-head was
glistening with new formed ice; and one of the sailors, when
engaged in casting over a haulser which he had just loosed, missed
footing on the treacherous margin, and fell into the sea. The
master knew his man could not swim; a powerful seaward tide
sweeps past the place with the first hours of the ebb; there was
not a moment to be lost; and, hastily throwing off his heavy
greatcoat, he plunged after him, and in an instant the strong
current swept them both out of sight. He succeeded, however, in
laying hold of the half-drowned man, and, striking with him from
out the perilous tideway into an eddy, with a Herculean effort he
regained the quay. On reaching it, his wife lay insensible in the
arms of her mother, and as she was at the time in the delicate
condition incidental to married women, the natural consequence
followed, and she never recovered the shock, but lingered for more

than a twelvemonth, the mere shadow of her former self; then a second event, as untoward as the first, too violently shook the fast ebbing sands, and precipitated her dissolution.

A prolonged tempest from the stormy north-east had swept the Moray Firth of its shipping, and congregated the storm-bound vessels by scores in the noble harbour of Cromarty, when the wind chopped suddenly round, and they all set out to sea—the sloop of the master among the rest. The other vessels kept the open Firth; but the master, thoroughly acquainted with its navigation, and in the belief that the change of wind was but temporary, went on hugging the land on the weather side, till, as he had anticipated, the breeze set full into the old quarter, and increased into a gale and then, when all the rest of the fleet had no other choice left them than just to scud back again, he struck out into the Firth in a long tack, and, doubling Kinnaird's Head and the dreaded Buchan Ness, succeeded in making good his voyage south. Next morning the wind-bound vessels were crowding the harbour of refuge as before, and only his sloop was amissing. The first war of the French Revolution had broken out at the time; it was known there were several French privateers hovering on the coast; and the report went abroad that the missing sloop had been captured by the French. There was a weather-brained tailor in the neighbourhood, who used to do very odd things, especially, it was said, when the moon was at the full, and whom the writer remembers from the circumstance that he fabricated for him his first jacket, and that, though he succeeded in sewing on one sleeve to the hole at the shoulder, where it ought to be, he committed the slight mistake of sewing on the other sleeve to one of the pocket-holes. Poor Andrew Fern had heard that his townsman's sloop had been captured by a privateer, and, fidgety with impatience till he had communicated the intelligence where he thought it would tell most effectively, he called on the master's wife, to ask whether she had not heard that all the wind-bound vessels had got back again save the master's, and to wonder no one had yet told her that, if *his* had not got back, it was simply because it had been taken by the French. The tailor's communication told more powerfully than he could have anticipated: in less than a week after, the master's wife was dead; and long ere her husband's return she was lying in the quiet family burying-place, in which— so heavy were the drafts made by accident and violent death on the family—the remains of none of the male members had been deposited for more than a hundred years.

The mother, now left, by the death of her daughter, to a dreary solitude, sought to relieve its tedium, during the absence of her son-in-law when on his frequent voyages, by keeping, as she had done ere his return from foreign parts, a humble school. It was attended by two little girls, the children of a distant relation but very dear friend, the wife of a tradesman of the place—a woman, like herself, of sincere though unpretending piety. Their similarity of character in this respect could hardly be traced to their common ancestor. He was the last curate of the neighbouring parish of Nigg; and, though not one of those intolerant Episcopalian ministers that succeeded in rendering their Church thoroughly hateful to the Scottish people—for he was a simple, easy man, of much good nature—he was, if tradition speak true, as little religious as any of them. In one of the earlier replies to that curious work, "Scotch Presbyterian Eloquence Displayed," I find a nonsensical passage from one of the curate's sermons, given as a set-off against the Presbyterian nonsense adduced by the other side. "Mr James MacKenzie,[1] curate of Nigg in Ross," says the writer, "describing eternity to his parishioners, told them that in that state they would be immortalized, so that nothing could hurt them: a slash of a broadsword could not hurt you, saith he; nay, a cannonball would play but *baff* on you." Most of the curate's descendants were staunch Presbyterians, and animated by a greatly stronger spirit than his; and there were none of them stauncher in their Presbyterianism than the two elderly women who counted kin from him in the fourth degree, and who, on the

[1] A great-grandchild of the curate was Henry MacKenzie, author of *The Man of Feeling*.

basis of a common faith, had become attached friends. The little girls were great favourites with the schoolmistress; and when, as she rose in years, her health began to fail, the elder of the two removed from her mother's house, to live with and take care of her; and the younger, who was now shooting up into a pretty young woman, used, as before, to pass much of her time with her sister and her old mistress.

Meanwhile the shipmaster was thriving. He purchased a site for a house beside that of his buccaneering grandfather, and built for himself and his aged relative a respectable dwelling, which cost him about four hundred pounds, and entitled his son, the writer, to exercise the franchise, on the passing, considerably more than thirty years after, of the Reform Bill. The new house was, however, never to be inhabited by its builder, for ere it was fully finished, he was overtaken by a sad calamity, that, to a man of less energy and determination, would have been ruin, and in consequence of which he had to content himself with the old house as before, and almost to begin the world anew. I have now reached a point in my narrative at which, from my connection with the two little girls—both of whom still live in the somewhat altered character of women far advanced in life—I can be as minute in its details as I please; and the details of the misadventure which stripped the shipmaster of the earnings of long years of carefulness and toil, blended as they are with what an old critic might term a curious *machinery* of the supernatural, seem not unworthy of being given unabridged.

Early in November 1797, two vessels—the one a smack in the London and Inverness trade, the other the master's square-rigged sloop—lay wind-bound for a few days on their passage north, in the port of Peterhead. The weather, which had been stormy and unsettled, moderated towards the evening of the fifth day of their detention; and the wind chopping suddenly into the east, both vessels loosed from their moorings, and, as a rather gloomy day was passing into still gloomier night, they bore out to sea. The breeze soon freshened into a gale; the gale swelled into a hurricane, accompanied by a thick snow-storm; and when, early next morning, the smack opened the Firth, she was staggering under her storm-jib, and a mainsail reefed to the cross. Whatever wind may blow, there is always shelter within the Sutors; and she was soon riding at anchor in the roadstead; but she had entered the bay alone; and when day broke, and for a brief interval the driving snow-rack cleared up towards the east, no second sail appeared in the offing. "Poor Miller!" exclaimed the master of the smack; "if he does not enter the Firth ere an hour, he will never enter it at all. Good sound vessel, and better sailor never stepped between stem and stern; but last night has, I fear, been too much for him. He should have been here long ere now." The hour passed; the day itself wore heavily away in gloom and tempest; and as not only the master, but also all the crew of the sloop, were natives of the place, groups of the town's-folk might be seen, so long as the daylight lasted, looking out into the storm from the salient points of the old coast-line that, rising immediately behind the houses, commands the Firth. But the sloop came not, and before they had returned to their homes, a second night had fallen, dark and tempestuous as the first.

Ere morning the weather moderated: a keen frost bound up the wind in its icy fetters; and during the following day, though a heavy swell continued to roll shorewards between the Sutors, and sent up its white foam high against the cliffs, the surface of the sea had become glassy and smooth. But the day wore on, and evening again fell; and even the most sanguine relinquished all hope of ever again seeing the sloop or her crew. There was grief in the master's dwelling—grief in no degree the less poignant from the circumstance that it was the tearless, uncomplaining grief of rigid old age. Her two youthful friends and their mother watched with the widow, now, as it seemed, left alone in the world. The town-clock had struck the hour of midnight, and still she remained as if tied to her seat, absorbed in silent, stupefying sorrow, when a heavy foot was heard pacing along the now silent street. It passed, and anon returned; ceased for a moment nearly opposite the window; then approached the door, where there was a second pause; and then there succeeded a faltering knock, that struck on the very hearts of the inmates within. One of the girls sprang up, and on undoing the bolt, shrieked out, as the door fell open, "Oh, mistress, here is Jack Grant the mate!" Jack, a tall, powerful seaman, but apparently in a state of utter exhaustion, staggered, rather than walked in, and flung himself into a chair. "Jack," exclaimed the old woman, seizing him convulsively by both his hands, "where's my cousin?—where's Hugh?" "The master's safe and well," said Jack; "but the poor *Friendship* lies in *spales*[1] on the bar of Findhorn."[2] "God be praised!" ejaculated the widow. "Let the gear go!"

I have often heard Jack's story related in Jack's own words, at a period of life when repetition never tires; but I am not sure that I can do it the necessary justice now. "We left Peterhead," he said, "with about half a cargo of coal—for we had lightened ship a day or two before—and the gale freshened as the night came on. We made all tight, however; and though the snow-drift was so blinding in the thick of the shower that I could scarce see my hand before me, and though it soon began to blow great guns, we had given the land a good offing, and the hurricane blew the right way. Just as we were loosening from the quay, a poor young woman, much knocked up, with a child in her arms, had come to the vessel's side, and begged hard of master to take her aboard. She was a soldier's wife and was travelling to join her husband at Fort George; but she was already worn out and penniless, she said; and now, as a snow-storm threatened to block up the roads, she could neither stay where she was, nor pursue her journey. Her infant, too—she was sure, if she tried to force her way through the hills, it would perish in the snow. The master, though unwilling to cumber us with a passenger in such weather, was induced, out of pity for the poor destitute creature, to take her aboard. And she was now, with her child, all alone, below in the cabin. I was

[1] Splinters.
[2] The River Findhorn, in Morayshire.

stationed ahead on the out-look beside the foresail *horse*: the night had grown pitch dark; and the lamp in the binnacle threw just light enough through the grey of the shower to show me the master at the helm. He looked more anxious, I thought, than I had almost ever seen him before, though I have been with him, mistress, in bad weather; and all at once I saw he had got company, and strange company too, for such a night: there was a woman moving round him, with a child in her arms. I could see her as distinctly as ever I saw anything—now on the one side, now on the other—at one time full in the light, at another half lost in the darkness. That, I said to myself, must be the soldier's wife and her child; but how in the name of wonder can the master allow a woman to come on deck in such a night as this, when we ourselves have just enough ado to keep footing? He takes no notice of her neither, but keeps looking on, quite in his wont, at the binnacle. 'Master,' I said, stepping up to him, 'the woman had surely better go below.' 'What woman, Jack?' said he; 'our passenger, you may be sure, is nowhere else.' I looked round, mistress, and found he was quite alone, and that the companion-head was hasped down. There came a cold sweat all over me. 'Jack,' said the master, 'the night is getting worse, and the roll of the waves heightening every moment. I'm convinced, too, our cargo is shifting: as the last sea struck us, I could hear the coals rattle below; and see how stiffly we heel to the larboard. Say nothing, however, to the men, but have all your wits about you; and look, meanwhile, to the boat-tackle and the oars. I have seen a boat live in as bad a night as this.' As he spoke, a blue light from above glimmered on the deck. We looked up, and saw a dead-fire sticking to the cross-trees. 'It's all over with us now, master,' said I. 'Nay, man,' replied the master, in his easy, humorous way, which I always like well enough except in bad weather, and then I see his humour is served out like his extra grog, to keep up hearts that have cause enough to get low— 'Nay, man,' he said, 'we can't afford to let your grandmother board us tonight. If you will insure *me* against the shifting coal, I'll be your guarantee against the dead-light. Why, it's as much a natural

14

appearance, man, as a flash of lightning. Away to your berth, and keep up a good heart: we can't be far from Covesea[1] now, where, when once past the Skerries, the swell will take off; and then, in two short hours, we may be snug within the Sutors.' I had scarcely reached my berth ahead, mistress, when a heavy sea struck us on the starboard quarter, almost throwing us on our beam-ends. I could hear the rushing of the coals below, as they settled on the larboard side, and though the master set us full before the wind, and gave instant orders to lighten every stitch of sail—and it was but little sail we had at the time to lighten—still the vessel did not rise, but lay unmanageable as a log, with her gunwale in the water. On we drifted, however, along the south coast, with little expectation save that every sea would send us to the bottom; until, in the first grey of the morning, we found ourselves among the breakers of the terrible bar of Findhorn. And shortly after, the poor *Friendship* took the ground right on the edge of the quicksands, for she would neither stay nor wear; and as she beat hard against the bottom, the surf came rolling over half-mast high.

"Just as we struck," continued Jack, "the master made a desperate effort to get into the cabin. The vessel couldn't miss we saw, to break up and fill; and though there was little hope of any of us ever setting foot ashore, he wished to give the poor woman below a chance with the rest. All of us but himself, mistress, had got up into the shrouds, and so we could see round us a bit; and he had just laid his hand on the companion-hasp to undo the door, when I saw a tremendous sea coming rolling towards us, like a moving wall, and shouted on him to hold fast. He sprang to the weather back-stay, and laid hold. The sea came tumbling on, and, breaking full twenty feet over his head buried him for a minute's space in the foam. We thought we should never see him more; but when it cleared away there was he still with his iron grip on the stay, though the fearful wave had water-logged the *Friendship* from bow to stern, and swept her companion-head as cleanly off by the deck as if it had been cut with a saw. No human aid could

---

[1] Lossiemouth, on the Coast of Moray.

avail the poor woman and her baby. Master could hear the terrible choking noise of her dying agony right under his feet, with but a two-inch plank between; and the sounds have haunted him ever since. But even had he succeeded in getting her on deck, she could not possibly have survived, mistress. For five long hours we clung to the rigging, with the seas riding over us all the time like wild horses; and though we could see, through the snow-drift and the spray, crowds on the shore, and boats lying thick beside the pier, none dared venture out to assist us, till near the close of the day, when the wind fell with the falling tide, and we were brought ashore, more dead than alive, by a volunteer crew from the harbour. The unlucky *Friendship* began to break up under us ere mid-day, and we saw the corpse of the drowned woman, with the dead infant still in its arms, come floating out through a hole in the side. But the surf soon tore mother and child asunder, and we lost sight of them as they drifted away to the west. Master would have crossed the Firth himself this morning to relieve your mind, but being less worn out than any of us, he thought it best to remain in charge of the wreck."

Such, in effect, was the narrative of Jack Grant, the mate. The master, as I have said, had well-nigh to commence the world anew, and was on the eve of selling his new house at a disadvantage, in order to make up the sum necessary for providing himself with a new vessel, when a friend interposed, and advanced him the balance required. He was assisted, too, by a sister in Leith, who was in tolerably comfortable circumstances; and so he got a new sloop, which, though not quite equal in size to the one he had lost, was built wholly of oak, every plank and beam of which he had superintended in the laying down, and a prime sailer to boot; and so, though he had to satisfy himself with the accommodation of the old domicile, with its little rooms and its small windows, and to let the other house to a tenant, he began to thrive again as before. Meanwhile his aged cousin was gradually sinking. The master was absent on one of his longer voyages, and she too truly felt that she could not survive till his return. She called to her bedside her two young friends, the sisters, who had been unwearied in their attentions to her, and poured out her blessing on them; first on the elder, and then on the younger. "But as for you, Harriet," she added, addressing the latter, "there waits for you one of the best blessings of this world also—the blessings of a good husband: you will be a gainer in the end, even in this life, through your kindness to the poor childless widow." The prophecy was a true one: the old woman had shrewdly marked where the eyes of her cousin had been falling of late; and in about a twelvemonth after her death her young friend and pupil had become the master's wife. There was a very considerable disparity between their ages—the master was forty-four, and his wife only eighteen—but never was there a happier marriage. The young wife was simple, confiding, affectionate; and the master of a soft and genial nature, with a large amount of buoyant humour about him, and so equable of temper, that, during six years of wedded life, his wife never saw him angry but once. I have heard her speak of the exceptional instance, however, as too terrible to be readily forgotten.

She had accompanied him on ship-board, during their first year of married life, to the upper parts of the Cromarty Firth. There his sloop was taking in a cargo of grain, and lay quietly embayed within two hundred yards of the southern shore. His mate had gone away for the night to the opposite side of the bay, to visit his parents, who resided in that neighbourhood; and the remaining crew consisted of but two seamen, both young and somewhat reckless men, and the ship-boy. Taking the boy with them to keep the ship's boat afloat, and wait their return, the two sailors went ashore, and, setting out for a distant public-house, remained there drinking till a late hour. There was a bright moon overhead, but the evening was chilly and frosty; and the boy, cold, tired, and half-overcome by sleep, after waiting on till past midnight, shoved off the boat, and, making his way to the vessel, got straightway into his hammock and fell asleep. Shortly after, the two men came to the shore much the worse of liquor; and, failing to make themselves heard by the boy, they stripped off their clothes, and, chilly as the night was, swam aboard. The master and his wife had been for hours snug in their bed, when they were awakened by the screams of the boy: the drunken men were unmercifully bastinading him with a rope's end apiece. The master, hastily rising, had to interfere in his behalf, and with the air of a man who knew that remonstrance in the circumstances would be of little avail, he sent them both off to their hammocks. Scarcely, however, had he again got into bed, when he was a second time aroused by the cries of the boy, uttered on this occasion in the shrill tones of agony and terror; and, promptly springing up, now followed by his wife, he found the two sailors again belabouring the boy, and that one of them, in his blind fury, had laid hold of a rope-end, armed, as is common on shipboard, with an iron thimble or ring, and that every blow produced a wound. The poor boy was streaming over with blood. The master, in the extremity of his indignation, lost command of himself. Rushing in, the two men were in a moment dashed against the deck;—they seemed powerless in his hands as children; and had not his wife, although very unfit at the time for mingling in a fray, run in and laid hold of him—a movement which calmed him at once—it was her serious impression that, unarmed as he was, he would have killed them both upon the spot. There are, I believe, few things more formidable than the unwonted anger of a good-natured man.

CHAPTER II

"Three stormy nights and stormy days
We tossed upon the raging main;
And long we strove our barque to save,
But all our striving was in vain."—LOWE

I WAS born, the first child of this marriage, on the 10th day of October 1802, in the low, long house built by my great-grandfather the buccaneer. My memory awoke early. I have recollections which date several months ere the completion of my third year; but, like those of the golden age of the world, they are chiefly of a mythologic character. I remember, for instance, getting out unobserved one day to my father's little garden, and seeing there a minute duckling covered with soft yellow hair, growing out of the soil by its feet, and beside it a plant that bore as its flowers a crop of little mussel shells of a deep red colour. I know not what prodigy of the vegetable kingdom produced the little ducklings; but the plant with the shells must, I think, have been a scarlet runner, and the shells themselves the papilionaceous blossoms. I have a distinct recollection, too—but it belongs to a later period—of seeing my ancestor, old John Feddes the buccaneer, though he must have been dead at the time considerably more than half a century. I had learned to take an interest in his story, as preserved and told in the antique dwelling which he had built more than a hundred years before. To forget a love disappointment, he had set out early in life for the Spanish Main, where, after giving and receiving some hard blows, he succeeded in filling a little bag with dollars and doubloons; and then coming home, he found his old sweetheart a widow, and so much inclined to listen to reason, that she ultimately became his wife. There were some little circumstances in his history which must have laid hold of my imagination; for I used over and over to demand its

19

repetition; and one of my first attempts at a work of art was to scribble his initials with my fingers, in red paint, on the house-door. One day, when playing all alone at the stair-foot—for the inmates of the house had gone out—something extraordinary had caught my eye on the landing-place above; and looking up, there stood John Feddes—for I somehow instinctively divined that it was none other than he—in the form of a large, tall, very old man, attired in a light-blue greatcoat. He seemed to be steadfastly regarding me with apparent complacency; but I was badly frightened; and for years after, when passing through the dingy, ill-lighted room out of which I inferred he had come, I used to feel not at all sure that I might not tilt against old John in the dark.

I retain vivid recollections of the joy which used to light up the household on my father's arrival; and I remember that I learned to distinguish for myself his sloop in the offing, by the two slim stripes of white which ran along her sides, and her two square topsails. I have my golden memories, too, of splendid toys that he used to bring home with him—among the rest, of a magnificent four-wheeled waggon of painted tin, drawn by four wooden horses and a string; and of getting it into a quiet corner, immediately on its being delivered over to me, and there breaking up every wheel and horse, and the vehicle itself, into their original bits, until not two of the pieces were left sticking together. Further, I still remember my disappointment at not finding something curious within at least the horses and the wheels; and as unquestionably the main enjoyment derivable from such things is to be had in the breaking of them, I sometimes wonder that our ingenious toymen do not fall upon the way of at once extending their trade, and adding to its philosophy, by putting some of their most brilliant things where nature puts the nut-kernel—inside. I shall advert to but one other recollection of this period. I have a dreamlike memory of a busy time, when men with gold lace on their breasts, and at least one gentleman with golden epaulets on his shoulders, used to call at my father's house, and fill my newly acquired pockets with coppers; and how they wanted, it was said, to bring my father along with them, to help them to sail their great vessel; but he preferred remaining, it was added, with his own little one. A ship of war, under the guidance of an unskilful pilot, had run aground on a shallow flat on the opposite side of the Firth, known as the *Inches*; and as the flood of a stream tide was at its height at the time, and straightway began to fall off, it was found, after lightening her of her guns and the greater part of her stores, that she still stuck fast. My father, whose sloop had been pressed into the service, and was loaded to the gunwale with the ordnance, had betrayed an unexpected knowledge of the points of a large war-vessel; and the commander, entering into conversation with him, was so impressed by his skill, that he placed his ship under his charge, and had his confidence repaid by seeing her hauled off into deep water in a single tide. Knowing the nature of the bottom—a soft arenaceous mud, which, if beat for some time by the foot or hand, resolved itself into a sort of quicksand, half-sludge, half-water, which, when covered by a competent depth of sea, could offer no effectual resistance to a ship's keel—the master had set half the crew to run in a body from side to side, till, by the motion generated in this way, the portion of the bank immediately beneath was beaten soft; and then the other moiety of the men, tugging hard on kedge and haulser, drew the vessel off a few feet at a time, till at length, after not a few repetitions of the process, she floated free. Of course, on a harder bottom the expedient would not have availed; but so struck was the commander by its efficiency and originality, and by the extent of the master's professional resources, that he strongly recommended him to part with his sloop, and enter the navy, where he thought he had influence enough, he said, to get him placed in a proper position. But as the master's previous experience of the service had been of a very disagreeable kind, and as his position, as at once master and owner of the vessel he sailed, was at least an independent one, he declined acting on the advice.

Such are some of my earlier recollections. But there was a time of sterner memories at hand. The kelp trade had not yet attained to the importance which it afterwards acquired, ere it fell before the first approaches of Free Trade; and my father, in collecting a supply for the Leith Glass Works, for which he occasionally acted both as agent and shipmaster, used sometimes to spend whole months amid the Hebrides, sailing from station to station, and purchasing here a few tons and there a few hundredweights, until he had completed his cargo. In his last kelp voyage he had been detained in this way from the close of August till the end of October; and at length, deeply laden, he had threaded his way round Cape Wrath, and through the Pentland and across the Moray Firths, when a severe gale compelled him to seek shelter in the harbour of Peterhead. From that port, on the 9th of November 1807, he wrote my mother the last letter she ever received from him; for on the day after he sailed from it there arose a terrible tempest, in which many seamen perished, and he and his crew were never more heard of. His sloop was last seen by a brother townsman and shipmaster, who, ere the storm came on, had been fortunate enough to secure an asylum for his barque in an English harbour on an exposed portion of the coast. Vessel after vessel had been coming ashore during the day; and the beach was strewed with wrecks and dead bodies; but he had marked his townsman's sloop in the offing from mid-day till near evening, exhausting every nautical shift and expedient to keep aloof from the shore; and at length as the night was falling, the skill and perseverance exerted seemed successful; for, clearing a formidable headland that had lain on the lee for hours, and was mottled with broken ships and drowned men, the sloop was seen stretching out in a long tack into the open sea. "Miller's seamanship has saved him once more!" said Matheson, the Cromarty skipper, as, quitting his place of outlook, he returned to his cabin; but the night fell tempestuous and wild, and no vestige of the hapless sloop was ever after seen. It was supposed that, heavy laden, and labouring in a mountainous sea, she must have started a plank and foundered. And thus perished—to borrow from the simple eulogium of his seafaring friends, whom I heard long after condoling with my mother—"one of the best sailors that ever sailed the Moray Firth."

The fatal tempest, as it had prevailed chiefly on the eastern coasts of England and the south of Scotland, was represented in the north by but a few bleak, sullen days, in which, with little wind, a heavy ground-swell came rolling in coastwards from the east, and sent up its surf high against the precipices of the northern Sutor. There were no forebodings in the master's dwelling; for his Peterhead letter—a brief but hopeful missive—had been just received; and my mother was sitting, on the evening after, beside the household fire, plying the cheerful needle, when the house door, which had been left unfastened, fell open, and I was despatched from her side to shut it. What follows must be regarded as simply the recollection, though a very vivid one, of a boy who had completed his fifth year only a month before. Day had not wholly disappeared, but it was fast posting on to night, and a grey haze spread a neutral tint of dimness over every more distant object, but left the nearer ones comparatively distinct, when I saw at the open door, within less than a yard of my breast, as plainly as ever I saw anything, a dissevered hand and arm stretched towards me. Hand and arm were apparently those of a female: they bore a livid and sodden appearance; and, directly fronting me, where the body ought to have been, there was only blank, transparent space, through which I could see the dim forms of the objects beyond. I was fearfully startled, and ran shrieking to my mother, telling what I had seen; and the house-girl whom she next sent to shut the door, apparently affected by my terror, also returned frightened, and said that she too had seen the woman's hand; which, however, did not seem to be the case. And finally, my mother going to the door, saw nothing, though she appeared much impressed by the extremeness of my terror and the minuteness of my description. I communicate the story as it lies fixed in my memory, without attempting to explain it. The supposed apparition may have been merely a momentary affection of the eye, of the nature described by Sir Walter Scott in his "Demonology," and Sir David Brewster in his "Natural Magic." But if so the affection was one of which I experienced no after-return; and its coincidence, in the case, with the probable time of my father's death, seems at least curious.

There followed a dreary season, on which I still look back in memory, as on a prospect which, sunshiny and sparkling for a time, has become suddenly enveloped in cloud and storm. I remember my mother's long fits of weeping, and the general gloom of the widowed household; and how, after she had sent my two little sisters to bed—for such had been the increase of the family—and her hands were set free for the evening, she used to sit up late at night engaged as a seamstress, in making pieces of dress for such of the neighbours as chose to employ her. My father's new house lay untenanted at the time; and though his sloop had been partially insured, the broker with whom he dealt was, it would seem, on the verge of insolvency, and having raised objections to paying the money, it was long ere any part of it could be realised. And so, with all my mother's industry, the household would have fared but ill, had it not been for the assistance lent her by her two brothers, industrious, hard-working men, who lived with their aged parents, and an unmarried sister, about a bow-shot away, and now not only advanced her money as she needed it, but also took her second child, the elder of my two sisters, a docile little girl of three years, to live with them. I remember I used to go wandering disconsolately about the harbour at this season, to examine the vessels which had come in during the night; and that I oftener than once set my mother a-crying, by asking her why the shipmasters who, when my father was alive, used to stroke my head and slip halfpence into my pockets, never now took any notice of me, or gave me anything? She well knew that the ship-masters—not an ungenerous class of men—had simply failed to recognise their old comrade's child; but the question was only too suggestive, notwithstanding, of both her own loss and mine. I used, too, to climb, day after day, a grassy protuberance of the old coast-line immediately behind my mother's house, that commands a wide reach of the Moray Firth, and to look wistfully out, long after every one else had ceased to hope, for the sloop with the two stripes of white and the two square top-sails. But months and years passed by, and the white stripes and the square topsails I never saw.

The antecedents of my father's life impressed me more powerfully during my boyhood than at least aught I acquired at school; and I have submitted them to the reader at considerable length, as not only curious in themselves, but as forming a first chapter in the story of my education. And the following stanzas, written at a time when, in opening manhood, I was sowing my wild oats in verse, may serve to show that they continued to stand out in bold relief on my memory, even after I had grown up:—

"Round Albyn's western shores, a lonely skiff
Is coasting slow;—the adverse winds detain;
And now she rounds secure the dreaded cliff,[1]
Whose horrid ridge beats back the northern main;
And now the whirling Pentland roars in vain
Her stern beneath, for favouring breezes rise;
The green isles fade, whitens the watery plain,
O'er the vexed waves with meteor speed she flies,
Till Moray's distant hills o'er the blue waves arise.

Who guides that vessel's wanderings o'er the wave?
A patient, hardy man, of thoughtful brow;
Serene and warm of heart, and wisely brave,
And sagely skill'd, when gurly breezes blow,
To press through angry waves the adventurous prow.
Age hath not quell'd his strength, nor quench'd desire
Of generous deed, nor chill'd his bosom's glow;
Yet to a better world his hopes aspire.
Ah! this must sure be thee! All hail, my honoured Sire!

Alas! thy latest voyage draws near a close,
For Death broods voiceless in the darkening sky;
Subsides the breeze; the untroubled waves repose;
The scene is peaceful all. Can Death be nigh,

---

[1] Cape Wrath (Miller)

When thus, mute and unarm'd, his vassals lie?
Mark ye that cloud! There toils the imprisoned gale;
E'en now it comes, with voice uplifted high;
Resound the shores, harsh screams the rending sail,
And roars th' amazed wave, and bursts the thunder peal!

Three days the tempest raged; on Scotia's shore
Wreck piled on wreck, and corse o'er corse was thrown;
Her rugged cliffs were red with clotted gore;
Her dark caves echoed back th' expiring moan;
And luckless maidens mourned their lovers gone,
And friendless orphans cried in vain for bread;
And widow'd mothers wandered forth alone;—
Restore, O wave, they cried,—restore our dead!
And then the breast they bared, and beat th' unsheltered head.

Of thee, my Sire, what mortal tongue can tell!
No friendly bay thy shattered barque received;
Ev'n when thy dust reposed in ocean cell,
Strange baseless tales of hope thy friends deceived,
Which oft they doubted sad, or gay believed.
At length, when deeper, darker, wax'd the gloom,
Hopeless they grieved; but 'twas in vain they grieved:
If God be truth, 'tis sure no voice of doom,
That bids the accepted soul its robes of joy assume."

I had been sent, previous to my father's death, to a dame's
school, where I was taught to pronounce my letters to such effect
in the old Scottish mode, that still, when I attempt spelling a word
aloud, which is not often—for I find the process a perilous one—
the *aa's* and *ee's*, and *uh's* and *vaus*, return upon me, and I have
to translate them with no little hesitation as I go along, into the
more modish sounds. A knowledge of the letters themselves I had
already acquired by studying the signposts of the place—rare
works of art, that excited my utmost admiration, with jugs, and
glasses, and bottles, and ships, and loaves of bread upon them; all
of which could, as the artists had intended, be actually recognised.
During my sixth year I spelt my way, under the dame, through
the Shorter Catechism, the Proverbs, and the New Testament, and

then entered upon her highest form, as a member of the Bible class; but all the while the process of acquiring learning had been a dark one, which I slowly mastered, in humble confidence in the awful wisdom of the schoolmistress, not knowing whither it tended, when at once my mind awoke to the meaning of that most delightful of all narratives—the story of Joseph. Was there ever such a discovery made before! I actually found out for myself, that the art of reading is the art of finding stories in books, and from that moment reading became one of the most delightful of my amusements. I began by getting into a corner at the dismissal of the school, and there conning over to myself the new-found story of Joseph; nor did one perusal serve; the other Scripture stories followed—in especial, the story of Samson and the Philistines, of David and Goliath, of the prophets Elijah and Elisha; and after these came the New Testament stories and parables. Assisted by my uncles, I began to collect a library in a box of birch-bark about nine inches square, which I found quite large enough to contain a great many immortal works—Jack the Giant-Killer, and Jack and the Bean-Stalk, and the Yellow Dwarf, and Blue Beard, and Sinbad the Sailor, and Beauty and the Beast, and Aladdin and the Wonderful Lamp, with several others of resembling character. Those intolerable nuisances the useful-knowledge books had not yet arisen, like tenebrious stars, on the educational horizon, to darken the world, and shed their blighting influence on the opening intellect of the "youth-hood"; and so, from my rudimental books—books that made themselves truly such by their thorough assimilation with the rudimental mind—I passed on, without being conscious of break or line of division, to books on which the learned are content to write commentaries and dissertations, but which I found to be quite as nice children's books as any of the others. Old Homer wrote admirably for little folk, especially in the "Odyssey"; a copy of which—in the only true translation extant— for, judging from its surpassing interest, and the wrath of critics, such I hold that of Pope to be—I found in the house of a neighbour. Next came the "Iliad"; not, however, in a complete copy, but represented by four of the six volumes of Bernard Lintot.[1] With what power, and at how early an age, true genius impresses! I saw, even at this immature period, that no other writer could cast a javelin with half the force of Homer. The missiles went whizzing athwart his pages; and I could see the momentary gleam of the steel, ere it buried itself deep in brass and bull-hide. I next succeeded in discovering for myself a child's book, of not less interest than even the "Iliad", which might, I was told, be read on Sabbaths, in a magnificent old edition of the " Pilgrim's Progress," printed on coarse whity-brown paper, and charged with numerous wood-cuts, each of which occupied an entire page, that, on principles of economy, bore letter-press on the other side. And such delightful prints as these were! It must have been some such volume that sat for its portrait to Wordsworth, and which he so exquisitely describes as—

> "Profuse in garniture of wooden cuts,
> Strange and uncouth; dire faces, figures dire,
> Sharp-knee'd, sharp-elbow'd, and lean-ankled too,
> With long and ghastly shanks,—forms which, once seen,
> Could never be forgotten."

In process of time I had devoured, besides these genial works, "Robinson Crusoe", "Gulliver's Travels", "Ambrose on Angels", the "judgment chapter" in Howie's "Scots Worthies", Byron's "Narrative", and the "Adventures of Philip Quarll", with a good many other adventures and voyages, real and fictitious, part of a very miscellaneous collection of books made by my father. It was a melancholy little library to which I had fallen heir. Most of the missing volumes had been with the master aboard his vessel when he perished. Of an early edition of Cook's "Voyages", all the volumes were now absent save the first; and a very tantalizing romance in four volumes—Mrs Radcliffe's "Mysteries of Udolpho," was represented by only the earlier two. Small as the collection was, it contained some rare books—among the rest, a curious little

[1] A bookseller (1675-1736) twice referred to in Pope's "Dunciad."

volume, entitled "The Miracles of Nature and Art," to which we find Dr Johnson referring, in one of the dialogues chronicled by Boswell, as scarce even in his day, and which had been published, he said, some time in the seventeenth century by a bookseller whose shop hung perched on Old London Bridge, between sky and water. It contained, too, the only copy I ever saw of the "Memoirs of a Protestant condemned to the Galleys of France for his Religion,"—a work interesting from the circumstance that—though it bore another name on its title-page—it had been translated from the French for a few guineas by poor Goldsmith, in his days of obscure literary drudgery, and exhibited the peculiar excellences of his style. The collection boasted, besides, of a curious old book, illustrated by very uncouth plates, that detailed the perils and sufferings of an English sailor who had spent his best years of life as a slave in Morocco. It had its volumes of sound theology, too, and of stiff controversy—Flavel's "Works", and Henry's "Commentary", and Hutchinson on the "Lesser Prophets", and a very old treatise on the Revelation, with the title-page away, and blind Jameson's volume on the Hierarchy, with first editions of "Naphthali", the "Cloud of Witnesses", and the "Hind let Loose". But with these solid authors I did not venture to grapple until long after this time. Of the works of fact and incident which it contained, those of the voyagers were my especial favourites. I perused with avidity the voyages of Anson, Drake, Raleigh, Dampier, and Captain Woods Rogers; and my mind became so filled with conceptions of what was to be seen and done in foreign parts, that I wished myself big enough to be a sailor, that I might go and see coral islands and burning mountains, and hunt wild beasts and fight battles.

I have already made mention of my two maternal uncles; and referred, at least incidentally, to their mother, as the friend and relative of my father's aged cousin, and, like her, a great-grandchild of the last curate of Nigg. The curate's youngest daughter had been courted and married by a somewhat wild young farmer, of the clan Ross, but who was known, like the celebrated Highland outlaw, from the colour of his hair, as Roy, or the Red. Donald Roy was the best club-player in the district; and as King James's "Book of Sports" was not deemed a very bad one in the semi-Celtic parish of Nigg, the games in which Donald took part were usually played on the Sabbath. About the time of the Revolution, however, he was laid hold of by strong religious convictions, heralded, say the traditions of the district, by events that approximated in character to the supernatural; and Donald became the subject of a mighty change. There is a phase of the religious character, which in the south of Scotland belongs to the first two ages of Presbytery, but which disappeared ere its third establishment under William of Nassau, that we find strikingly exemplified in the Welches, Pedens, and Cargills of the times of the persecution, and in which a sort of wild machinery of the supernatural was added to the commoner aspects of a living Christianity. The men in whom it was exhibited were seers of visions and dreamers of dreams; and, standing on the very verge of the natural world, they looked far into the world of spirits, and had at times their strange glimpses of the distant and the future. To the north of the Grampians, as if born out of due season, these seers pertain to a later age. They flourished chiefly in the early part of the last century; for it is a not uninstructive fact, that in the religious history of Scotland, the eighteenth century of the Highland and semi-Highland districts of the north corresponded in many of its traits to the seventeenth century of the Saxon-peopled districts of the south; and Donald Roy was one of the most notable of the class. The anecdotes regarding him which still float among the old recollections of Ross-shire, if transferred to Peden or Welch, would be found entirely in character with the strange stories that inlay the biographies of these devoted men, and live so enduringly in the memory of the Scottish people. Living, too, in an age in which, like the Covenanters of a former century, the Highlander still retained his weapons, and knew how to use them, Donald had, like the Patons, Hackstons, and Balfours of the south, his dash of the warlike spirit; and after assisting his minister, previous to the rebellion of 1745, in what was known as the great religious revival of Nigg, he had to assist him, shortly after, in pursuing a band of armed Caterans, that, descending from the hills, swept the parish of its cattle. And coming up with the outlaws in the gorge of a wild Highland glen, no man of his party was more active in the fray that followed than old Donald, or exerted himself to better effect in re-capturing the cattle. I need scarcely add, that he was an attached member of the Church of Scotland: but he was not destined to die in her communion.

Donald's minister, John Balfour of Nigg—a man whose memory is still honoured in the north—died in middle life, and an unpopular presentee was obtruded on the people. The policy of Robertson[1] prevailed at the time; Gillespie[2] had been deposed only four years previous, for refusing to assist in the disputed settlement of Inverkeithing; and four of the Nigg Presbytery, overawed by the stringency of the precedent, repaired to the parish church to conduct the settlement of the obnoxious licentiate, and introduce him to the parishioners. They found, however, only an empty building; and, notwithstanding the ominous absence of the people, they were proceeding in shame and sorrow with their work, when a venerable man, far advanced in life, suddenly appeared before them, and, solemnly protesting against the utter mockery of such a proceeding, impressively declared "that if they settled a man to the *walls* of that kirk, the blood of the parish of Nigg would be required at their hands." Both Dr Hetherington and Dr Merle d'Aubigné record the event; but neither of these accomplished historians seems to have been aware of the peculiar emphasis which a scene that would have been striking in any circumstances derived from the character of the protester—old

[1] William Robertson (1721-93), author of a "History of Scotland" (1759), Moderator of the General Assembly of the Church of Scotland in 1763, and Principal of Edinburgh University.

[2] Thomas Gillespie (1708-74) was deposed from his living at Carnock, Fife, for leading the Dunfermline presbytery in refusing to ordain an appointed Minister to Inverkeithing. Together with his own and two other congregations at Jedburgh and Colinsburgh, he formed the so-called Relief Church in 1762, a small but influential anti-patronage secession group.

Donald Roy. The Presbytery, appalled, stopped short in the middle of its work; nor was it resumed till an after day, when, at the command of the Moderate majority of the Church—a command not unaccompanied by significant reference to the fate of Gillespie—the forced settlement was consummated. Donald, who carried the entire parish with him, continued to cling to the national Church for nearly ten years after, much befriended by one of the most eminent and influential divines of the north— Fraser of Alness—the author of a volume on Sanctification, still regarded as a standard work by Scottish theologians. But as neither the people nor their leader ever entered on any occasion the parish church, or heard the obnoxious presentee, the Presbytery at length refused to tolerate the irregularity by extending to them, as before, the ordinary Church privileges; and so they were lost to the Establishment, and became Seceders. And in the communion of that portion of the Secession known as the Burghers,[1] Donald died several years after, at a patriarchal old age.

Among his other descendants, he had three grand-daughters, who were left orphans at an early age by the death of both their parents, and whom the old man, on their bereavement, had brought to his dwelling to live with him. They had small portions apiece, derived from his son-in-law, their father, which did not grow smaller under the care of Donald; and as each of the three was married in succession out of his family, he added to all his other kindnesses the gift of a gold ring. They had been brought up under his eye sound in the faith; and Donald's ring had, in each case, a mystic meaning—they were to regard it, he told them, as the wedding ring of their *other Husband*, the head of the Church, and to be faithful spouses to Him in their several households. Nor did the injunction, nor the significant symbol with which it was accompanied, prove idle in the end. They all brought the savour of sincere piety into their families. The grand-daughter with whom the writer was more directly connected, had been courted

[1] One of the bodies into which the Secession divided in 1747 over the question of the propriety of taking the Burgess Oath to an uncovenanted king. Their opponents were Anti-burghers.

and married by an honest and industrious but somewhat gay young tradesman, but she proved, under God, the means of his conversion; and their children, of whom eight grew up to be men and women, were reared in decent frugality, and the exercise of honest principles carefully instilled. Her husband's family had, like that of my paternal ancestors, been a seafaring one. His father, after serving for many years on shipboard, passed the latter part of his life as one of the armed boatmen that, during the last century, guarded the coasts in behalf of the revenue; and his only brother, the boatman's son, an adventurous young sailor, had engaged in Admiral Vernon's unfortunate expedition, and left his bones under the walls of Carthagena; but he himself pursued the peaceful occupation of a shoemaker, and, in carrying on his trade, usually employed a few journeymen, and kept a few apprentices. In course of time the elder daughters of the family married, and got households of their own; but the two sons, my uncles, remained under the roof of their parents, and at the time when my father perished, they were both in middle life. And, deeming themselves called on to take his place in the work of instruction and discipline, I owed to them much more of my real education than to any of the teachers whose schools I afterwards attended. They both bore a marked individuality of character, and were much the reverse of commonplace or vulgar men.

My elder uncle, James, added to a clear head and much native sagacity, a singularly retentive memory, and great thirst of information. He was a harness-maker, and wrought for the farmers of an extensive district of country; and, as he never engaged either journeyman or apprentice, but executed all his work with his own hands, his hours of labour, save that he indulged in a brief pause as the twilight came on, and took a mile's walk or so, were usually protracted from six o'clock in the morning till ten at night. Such incessant occupation left him little time for reading; but he often found some one to read beside him during the day; and in the winter evenings his portable bench used to be brought from his shop at the other end of the dwelling, into the family sitting-room, and placed beside the circle round the hearth, where his brother Alexander, my younger uncle, whose occupation left his evenings free, would read aloud from some interesting volume for the general benefit—placing himself always at the opposite side of the bench, so as to share in the light of the worker. Occasionally the family circle would be widened by the accession of from two to three intelligent neighbours, who would drop in to listen; and then the book, after a space, would be laid aside, in order that its contents might be discussed in conversation. In the summer months Uncle James always spent some time in the country, in looking after and keeping in repair the harness of the farmers for whom he wrought; and during his journeys and twilight walks on these occasions there was not an old castle, or hill-fort, or ancient encampment, or antique ecclesiastical edifice, within twenty miles of the town, which he had not visited and examined over and over again. He was a keen local antiquary; knew a good deal about the architectural styles of the various ages, at a time when these subjects were little studied or known; and possessed more traditionary lore, picked up chiefly in his country journeys, than any man I ever knew. What he once heard he never forgot; and the knowledge which he had acquired he could communicate pleasingly and succinctly, in a style which, had he been a writer of books, instead of merely a reader of them, would have had the merit of being clear and terse, and more laden with meaning than words. From his reputation for sagacity, his advice used to be much sought after by the neighbours in every little difficulty that came their way; and the counsel given was always shrewd and honest. I never knew a man more entirely just in his dealings than Uncle James, or who regarded every species of meanness with a more thorough contempt. I soon learned to bring my story-books to his workshop, and became, in a small way, one of his readers—greatly more, however, as may be supposed, on my own account than his. My books were not yet of the kind which he would have chosen for himself; but he took an interest in my interest; and his explanations of all the hard words saved me the trouble of turning over a dictionary. And when tired of reading, I never failed to find rare delight in his anecdotes and old-world stories, many of which were not to be found in books, and all of which, without apparent effort on his own part, he could render singularly amusing. Of these narratives, the larger part died with him; but a portion of them I succeeded in preserving in a little traditionary work published a few years after his death. I was much a favourite with Uncle James—even more, I am disposed to think, on my father's account than on that of his sister, my mother. My father and he had been close friends for years; and in the vigorous and energetic sailor he had found his *beau-idéal* of a man.

My Uncle Alexander was of a different cast from his brother, both in intellect and temperament; but he was characterized by the same strict integrity; and his religious feelings, though quiet and unobtrusive, were perhaps more deep. James was somewhat of a humorist, and fond of a good joke. Alexander was grave and serious; and never, save on one solitary occasion, did I know him even attempt a jest. On hearing an intelligent but somewhat eccentric neighbour observe, that "all flesh is grass," in a strictly physial sense, seeing that all the flesh of the herbivorous animals is elaborated from vegetation, and all the flesh of the carnivorous animals from that of the herbivorous ones, Uncle Sandy remarked that, knowing, as he did, the piscivorous habits of the Cromarty folk, he should surely make an exception in his generalization, by admitting that in at least one village "all flesh is fish." My uncle had acquired the trade of the cartwright, and was employed in a workshop at Glasgow at the time the first war of the French Revolution broke out; when, moved by some such spirit as possessed his uncle—the victim of Admiral Vernon's unlucky expedition— or Old Donald Roy, when he buckled himself to his Highland broadsword, and set out in pursuit of the Caterans—he entered the navy. And during the eventful period which intervened between the commencement of the war and the peace of 1802, there was little either suffered or achieved by his country-

35

men in which he had not a share. He sailed with Nelson; witnessed the mutiny at the Nore; fought under Admiral Duncan at Camperdown, and under Sir John Borlase Warren at Loch Swilly; assisted in capturing the *Généreux* and *Guillaume Tell*, two French ships of the line; was one of the seamen who, in the Egyptian expedition, were drafted out of Lord Keith's fleet to supply the lack of artillerymen in the army of Sir Ralph Abercromby; had a share in the danger and glory of the landing in Egypt; and fought in the battle of 13th March, and in that which deprived our country of one of her most popular generals. He served, too, at the siege of Alexandria. And then, as he succeeded in procuring his discharge during the short peace of 1802, he returned home with a small sum of hardly-earned prize-money, heartily sick of war and bloodshed. I was asked not long ago by one of his few surviving comrades, whether my uncle had ever told me that their gun was the first landed in Egypt, and the first dragged up the sand-bank immediately over the beach, and how hot it grew under their hands, as, with a rapidity unsurpassed along the line, they poured out in thick succession its iron discharges upon the enemy. I had to reply in the negative. All my uncle's narratives were narratives of what he had seen—not of what he had done; and when, perusing, late in life, one of his favourite works—Dr Keith's "Signs of the Times"—he came to the chapter in which that excellent writer describes the time of hot naval warfare which immediately followed the breaking out of war, as the period in which the second vial was poured out on the sea, and in which the waters "became as the blood of a dead man, so that every living soul died in the sea," I saw him bend his head in reverence as he remarked, "Prophecy, I find, gives to all our glories but a single verse, and it is a verse of judgment." Uncle Sandy, however, did not urge the peace principles which he had acquired amid scenes of death and carnage, into any extravagant consequences; and on the breaking out, in 1803, of the second war of the Revolution, when Napoleon threatened invasion from Brest and Boulogne, he at once shouldered his musket as a volunteer. He had not his brother's fluency of speech; but his narratives of what he had seen were singularly truthful and graphic; and his descriptions of foreign plants and animals, and of the aspect of the distant regions which he had visited, had all the careful minuteness of those of a Dampier. He had a decided turn for natural history. My collection contains a murex, not unfrequent in the Mediterranean, which he found time enough to transfer, during the heat of the landing in Egypt, from the beach to his pocket; and the first ammonite I ever saw was a specimen, which I still retain, that he brought home with him from one of the Liassic deposits of England.

Early on the Sabbath evenings I used regularly to attend at my uncle's with two of my maternal cousins, boys of about my own age, and latterly with my two sisters, to be catechized, first on the Shorter Catechism, and then on the Mother's Catechism of Willison. On Willison my uncles always cross-examined us, to make sure that we understood the short and simple questions; but, apparently regarding the questions of the Shorter Catechism as seed sown for a future day, they were content with having them well fixed in our memories. There was a Sabbath class taught in the parish church at the time by one of the elders; but Sabbath-schools my uncles regarded as merely compensatory institutions, highly creditable to the teachers, but very discreditable indeed to the parents and relatives of the taught; and so they of course never thought of sending us there. Later in the evening, after a short twilight walk, for which the sedentary occupation of my Uncle James formed an apology, but in which my Uncle Alexander always shared, and which usually led them into solitary woods, or along an unfrequented sea-shore, some of the old divines were read; and I used to take my place in the circle, though, I am afraid, not to much advantage. I occasionally caught a fact, or had my attention arrested for a moment by a simile or metaphor; but the trains of close argument, and the passages of dreary "application," were always lost.

CHAPTER III

"At Wallace' name what Scottish blood
But boils up in a spring-tide flood!
Oft have our fearless fathers strode
        By Wallace' side,
Still pressing onward, red wat shod,
        Or glorious died."—BURNS.

I FIRST became thoroughly a Scot some time in my tenth year; and the consciousness of country has remained tolerably strong within me ever since. My Uncle James had procured for me from a neighbour the loan of a common stall-edition of Blind Harry's "Wallace," as modernized by Hamilton; but after reading the first chapter—a piece of dull genealogy, broken into very rude rhyme—I tossed the volume aside as uninteresting; and only resumed it at the request of my uncle, who urged that, simply for *his* amusement and gratification, I should read some three or four chapters more. Accordingly, the three or four chapters more I did read;—I read "how Wallace killed young Selbie the Constable's son"; "how Wallace fished in Irvine Water"; and "how Wallace killed the Churl with his own staff in Ayr"; and then Uncle James told me, in the quiet way in which he used to make a joke tell, that the book seemed to be rather a rough sort of production, filled with accounts of quarrels and bloodshed, and that I might read no more of it unless I felt inclined. But I now did feel inclined very strongly, and read on with increasing astonishment and delight. I was intoxicated with the fiery narratives of the blind minstrel—with his fierce breathings of hot, intolerant patriotism, and his stories of astonishing prowess; and, glorying in being a Scot, and the countryman of Wallace and the Graham, I longed for a war with the Southron, that the wrongs and sufferings of these noble heroes might yet be avenged. All I had previously heard and read of the marvels of foreign parts, of the glories of modern battles, seemed tame and commonplace, compared with the incidents in the life of Wallace; and I never after vexed my mother by wishing myself big enough to be a sailor. My Uncle Sandy, who had some taste for the refinements of poetry, would fain have led me on from the exploits of Wallace to the "Life of the Bruce," which, in the form of a not very vigorous imitation of Dryden's "Virgil," by one Harvey, was bound up in the same volume, and which my uncle deemed the better-written life of the two. And so far as the mere amenities of style were concerned, he was, I daresay, right. But I could not agree with him. Harvey was by much too fine and too learned for me; and it was not until some years after, when I was fortunate enough to pick up one of the later editions of Barbour's "Bruce," that the Hero-King of Scotland assumed his right place in my mind beside its Hero-Guardian. There are stages of development in the immature youth of individuals, that seem to correspond with stages of development in the immature youth of nations; and the recollections of this early time enable me, in some measure, to understand how it was that, for hundreds of years, Blind Harry's "Wallace," with its rude and naked narrative, and its exaggerated incident, should have been, according to Lord Hailes, the Bible of the Scotch people.

I quitted the dame's school at the end of the first twelvemonth, after mastering that grand acquirement of my life—the art of holding converse with books; and was transferred straightforth to the grammar school of the parish, at which there attended at this time about a hundred and twenty boys, with a class of about thirty individuals more, much looked down upon by the others, and not deemed greatly worth the counting, seeing that it consisted of only *lassies*. And here, too, the early individual development seems nicely correspondent with an early national one. In his depreciatory estimate of contemporary woman, the boy is always a true savage. The old parish school of the place had been nobly situated in a snug corner, between the parish churchyard and a thick wood;

and from the interesting centre which it formed, the boys, when tired of making dragoon-horses of the erect headstones, or of leaping along the flat-laid memorials, from end to end of the graveyard, "without touching grass," could repair to the taller trees, and rise in the world by climbing among them. As, however, they used to encroach, on these latter occasions, upon the laird's pleasure-grounds, the school had been removed ere my time to the sea-shore; where, though there were neither tombstones nor trees, there were some balancing advantages, of a kind which perhaps only boys of the old school could have adequately appreciated. As the school-windows fronted the opening of the Firth, not a vessel could enter the harbour that we did not see; and, improving through our opportunities, there was perhaps no educational institution in the kingdom in which all sorts of barques and carvels, from the fishing yawl to the frigate, could be more correctly drawn on the slate, or where any defect in hulk or rigging, in some faulty delineation, was surer of being more justly and unsparingly criticised. Further, the town, which drove a great trade in salted pork at the time, had a killing-place not thirty yards from the school-door, where from eighty to a hundred pigs used sometimes to die for the general good in a single day; and it was a great matter to hear, at occasional intervals, the roar of death outside rising high over the general murmur within, or to be told by some comrade, returned from his five minutes' leave of absence, that a hero of a pig had taken three blows of the hatchet ere it fell, and that even after its subjection to the sticking process, it had got hold of Jock Keddie's hand in its mouth, and almost smashed his thumb. We learned, too, to know, from our signal opportunities of observation, not only a good deal about pig-anatomy—especially about the detached edible parts of the animal, such as the spleen and the pancreas, and at least one other very palatable viscus besides—but became knowing also about the *take* and curing of herrings. All the herring boats during the fishing season passed our windows on their homeward way to the harbour; and, from their depth in the water, we became skilful enough to predicate the number of crans[1] aboard of each with wonderful judgment and correctness. In days of good general fishings, too, when the curing-yards proved too small to accommodate the quantities brought ashore, the fish used to be laid in glittering heaps opposite the school-house door; and an exciting scene, that combined the bustle of the workshop with the confusion of the crowded fair, would straightway spring up within twenty yards of the forms at which we sat, greatly to our enjoyment, and, of course, not a little to our instruction. We could see, simply by peering over book or slate, the curers going about rousing their fish with salt, to counteract the effects of the dog-day sun; bevies of young women employed as gutters, and horridly incarnadined with blood and viscera, squatting around the heaps, knife in hand, and plying with busy fingers their well-paid labours, at the rate of sixpence per hour; relays of heavily-laden fish-wives bringing ever and anon fresh heaps of herrings in their creels; and outside of all, the coopers hammering as if for life and death—now tightening hoops, and now slackening them, and anon caulking with bulrush the leaky seams. It is not every grammar school in which such lessons are taught as those in which all were initiated, and in which all became in some degree accomplished, in the grammar school of Cromarty!

The building in which we met was a low, long, straw-thatched cottage, open from gable to gable, with a mud floor below, and an unlathed roof above; and stretching along the naked rafters, which, when the master chanced to be absent for a few minutes, gave noble exercise in climbing, there used frequently to lie a helm, or oar, or boathook, or even a foresail—the spoil of some hapless peat-boat from the opposite side of the Firth. The Highland boatmen of Ross had carried on a trade in peats for ages with the Saxons of the town; and as every boat owed a long-derived perquisite of twenty peats to the grammar school, and as payment

---

[1] A measure of capacity used in Scotland, in the form of baskets, for herring from the net—containing $37^1/_2$ imperial gallons, or about 750 herrings.

was at times foolishly refused, the party of boys commissioned by the master to exact it almost always succeeded, either by force or stratagem, in securing and bringing along with them, in behalf of the institution, some spar, or sail, or piece of rigging, which, until redeemed by special treaty, and the payment of the peats, was stowed up over the rafters. These peat expeditions, which were intensely popular in the school, gave noble exercise to the faculties. It was always a great matter to see, just as the school met, some observant boy appear, cap in hand, before the master, and intimate the fact of an arrival at the shore, by the simple words, "Peat-boat, Sir." The master would then proceed to name a party, more or less numerous, according to the exigency; but it seemed to be matter of pretty correct calculation that, in the cases in which the peat claim was disputed, it required about twenty boys to bring home the twenty peats, or, lacking these, the compensatory sail or spar. There were certain ill-conditioned boatmen who almost always resisted, and who delighted to tell us—invariably, too, in very bad English—that our perquisite was properly the hangman's perquisite,[1] made over to us because we were *like him*; not seeing—blockheads as they were!—that the very admission established in full the rectitude of our claim, and gave to us, amid our dire perils and faithful contendings, the strengthening consciousness of a just quarrel. In dealing with these recusants, we used ordinarily to divide our forces into two bodies, the larger portion of the party filling their pockets with stones, and ranging themselves on some point of vantage, such as the pier-head; and the smaller stealing down as near the boat as possible, and mixing themselves up with the purchasers of the peats. We then, after due warning, opened fire upon the boatmen; and, when the pebbles were hopping about them like hailstones, the boys below commonly succeeded in securing, under cover of the fire, the desired boathook or oar. And such were the ordinary circumstances and details of this piece of Spartan education; of which a

---

[1] There may have been truth in the allegation; at least the hangman of Inverness enjoyed, from time immemorial, a similar perquisite—a peat out of every creel brought to the burgh market (Miller).

townsman has told me he was strongly reminded when boarding, on one occasion, under cover of a well-sustained discharge of musketry, the vessel of an enemy that had been stranded on the shores of Berbice.

The parish schoolmaster was a scholar and an honest man, and if a boy really wished to learn, *he* certainly could teach him. He had attended the classes at Aberdeen during the same sessions as the late Dr Mearns,[1] and in mathematics and the languages had disputed the prize with the Doctor; but he had failed to get on equally well in the world; and now, in middle life, though a licentiate of the Church, he had settled down to be what he subsequently remained—the teacher of a parish school. There were usually a few grown-up lads under his tuition—careful sailors, that had stayed ashore during the winter quarter to study navigation as a science—or tall fellows, happy in the patronage of the great, who, in the hope of being made excisemen, had come to school to be initiated in the mysteries of gauging—or grown young men, who, on second thoughts, and somewhat late in the day, had recognised the Church as their proper vocation; and these used to speak of the master's acquirements and teaching ability in the very highest terms. He himself, too, could appeal to the fact, that no teacher in the north had ever sent more students to college, and that his better scholars almost always got on well in life. But then, on the other hand, the pupils who wished to do nothing— a description of individuals that comprised fully two-thirds of all the younger ones—were not required to do much more than they wished; and parents and guardians were loud in their complaints that he was no suitable schoolmaster for them; though the boys themselves usually thought him quite suitable enough.

He was in the habit of advising the parents or relations of those he deemed his clever lads, to give them a classical education; and meeting one day with Uncle James, he urged that I should be put on Latin. I was a great reader, he said; and he found that when

[1] Dr Duncan Mearns (1779-1852), Professor of Divinity at King's College, Aberdeen. Moderator of the General Assembly in 1821, and a leading moderate in religious affairs.

I missed a word in my English tasks, I almost always substituted a synonym in the place of it. And so, as Uncle James had arrived, on data of his own, at a similar conclusion, I was transferred from the English to the Latin form, and, with four other boys, fairly entered on the "Rudiments." I laboured with tolerable diligence for a day or two; but there was no one to tell me what the rules meant, or whether they really meant anything; and when I got on as far as *penna*, a pen, and saw how the changes were rung on one poor word, that did not seem to be of more importance in the old language than in the modern one, I began miserably to flag, and to long for my English reading, with its nice amusing stories, and its picture-like descriptions. The "Rudiments" was by far the dullest book I had ever seen. It embodied no thought that I could perceive—it certainly contained no narrative—it was a perfect contrast to not only the "Life and Adventures of Sir William Wallace," but to even the Voyages of Cook and Anson. None of my class-fellows were by any means bright—they had been all set on Latin without advice of the master; and yet, when he learned, which he soon did, to distinguish and call us up to our tasks by the name of the "heavy class," I was, in most instances, to be found at its nether end. Shortly after, however, when we got a little farther on, it was seen that I had a decided turn for translation. The master, good simple man that he was, always read to us in English, as the school met, the piece of Latin given us as our task for the day; and as my memory was strong enough to carry away the whole translation in its order, I used to give him back in the evening, word for word, his own rendering, which satisfied him on most occasions tolerably well. There were none of us much looked after; and I soon learned to bring books of amusement to the school with me, which, amid the Babel confusion of the place, I contrived to read undetected. Some of them, save in the language in which they were written, were identical with the books proper to the place. I remember perusing by stealth in this way, Dryden's "Virgil," and the "Ovid" of Dryden and his friends; while Ovid's own "Ovid," and Virgil's own "Virgil," lay beside me, sealed up in the fine old tongue, which I was thus throwing away my only chance of acquiring.

One morning, having the master's English rendering of the day's task well fixed in my memory, and no book of amusement to read, I began gossiping with my nearest class-fellow, a very tall boy, who ultimately shot up into a lad of six feet four, and who on most occasions sat beside me, as lowest in the form save one. I told him about the tall Wallace and his exploits; and so effectually succeeded in awakening his curiosity, that I had to communicate to him, from beginning to end, every adventure recorded by the blind minstrel. My story-telling vocation once fairly ascertained, there was, I found, no stopping in my course. I had to tell all the stories I ever heard or read; all my father's adventures, so far as I knew them, and all my Uncle Sandy's—with the story of Gulliver, and Philip Quarll, and Robinson Crusoe—of Sinbad, and Ulysses, and Mrs Radcliffe's heroine Emily, with, of course, the love-passages left out; and at length, after weeks and months of narrative, I found my available stock of acquired fact and fiction fairly exhausted. The demand on the part of my class-fellows was, however, as great and urgent as ever; and, setting myself, in the extremity of the case, to try my ability of original production, I began to dole out to them by the hour and the diet, long extempore biographies, which proved wonderfully popular and successful. My heroes were usually warriors like Wallace, and voyagers like Gulliver, and dwellers in desolate islands like Robinson Crusoe; and they had not unfrequently to seek shelter in huge deserted castles, abounding in trap-doors and secret passages, like that of Udolpho. And finally, after much destruction of giants and wild beasts, and frightful encounters with magicians and savages, they almost invariably succeeded in disentombing hidden treasures to an enormous amount, or in laying open gold mines, and then passed a luxurious old age, like that of Sinbad the Sailor, at peace with all mankind, in the midst of confectionery and fruits. The master had a tolerably correct notion of what was going on in the "heavy class"—the stretched-out necks, and the heads clustered together, always told their own special story when I was engaged in telling mine; but, without hating the child, he spared the rod, and simply did what he sometimes allowed himself to do—bestowed a nickname upon me. I was the *Sennachie*,[1] he said; and as the Sennachie I might have been known so long as I remained under his charge, had it not been that, priding himself upon his Gaelic, he used to bestow upon the word the full Celtic pronunciation, which, agreeing but ill with the Teutonic mouths of my school-fellows, militated against its use; and so the name failed to take. With all my carelessness, I continued to be a sort of favourite with the master; and, when at the general English lesson, he used to address to me little quiet speeches, vouchsafed to no other pupil, indicative of a certain literary ground common to us, on which the others had not entered. "That, Sir," he has said, after the class had just perused, in the school collection, a *Tatler* or *Spectator*—"That, Sir, is a good paper—it's an Addison"; or, "That's one of Steele's, Sir"; and on finding in my copy-book, on one occasion, a page filled with rhymes, which I had headed "Poem on Care," he brought it to his desk, and, after reading it carefully over, called me up, and with his closed pen-knife, which served as a pointer, in the one hand, and the copy-book brought down to the level of my eyes in the other, began his criticism. "That's bad grammar, Sir," he said, resting the knife-handle on one of the lines; "and here's an ill-spelt word; and there's another; and you have not at all attended to the punctuation; but the general sense of the piece is good—very good - indeed, Sir." And then he added, with a grim smile, "*Care*, Sir, is, I daresay, as you remark, a very bad thing; but you may safely bestow a little more of it on your spelling and your grammar."

The school, like almost all the other grammar-schools of the period in Scotland, had its yearly cock-fight, preceded by two holidays and a half, during which the boys occupied themselves in collecting and bringing up their cocks. And such always was the array of fighting birds mustered on the occasion, that the day of

[1] Gaelic: story-teller, historian. 'S' in pronunciation = sh.

the festival, from morning till night, used to be spent in fighting out the battle. For weeks after it had passed, the school-floor would continue to retain its deeply-stained blotches of blood, and the boys would be full of exciting narratives regarding the glories of gallant birds, who had continued to fight until both their eyes had been picked out, or who, in the moment of victory, had dropped dead in the middle of the cock-pit. The yearly fight was the relic of a barbarous age; and, in at least one of its provisions, there seemed evidence that it was that of an intolerant age also: every pupil at school, without exemption, had his name entered on the subscription-list, as a cock-fighter, and was obliged to pay the master at the rate of twopence per head, ostensibly for leave to bring his birds to the pit; but, amid the growing humanities of a better time, though the twopences continued to be exacted, it was no longer imperative to bring the birds; and, availing myself of the liberty, I never brought any. Nor, save for a few minutes, on two several occasions, did I ever attend the fight. Had the combat been one among the boys themselves, I would readily enough have done my part, by meeting with any opponent of my years and standing; but I could not bear to look at the bleeding birds. And so I continued to pay my yearly sixpence, as a holder of three cocks—the lowest sum deemed in any degree genteel—but remained simply a fictitious or paper cock-fighter, and contributed in no degree to the success of the *head-stock* or leader, to whose party, in the general division of the school, it was my lot to fall. Neither, I must add, did I learn to take an interest in the sacrificial orgies of the adjoining slaughterhouse. A few of the chosen school-boys were permitted by the killers to exercise at times the privilege of knocking down a pig, and even, on rare occasions, to essay the sticking; but I turned with horror from both processes; and if I drew near at all, it was only when some animal, scraped and cleaned, and suspended from the beam, was in the course of being laid open by the butcher's knife, that I might mark the forms of the viscera, and the positions which they occupied. To my dislike of the annual cock-fight my uncles must have contributed. They were loud in their denunciations of the enormity; and on one occasion, when a neighbour was unlucky enough to remark, in extenuation, that the practice had been handed down to us by pious and excellent men, who seemed to see nothing wrong in it, I saw the habitual respect for the old divines give way, for at least a moment. Uncle Sandy hesitated under apparent excitement; but, quick and fiery as lightning, Uncle James came to his rescue. "Yes, excellent men!" said my uncle, "but the excellent men of a rude and barbarous age; and, in some parts of their character, tinged by its barbarity. For the cock-fight which these excellent men have bequeathed to us, they ought to have been sent to Bridewell for a week, and fed upon bread and water." Uncle James was, no doubt, over hasty, and felt so a minute after; but the practice of fixing the foundations of ethics on a *They themselves did it*, much after the manner in which the Schoolmen fixed the foundations of their nonsensical philosophy on a "*He himself said it*," is a practice which, though not yet exploded in even very pure Churches, is always provoking, and not quite free from peril to the worthies, whether dead or alive, in whose precedents the moral right is made to rest. In the class of minds represented among the people by that of Uncle James, for instance, it would be much easier to bring down even the old divines, than to bring up cock-fighting.

My native town had possessed, for at least an age or two previous to that of my boyhood, its sprinkling of intelligent, book-consulting mechanics and tradesfolk; and as my acquaintance gradually extended among their representatives and descendants, I was permitted to rummage, in the pursuit of knowledge, delightful old chests and cupboards, filled with tattered and dusty volumes. The moiety of my father's library which remained to me consisted of about sixty several works; my uncle possessed about a hundred and fifty more; and there was a literary cabinet-maker in the neighbourhood, who had once actually composed a poem of thirty lines on the Hill of Cromarty, whose collection of books, chiefly poetical, amounted to from about eighty to a hundred. I used to be often at nights in the workshop of the cabinet-maker, and was sometimes privileged to hear him repeat his poem. There was not much admiration of poets or poetry in the place; and my praise, though that of a very young critic, had always the double merit of being both ample and sincere. I knew the very rocks and trees which his description embraced—had heard the birds to which he referred, and seen the flowers; and as the Hill had been of old a frequent scene of executions, and had borne the gallows of the sheriffdom on its crest, nothing could be more definite than the grave reference, in his opening line, to

"The verdant rising of the *Gallow*-hill."

And so I thought a very great deal of his poem, and what I thought I said; and he, on the other hand, evidently regarded me as a lad of extraordinary taste and discernment for my years. There was another mechanic in the neighbourhood—a house-carpenter, who, though not a poet, was deeply read in books of all kinds, from the plays of Farquhar to the sermons of Flavel;[1] and as both his father and grandfather—the latter, by the way, a Porteous-mob man, and the former a personal friend of poor Fergusson the poet—had also been readers and collectors of books, he possessed a whole pressful of tattered, hard-working volumes, some of them very curious ones; and to me he liberally extended, what literary men always value, "the full freedom of the press." But of all my occasional benefactors in this way, by far the greatest was poor old Francie, the retired clerk and supercargo.

Francie was naturally a man of fair talent and active curiosity. Nor was he by any means deficient in acquirement. He wrote and figured well, and knew a good deal about at least the theory of business; and when articled in early life to a Cromarty merchant and shopkeeper, it was with tolerably fair prospects of getting on in the world. He had, however, a certain infirmity of brain, which rendered both talent and acquirement of but little avail, and that

[1] George Farquhar (1678-1707), the Dublin playwright, author of "The Recruiting Officer"; John Flavel (1630?-1691), a presbyterian divine of Gloucestershire.

began to manifest itself very early. While yet an apprentice, on ascertaining that the way was clear, he used, though grown a tall lad, to bolt out from behind the counter into the middle of a green directly opposite, and there, joining in the sports of some group of youngsters, which the place rarely wanted, he would play out half a game at marbles, or honey-pots, or hy-spy, and, when he saw his master or a customer approaching, bolt back again. The thing was not deemed seemly; but Francie, when spoken to on the subject, could speak as sensibly as any young person of his years. He needed relaxation, he used to say, though he never suffered it to interfere with his proper business; and where was there safer relaxation to be found than among innocent children? This, of course, was eminently rational, and even virtuous. And so, when his term of apprenticeship had expired, Francie was despatched, not without hope of success, to Newfoundland—where he had relations extensively engaged in the fishing trade—to serve as one of their clerks. He was found to be a competent clerk; but unluckily there was but little known of the interior of the island at the time; and some of the places most distant from St John's, such as the Bay and River of Exploits, bore tempting names; and so, after Francie had made many inquiries at the older inhabitants regarding what was to be seen amid the scraggy brushwood and broken rocks of the inner country, a morning came in which he was reported missing at the office; and little else could be learned respecting him, than that at early dawn he had been seen setting out for the woods, provided with staff and knapsack. He returned in about a week, worn out and half-starved. He had not been so successful as he had anticipated, he said, in providing himself by the way with food, and so he had to turn back ere he could reach the point on which he had previously determined; but he was sure he would be happier in his next journey. It was palpably unsafe to suffer him to remain exposed to the temptation of an unexplored country; and as his friends and superiors at St John's had just laden a vessel with fish for the Italian market during Lent, Francie was despatched with her as supercargo, to look after

50

the sales, in a land of which every footbreadth had been familiar to men for thousands of years, and in which it was supposed he would have no inducement to wander. Francie, however, had read much about Italy; and finding, on landing at Leghorn, that he was within a short distance of Pisa, he left ship and cargo to take care of themselves, and set out on foot to see the famous hanging-tower, and the great marble cathedral. And tower and cathedral he did see: but it was meanwhile found that he was not quite suited for a supercargo; and he had shortly after to return to Scotland, where his friends succeeded in establishing him in the capacity of clerk and overseer upon a small property in Forfarshire, which was farmed by the proprietor on what was then the newly introduced modern system. He was acquainted, however, with the classical description of Glammis Castle, in the letters of the poet Gray; and after visiting the castle, he set out to examine the ancient encampment at Ardoch—the *Lindum* of the Romans. Finally, all hopes of getting him settled at a distance being given up by his friends, he had to fall back upon Cromarty, where he was yet once more appointed to a clerkship. The establishment with which he was now connected was a large hempen manufactory; and it was his chief employment to register the quantities of hemp given out to the spinners, and the numbers of hanks of yarn into which they had converted it, when given in. He soon, however, began to take long walks; and the old women, with their yarn, would be often found accumulated, ere his return, by tens and dozens at his office-door. At length, after taking a very long walk indeed, for it stretched from near the opening to the head of the Cromarty Firth, a distance of about twenty miles, and included in its survey the antique tower of Kinkell and the old Castle of Craighouse, he was relieved from the duties of his clerkship, and left to pursue his researches undisturbed, on a small annuity, the gift of his friends. He was considerably advanced in life ere I knew him, profoundly grave, and very taciturn, and, though he never discussed politics, a mighty reader of the newspapers. "Oh! this is terrible," I have heard him exclaim, when on one occasion a snow

51

storm had blocked up both the coast and the highland roads for a week together, and arrested the northward course of the mails— "It is terrible to be left in utter ignorance of the public business of the country!"

Francie, whom every one called Mr— to his face, and always Francie when his back was turned, chiefly because it was known he was punctilious on the point, and did not like the more familiar term, used in the winter evenings to be a regular member of the circle that met beside my Uncle James's work-table. And, chiefly through the influence, in the first instance, of my uncles, I was permitted to visit him in his own room—a privilege enjoyed by scarce any one else—and even invited to borrow his books. His room—a dark and melancholy chamber, grey with dust—always contained a number of curious but not very rare things, which he had picked up in his walks—prettily coloured fungi, vegetable monstrosities of the commoner kind, such as "fause craws' nests," and flattened twigs of pine—and with these, as the representatives of another department of natural science, fragments of semi-transparent quartz or of glittering feldspar,[1] and sheets of mica a little above the ordinary size. But the charm of the apartment lay in its books. Francie was a book-fancier, and lacked only the necessary wealth to be in the possession of a very pretty collection. As it was, he had some curious volumes; among others, a first-edition copy of the "Nineteen Years' Travels of William Lithgow," with an ancient woodcut, representing the said William in the background, with his head brushing the skies, and, far in front, two of the tombs which covered the heroes of Ilium, barely tall enough to reach half-way to his knee, and of the length, in proportion to the size of the traveller, of ordinary octavo volumes. He had black-letter books, too, on astrology, and on the planetary properties of vegetables; and an ancient book on medicine, that recommended as a cure for the toothache a bit of the jaw of a suicide, well triturated; and, as an infallible remedy for the falling-sickness, an ounce or two of the brains of a young man, carefully

[1] Or felspar, a milky or sometimes pinkish rock, one of the components of granite.

dried over the fire. Better, however, than these, for at least my purpose, he had a tolerably complete collection of the British essayists, from Addison to Mackenzie, with the "Essays" and "Citizen of the World" of Goldsmith; several interesting works of travels and voyages, translated from the French; and translations from the German, of Lavater, Zimmerman, and Klopstock. He had a good many of the minor poets too; and I was enabled to cultivate, mainly from his collection, a tolerably adequate acquaintance with the wits of the reign of Queen Anne. Poor Francie was at bottom a kindly and honest man; but the more intimately one knew him, the more did the weakness and brokenness of his intellect appear. His mind was a labyrinth without a clue, in whose recesses there lay stored up a vast amount of book-knowledge, that could never be found when wanted, and was of no sort of use to himself, or any one else. I got sufficiently into his confidence to be informed, under the seal of strict secrecy, that he contemplated producing a great literary work, whose special character he had not quite determined, but which was to be begun a few years hence. And when death found him, at an age which did not fall far short of the allotted threescore and ten, the great unknown work was still an undefined idea, and had still to be begun.

There were several other branches of my education going on at this time outside the pale of the school, in which, though I succeeded in amusing myself, I was no trifler. The shores of Cromarty are strewed over with water-rolled fragments of the primary rocks derived chiefly from the west during the ages of the boulder clay[1]; and I soon learned to take a deep interest in sauntering over the various pebble-beds when shaken up by recent storms, and in learning to distinguish their numerous components. But I was sadly in want of a vocabulary; and as, according to Cowper, "the growth of what is excellent is slow," it was not until long after that I bethought me of the obvious enough expedient of representing the various species of simple rocks, by certain

[1] A stiff, sandy clay usually studded with "boulders" great and small; a deposit of the ice age.

numerals, and the compound ones by the numerals representative of each separate component, ranged, as in vulgar fractions, along a medial line, with the figures representative of the prevailing materials of the mass above, and those representative of the materials in less proportions below. Though, however, wholly deficient in the signs proper to represent what I knew, I soon acquired a considerable quickness of eye in distinguishing the various kinds of rock, and tolerably definite conceptions of the generic character of the porphyries[1], granites, gneisses[2], quartz-rocks, clay-slates, and mica-schists[3], which everywhere strewed the beach. In the rocks of mechanical origin I was at this time much less interested; but in individual, as in general history, mineralogy almost always precedes geology. I was fortunate enough to discover, one happy morning, among the lumber and debris of old John Feddes's dark room, an antique-fashioned hammer, which had belonged, my mother told me, to old John himself more than a hundred years before. It was an uncouth sort of implement, with a handle of strong black oak, and a short, compact head, square on the one face, and oblong on the other. And though it dealt rather an obtuse blow, the temper was excellent, and the shaft firmly set; and I went about with it, breaking into all manner of stones, with great perseverance and success. I found, in a large-grained granite, a few sheets of beautiful black mica, that, when split exceedingly thin, and pasted between slips of mica of the ordinary kind, made admirably-coloured eye-glasses, that converted the landscapes around into richly-toned drawings in sepia; and numerous crystals of garnet embedded in mica-schist, that were, I was sure, identical with the stones set in a little gold brooch, the property of my mother. To this last surmise, however, some of the neighbours to whom I showed my prize demurred. The stones in my mother's brooch were precious stones, they said; whereas what I had found was merely a "stone upon the shore."

[1] Rocks showing large conspicuous crystals.
[2] Rocks of the composition of granite in which, however, the minerals are arranged in irregular layers: the prevailing type of rock in the Highlands.
[3] Rocks made up of alternate sheets of quartz and mica.

My friend the cabinet-maker went so far as to say that the specimen was but a mass of plum-pudding stone, and its dark-coloured enclosures simply the currants; but then, on the other hand, Uncle Sandy took my view of the matter: the stone was not plum-pudding stone, he said: he had often seen plum-pudding stone in England, and knew it to be a sort of rough conglomerate of various components; whereas my stone was composed of a finely-grained silvery substance, and the crystals which it contained were, he was sure, gems like those in the brooch, and, so far as he could judge, real garnets. This was a great decision; and, much encouraged in consequence, I soon ascertained that garnets are by no means rare among the pebbles of the Cromarty shore. Nay, so mixed up are they with its sands even—a consequence of the abundance of the mineral among the primary rocks of Ross— that after a heavy surf has beaten the exposed beach of the neighbouring hill, there may be found on it patches of comminuted garnet, from one to three square yards in extent, that resemble, at a little distance, pieces of crimson carpeting, and nearer at hand, sheets of crimson bead-work, and of which almost every point and particle is a gem. From some unexplained circumstance, connected apparently with the specific gravity of the substance, it separates in this style from the general mass, on coasts much beaten by the waves; but the garnets of these curious pavements, though so exceedingly abundant, are in every instance exceedingly minute. I never detected in them a fragment greatly larger than a pin-head; but it was always with much delight that I used to fling myself down on the shore beside some newly-discovered patch, and bethink me, as I passed my fingers along the larger grains, of the heaps of gems in Aladdin's cavern, or of Sinbad's valley of diamonds.

The Hill of Cromarty formed at this time at once my true school and favourite playground; and if my master did wink at times harder than master ought, when I was playing truant among its woods or on its shores, it was, I believe, whether he thought so or no, all for the best. My Uncle Sandy had, as I have already said, been bred a cartwright; but finding, on his return, after his seven years' service on board a man-of-war, that the place had cartwrights enough for all the employment, he applied himself to the humble but not unremunerative profession of a sawyer, and used often to pitch his saw-pit, in the more genial seasons of the year, among the woods of the hill. I remember, he never failed setting it down in some pretty spot, sheltered from the prevailing winds under the lee of some fern-covered rising ground or some bosky thicket, and always in the near neighbourhood of a spring; and it used to be one of my most delightful exercises to find out for myself among the thick woods, in some holiday journey of exploration, the place of a newly-formed pit. With the saw-pit as my base-line of operations, and secure always of a share in Uncle Sandy's dinner, I used to make excursions of discovery on every side—now among the thicker tracts of wood, which bore among the town-boys, from the twilight gloom that ever rested in their recesses, the name of "the dungeons"; and anon to the precipitous seashore, with its wild cliffs and caverns. The Hill of Cromarty is one of a chain belonging to the great Ben Nevis line of elevation; and, though it occurs in a sandstone district, is itself a huge primary mass, upheaved of old from the abyss, and composed chiefly of granitic gneiss and a red splintery hornstone. It contains also numerous veins and beds of hornblend[1] rock and chlorite-schist[2], and of a peculiar-looking granite, of which the quartz is white as milk, and the feldspar red as blood. When still wet by the receding tide, those veins and beds seem as if highly polished, and present a beautiful aspect; and it was always with great delight that I used to pick my way among them, hammer in hand, and fill my pockets with specimens.

There was one locality which I in especial loved. No path runs the way. On the one side, an abrupt iron-tinged promontory, so remarkable for its human-like profile, that it seems part of a half-buried sphinx, protrudes into the deep green water. On the

[1] A usually dark green mineral.
[2] A rock composed of fine layers (schist) of a light green rock (Gr, *chloros*, green) and felspar.

other—less prominent, for even at full tide the traveller can wind between its base and the sea—there rises a shattered and ruined precipice, seamed with blood-red ironstone, that retains on its surface the bright metallic gleam, and amid whose piles of loose and fractured rock one may still detect fragments of stalactite. The stalactite is all that remains of a spacious cavern, which once hollowed the precipice, but which, more than a hundred years before, had tumbled down during a thunderstorm, when filled with a flock of sheep, and penned up the poor creatures for ever. The space between these headlands forms an irregular crescent of great height, covered with wood a-top, and amid whose lichened crags, and on whose steep slopes, the hawthorn, and bramble, and wild rasp, and rock strawberry, take root, with many a scraggy shrub and sweet wild flower besides; while along its base lie huge blocks of green hornblend, on a rude pavement of granitic gneiss, traversed at one point, for many yards, by a broad vein of milk-white quartz. The quartz vein formed my central point of attraction in this wild paradise. The white stone, thickly traversed by threads of purple and red, is a beautiful though unworkable rock; and I soon ascertained that it is flanked by a vein of feldspar broader than itself, of a brick-red tint, and the red stone flanked, in turn, by a drab-coloured vein of the same mineral, in which there occur in great abundance masses of a homogeneous mica— mica not existing in lamina, but, if I may use the term, as a sort of micaceous felt. It would almost seem as if some gigantic experimenter of the old world had set himself to separate into their simple mineral components the granitic rocks of the hill, and that the three parallel veins were the results of his labour. Such, however, was not the sort of idea which they at this time suggested to me. I had read in Sir Walter Raleigh's voyage to Guiana, the poetic description of that upper country in which the knight's exploration of the river Corale terminated, and where, amid lovely prospects of rich valleys, and wooded hills and winding waters, almost every rock bore on its surface the yellow gleam of gold. True, according to the voyager, the precious metal was itself absent. But Sir Walter, on afterwards showing "some of the stones to a Spaniard of the Caraccas, was told by him they were *el madre del ora*, that is, the mother of gold, and that the mine itself was further in the ground." And though the quartz vein of the Cromarty Hill contained no metal more precious than iron, and but little even of that, it was, I felt sure, the "mother" of something very fine. As for silver, I was pretty certain I had found the "mother" of *it*, if not, indeed, the precious metal itself, in a cherty boulder enclosing numerous cubes of rich galena;[1] and occasional masses of iron pyrites gave, as I thought, large promise of gold. But though sometimes asked in humble irony, by the farm-servants who came to load their carts with sea-weed along the Cromarty beach, whether I was "getting siller in the stanes," I was so unlucky as never to be able to answer their question in the affirmative.

[1] Sulphide of lead.

CHAPTER IV

"Strange marble stones, here larger and there less,
And of full various forms, which still increase
In height and bulk by a continual drop,
Which upon each distilling from the top,
And falling still exactly on the crown,
There break themselves to mists, which, trickling down,
Crust into stone, and (but with leisure) swell
The sides, and still advance the miracle."—CHARLES COTTON.

It is low water in the Firth of Cromarty during stream tides, between six and seven o'clock in the evening; and my Uncle Sandy, in returning from his work at the close of the day, used not unfrequently, when, according to the phrase of the place, "there was a tide in the water," to strike down the hillside, and spend a quiet hour in the ebb. I delighted to accompany him on these occasions. There are professors of Natural History that know less of living nature than was known by Uncle Sandy; and I deemed it no small matter to have all the various productions of the sea with which he was acquainted pointed out to me in these walks, and to be in possession of his many curious anecdotes regarding them.

He was a skilful crab and lobster fisher, and knew every hole and cranny, along several miles of rocky shore, in which the creatures were accustomed to shelter, with not a few of their own peculiarities of character. Contrary to the view taken by some of our naturalists, such as Agassiz, who hold that the crab—a genus comparatively recent in its appearance in creation—is less embryotic in its character, and higher in its standing, than the more ancient lobster, my uncle regarded the lobster as a more highly developed and more intelligent animal than the crab. The hole in which the lobster lodges has almost always two openings, he has said, through one of which it sometimes contrives to escape when the other is stormed by the fisher; whereas the crab is usually content, like the "rat devoid of soul," with a hole of only one opening; and, besides, gets so angry in most cases with his assailant, as to become more bent on assault than escape, and so loses himself through sheer loss of temper. And yet the crab has, he used to add, some points of intelligence about him too. When, as sometimes happened, he got hold, in his dark narrow recess in the rock, of some luckless digit, my uncle showed me how that, after the first tremendous squeeze, he began always to experiment upon what he had got, by alternately slackening and straitening his grasp, as if to ascertain whether it had life in it, or was merely a piece of dead matter; and that the only way to escape him, on these trying occasions, was to let the finger lie passively between his nippers, as if it were a bit of stick or tangle; when, apparently deeming it such, he would be sure to let it go; whereas, on the least attempt to withdraw it, he would at once straiten his gripe, and not again relax it for mayhap half an hour. In dealing with the lobster, on the other hand, the fisher had to beware that he did not depend too much on the hold he had got of the creature, if it was merely a hold of one of the great claws. For a moment it would remain passive in his grasp; he would then be sensible of a slight tremor in the captured limb, and mayhap hear a slight crackle; and, presto, the captive would straightway be off like a dart through the deep-water hole, and only the limb remain in the fisher's hand. My uncle has, however, told me that lobsters do not always lose their limbs with the necessary judgment. They throw them of when suddenly frightened, without first waiting to consider whether the sacrifice of a pair of legs is the best mode of obviating the danger. On firing a musket immediately over a lobster just captured, he has seen it throw off both its great claws in the sudden extremity of its terror, just as a panic-struck soldier sometimes throws away his weapons. Such, in kind, were the anecdotes of Uncle Sandy. He instructed me, too, how to find, amid thickets of laminaria and fuci[1] the nest of the lump-fish, and

[1] Tangle and wrack

taught me to look well in its immediate neighbourhood for the male and female fish, especially for the male; and showed me further, that the hard-shelled spawn of this creature may, when well washed, be eaten raw, and forms at least as palatable a viand in that state as the imported caviare of Russia and the Caspian. There were instances in which the common crow acted as a sort of jackal to us in our lump-fish explorations. We would see him busied at the side of some fuci-covered pool, screaming and cawing as if engaged in combating an enemy; and, on going up to the place, we used to find the lump-fish he had killed fresh and entire, but divested of the eyes, which we found, as a matter of course, that the assailant, in order to make sure of victory, had taken the precaution of picking out at an early stage of the contest.

Nor was it with merely the edible that we busied ourselves on these journeys. The brilliant metallic *plumage* of the sea-mouse (*Aphrodita*), steeped as in the dyes of the rainbow, excited our admiration time after time; and still higher wonder used to be awakened by a much rarer annelid, brown, and slender as a piece of rope-yarn, and from thirty to forty feet in length, which no one save my uncle had ever found along the Cromarty shores, and which, when broken in two, as sometimes happened in the measuring, divided its vitality so equally between the pieces, that each was fitted, we could not doubt, though unable to repeat in the case the experiment of Spallanzani, to set up as an independent existence, and carry on business for itself. The annelids, too, that form for themselves tubular dwellings built up of large grains of sand (*amphitrites*), always excited our interest. Two hand-shaped tufts of golden-hued setæ—furnished, however, with greatly more than the typical number of fingers—rise from the shoulders of these creatures, and must, I suspect, be used as hands in the process of building; at least the hands of the most practised builder could not set stones with nicer skill than is exhibited by these worms in the setting of the grains which compose their cylindrical dwellings—dwellings that, from their form and structure, seem suited to remind the antiquary of the round towers of Ireland, and, from the style of their masonry, of old Cyclopean walls. Even the mason-wasps and bees are greatly inferior workmen to these mason *amphitrites*. I was introduced also, in our ebb excursions, to the cuttle-fish and the sea-hare, and shown how the one, when pursued by an enemy, discharges a cloud of ink to conceal its retreat, and that the other darkens the water around it with a lovely purple pigment, which my uncle was pretty sure would make a rich dye, like that extracted of old by the Tyrians from a whelk which he had often seen on the beach near Alexandria. I learned, too, to cultivate an acquaintance with some two or three species of doris, that carry their arboraceous, tree-like lungs on their backs, as Macduff's soldiers carried the boughs of Birnam wood to the Hill of Dunsinane; and I soon acquired a sort of affection for certain shells, which bore, as I supposed, a more exotic aspect than their neighbours. Among these were *Trochus Zizyphinus*,[1] with its flame-like markings of crimson, on a ground of paley-brown; *Patella pellucida*,[2] with its lustrous rays of vivid blue on its dark epidermis, that resemble the sparks of a firework breaking against a cloud; and, above all, *Cyprœa Europea*,[3] a not rare shell further to the north, but so little abundant in the Firth of Cromarty, as to render the live animal, when once or twice in a season I used to find it creeping on the laminaria at the extreme outer edge of the tide-line, with its wide orange mantle flowing liberally around it, somewhat of a prize. In short, the tract of sea-bottom laid dry by the ebb formed an admirable school, and Uncle Sandy an excellent teacher, under whom I was not in the least disposed to trifle; and when, long after, I learned to detect old-marine bottoms far out of sight of the sea—now amid the ancient forest-covered Silurians[4] of central England, and anon opening to the light on some hillside among the Mountain Limestones of our country—I have felt how very much I owed to his instructions.

[1] The common Top Shell.
[2] The Smooth Limpet.
[3] The Cowry, a sea snail.
[4] The System of rocks overlying the Old Red Sandstone, familiar in the south of Scotland, and represented in Sutherlandshire.

His facts wanted a vocabulary adequately fitted to represent them; but though they "lacked a commodity of good names," they were all founded on careful observation, and possessed that first element of respectability—perfect originality: they were all acquired by himself. I owed more, however, to the habit of observation which he assisted me in forming, than even to his facts; and yet some of these were of high value. He has shown me, for instance, that an immense granitic boulder in the neighbourhood of the town, known for ages as the Clach Malloch, or Cursed Stone, stands so exactly in the line of low water, that the larger stream-tides of March and September lay dry its inner side, but never its outer one—round the outer side there are always from two to four inches of water; and such had been the case for at least a hundred years before, in his father's and grandfather's days—evidence enough of itself, I have heard him say, that the relative levels of sea and land were not altering; though during the lapsed century the waves had so largely encroached on the low flat shores, that elderly men of his acquaintance, long since passed away, had actually held the plough when young where they had held the rudder when old. He used, too, to point out to me the effect of certain winds upon the tides. A strong hasty gale from the east, if coincident with a spring-tide, sent up the waves high upon the beach, and cut away whole roods of the soil; but the gales that usually kept larger tides from falling during ebb were prolonged gales from the west. A series of these, even when not very high, left not unfrequently from one to two feet of water round the Clach Malloch, during stream-tides, that would otherwise have laid its bottom bare—a proof, he used to say, that the German Ocean, from its want of breadth, could not be heaped up against our coasts to the same extent, by the violence of a very powerful east wind, as the Atlantic by the force of a comparatively moderate westerly one. It is not improbable that the philosophy of the Drift Current, and of the apparently reactionary Gulf Stream, may be embodied in this simple remark.

The woods on the lower slopes of the hill, when there was no access to the zones covered save at low ebb by the sea, furnished me with employment of another kind. I learned to look with interest on the workings of certain insects, and to understand some of at least their simpler instincts. The large Diadem Spider, which spins so strong a web, that, in pressing my way through the furze thickets, I could hear its white silken cords crack as they yielded before me, and which I found skilled, like an ancient magician, in the strange art of rendering itself invisible in the clearest light, was an especial favourite; though its great size, and the wild stories I had read about the bite of its cogener the tarantula, made me cultivate its acquaintance somewhat at a distance. Often, however, have I stood beside its large web, when the creature occupied its place in the centre, and, touching it with a withered grass stalk, I have seen it sullenly swing on the lines "with its hands," and then shake them with a motion so rapid, that—like Carathis, the mother of the Caliph Vathek[1], who, when her hour of doom had come, "glanced off in a rapid whirl, which rendered her invisible"—the eye failed to see either web or insect for minutes together. Nothing appeals more powerfully to the youthful fancy than those coats, rings, and amulets of eastern lore, that conferred on their possessors the gift of invisibility. I learned, too, to take an especial interest in what, though they belong to a different family, are known as the Water *Spiders*; and have watched them speeding by fits and starts, like skaters on the ice, across the surface of some woodland spring or streamlet—fearless walkers on the waters, that, with true faith in the integrity of the implanted instinct, never made shipwreck in the eddy or sank in the pool. It is to these little creatures that Wordsworth refers in one of his sonnets on sleep:—

> "O sleep, thou art to me
> A fly that up and down himself doth shove
> Upon a fretful rivulet; now *above*,
> Now *on* the water, vexed with mockery."

---

[1] From Beckford's Oriental romance, "Vathek" (1786).

As shown, however, to the poet himself on one occasion, somewhat to his discomfort, by assuredly no mean authority—Mr James Wilson—the "vexed" "fly," though one of the hemipterous insects, never uses its wings, and so never gets "above" the water. Among my other favourites were the splendid dragonflies, the crimson-speckled Burnet moths, and the small azure butterflies, that, when fluttering among delicate harebells and crimson-tipped daisies, used to suggest to me, long ere I became acquainted with the pretty figure of Moore,[1] or even ere the figure had been produced, the idea of flowers that had taken to flying. The wild honey bees, too, in their several species, had peculiar charms for me. There were the buff-coloured carders, that erected over their honey-jars domes of moss; the lapidary red-tipped bees, that built amid the recesses of ancient cairns, and in old dry stone walls, and were so invincibly brave in defending their homesteads, that they never gave up the quarrel till they died; and, above all, the yellow-zoned humble-bees, that lodged deep in the ground along the dry sides of grassy banks, and were usually wealthier in honey than any of their cogeners, and existed in larger communities. But the herd-boys of the parish, and the foxes of its woods and brakes, shared in my interest in the wild honey bees, and, in the pursuit of something else than knowledge, were ruthless robbers of their nests. I often observed that the fox, with all his reputed shrewdness, is not particularly knowing on the subject of bees. He makes as dead a set on a wasp's nest as on that of the carder or humble-bee, and gets, I doubt not, heartily stung for his pains; for though, as shown by the marks of his teeth, left on fragments of the paper combs scattered about, he attempts eating the young wasps in the chrysalis state, the undevoured remains seem to argue that he is but little pleased with them as food. There were occasions, however, in which even the herd-boys met with only disappointment in their bee-hunting excursions; and in one

---

[1] "The beautiful blue damsel flies,
    That fluttered round the jasmine stems,
    Like wingéd flowers or flying gems.
            PARADISE AND THE PERI (Miller).

notable instance, the result of the adventure used to be spoken of in school and elsewhere, under our breath and in secret, as something very horrible. A party of boys had stormed a humble-bees' nest on the side of the old chapel-brae, and, digging inwards along the narrow winding earth passage, they at length came to a grinning human skull, and saw the bees issuing thick from out a round hole at its base—the *foramen magnum*. The wise little workers had actually formed their nest within the hollow of the head, once occupied by the busy brain; and their spoilers, more scrupulous than Samson of old, who seems to have enjoyed the meat brought forth out of the eater, and the sweetness extracted from the strong, left in very great consternation their honey all to themselves.

One of my discoveries of this early period would have been deemed a not unimportant one by the geologist. Among the woods of the hill, a short half-mile from the town, there is a morass of comparatively small extent, but considerable depth, which had been laid open by the bursting of a waterspout on the uplands, and in which the dark peaty chasm remained unclosed, though the event had happened ere my birth, until I had become old and curious enough thoroughly to explore it. It was a black miry ravine some ten or twelve feet in depth. The bogs around waved thick with silvery willows of small size; but sticking out from the black sides of the ravine itself, and in some instances stretched across it from side to side, lay the decayed remains of huge giants of the vegetable world, that had flourished and died long ages ere, in at least our northern part of the island, the course of history had begun. There were oaks of enormous girth, into whose coal-black substance one could dig as easily with a pickaxe as one digs into a bank of clay; and at least one noble elm, which ran across the little stream that trickled, rather than flowed, along the bottom of the hollow, and which was in such a state of keeping, that I have scooped out of its trunk, with the unassisted hand, a way for the water. I have found in the ravine—which I learned very much to like as a scene of exploration, though I never failed to quit it sadly bemired—handfuls of hazel-nuts, of the ordinary size, but black as jet, with the cups of acorns, and with twigs of birch that still retained almost unchanged their silvery outer crust of bark, but whose ligneous interior existed as a mere pulp. I have even laid open, in layers of a sort of unctuous clay, resembling fuller's earth, leaves of oak, birch, and hazel, that had fluttered in the wind thousands of years before; and there was one happy day in which I succeeded in digging from out the very bottom of the excavation a huge fragment of an extraordinary-looking deer's horn. It was a broad, massive, strange-looking piece of bone, evidently old-fashioned in its type; and so I brought it home in triumph to Uncle James, as the antiquary of the family, assured that he could tell me all about it. Uncle James paused in the middle of his work; and, taking the horn in his hand, surveyed it leisurely on every side. "That is the horn, boy," he at length said, "of no deer that now lives in this country. We have the red deer, and the fallow deer, and the roe; and none of them have horns at all like that. I never saw an elk; but I am pretty sure this broad, plank-like horn can be none other than the horn of an elk." My uncle set aside his work; and, taking the horn in his hand, went out to the shop of a cabinet-maker in the neighbourhood, where there used to work from five to six journeymen. They all gathered round him to examine it, and agreed in the decision that it was an entirely different sort of horn from any borne by the existing deer of Scotland, and that this surmise regarding it was probably just. And, apparently to enhance the marvel, a neighbour, who was lounging in the shop at the time, remarked, in a tone of sober gravity, that it had lain in the Moss of the Willows "for perhaps half a century." There was positive anger in the tone of my uncle's reply. "Half a century, Sir!" he exclaimed; "was the elk a native of Scotland half a century ago? There is no notice of the elk, Sir, in British history. That horn must have lain in the Moss of the Willows for thousands of years!" "Ah, ha, James, ah, ha," ejaculated the neighbour, with a sceptical shake of the head; but as neither he nor any one else dared meet my uncle on historical ground, the controversy took end with the ejaculation. I soon added to the horn of the elk that of a roe, and part of that of a red deer, found in the same ravine; and the neighbours, impressed by Uncle James's view, used to bring strangers to look at them. At length, unhappily, a relation settled in the south, who had shown me kindness, took a fancy to them; and, smit by the charms of a gorgeous paint-box which he had just sent me, I made them over to him entire. They found their way to London, and were ultimately lodged in the collection of some obscure virtuoso, whose locality or name I have been unable to trace.

The Cromarty Sutors have their two lines of caves—an ancient line hollowed by the waves many centuries ago, when the sea stood, in relation to the land, from fifteen to thirty feet higher along our shores than it does now; and a modern line, which the surf is still engaged in scooping out. Many of the older caves are lined with stalactites, deposited by springs that, filtering through the cracks and fissures of the gneiss, find lime enough in their passage to acquire what is known as a *petrifying*, though, in reality, only an incrusting quality. And these stalactites, under the name of "white stones made by the water," formed of old—as in that Cave of Slains specially mentioned by Buchanan and the Chroniclers, and in those caverns of the Peak so quaintly described by Cotton—one of the grand marvels of the place. Almost all the old gazetteers sufficiently copious in their details to mention Cromarty at all, refer to its "Dropping Cave" as a marvellous marble-producing cavern; and this "Dropping Cave" is but one of many that look out upon the sea from the precipices of the southern Sutor, in whose dark recesses the drops ever tinkle, and the stony ceilings ever grow. The wonder could not have been deemed a great or very rare one by a man like the late Sir George Mackenzie of Coul, well known from his travels in Iceland, and his experiments on the inflammability of the diamond; but it so happened, that Sir George, curious to see the sort of stones to which the old gazetteers referred, made application to the minister of the parish for a set of specimens; and the minister straightway deputed the commission, which he believed to be not a difficult one, to one of his poorer parishioners, an old nailer, as a means of putting a few shillings in his way.

It so happened, however, that the nailer had lost his wife by a sad accident, only a few weeks before; and the story went abroad that the poor woman was, as the townspeople expressed it, "coming back." She had been very suddenly hurried out of the world. When going down the quay after nightfall one evening, with a parcel of clean linen for a sailor, her relative, she had missed footing on the pier edge, and, half-brained, half-drowned, had been found in the morning, stone dead, at the bottom of the harbour. And now, as if pressed by some unsettled business, she used to be seen, it was said, hovering after nightfall about her old dwelling, or sauntering along the neighbouring street; nay, there were occasions, according to the general report, in which she had even exchanged words with some of the neighbours, little to their satisfaction. The words, however, seemed in every instance to have wonderfully little to do with the affairs of another world. I remember seeing the wife of a neighbour rush into my mother's one evening about this time, speechless with terror, and declare, after an awful pause, during which she had lain half-fainting in a chair, that she had just seen Christy. She had been engaged, as the night was falling, but ere darkness had quite set in, in piling up a load of brushwood for fuel outside the door, when up started the spectre on the other side of the heap, attired in the ordinary work-day garb of the deceased, and, in a light and hurried tone, asked, as Christy might have done ere the fatal accident, for a share of the brushwood. "Give me some of that *hag*,[1]" said the ghost; "you have plenty—I have none." It was not known whether or no the nailer had seen the apparition; but it was pretty certain he believed in it; and as the "Dropping Cave" is both dark and solitary, and had forty years ago a bad name to boot—for the mermaid had been observed disporting in front of it even at mid-day, and lights and screams heard from it at nights—it must have

---

[1] Cut wood.

been a rather formidable place to a man living in the momentary expectation of a visit from a dead wife. So far as could be ascertained—for the nailer himself was rather close in the matter—he had not entered the cave at all. He seemed, judging from the marks of scraping left along the sides for about two or three feet from the narrow opening, to have taken his stand outside, where the light was good, and the way of retreat clear, and to have raked outwards to him, as far as he could reach, all that stuck to the walls, including ropy slime and mouldy damp, but not one particle of stalactite. It was, of course, seen that his specimens would not suit Sir George; and the minister, in the extremity of the case, applied to my uncles, though with some little unwillingness, as it was known that no remuneration for their trouble could be offered to them. My uncles were, however, delighted with the commission—it was all for the benefit of science; and, providing themselves with torches and a hammer, they set out for the caves. And I, of course, accompanied them— a very happy boy—armed, like themselves, with hammer and torch, and prepared devotedly to labour in behalf of science and Sir George.

I had never before seen the caves by torch-light; and though what I now witnessed did not quite come up to what I had read regarding the Grotto of Antiparos, or even the wonders of the Peak, it was unquestionably both strange and fine. The celebrated Dropping Cave proved inferior—as is not unfrequently the case with the celebrated—to a cave almost entirely unknown, which opened among the rocks a little further to the east; and yet even it had its interest. It widened, as one entered, into a twilight chamber, green with velvety mosses, that love the damp and the shade; and terminated in a range of crystalline wells, fed by the perpetual dropping, and hollowed in what seemed an altar-piece of the deposited marble. And above, and along the sides, there depended many a draped fold, and hung many a translucent icicle. The other cave, however, we found to be of much greater extent, and of more varied character. It is one of three caves of the old coast line, known as the Doocot or Pigeon Caves, which open upon a piece of rocky beach, overhung by a rudely semicircular range of gloomy precipices. The points of the semicircle project on either side into deep water—into at least water so much deeper than the fall of ordinary neaps, that it is only during the ebb of stream tides that the place is accessible by land; and in each of these bold promontories—the terminal horns of the crescent—there is a cave of the present coast-line, deeply hollowed, in which the sea stands from ten to twelve feet in depth when the tide is at full, and in which the surf thunders, when gales blow hard from the stormy north-coast, with the roar of whole parks of artillery. The cave in the western promontory, which bears among the townsfolk the name of the "Puir Wife's Meal Kist," has its roof drilled by two small perforations—the largest of them not a great deal wider than the blow-hole of a porpoise—that open externally among the cliffs above; and when, during storms from the sea, the huge waves come rolling ashore like green moving walls, there are certain times of the tide in which they shut up the mouth of the cave, and so compress the air within, that it rushes upwards through the openings, roaring in its escape as if ten whales were blowing at once, and rises from amid the crags overhead in two white jets of vapour, distinctly visible, to the height of from sixty to eighty feet. If there be critics who have deemed it one of the extravagances of Goethe that he should have given life and motion, as in his famous witch-scene in "Faust," to the Hartz crags, they would do well to visit this bold headland during some winter tempest from the east, and find his description perfectly sober and true:

"See the giant crags, oh ho!
How they snort and how they blow!"

Within, at the bottom of the crescent, and where the tide never reaches when at the fullest, we found the large pigeon cave which we had come to explore, hollowed for about a hundred and fifty feet in the line of a fault. There runs across the opening the broken remains of a wall erected by some monopolizing proprietor of the neighbouring lands, with the intention of appropriating to himself the pigeons of the cavern; but his day, even at this time, had been long gone by, and the wall had sunk into a ruin. As we advanced, the cave caught the echoes of our footsteps, and a flock of pigeons, startled from their nests, came whizzing out, almost brushing us with their wings. The damp floor sounded hollow to the tread; we saw the green mossy sides, which close in the uncertain light, more than twenty feet overhead, furrowed by ridges of stalactites, that became whiter and purer as they retired from the vegetative influences; and marked that the last plant which appeared as we wended our way inwards was a minute green moss, about half an inch in length, which slanted outwards on the prominence of the icicles, and overlay myriads of similar sprigs of moss, long before converted into stone, but which, faithful in death to the ruling law of their lives, still pointed, like the others, to the free air and the light. And then, in the deeper recesses of the cave, where the floor becomes covered with uneven sheets of stalagmite, and where long spear-like icicles and drapery-like foldings, pure as the marble of the sculptor, descend from above, or hang pendent over the sides, we found in abundance magnificent specimens for Sir George. The entire expedition was one of wondrous interest; and I returned next day to school, big with description and narrative, to excite, by truths more marvellous than fiction, the curiosity of my class-fellows.

I had previously introduced them to the marvels of the hill; and during our Saturday half-holidays some of them had accompanied me in my excursions to it. But it had failed, somehow, to catch their fancy. It was too solitary, and too far from home, and, as a scene of amusement, not at all equal to the town-links, where they could play at "shinty" and "French and English," almost within hail of their parents' homesteads. The very tract along its flat, moory summit, over which, according to tradition, Wallace had once driven before him in headlong rout a strong body of English, and which was actually mottled with sepulchral tumuli, still visible amid the heath, failed in any marked degree to engage them; and though they liked well enough to hear about the caves, they seemed to have no very great desire to see them. There was, however, one little fellow, who sat in the Latin form—the member of a class lower and brighter than the heavy one, though it was not particularly bright either—who differed in this respect from all the others. Though he was my junior by about a twelvemonth, and shorter by about half a head, he was a diligent boy in even the Grammar School, in which boys were so rarely diligent, and, for his years, a thoroughly sensible one, without a grain of the dreamer in his composition. I succeeded, however, notwithstanding his sobriety, in infecting him thoroughly with my peculiar tastes, and learned to love him very much, partly because he doubled my amusements by sharing in them, and partly, I daresay—on the principle on which Mahomet preferred his old wife to his young one—because "he believed in me." Devoted to him as Caliban in the *Tempest* to his friend Trinculo—

"I showed him the best springs, I plucked him berries,
And I with my long nails did dig him pig-nuts."

His curiosity on this occasion was largely excited by my description of the Doocot Cave; and, setting out one morning to explore its wonders, armed with John Feddes's hammer, in the benefits of which my friend was permitted liberally to share, we failed, for that day at least, in finding our way back.

It was on a pleasant spring morning that, with my little curious friend beside me, I stood on the beach opposite the eastern promontory, that, with its stern granitic wall, bars access for ten days out of every fourteen to the wonders of the Doocot; and saw it stretching provokingly out into the green water. It was hard to be disappointed, and the caves so near. The tide was a low neap, and if we wanted a passage dry-shod, it behoved us to wait for at least a week; but neither of us understood the philosophy of neap-tides at the period. I was quite sure I had got round at low water with my uncles not a great many days before, and we both inferred, that if we but succeeded in getting round now, it would be quite a pleasure to wait among the caves inside until such time as the fall of the tide should lay bare a passage for our return. A narrow and broken shelf runs along the promontory, on which, by the assistance of the naked toe and the toe nail, it is just possible to creep. We succeeded in scrambling up to it; and then, crawling outwards on all fours—the precipice, as we proceeded, beetling more and more formidable from above, and the water becoming greener and deeper below—we reached the outer point of the promontory; and then doubling the cape on a still narrowing margin—the water, by a reverse process, becoming shallower and less green as we advanced inwards—we found the ledge terminating just where, after clearing the sea, it overhung the gravelly beach at an elevation of nearly ten feet. Adown we both dropped, proud of our success; up splashed the rattling gravel as we fell; and for at least the whole coming week— though we were unaware of the extent of our good luck at the time—the marvels of the Doocot Cave might be regarded as solely and exclusively our own. For one short seven days—to borrow emphasis from the phraseology of Carlyle—"they were our own, and no other man's."

The first few hours were hours of sheer enjoyment. The larger cave proved a mine of marvels; and we found a great deal additional to wonder at on the slopes beneath the precipices, and along the piece of rocky sea-beach in front. We succeeded in discovering for ourselves, in creeping, dwarf bushes, that told of the blighting influences of the sea-spray; the pale yellow honeysuckle, that we had never seen before, save in gardens and shrubberies; and on a deeply-shaded slope that leaned against one of the steeper precipices, we detected the sweet-scented woodroof of the flower-plot and parterre, with its pretty verticillate leaves, that become the more odoriferous the more they are crushed, and its white delicate flowers. There, too, immediately in the opening of the deeper cave, where a small stream came pattering in detached drops from the over-beetling precipice above, like the first drops of a heavy thunder-shower, we found the hot, bitter scurvy grass, with its minute cruciform flowers, which the great

Captain Cook had used in his voyages; above all, *there* were the caves with their pigeons—white, variegated, and blue—and their mysterious and gloomy depths, in which plants hardened into stone, and water became marble. In a short time we had broken off with our hammers whole pocketfuls of stalactites and petrified moss. There were little pools at the side of the cave, where we could see the work of congelation going on, as at the commencement of an October frost, when the cold north wind ruffles, and but barely ruffles, the surface of some mountain lochan or sluggish moorland stream, and shows the newly-formed needles of ice projecting mole-like from the shores into the water. So rapid was the course of deposition, that there were cases in which the sides of the hollows seemed growing almost in proportion as the water rose in them; the springs, lipping over, deposited their minute crystals on the edges; and the reservoirs deepened and became more capacious as their mounds were built up by this curious masonry. The long telescopic prospect of the sparkling sea, as viewed from the inner extremity of the cavern, while all around was dark as midnight—the sudden gleam of the sea-gull, seen for a moment from the recess, as it flitted past in the sunshine—the black heaving bulk of the grampus, as it threw up its slender jets of spray, and then, turning downwards, displayed its glossy back and vast angular fin—even the pigeons, as they shot whizzing by, one moment scarce visible in the gloom, the next radiant in the light—all acquired a new interest, from the peculiarity of the *setting* in which we saw them. They formed a series of sun-gilt vignettes, framed in jet; and it was long ere we tired of seeing and admiring in them much of the strange and the beautiful. It did seem rather ominous, however, and perhaps somewhat supernatural to boot, that about an hour after noon, the tide, while there was yet a full fathom of water beneath the brow of the promontory, ceased to fall, and then, after a quarter of an hour's space, began actually to creep upwards on the beach. But just hoping that there might be some mistake in the matter, which the evening tide would scarce fail to rectify, we continued to amuse ourselves, and to hope on. Hour after hour passed, lengthening as the shadows lengthened, and yet the tide still rose. The sun had sunk behind the precipices, and all was gloom along their bases, and double gloom in their caves; but their rugged brows still caught the red glare of evening. The flush rose higher and higher, chased by the shadows; and then, after lingering for a moment on their crests of honeysuckle and juniper, passed away, and the whole became sombre and grey. The sea-gull sprang upwards from where he had floated on the ripple, and hied him slowly away to his lodge in his deep-sea stack; the dusky cormorant flitted past, with heavier and more frequent stroke, to his whitened shelf high on the precipice; the pigeons came whizzing downwards from the uplands and the opposite land, and disappeared amid the gloom of their caves; every creature that had wings made use of them in speeding homewards; but neither my companion nor myself had any; and there was no possibility of getting home without them. We made desperate efforts to scale the precipices, and on two several occasions succeeded in reaching mid-way shelves among the crags, where the sparrowhawk and the raven build; but though we had climbed well enough to render our return a matter of bare possibility, there was no possibility whatever of getting farther up: the cliffs had never been scaled before, and they were not destined to be scaled now. And so, as the twilight declined, and the precarious footing became every moment more doubtful and precarious still, we had just to give up in despair. "Wouldn't care for myself," said the poor little fellow, my companion, bursting into tears, "if it were not for my mother; but what will my mother say?" "Wouldn't care neither," said I, with a heavy heart; "but it's just back water, and we'll get out at twall." We retreated together into one of the shallower and drier caves, and, clearing a little spot of its rough stones, and then groping along the rocks for the dry grass that in the spring season hangs from them in withered tufts, we formed for ourselves a most uncomfortable bed, and lay down in one another's arms. For the last few hours mountainous piles of clouds had been rising dark and stormy in the sea-mouth: they had flared portentously in the setting sun, and had worn, with the decline of evening, almost every meteoric tint of anger, from fiery red to a sombre thundrous brown, and from sombre brown to doleful black. And we could now at least hear what they portended, though we could no longer see. The rising wind began to howl mournfully amid the cliffs, and the sea, hitherto so silent, to beat heavily against the shore, and to boom, like distress-guns, from the recesses of the two deep-sea caves. We could hear, too, the beating rain, now heavier, now lighter, as the gusts swelled or sank; and the intermittent patter of the streamlet over the deeper cave, now driving against the precipices, now descending heavily on the stones.

My companion had only the real evils of the case to deal with, and so, the hardness of our bed and the coldness of the night considered, he slept tolerably well; but I was unlucky enough to have evils greatly worse than the real ones to annoy me. The corpse of a drowned seaman had been found on the beach about a month previous, some forty yards from where we lay. The hands and feet, miserably contracted, and corrugated into deep folds at every joint, yet swollen to twice their proper size, had been bleached as white as pieces of alumed sheep-skin; and where the head should have been, there existed only a sad mass of rubbish. I had examined the body, as young people are apt to do, a great deal too curiously for my peace; and, though I had never done the poor nameless seaman any harm, I could not have suffered more from him during that melancholy night had I been his murderer. Sleeping or waking, he was continually before me. Every time I dropped into a doze, he would come stalking up the beach from the spot where he had lain, with his stiff white fingers, that stuck out like eagle's toes, and his pale, broken pulp of a head, and attempt striking me; and then I would awaken with a start, cling to my companion, and remember that the drowned sailor had lain festering among the identical bunches of sea-weed that still rotted on the beach not a stone-cast away. The near neighbourhood of a score of living bandits would have inspired less horror than the recollection of that one dead seaman.

Towards midnight the sky cleared and the wind fell, and the moon, in her last quarter, rose red as a mass of heated iron out of the sea. We crept down, in the uncertain light, over the rough slippery crags, to ascertain whether the tide had not fallen sufficiently far to yield us a passage; but we found the waves chafing among the rocks just where the tide-line had rested twelve hours before, and a full fathom of sea enclasping the base of the promontory. A glimmering idea of the real nature of our situation at length crossed my mind. It was not imprisonment for a tide to which we had consigned ourselves; it was imprisonment for a week. There was little comfort in the thought, arising, as it did, amid the chills and terrors of a dreary midnight; and I looked wistfully on the sea as our only path of escape. There was a vessel crossing the wake of the moon at the time, scarce half a mile from the shore; and, assisted by my companion, I began to shout at the top of my lungs, in the hope of being heard by the sailors. We saw her dim bulk falling slowly athwart the red glittering belt of light that had rendered her visible, and then disappearing in the murky blackness; and just as we lost sight of her for ever, we could hear an indistinct sound mingling with the dash of the waves—the shout, in reply, of the startled helmsman. The vessel, as we afterwards learned, was a large stone-lighter, deeply laden, and unfurnished with a boat; nor were her crew at all sure that it would have been safe to attend to the midnight voice from amid the rocks, even had they had the means of communication with the shore. We waited on and on however, now shouting by turns, and now shouting together; but there was no second reply; and at length, losing hope, we groped our way back to our comfortless bed, just as the tide had again turned on the beach, and the waves began to roll upwards higher and higher at every dash.

As the moon rose and brightened, the dead seaman became less troublesome; and I had succeeded in dropping as soundly asleep as my companion, when we were both aroused by a loud shout. We started up, and again crept downwards among the crags to the shore; and as we reached the sea the shout was repeated. It was that of at least a dozen harsh voices united. There was a brief pause, followed by another shout; and then two boats, strongly manned, shot round the western promontory, and the men, resting on their oars, turned towards the rock, and shouted yet again. The whole town had been alarmed by the intelligence that two little boys had straggled away in the morning to the rocks of the southern Sutor, and had not found their way back. The precipices had been a scene of frightful accidents from time immemorial, and it was at once inferred that one other sad accident had been added to the number. True, there were cases remembered of people having been tidebound in the Doocot Caves, and not much the worse in consequence; but as the caves were inaccessible during neaps, we could not, it was said, possibly be in them; and the sole remaining ground of hope, was that, as had happened once before, only one of the two had been killed, and that the survivor was lingering among the rocks, afraid to come home. And in this belief, when the moon rose and the surf fell, the two boats had been fitted out. It was late in the morning ere we reached Cromarty, but a crowd on the beach awaited our arrival; and there were anxious-looking lights glancing in the windows, thick and manifold; nay, such was the interest elicited, that some enormously bad verses, in which the writer described the incident a few days after, became popular enough to be handed about in manuscript, and read at tea-parties by the elite of the town. Poor old Miss Bond, who kept the town boarding-school, got the piece nicely dressed up, somewhat on the principle upon which Macpherson translated Ossian; and at our first school-examination—proud and happy day for the author!—it was recited with vast applause, by one of her prettiest young ladies, before the assembled taste and fashion of Cromarty.

CHAPTER V

"The wise
Shook their white aged hands o'er me, and said,
Of such materials wretched men were made."—BYRON.

THE report went abroad about this time, not without some foundation, that Miss Bond purposed patronizing me. The copy of my verses which had fallen into her hands—a genuine holograph—bore a-top a magnificent view of the Doocot, in which horrid crags of burnt umber were perforated by yawning caverns of Indian ink, and crested by a dense pine-forest of sap-green; while vast waves, blue on the one side and green on the other, and bearing blotches of white lead a-top, rolled frightfully beneath. And Miss Bond had concluded, it was said, that such a genius as that evinced by the sketch and the "poem" for those sister arts of painting and poesy in which she herself excelled, should not be left to waste itself uncared for in the desert wilderness. She had published, shortly before, a work, in two slim volumes, entitled, "Letters of a Village Governess"—a curious kind of medley, little amenable to the ordinary rules, but a genial book notwithstanding, with more heart than head about it; and not a few of the incidents that it related had the merit of being true. It was an unlucky merit for poor Miss Bond. She dated her book from Fortrose, where she taught what was designated in the Almanac as the boarding-school of the place, but which, according to Miss Bond's own description, was the school of the "village governess." And as her tales were found to be a kind of mosaics composed of droll bits of fact picked up in the neighbourhood, Fortrose soon became considerably too hot for her. She had drawn, under the over-transparent guise of the niggardly Mrs Flint, the skin-flint wife of a "paper minister," who had ruined at one fell blow her best silk dress, and a dozen of good eggs to boot, by putting the eggs in her pocket when going out to a party, and then stumbling over a stone. And, of course, Mrs Skinflint and the Rev. Mr Skinflint, with all their blood-relations, could not be other than greatly gratified to find the story furbished up in the printed form, and set in fun. There were other stories as imprudent and as amusing—of young ladies caught eavesdropping at their neighbours' windows; and of gentlemen, ill at ease in their families, sitting soaking among vulgar companions in the public-house; and so the authoress, shortly after the appearance of her work, ceased to be the village governess of Fortrose, and became the village governess of Cromarty.

It was on this occasion that I saw, for the first time, with mingled admiration and awe, a human creature—not dead and gone, and merely a printed name—that had actually published a book. Poor Miss Bond was a kindly sort of person, fond of children, and mightily beloved by them in turn; and, though keenly alive to the ludicrous, without a grain of malice in her. I remember how, about this time, when, assisted by some three or four boys more, I succeeded in building a huge house, full four feet long and three feet high, that contained us all, and a fire, and a great deal of smoke to boot, Miss Bond the authoress came, and looked in upon us, first through the little door, and then down through the chimney, and gave us kind words, and seemed to enjoy our enjoyment very much; and how we all deemed her visit one of the greatest events that could possibly have taken place. She had been intimate with the parents of Sir Walter Scott; and, on the appearance of Sir Walter's first publication, the "Minstrelsy of the Scottish Border," she had taken a fit of enthusiasm, and written to him; and, when in the cold paroxysm, and inclined to think she had done something foolish, had received from Sir Walter, then Mr Scott, a characteristically warm-hearted reply. She experienced much kindness at his hands ever after; and when she herself became an author, she dedicated her book to him. He now and then procured boarders for her; and when, after leaving Cromarty for Edinburgh, she opened a school in the latter place, and got on with but indifferent success, Sir Walter—though struggling with his own difficulties at the time—sent her an enclosure of ten pounds, to scare, as he said in his note, "the wolf from the door." But Miss Bond, like the original of his own Jeanie Deans, was a "proud bodie"; and the ten pounds were returned, with the intimation that the wolf had not *yet* come to the door. Poor lady! I suspect he came to the door at last. Like many other writers of books, her voyage through life skirted, for the greater part of the way, the bleak lee-shore of necessity; and it cost her not a little skilful steering at times to give the strand a respectable offing. And in her solitary old age, she seemed to have got fairly aground. There was an attempt made by some of her former pupils to raise money enough to purchase for her a small annuity; but when the design was in progress, I heard of her death. She illustrated in her life the remark recorded by herself in her "Letters," as made by a humble friend:—"It's no an easy thing, Mem, for a woman to go through the world *without a head*," i.e., single and unprotected.

From some unexplained cause, Miss Bond's patronage never reached me. I am sure the good lady intended giving me lessons in both drawing and composition; for she had said it, and her heart was a kind one; but then her time was too much occupied to admit of her devoting an occasional hour to myself alone; and as for introducing me to her young-lady classes, in my rough garments, ever greatly improved the wrong way by my explorations in the ebb and the peat-moss, and frayed, at times, beyond even my mother's ability of repair, by warping to the tops of great trees, and by feats as a cragsman—that would have been a piece of Jack-Cadeism, on which, then or now, no village governess could have ventured. And so I was left to get on in verse and picture-making quite in the wild way, without care or culture.

My schoolfellows liked my stories well enough—better at least, on most occasions, than they did the lessons of the master; but, beyond the common ground of enjoyment which these ex-tempore compositions furnished to both the "sennachie" and his auditors, our tracts of amusement lay widely apart. I disliked, as I have said, the yearly cock-fight—found no pleasure in cat-killing, or in teasing at nights, or on the street, the cross-tempered, half-witted *eccentrics* of the village—usually kept aloof from the ordinary play-grounds, and very rarely mingled in the old hereditary games. On the other hand, with the exception of my little friend of the cave, who, even after that disastrous incident, evinced a tendency to trust and follow me as implicitly as before, my schoolmates cared as little for my amusements as I did for theirs; and, having the majority on their side, they of course voted mine to be the foolish ones. And certainly a run of ill-luck followed me in my sports about this time, that did give some show of reason to their decision.

In the course of my book-hunting, I had fallen in with two old-fashioned military treatises, part of the small library of a retired officer lately deceased, of which the one entitled the "Military Medley," discussed the whole art of marshalling troops, and contained numerous plans, neatly coloured, of battalions drawn up in all possible forms, to meet all possible exigencies; while the other, which also abounded in prints, treated of the noble science of fortification according to the system of Vauban. I pored over both works with much perseverance; and, regarding them as admirable toy-books, set myself to construct, on a very small scale, some of the toys with which they specially dealt. The sea-shore in the immediate neighbourhood of the town appeared to my inexperienced eye an excellent field for the carrying on of a campaign. The sea-sand I found quite coherent enough, when still moistened by the waters of the receding tide, to stand up in the form of towers and bastions, and long lines of rampart; and there was one of the commonest of the Littorinidæ—*Littorina littoralis*,[1] that in one of its varieties is of a rich yellow colour, and in another of a bluish-green tint—which supplied me with soldiers enough to execute all the evolutions figured and described in the "Medley." The warmly-hued yellow shells represented Britons in their scarlet—the more dingy ones, the French in their uniforms

---

[1] The small red or yellow Winkle Shell.

of dirty blue; well-selected specimens of *Purpura lapillus*,[1] just tipped on their backs with a speck of paint, blue or red, from my box, made capital dragoons; while a few dozens of the slender pyramidal shells of *Turritella communis*[2] formed complete parks of artillery. With such unlimited stores of the *matériel* of war at my command, I was enabled, more fortunate than Uncle Toby of old, to fight battles and conduct retreats, assault and defend, build up fortifications, and then batter them down again, at no expense at all; and the only drawback on such a vast amount of advantage that I could at first perceive consisted in the circumstance, that the shore was exceedingly open to observation, and that my new amusements, when surveyed at a little distance, did greatly resemble those of the very young children of the place, who used to repair to the same arenaceous banks and shingle-beds, to bake dirt-pies in the sand, or range lines of shells on little shelves of stone, imitative of the crockery cupboard at home. Not only my school-fellows, but also some of their parents, evidently arrived at the conclusion that the two sets of amusements—mine and those of the little children—were identical; for the elder folk said, that "in their time, poor Francie had been such another joy, and every one saw what he had come to"; while the younger, more energetic in their manifestations, and more intolerant of folly, have even paused in their games of marbles, or ceased spinning their tops, to hoot at me from a safe distance. But the campaign went on; and I solaced myself by reflecting, that neither the big folk nor the little folk could bring a battalion of troops across a bridge of boats in the face of an enemy, or knew that a regular fortification could be constructed on only a regular polygon.

I at length discovered, however, that as a sea-shore is always a sloping plane, and the Cromarty beach, in particular, a plane of a rather steep slope, it afforded no proper site for a fortress fitted to stand a protracted siege, seeing that, fortify the place as I might, it could be easily commanded by batteries raised on the higher

[1] The Dog Winkle.
[2] The Turret Shell.

side. And so, fixing upon a grassy knoll among the woods, in the immediate neighbourhood of a scaur of boulder clay, capped by a thick stratum of sand, as a much better scene of operations, I took possession of the knoll somewhat irregularly; and carrying to it large quantities of sand from the scaur, converted it into the site of a magnificent stronghold. First I erected an ancient castle, consisting of four towers built on a rectangular base, and connected by straight curtains embrasured a-top. I then surrounded the castle by outworks in the modern style, consisting of greatly lower curtains than the ancient ones, flanked by numerous bastions, and bristling with cannon of huge calibre, made of the jointed stalks of the hemlock; while, in advance of these, I laid down ravelins, horn-works, and tenailles. I was vastly delighted with my work: it would, I was sure, be no easy matter to reduce such a fortress; but observing an eminence in the immediate neighbourhood which could, I thought, be occupied by a rather annoying battery, I was deliberating how I might best take possession of it by a redoubt, when out started, from behind a tree, the factor of the property on which I was trespassing, and rated me soundly for spoiling the grass in a manner so wantonly mischievous. Horn-work and half-moon, tower and bastion, proved of no manner of effect in repelling an attack of a kind so little anticipated. I did think that the factor, who was not only an intelligent man, but had also seen much service in his day on the town links, as the holder of a commission in the Cromarty volunteers, might have perceived that I was labouring on scientific principles, and so deem me worthy of some tolerance on that account; but I suppose he did not; though, to be sure, his scold died out good-naturedly enough in the end, and I saw him laugh as he turned away. But so it was, that in the extremity of my mortification I gave up generalship and bastion-building for the time; though, alas! my next amusement must have worn in the eyes of my youthful compeers as suspicious an aspect as either.

My friend of the cave had lent me what I had never seen before—a fine quarto edition of Anson's "Voyages," containing the original prints (my father's copy had only the maps); among the others, Mr Brett's elaborate delineation of that strangest of vessels, a proa of the Ladrone Islands. I was much struck by the singularity of the construction of a barque that, while its head and stern were exactly alike, had sides that totally differed from each other, and that, with the wind upon the beam, outsailed, it was said, all other vessels in the world; and, having the command of the little shop in which my Uncle Sandy made occasional carts and wheelbarrows when unemployed abroad, I set myself to construct a miniature proa, on the model given in the print, and succeeded in fabricating a very extraordinary proa indeed. While its lee side was perpendicular as a wall, its windward one, to which there was an outrigger attached, resembled that of a flat-bottomed boat; head and stern were exactly alike, so as to fit each for performing in turn the part of either; a moveable yard, which supported the sail, had to be shifted towards the end converted into the stern for the time, at each tack; while the sail itself—a most uncouth-looking thing—formed a scalene triangle. Such was the vessel—some eighteen inches long or so—with which I startled from their propriety the mimic navigators of a horse-pond in the neighbour-hood—all very masterly critics in all sorts of barques and barges known on the Scottish coast. According to Campbell,

> "'Twas a thing beyond
> Description wretched; such a wherry,
> Perhaps, ne'er ventured on a pond,
> Or crossed a ferry."

And well did my fellows appreciate its extreme ludicrousness. It was certainly rash to "venture" it on this especial "pond"; for, greatly to the damage of the rigging, it was fairly pelted off, and I was sent to test elsewhere its sailing qualities, which were, as I ascertained, not very remarkable after all. And thus, after a manner so unworthy, were my essays in strategy and barque-building received by a censorious age, that judged ere it knew. Were I sentimental, which luckily I am not, I might well exclaim, in the very vein of Rousseau, Alas! it has been ever the misfortune of my life that, save by a few friends, I have never been understood!

I was evidently out-Francieing Francie; and the parents of my young friend, who saw that I had acquired considerable influence over him, and were afraid lest I should make another Francie of *him*, had become naturally enough desirous to break off our intimacy, when there occurred an unlucky accident, which served materially to assist them in the design. My friend's father was the master of a large trading smack, which, in war times, carried a few twelve-pounders, and was furnished with a small magazine of powder and shot; and my friend having secured for himself from the general stock, through the connivance of the ship-boy, an entire cannon cartridge, containing some two or three pounds of gunpowder, I was, of course, let into the secret, and invited to share in the sport and the spoil. We had a glorious day together in his mother's garden: never before did such magnificent volcanoes break forth out of mole-hills, or were plots of daisies and violets so ruthlessly scorched and torn by the explosion of deep-laid mines; and though a few mishaps did happen to over-forward fingers, and to eye-brows that were in the way, our amusements passed off innocuously on the whole, and evening saw nearly the half of our precious store unexhausted. It was garnered up by my friend in an unsuspected corner of the garret in which he slept, and would have been safe, had he not been seized, when going to bed, with a yearning desire to survey his treasure by candle-light; when an unlucky spark from the flame exploded the whole. He was so sadly burnt about the face and eyes as to be blind for several days after; but, amid smoke and confusion, he gallantly bolted his garret-door, and, while the inmates of the household, startled by the shock and the noise, came rushing upstairs, sturdily refused to let any of them in. Volumes of gunpowder reek issued from every crack and cranny, and his mother and sisters were prodigiously alarmed. At length, however, he capitulated—terms unknown; and I, next morning, heard with horror and dismay of the accident. It had been matter of agreement between us on the previous day, mainly in order to screen the fine fellow of a ship-boy, that I should be regarded as the owner of the powder; but here was a consequence on which I had not calculated; and the strong desire to see my poor friend was dashed by the dread of being held responsible by his parents and sisters for the accident. And so, more than a week elapsed ere I could muster up courage enough to visit him. I was coldly received by his mother, and, what vexed me to the heart, coldly received by himself; and suspecting that he had been making an ungenerous use of our late treaty, I took leave in high dudgeon, and came away. My suspicions, however, wronged him: he had stoutly denied, as I afterwards learned, that I had any share in the powder; but his friends deeming the opportunity a good one for breaking with me, had compelled him, very unwillingly, and after much resistance, to give me up. And from this period more than two years elapsed, though our hearts beat quick and high every time we accidentally met, ere we exchanged a single word. On one occasion, however, shortly after the accident, we did exchange letters. I wrote to him from the school-form, when, of course, I ought to have been engaged with my tasks, a stately epistle, in the style of the billets in the "Female Quixote," which began, I remember, as follows:—"I once thought I had a friend whom I could rely upon; but experience tells me he was only nominal. For, had he been a real friend, no accident could have interfered with, or arbitrary command annihilated, his affection," &c., &c. As I was rather an indifferent scribe at the time, one of the lads known as the "copper-plate writers" of the class, made for me a fair copy of my lucubration, full of all manner of elegant dashes, and in which the spelling of every word was scrupulously tested by the dictionary. And, in due course, I received a carefully engrossed note in reply, of which the manual portion was performed by my old companion, but the composition, as he afterwards told me, elaborated by some one else. It assured me he was still my friend, but that there were "certain circumstances" which would prevent us from meeting for the future on our old terms. We were, however, destined to meet pretty often in the future, notwithstanding; and narrowly missed going to the bottom together many years after, in the Floating Manse,[1] grown infirm in her nether parts at the time, when he was the outed minister of Small Isles, and I editor of the *Witness* newspaper.

I had a maternal aunt long settled in the Highlands of Sutherland, who was so much older than her sister, my mother, that, when nursing her eldest boy, she had, when on a visit to the low country, assisted also in nursing her. The boy had shot up into a very clever lad, who, having gone to seek his fortune in the south, rose, through the several degrees of clerkship in a mercantile firm, to be the head of a commercial house of his own, which, though ultimately unsuccessful, seemed for some four or five years to be in a fair way of thriving. For about three of these the portion of the profits which fell to my cousin's share did not fall short of fifteen hundred pounds per annum; and on visiting his parents in their Highland home in the heyday of his prosperity, after an absence of years, it was found that he had a great many friends in his native district on whom he had not calculated, and of a class that had not been greatly in the habit of visiting his mother's cottage, but who now came to lunch and dine, and take their wine with him, and who seemed to value and admire him very much. My aunt, who was little accustomed to receive high company, and found herself, like Martha of old, "cumbered about much serving," urgently besought my mother, who was young and active at the time, to visit and assist her; and, infinitely to my delight, I was included in the invitation. The place was not much above thirty miles from Cromarty; but then it was in the *true* Highlands, which I had never before seen, save on the distant horizon; and, to a boy who had to walk all the way, even thirty

[1] The Free Church yacht, *Betsey*, which served as a means of visiting and preaching for the Free Church minister of the small isles near Skye. The Rev. Mr Swanson, Miller's friend, had "come out" at the Disruption, and so lost his manse in Eigg. The proprietor of the island refused a site for Free Church purposes. See Miller's "Cruise of the *Betsey*."

miles, in an age when railways were not, and ere even mail gigs had penetrated so far, represented a journey of no inconsiderable distance. My mother, though rather a delicate-looking woman, walked remarkably well; and early on the evening of the second day, we reached together my aunt's cottage, in the ancient Barony of Gruids. It was a low, long, dingy edifice of turf, four or five rooms in length, but only one in height, that, lying along a gentle acclivity, somewhat resembled at a distance a huge black snail creeping up the hill. As the lower apartment was occupied by my uncle's half-dozen milk-cows, the declination of the floor, consequent on the nature of the site, proved of signal importance, from the free drainage which it secured; the second apartment, reckoning upwards, which was of considerable size, formed the sitting-room of the family, and had, in the old Highland style, its fire full in the middle of the floor, without back or sides; so that, like a bonfire kindled in the open air, all the inmates could sit around it in a wide circle—the women invariably ranged on the one side, and the men on the other; the apartment beyond was partitioned into small and very dark bed-rooms; while, further on still, there was a closet with a little window in it, which was assigned to my mother and me; and beyond all lay what was emphatically "the room," as it was built of stone, and had both window and chimney, with chairs, and table, and chest of drawers, a large box-bed, and a small but well-filled bookcase. And "the room" was, of course, for the time, my cousin the merchant's apartment—his dormitory at night, and the hospitable refectory in which he entertained his friends by day.

My aunt's family was one of solid worth. Her husband—a compactly-built, stout-limbed, elderly Highlander, rather below the middle size, of grave and somewhat melancholy aspect, but in reality of a temperament rather cheerful than otherwise—had been somewhat wild in his young days. He had been a good shot and a skilful angler, and had danced at bridals, and, as was common in the Highlands at the time, at lyke-wakes; nay, on one occasion he had succeeded in inducing a new-made widow to take the floor in a strathspey, beside her husband's corpse, when every one else had failed to bring her up, by roguishly remarking, in her hearing, that whoever else might have refused to dance at poor Donald's death-wake, he little thought it would have been she. But a great change had passed over him; and he was now a staid, thoughtful, God-fearing man, much respected in the Barony for honest worth and quiet unobtrusive consistency of character. His wife had been brought, at an early age, under the influence of Donald Roy's ring, and had, like her mother, been the means of introducing the vitalities of religion into her household. They had two other sons besides the merchant—both well-built, robust men, somewhat taller than their father, and of such character, that one of my Cromarty cousins, in making out his way, by dint of frequent and sedulous inquiry, to their dwelling, found the general verdict of the district embodied in the very bad English of a poor old woman, who, after doing her best to direct him, certified her knowledge of the household by remarking, "It's a goot mistress— it's a goot maister—it's a goot, goot two lads." The older of the two brothers superintended, and partly wrought, his father's little farm; for the father himself found employment enough in acting as a sort of humble factor for the proprietor of the Barony, who lived at a distance, and had no dwelling upon the land. The younger was a mason and slater, and was usually employed, in the working seasons, at a distance; but in winter, and, on this occasion, for a few weeks during the visit of his brother the merchant, he resided with his father. Both were men of marked individuality of character. The elder, Hugh, was an ingenious, self-taught mechanic, who used in the long winter evenings to fashion a number of curious little articles by the fireside—among the rest, Highland snuff-mulls, with which he supplied all his friends; and he was at this time engaged in building for his father a Highland barn, and, to vary the work, fabricating for him a Highland plough. The younger, George, who had wrought for a few years at his trade in the south of Scotland, was a great reader, wrote very tolerable prose, and verse which, if not poetry, to which he made

91

no pretensions, was at least quaintly-turned rhyme. He had, besides, a competent knowledge of geometry, and was skilled in architectural drawing; and—strange accomplishment for a Celt— he was an adept in the noble science of self-defence. But George never sought out quarrels; and such was his amount of bone and muscle, and such the expression of manly resolution stamped on his countenance, that they never came in his way unsought.

At the close of the day, when the members of the household had assembled in a wide circle round the fire, my uncle "took the Book," and I witnessed, for the first time, family-worship conducted in Gaelic. There was, I found, an interesting peculiarity in one portion of the services which he conducted. He was, as I have said, an elderly man, and had worshipped in his family ere Dr Stewart's Gaelic translation of the Scriptures[1] had been introduced into the county; and as he possessed in those days only the English Bible, while his domestics understood only Gaelic, he had to acquire the art, not uncommon in Sutherland at the time, of translating the English chapter for them, as he read, into their native tongue; and this he had learned to do with such ready fluency, that no one could have guessed it to be other than a Gaelic work from which he was reading. Nor had the introduction of Dr Stewart's translation rendered the practice obsolete in his household. His Gaelic was *Sutherlandshire* Gaelic, whereas that of Dr Stewart was Argyleshire Gaelic. His family understood his rendering better, in consequence, than that of the Doctor; and so he continued to translate from his English Bible *ad aperturam libri,*[2] many years after the Gaelic edition had been spread over the country. The concluding evening prayer was one of great solemnity and unction. I was unacquainted with the language in which it was couched; but it was impossible to avoid being struck, notwithstanding, with its wrestling earnestness and fervour. The man who poured it forth evidently believed there was an unseen

[1] James Stewart (1700-89), minister of Killin from 1737 until his death, translated the New Testament from Greek into Gaelic—his translation was first published in 1767.

[2] At sight.

ear open to it, and an all-seeing presence in the place, before whom every secret thought lay exposed. The entire scene was a deeply impressive one; and when I saw, in witnessing the celebration of high mass in a Popish cathedral many years after, the altar suddenly enveloped in a dim and picturesque obscurity, amid which the curling smoke of the incense ascended, and heard the musically-modulated prayer sounding in the distance from within the screen, my thoughts reverted to the rude Highland cottage, where, amid solemnities not theatric, the red umbry light of the fire fell with uncertain glimmer upon dark walls, and bare black rafters, and kneeling forms, and a pale expanse of dense smoke, that, filling the upper portion of the roof, overhung the floor like a ceiling, and there arose amid the gloom the sounds of prayer truly God-directed, and poured out from the depths of the heart; and I felt that the stoled priest of the cathedral was merely an artist, though a skilful one, but that in the "priest and father" of the cottage there were the truth and reality from which the artist drew. No bolt was drawn across the outer door as we retired for the night. The philosophic Biot,[1] when employed with his experiments on the second pendulum, resided for several months in one of the smaller Shetland islands; and, fresh from the troubles of France—his imagination bearing about with it, if I may so speak, the stains of the guillotine—the state of trustful security in which he found the simple inhabitants filled him with astonishment. "Here during the twenty-five years in which Europe has been devouring herself," he exclaimed, "the door of the house I inhabit has remained open day and night." The interior of Sutherland was at the time of my visit in a similar condition. The door of my uncle's cottage, unfurnished with lock or bar, opened, like that of the hermit in the ballad, with a latch; but, unlike that of the hermit, it was not because there were no stores within to demand the care of the master, but because at that comparatively recent period the crime of theft was unknown in the district.

[1] Jean Baptiste Biot, a French astronomer and physicist (1774-1862). He was in Shetland in 1817.

I rose early next morning, when the dew was yet heavy on grass and lichen, curious to explore a locality so new to me. The tract, though a primary one, forms one of the tamer gneiss districts of Scotland; and I found the nearer hills comparatively low and confluent, and the broad valley in which lay my uncle's cottage, flat, open, and unpromising. Still there were a few points to engage me; and the more I attached myself to them, the more did their interest grow. The western slopes of the valley are mottled by grassy tomhans—the moraines of some ancient glacier, around and over which there rose, at this period, a low widely-spreading wood of birch, hazel, and mountain ash—of hazel, with its nuts fast filling at the time, and of mountain ash, with its berries glowing bright in orange and scarlet. In looking adown the hollow, a group of the green tomhans might be seen relieved against the blue hills of Ross; in looking upwards, a solitary birch-covered hillock of similar origin, but larger proportions, stood strongly out against the calm waters of Loch Shin and the purple peaks of the distant Ben Hope. In the bottom of the valley, close beside my uncle's cottage, I marked several low swellings of the rock beneath, rising above the general level; and, ranged along these, there were groups of what seemed to be huge boulder stones, save that they were less rounded and water-worn than ordinary boulders, and were, what groups of boulders rarely are, all of one quality. And on examination, I ascertained that some of their number, which stood up like broken obelisks, tall, and comparatively narrow of base, and all hoary with moss and lichen, were actually still connected with the mass of rock below. They were the wasted upper portions of vast dikes[1] and veins of a grey, large-grained syenite[2], that traverse the fundamental gneiss of the valley, and which I found veined, in turn, by threads and seams of a white quartz, abounding in drusy cavities[3], thickly lined along their sides with sprig crystals. Never had I seen such lovely crystals on the shores of Cromarty, or anywhere else. They were clear and

[1] Vertical intrusions of eruptive rock.
[2] A rather rare bluish rock; granite without quartz.
[3] Cavities in a rock filled with crystals or some other mineral.

transparent as the purest spring water, furnished each with six sides, and sharpened a-top into six facets. Borrowing one of Cousin George's hammers, I soon filled a little box with these gems, which even my mother and aunt were content to admire, as what of old used, they said, to be called Bristol diamonds, and set in silver brooches and sleeve buttons. Further, within less than a hundred yards of the cottage, I found a lively little stream, brown, but clear as a cairngorm of the purest water, and abounding, as I soon ascertained, in trout, lively and little like itself, and gaily speckled with scarlet. It wound through a flat, dank meadow, never disturbed by the plough; for it had been a burying-ground of old, and flat undressed stones lay thick amid the rank grass. And in the lower corner, where the old turf-wall had sunk into an inconspicuous mound, there stood a mighty tree, all solitary, for its fellows had long before disappeared, and so hollow-hearted in its corrupt old age, that though it still threw out every season a mighty expanse of foliage, I was able to creep into a little chamber in its trunk, from which I could look out through circular openings where boughs once had been, and listen, when a sudden shower came sweeping down the glen, to the pattering of the rain-drops amid the leaves. The valley of the Gruids was perhaps not one of the finest or most beautiful of Highland valleys, but it was a very admirable place after all; and amid its woods, and its rocks, and its tomhans, and at the side of its little trouting stream, the weeks passed delightfully away.

My cousin William, the merchant, had, as I have said, many guests; but they were all too grand to take any notice of me. There was, however, one delightful man, who was said to know a great deal about rocks and stones, that, having heard of my fine large crystals, desired to see both them and the boy who had found them; and I was admitted to hear him talk about granites, and marbles, and metallic veins, and the gems that lie hid among the mountains in nooks and crannies. I am afraid I would not now deem him a very accomplished mineralogist: I remember enough of his conversation to conclude that he knew but little, and that little not very correctly: but not before Werner or Hutton could I have bowed down with a profounder reverence. He spoke of the marbles of Assynt—of the petrifactions of Helmsdale and Brora—of shells and plants embedded in solid rocks, and of forest trees converted into stone; and my ears drank in knowledge eagerly, as those of the Queen of Sheba of old when she listened to Solomon. But all too soon did the conversation change. My cousin was mighty in Gaelic etymology, and so was the mineralogist; and while my cousin held that the name of the Barony of Gruids was derived from the great hollow tree, the mineralogist was quite as certain that it was derived from its syenite, or, as he termed it, its *granite*, which resembled, he remarked, from the whiteness of its feldspar, a piece of curd. *Gruids*, said the one, means the place of the great tree; *Gruids*, said the other, means the place of the curdled stone. I do not remember how they settled the controversy; but it terminated, by an easy transition, in a discussion respecting the authenticity of Ossian—a subject on which they were both perfectly agreed. There could exist no manner of doubt regarding the fact that the poems given to the world by Macpherson had been sung in the Highlands by Ossian, the son of Fingal, more than fourteen hundred years before. My cousin was a devoted member of the Highland Society; and the Highland Society, in these days, was very much engaged in ascertaining the right cut of the philabeg, and in determining the chronology and true sequence of events in the Ossianic age.

Happiness perfect and entire is, it is said, not to be enjoyed in this sublunary state; and even in the Gruids, where there was so much to be seen, heard, and found out, and where I was separated by more than thirty miles from my Latin—for I had brought none of it from home with me—this same Ossianic controversy rose like a Highland fog on my horizon, to chill and darken my hours of enjoyment. My cousin possessed everything that had been written on the subject, including a considerable amount of manuscript of his own composition; and as Uncle James had inspired him with the belief that I could master anything to which in good earnest

I set my mind, he had determined that it should be no fault of his if I did not become mighty in the controversy regarding the authenticity of Ossian. This was awful. I liked Blair's Dissertation well enough, nor did I greatly quarrel with that of Kames; and as for Sir Walter's critique in the *Edinburgh*, on the opposite side, I thought it not only thoroughly sensible, but, as it furnished me with arguments against the others, deeply interesting to boot. But then there succeeded a vast ocean of dissertation, emitted by Highland gentlemen and their friends, as the dragon in the Apocalypse emitted the great flood which the earth swallowed up; and, when once fairly embarked upon it, I could see no shore and find no bottom. And so at length, though very unwillingly—for my cousin was very kind—I fairly mutinied and struck work, just as he had begun to propose that, after mastering the authenticity controversy, I should set myself to acquire Gaelic, in order that I might be able to read Ossian in the original. My cousin was not well pleased; but I did not choose to aggravate the case by giving expression to the suspicion which, instead of lessening, has rather grown upon me since, that as I possessed an English copy of the poems, I had read the true Ossian in the original already. With Cousin George, however, who, though strong on the authenticity side, liked a joke rather better than he did Ossian, I was more free; and to him I ventured to designate his brother's fine Gaelic copy of the poems, with a superb head of the ancient bard affixed, as "The Poems of Ossian in Gaelic, translated from the original English by their author." George looked grim, and called me infidel, and then laughed, and said he would tell his brother. But he didn't; and as I really liked the poems, especially "Temora" and some of the smaller pieces, and could read them with more real pleasure than the greater part of the Highlanders who believed in them, I did not wholly lose credit with my cousin the merchant. He even promised to present me with a finely bound edition of the "Elegant Extracts," in three bulky octavo volumes, whenever I should have gained my first prize at College; but I unluckily failed to qualify myself for the gift; and my copy of the "Extracts"

I had to purchase for myself ten years after, at a book-stall, when working in the neighbourhood of Edinburgh as a journeyman mason.

It is not every day one meets with so genuine a Highlander as my cousin the merchant; and though he failed to inspire me with all his own Ossianic faith and zeal, there were some of the little Celtic practices which he resuscitated *pro tempore* in his father's household, that I learned to like very much. He restored the genuine Highland breakfasts; and, after hours spent in busy exploration outside, I found I could as thoroughly admire the groaning table, with its cheese, and its trout, and its cold meat, as even the immortal Lexicographer himself.[1] Some of the dishes, too, which he revived, were at least curious. There was a supply of *gradden*-meal prepared—i.e., grain dried in a pot over the fire, and then coarsely ground in a hand-mill—which made cakes that, when they had hunger for their sauce, could be eaten; and on more than one occasion I shared in a not unpalatable sort of blood-pudding, enriched with butter, and well seasoned with pepper and salt, the main ingredient of which was derived, through a judicious use of the lancet, from the *yeld* cattle[2] of the farm. The practice was an ancient, and by no means unphilosophic one. In summer and early autumn there is plenty of grass in the Highlands; but, of old at least, there used to be very little grain in it before the beginning of October; and as the cattle could, in consequence, provide themselves with a competent supply of blood from the grass, when their masters, who could not eat grass, and had little else that they could eat, were able to acquire very little, it was opportunely discovered that, by making a division in this way of the all-essential fluid, accumulated as a common stock, the circumstances of the cattle and their owners could be in some degree equalized. With these peculiarly Highland dishes there mingled others not less genuine—now and then a salmon from the river, and a haunch of venison from the hill-side—which I

[1] i.e. Dr Johnson.
[2] Cattle not giving milk.

relished better still; and if all Highlanders live but as well in the present day as I did during my stay with my aunt and cousins, they would be rather unreasonable were they greatly to complain.

There were some of the other Highland restorations affected by my cousin that pleased me much. He occasionally gathered at night around the central "Ha'" fire a circle of the elderly men of the neighbourhood, to repeat long-derived narratives of the old clan feuds of the district, and wild Fingalian legends; and though, of course, ignorant of the language in which the stories were conveyed, by taking my seat beside Cousin George, and getting him to translate for me in an undertone, as the narratives went on, I contrived to carry away with me at least as much of the clan stories and legends as I ever after found use for. The clan stories were waxing at the time rather dim and uncertain in Sutherland. The county, through the influence of its good Earls and its godly Lords Reay, had been early converted to Protestantism; and its people had in consequence ceased to take liberties with the throats and cattle of their neighbours, about a hundred years earlier than in any other part of the Scotch Highlands. And as for the Fingalian legends, they were, I found, very wild legends indeed. Some of them immortalized wonderful hunters, who had excited the love of Fingal's lady, and whom her angry and jealous husband had sent out to hunt monstrous wild boars with poisonous bristles on their backs—secure, in this way, of getting rid of them. And some of them embalmed the misdeeds of spiritless diminutive Fions, not very much above fifteen feet in height, who, unlike their more active companions, could not leap across the Cromarty or Dornoch Firths on their spears, and who, as was natural, were very much despised by the women of the tribe. The pieces of fine sentiment and brilliant description discovered by Macpherson seemed never to have found their way into this northern district. But, told in fluent Gaelic, in the great "Ha'," the wild legends served every necessary purpose equally well. The "Ha'" in the autumn nights, as the days shortened and the frosts set in, was a genial place; and so attached was my cousin to its distinctive principle—the fire in the midst—as handed down from the "days of other years," that in the plan of a new two-storeyed house for his father, which he had procured from a London architect, one of the nether rooms was actually designed in the circular form; and a hearth like a millstone, placed in the centre, represented the place of the fire. But there was, as I remarked to Cousin George, no corresponding central hole in the room above, through which to let up the smoke; and I questioned whether a nicely plastered apartment, round as a band-box, with the fire in the middle, like the sun in the centre of an Orrery,[1] would have been quite like anything ever seen in the Highlands before. The plan, however, was not destined to encounter criticism, or give trouble in the execution of it.

On Sabbaths my cousin and his two brothers attended the parish church, attired in the full Highland dress; and three handsome, well-formed men they were; but my aunt, though mayhap not quite without the mother's pride, did not greatly relish the exhibition; and oftener than once I heard her say so to her sister my mother; though she, smitten by the gallant appearance of her nephews, seemed inclined rather to take the opposite side. My uncle, on the other hand, said nothing either for or against the display. He had been a keen Highlander in his younger days; and when the inhibition against wearing tartan and the philabeg had been virtually removed, in consideration of the achievements of the "hardy and dauntless men" who, according to Chatham, conquered for England "in every quarter of the globe," he had celebrated the event in a merry-making, at which the dance was kept up from night till morning; but though he retained, I suspect, his old partialities, he was now a sobered man; and when I ventured to ask him, on one occasion, why he too did not get a Sunday kilt, which, by the way, he would "*have set*," notwithstanding his years, as well as any of his sons, he merely replied with a quiet, "No, no; there's no fool like an old fool."

[1] A clockwork model of the solar system, named after Charles Boyle, 4th Earl of Orrery (1676-1731) for whom one was made.

CHAPTER VI

"When they sawe the darksome night,
They sat them downe and cryed."—BABES IN THE WOOD.

I SPENT the holidays of two other autumns in this delightful Highland valley. On the second, as on the first occasion, I had accompanied my mother, specially invited; but the third journey was an unsanctioned undertaking of my own and a Cromarty cousin, my contemporary, to whom, as he had never travelled the way, I had to act as protector and guide. I reached my aunt's cottage without mishap or adventure of any kind; but found, that during the twelvemonth which had just elapsed, great changes had taken place in the circumstances of the household. My cousin George, who had married in the interim, had gone to reside in a cottage of his own; and I soon ascertained that my cousin William, who had been for several months resident with his father, had not nearly so many visitors as before; nor did presents of salmon and haunches of venison come at all so often the way. Immediately after the final discomfiture of Napoleon, an extensive course of speculation in which he had ventured to engage had turned out so ill, that, instead of making him a fortune, as at first seemed probable, it had landed him in the *Gazette*; and he was now tiding over the difficulties of a time of settlement, six hundred miles from the scene of disaster, in the hope of being soon enabled to begin the world anew. He bore his losses with quiet magnanimity; and I learned to know and like him better during his period of eclipse than in the previous time, when summer friends had fluttered around him by scores. He was a generous, warm-hearted man, who felt, with the force of an implanted instinct not vouchsafed to all, that it is more blessed to give than to receive; and it was doubtless a wise provision of nature, and worthy, in this point of view, the special attention of moralists and philosophers, that his old associates, the grand gentlemen, did not now often come his way; seeing that his inability any longer to give would cost him, in the circumstances, great pain.

I was much with my cousin George in his new dwelling. It was one of the most delightful of Highland cottages, and George was happy in it, far above the average lot of humanity, with his young wife. He had dared, in opposition to the general voice of the district, to build it half-way up the slope of a beautiful tomhan, that, waving with birch from base to summit, rose regular as a pyramid from the bottom of the valley, and commanded a wide view of Loch Shin on the one hand, with the moors and mountains that lie beyond; and overlooked, on the other, with all the richer portions of the Barony of Gruids, the church and picturesque hamlet of Lairg. Half-hidden by the graceful birchen trees that sprang up thick around, with their silvery boles and light foliage, it was rather a nest than a house; and George, emancipated, by his reading, and his residence for a time in the south, from at least the wilder beliefs of the locality, failed to suffer, as had been predicted, for his temerity; as the "good people,"[1] who, much to their credit, had made choice of the place for themselves long before, never, to his knowledge, paid him a visit. He had brought his share of the family library with him; and it was a large share. He had mathematical instruments too, and a colour-box, and the tools of his profession; in especial, large hammers fitted to break great stones; and I was generously made free of them all—books, instruments, colour-box, and hammers. His cottage, too, commanded, from its situation, a delightful variety of most interesting objects. It had all the advantages of my uncle's domicile and a great many more.

The nearer shores of Loch Shin were scarce half a mile away; and there was a low long promontory which shot out into the lake, that was covered at that time by an ancient wood of doddered time-worn trees, and bore amid its outer solitudes, where the waters circled round its terminal apex, one of those towers of hoary

---

[1] The fairies.

eld—memorials, mayhap, of the primeval stone-period in our island, to which the circular erections of Glenelg and Dornadilla belong. It was formed of undressed stones of vast size, uncemented by mortar; and through the thick walls ran winding passages— the only covered portions of the building, for the inner area had never been furnished with a roof—in which, when a sudden shower descended, the loiterer amid the ruins could find shelter. It was a fascinating place to a curious boy. Some of the old trees had become mere whitened skeletons, that stretched forth their blasted arms to the sky, and had so slight a hold of the soil, that I have overthrown them with a delightful crash, by merely running against them; the heath rose thick beneath, and it was a source of fearful joy to know that it harboured snakes full three feet long; and though the loch itself is by no means one of our finer Highland lochs, it furnished, to at least my eye at this time, a delightful prospect in still October mornings, when the light gossamer went sailing about in white filmy threads, and birch and hazel, glorified by decay, served to embroider with gold the brown hillsides which, standing up on either hand in their long vista of more than twenty miles, form the barriers of the lake; and when the sun, still struggling with a blue diluted haze, fell delicately on the smooth surface, or twinkled for a moment on the silvery coats of the little trout, as they sprang a few inches into the air, and then broke the water into a series of concentric rings in their descent. When I last passed the way, both the old wood and the old tower were gone; and for the latter, which, though much a ruin, might have survived for ages, I found only a long extent of dry-stone dike, and the wide ring formed by the old foundation-stones, which had proved too massive to be removed. A greatly more entire erection of the same age and style, known of old as Dunaliscag—which stood on the Ross-shire side of the Dornoch Firth, and within whose walls, forming, as it did, a sort of half-way stage, I used, on these Sutherlandshire journeys, to eat my piece of cake with a double relish—I found, on last passing the way, similarly represented. Its grey venerable walls, and dark winding passages of many steps—even the huge pear-shaped lintel, which had stretched over its little door, and which, according to tradition, a great Fingalian lady had once thrown across the Dornoch Firth from off the point of her spindle—had all disappeared, and I saw instead, only a dry-stone wall. The men of the present generation do certainly live in a most enlightened age—an age in which every trace of the barbarism of our early ancestors is fast disappearing; and were we but more zealous in immortalizing the public benefactors who efface such dark memorials of the past as the tower of Dunaliscag and the promontory of Loch Shin, it would be, doubtless, an encouragement to others to speed us yet further on in the march of improvement. It seems scarce fair that the enlightened destroyers of Arthur's Oven or of the bas-relief known as Robin of Redesdale, or of the Town-cross of Edinburgh, should enjoy all the celebrity attendant on such acts, while the equally deserving iconoclasts of Dunaliscag and the tower of Loch Shin should be suffered to die without their fame.

I remember spending one singularly delightful morning with Cousin George beside the ancient tower. He pointed out to me, amid the heath, several plants to which the old Highlanders used to attach occult virtues—plants that disenchanted bewitched cattle, not by their administration as medicines to the sick animals, but by bringing them in contact, as charms, with the injured milk; and plants which were used as philters, either for procuring love, or exciting hatred. It was, he showed me, the root of a species of orchis that was employed in making the philters. While most of the radical fibres of the plant retain the ordinary cylindrical form, two of their number are usually found developed into starchy tubercles; but, belonging apparently to different seasons, one of the two is of a dark colour and of such gravity that it sinks in water; while the other is light-coloured, and floats. And a powder made of the light-coloured tubercle formed the main ingredient, said my cousin, in the love philter; while a powder made of the dark-coloured one excited, it was held, only antipathy and dislike. And then George would speculate on the origin of a belief which could, he said, neither be suggested by reason, nor tested by experience. Living, however, among a people with whom beliefs of the kind were still vital and influential, he did not wholly escape the influence; and I saw him, in one instance, administer to an ailing cow a little live trout, simply because the traditions of the district assured him, that a trout swallowed alive by the creature was the only specific in the case. Some of his Highland stories were very curious. He communicated to me, for example, beside the broken tower, a tradition illustrative of the Celtic theory of dreaming, of which I have since often thought. Two young men had been spending the early portion of a warm summer day in exactly such a scene as that in which he communicated the anecdote. There was an ancient ruin beside them, separated however, from the mossy bank on which they sat, by a slender runnel, across which there lay, immediately over a miniature cascade, a few withered grass stalks. Overcome by the heat of the day, one of the young men fell asleep; his companion watched drowsily beside him; when all at once the watcher was aroused to attention by seeing a little indistinct form, scarce larger than a humble-bee, issue from the mouth of the sleeping man, and, leaping upon the moss, move downwards to the runnel, which it crossed along the withered grass stalks, and then disappeared amid the interstices of the ruin. Alarmed by what he saw, the watcher hastily shook his companion by the shoulder and awoke him; though, with all his haste, the little cloud-like creature, still more rapid in its movements, issued from the interstice into which it had gone, and, flying across the runnel instead of creeping along the grass stalks and over the sward, as before, it re-entered the mouth of the sleeper, just as he was in the act of awakening. "What is the matter with you?" said the watcher, greatly alarmed. "What ails you?" "Nothing ails me," replied the other; "but you have robbed me of a most delightful dream. I dreamed I was walking through a fine rich country, and came at length to the shores of a noble river; and, just where the clear water went thundering down a precipice, there was a bridge all of silver, which I crossed; and then, entering a noble palace on the opposite side, I saw great heaps of gold and jewels, and I was just going to load myself with treasure, when you rudely awoke me, and I lost all." I know not what the asserters of the clairvoyant faculty may think of the story; but I rather believe I have occasionally seen them make use of anecdotes that did not rest on evidence a great deal more solid than the Highland legend, and that illustrated not much more clearly the philosophy of the phenomena with which they profess to deal.

Of all my cousins, Cousin George was the one whose pursuit most nearly resembled my own, and in whose society I most delighted to share. He did sometimes borrow a day from his work, even after his marriage; but then, according to the poet, it was

"The love he bore to science was in fault."

The borrowed day was always spent in transferring to paper some architectural design, or in working out some mathematical problem, or in rendering some piece of Gaelic verse into English, or some piece of English prose into Gaelic; and as he was a steady, careful man, the appropriated day was never seriously missed. The winter, too, was all his own, for, in those northern districts, masons are never employed from a little after Hallow-day, till the second, or even third month of spring—a circumstance which I carefully noted at this time in its bearing on the amusements of my cousin, and which afterwards weighed not a little with me when I came to make choice of a profession for myself. And George's winters were always ingeniously spent. He had a great command of Gaelic, and a very tolerable command of English; and so a translation of Bunyan's "Visions of Heaven and Hell," which he published several years subsequent to this period, was not only well received by his country folk of Sutherland and Ross, but was said by competent judges to be really a not inadequate rendering of the meaning and spirit of the noble old tinker of Elstow. I, of course, could be no authority respecting the merits of a translation, the language of which I did not understand; but living much amid the literature of a time when almost every volume, whether the "Virgil "of a Dryden, or the "Meditations" of a Harvey, was heralded by its sets of complimentary verses, and having a deep interest in whatever Cousin George undertook and performed, I addressed to him, in the old style, a few introductory stanzas, which, to indulge me in the inexpressible luxury of seeing myself in print for the first time, he benevolently threw into type. They survive to remind me that my cousin's belief in Ossian did exert some little influence over my phraseology when I addressed myself to him, and that, with the rashness natural to immature youth, I had at this time the temerity to term myself "poet."

> Yes, oft I've said, as oft I've seen
> The men who dwell its hills among,
> That Morven's land has ever been
> A land of valour, worth, and song.
>
> But Ignorance, of darkness dire,
> Has o'er that land a mantle spread;
> And all untuned and rude the lyre
> That sounds beneath its gloomy shade.
>
> With muse of calm untiring wing,
> Oh, be it thine, my friend, to show
> The Celtic swain how Saxons sing
> Of Hell's dire gloom and Heaven's glow!
>
> So shall the meed of fame be thine,
> The glistening bay-wreath green and gay;
> Thy *poet*, too, though weak his line,
> Shall frame for thee th' approving lay.

Longing for some profession in which his proper work would give exercise to the faculties which he most delighted to cultivate, my cousin resolved on becoming candidate for a Gaelic Society school—a poor enough sort of office then, as now; but which, by investing a little money in cattle, by tilling a little croft, and by now and then emitting from the press a Gaelic translation, might, he thought, be rendered sufficiently remunerative to supply the very moderate wants of himself and his little family. And so he set out for Edinburgh, amply furnished with testimonials that meant more in his case than testimonials usually mean, to stand an examination before a Committee of the Gaelic School Society. Unluckily for his success, however, instead of bringing with him his ordinary Sabbath-day suit of dark brown and blue (the kilt had been assumed for but a few weeks, to please his brother William), he had provided himself with a suit of tartan, as at once cheap and respectable, and appeared before the Committee—if not in the garb, in at least the many-coloured hues, of his clan—a robust manly Highlander, apparently as well suited to enact the part of colour-serjeant to the Forty-Second, as to teach children their letter. A grave member of the Society, at that time in high repute for sanctity of character, but who afterwards, becoming righteous overmuch, was loosened from his charge, and straightaway, spurning the ground, rose into an Irvingite angel, came at once to the conclusion that no such type of man, encased in clan-tartan, could possibly have the root of the matter in him; and so he determined that Cousin George should be cast in the examination. But then, as it could not be alleged with any decency that my cousin was inadmissible on the score of his having too much tartan, it was agreed that he should be declared inadmissible on the score of his having too little Gaelic. And, of course, at this result the examinators arrived; and George, ultimately to his advantage, was cast accordingly. I still remember the astonishment evinced by a worthy catechist of the north—himself a Gaelic teacher—on being told how my cousin had fared. "George Munro was not allowed to pass," he said, "for want of right Gaelic! Why, he has more right Gaelic in his own self than all the Society's teachers in this corner of Scotland put together. They are the *curiousest* people, some of these good gentlemen of the Edinburgh Committees, that I ever heard of: they're just like our country lawyers." It would, however, be far from fair to regard this transaction, which took place, I may mention, so late as the year 1829, as a specimen of the actings of either civic societies or country lawyers. George's chief examinator on the occasion was the minister of the Gaelic Chapel of the place, at that time one of the Society's Committee for the year; and, not being a remarkably scrupulous man, he seems to have stretched a point or two, in compliance with the pious wishes and occult judgment of the Society's Secretary. But the anecdote is not without its lesson. When devout Walter Taits set themselves ingeniously to manoeuvre with the purest of intentions, and for what they deem the best of purposes—when, founding their real grounds of objection on one set of appearances, they found their ostensible grounds of objection on another and entirely different set—they are always exposed to the signal danger of—getting indevout Duncan M'Caigs to assist them. Only two years from the period of my cousin's examination before the Society, his reverend examinator received at the bar of the High Court of Justiciary, in the character of a thief convicted of eleven acts of stealing, sentence of transportation for fourteen years.

I had several interesting excursions with my cousin William. We found ourselves one evening—on our way home from a mineral spring which he had discovered among the hills—in a little lonely valley, which opened transversely into that of the Gruids, and which, though its sides were mottled with green furrow-marked patches, had not at the time a single human habitation. At the upper end, however, there stood the ruins of a narrow two-storeyed house, with one of its gables still entire from foundation-stone to the shattered chimney-top, but with the other gable, and the larger part of the front wall, laid prostrate along the sward. My cousin, after bidding me remark the completeness of the solitude, and that the eye could not command from the site of the ruin a single spot where man had ever dwelt, told me that it had been the scene of the strict seclusion, amounting almost to imprisonment, about eighty years before, of a lady of high birth, over whom, in early youth, there had settled a sad cloud of infamy. She had borne a child to one of the menials of her father's house, which, with the assistance of her paramour, she had murdered;

and being too high for the law to reach in these northern parts, at a time when the hereditary jurisdiction still existed entire, and her father was the sole magistrate, possessed of the power of life and death in the district, she was sent by her family to wear out life in this lonely retreat, in which she remained secluded from the world for more than half a century. And then, long after the abolition of the local jurisdictions, and when her father and brother, with the entire generation that knew of her crime, had passed away, she was permitted to take up her abode in one of the seaport towns of the north, where she was still remembered at this time as a crazy old lady, invariably silent and sullen, that used to be seen in the twilight flitting about the more retired lanes and closes, like an unhappy ghost. The story, as told me in that solitary valley, just as the sun was skulking over the hill beyond, powerfully impressed my fancy. Crabbe would have delighted to tell it; and I now relate it, as it lies fast wedged in my memory, mainly for the peculiar light which it casts on the times of the hereditary jurisdictions. It forms an example of one of the judicial banishments of an age that used, in ordinary cases, to save itself all sorts of trouble of the kind, by hanging its victims. I may add, that I saw a good deal of the neighbourhood at this time in the company of my cousin, and gleaned, from my visits to shieling and cottage, most of my conceptions of the state of the Northern Highlands, ere the clearance system had depopulated the interior of the country, and precipitated its poverty-stricken population upon the coasts.

There was, however, one of my excursions with Cousin William, that turned out rather unfortunately. The river Shin has its bold salmon-leap, which even yet, after several hundred pounds' worth of gunpowder have been expended in sloping its angle of ascent, to facilitate the passage of the fish, is a fine picturesque object, but which at this time, when it presented all its original abruptness, was a finer object still. Though distant about three miles from my uncle's cottage, we could distinctly hear its roarings from beside his door, when October nights were frosty and still; and as we had been told many strange stories regarding it—stories about bold fishers who had threaded their dangerous way between the overhanging rock and the water, and who, striking outwards, had speared salmon through the foam of the cataract as they leaped—stories, too, of skilful sportsmen, who, taking their stand in the thick wood beyond, had shot the rising animals, as one shoots a bird flying—both my Cromarty cousin and myself were extremely desirous to visit the scene of such feats and marvels; and Cousin William obligingly agreed to act as our guide and instructor by the way. He did look somewhat askance at our naked feet; and we heard him remark, in an undertone, to his mother, that when he and his brothers were boys, she never suffered *them* to visit her Cromarty relations unshod; but neither Cousin Walter nor myself had the magnanimity to say, that *our* mothers had also taken care to see us shod; but that, deeming it lighter and cooler to walk barefoot, the good women had no sooner turned their backs than we both agreed to fling our shoes into a corner, and set out on our journey without them. The walk to the salmon-leap was a thoroughly delightful one. We passed through the woods of Achanie, famous for their nuts; startled, as we went, a herd of roe deer; and found the leap itself far exceeded all anticipation. The Shin becomes savagely wild in its lower reaches. Rugged precipices of gneiss, with scattered bushes fast anchored in the crevices, overhang the stream, which boils in many a dark pool, and foams over many a steep rapid; and immediately beneath, where it threw itself headlong, at this time, over the leap—for it now merely rushes in snow adown a steep slope—there was a cauldron, so awfully dark and profound, that, according to the accounts of the district, it had no bottom; and so vexed was it by a frightful whirlpool, that no one ever fairly caught in its eddies had succeeded, it was said, in regaining the shore. We saw, as we stood amid the scraggy trees of an overhanging wood, the salmon leaping up by scores, most of them, however, to fall back again into the pool—for only a very few stray fish that attempted the cataract at its edges seemed to succeed in forcing their upward way; we saw, too, on a shelf of the precipitous but wooded bank, the rude hut, formed of undressed logs, where a solitary watcher used to take his stand, to protect them from the spear and fowling-piece of the poacher, and which in stormy nights, when the cry of the kelpie mingled with the roar of the flood, must have been a sublime lodge in the wilderness, in which a poet might have delighted to dwell. I was excited by the scene; and, when heedlessly leaping from a tall lichened stone into the long heath below, my right foot came so heavily in contact with a sharp-edged fragment of rock concealed in the moss, that I almost screamed aloud with pain. I, however, suppressed the shriek, and, sitting down and setting my teeth close, bore the pang, until it gradually moderated, and my foot, to the ankle, seemed as if almost divested of feeling. In our return, I halted as I walked, and lagged considerably behind my companions; and during the whole evening the injured foot seemed as if dead, save that it glowed with an intense heat. I was, however, at ease enough to write a sublime piece of blank verse on the cataract; and, proud of my production, I attempted reading it to Cousin William. But William had taken lessons in recitation under the great Mr Thelwall, politician and elocutionist; and deeming it proper to set me right in all the words which I mispronounced—three out of every four at least, and not unfrequently the fourth word also— the reading of the piece proved greatly stiffer and slower work than the writing of it; and, somewhat to my mortification, my cousin declined giving me any definite judgment on its merits, even when I had done. He insisted, however, on the signal advantages of reading well. He had an acquaintance, he said, a poet, who had taken lessons under Mr Thelwall, and who, though his verses, when he published, met with no great success, was so indebted to his admirable elocution, as to be invariably successful when he read them to his friends.

Next morning my injured foot was stiff and sore; and, after a few days of suffering, it suppurated and discharged great quantities of blood and matter. It was, however, fast getting well again, when, tired of inaction, and stirred up by my cousin Walter, who wearied sadly of the Highlands, I set out with him, contrary to all advice, on my homeward journey, and, for the first six or eight miles, got on tolerably well. My cousin, a stout active lad, carried the bag of Highland luxuries—cheese, and butter, and a full peck of nuts—with which we had been laden by my aunt; and, by way of indemnity for taking both my share of the burden and his own, he demanded of me one of my long extempore stories, which, shortly after leaving my aunt's cottage, I accordingly began. My stories, when I had cousin Walter for my companion, were usually co-extensive with the journey to be performed: they became ten, fifteen, or twenty miles long, agreeably to the measure of the road, and the determination of the milestones; and what was at present required was a story of about thirty miles in length, whose one end would touch the Barony of Gruids, and the other the Cromarty Ferry. At the end, however, of the first six or eight miles, my story broke suddenly down, and my foot, after becoming very painful, began to bleed. The day, too, had grown raw and unpleasant, and after twelve o'clock there came on a thick, wetting drizzle. I limped on silently in the rear, leaving at every few paces a blotch of blood upon the road, until, in the parish of Edderton, we both remembered that there was a short cut through the hills, which two of our older cousins had taken during the previous year, when on a similar journey; and as Walter deemed himself equal to anything which his elder cousins could perform, and as I was exceedingly desirous to get home as soon as possible, and by the shortest way, we both struck up the hill-side, and soon found ourselves in a dreary waste, without trace of human habitation.

Walter, however, pushed on bravely and in the right direction; and, though my head was now becoming light and my sight dim, I succeeded in struggling after him, until, just as the night was falling, we reached a heathy ridge, which commands the northern sea-board of the Cromarty Firth, and saw the cultivated country and the sands of Nigg lying only a few miles below. The sands are dangerous at certain hours of the tide, and accidents frequently happen in the fords; but then there could, we thought, be no fear of us; for though Walter could not swim, I could; and as I was to lead the way, he of course would be safe, by simply avoiding the places where I lost footing. The night fell rather thick than dark, for there was a moon overhead, though it could not be seen through the cloud; but, though Walter steered well, the downward way was exceedingly rough and broken, and we had wandered from the path. I retain a faint but painful recollection of a scraggy moor, and of dark patches of planting, through which I had to grope onwards, stumbling as I went; and then, that I began to feel as if I were merely dreaming, and that the dream was a very horrible one, from which I could not awaken. And finally, on reaching a little cleared spot on the edge of the cultivated country, I dropped down as suddenly as if struck by a bullet, and, after an ineffectual attempt to rise, fell fast asleep. Walter was much frightened; but he succeeded in carrying me to a little rick of dried grass which stood up in the middle of the clearing; and after covering me well up with the grass, he laid himself down beside me. Anxiety, however, kept him awake; and he was frightened, as he lay, to hear the sounds of psalm-singing, in the old Gaelic style, coming apparently from a neighbouring clump of wood. Walter believed in the fairies; and, though psalmody was not one of the reputed accomplishments of the "good people" in the low country, he did not know but that in the Highlands the case might be different. Some considerable time after the singing had ceased, there was a slow, heavy step heard approaching the rick; an exclamation in Gaelic followed; and then a rough hard hand grasped Walter by the naked heel. He started up, and found himself confronted by an old, grey-headed man, the inmate of a cottage, which, hidden in the neighbouring clump, had escaped his notice.

The old man, in the belief that we were gipsies, was at first disposed to be angry at the liberty we had taken with his hay-rick; but Walter's simple story mollified him at once, and he expressed deep regret that "poor boys, who had met with an accident," should have laid them down in such a night under the open sky, and a house so near. "It was putting disgrace," he said, "on a Christian land." I was assisted into his cottage, whose only other inmate, an aged woman, the old Highlander's wife, received us with great kindness and sympathy; and on Walter's declaring our names and lineage, the hospitable regrets and regards of both host and hostess waxed stronger and louder still. They knew our maternal grandfather and grandmother, and remembered old Donald Roy; and when my cousin named my father, there was a strongly-expressed burst of sorrow and commiseration, that the son of a man whom they had seen so "well to do in the world" should be in circumstances so deplorably destitute. I was too ill to take much note of what passed. I only remember, that of the food which they placed before me, I could partake of only a few spoonfuls of milk; and that the old woman, as she washed my feet, fell a-crying over me. I was, however, so greatly recruited by a night's rest in their best bed, as to be fit in the morning to be removed, in the old man's *rung*-cart, to the house of a relation in the parish of Nigg, from which, after a second day's rest, I was conveyed in another cart to the Cromarty Ferry. And thus terminated the last of my boyish visits to the Highlands.

Both my grandfather and grandmother had come of long-lived races, and Death did not often knock at the family door. But the time when the latter "should cross the river," though she was some six or eight years younger than her husband, came first; and so, according to Bunyan, she "called for her children, and told them that her hour had come." She was a quiet, retiring woman, and, though intimately acquainted with her Bible, not in the least fitted to make a female Professor of Theology: she could *live* her religion better than *talk* it; but she now earnestly recommended to her family the great interests once more; and, as its various members gathered round her bed, she besought one of her daughters to read to her, in their hearing, that eighth chapter of the Romans which declares that "there is now no condemnation to them which are in Christ Jesus, who walk not after the flesh, but after the Spirit." She, repeated, in a sinking voice, the concluding verses—"For I am persuaded, that neither death nor life, nor angels nor principalities nor powers, nor things present nor things to come, nor height nor depth, nor any other creature, shall be able to separate us from the love of God, which is in Christ Jesus our Lord." And, resting in confidence on the hope which the passage so powerfully expresses, she slept her last sleep, in simple trust that all would be well with her in the morning of the general awakening. I retain her wedding-ring, the gift of Donald Roy. It is a sorely-wasted fragment, worn through on one of the sides, for she had toiled long and hard in her household, and the breach in the circlet, with its general thinness, testify to the fact; but its gold is still bright and pure; and, though not much of a relic-monger, I would hesitate to exchange it for the Holy Coat of Trèves, or for waggon-loads of the wood of the "true cross."

My grandmother's term of life had exceeded by several twelvemonths the full threescore and ten; but when, only a few years after, Death next visited the circle, it was on its youngest members that his hand was laid. A deadly fever swept over the place, and my two sisters—the one in her tenth, the other in her twelfth year—sank under it within a few days of each other. Jean, the elder, who resided with my uncles, was a pretty little girl, of fine intellect, and a great reader; Catherine, the younger, was lively and affectionate, and a general favourite; and their loss plunged the family in deep gloom. My uncles made little show of grief, but they felt strongly: my mother for weeks and months wept for her children, like Rachel of old, and refused to be comforted, because they were not; but my grandfather, now in his eighty-fifth year, seemed to be rendered wholly bankrupt in heart by their loss. As is perhaps not uncommon in such cases, his warmer affections strode across the generation of grown-up men and women—his sons and daughters—and luxuriated among the children their descendants. The boys, his grandsons, were too wild for him; but the two little girls—gentle and affectionate—had

116

seized on his whole heart; and now that they were gone, it seemed as if he had nothing in the world left to care for. He had been, up till this time, notwithstanding his great age, a hale and active man. In 1803, when France threatened invasion, he was, though on the verge of seventy, one of the first men in the place to apply for arms as a volunteer; but now he drooped and gradually sunk, and longed for the rest of the grave. "It is God's will," I heard him say about this time, to a neighbour who congratulated him on his long term of life and unbroken health—"It is God's will, but not my desire." And in rather more than a twelvemonth after the death of my sisters, he was seized by almost his only illness—for, for nearly seventy years he had not been confined to bed for a single day— and was carried off in less than a week. During the last few days, the fever under which he sank mounted to his brain; and he talked in unbroken narrative of the events of his past life. He began with his earliest recollections; described the battle of Culloden as he had witnessed it from the Hill of Cromarty, and the appearance of Duke William and the royal army as seen during a subsequent visit to Inverness; ran over the after events of his career—his marriage, his interviews with Donald Roy, his business transactions with neighbouring proprietors, long dead at the time; and finally, after reaching, in his oral history, his term of middle life, he struck off into another track, and began laying down, with singular coherency, the statements of doctrine in a theological work of the old school, which he had been recently perusing. And finally, his mind clearing as his end approached, he died in good hope. It is not uninteresting to look back on two such generations of Scotchmen as those to which my uncles and grandfather belonged. They differed very considerably in some respects. My grandfather, with most of his contemporaries of the same class, had a good deal of the Tory in his composition. He stood by George III in the early policy of his reign, and by his adviser Lord Bute; reprobated Wilkes and Junius; and gravely questioned whether Washington and his coadjutors, the American Republicans, were other than bold rebels. My uncles, on the contrary, were staunch Whigs, who looked upon Washington as perhaps the best and greatest man of modern times—stood firm by the policy of Fox, as opposed to that of Pitt—and held that the war with France, which immediately succeeded the First Revolution, was, however thoroughly it changed its character afterwards, one of unjustifiable aggression. But however greatly my uncles and grandfather may have differed on these points, they were equally honest men.

The rising generation can perhaps form no very adequate conception of the number and singular interest of the links which serve to connect the recollections of a man who has seen his fiftieth birthday, with what to them must appear a remote past. I have seen at least two men who fought at Culloden—one on the side of the King, the other on that of the Prince—and, with these, not a few who witnessed the battle from a distance. I have conversed with an aged woman that had conversed, in turn, with an aged man who had attained to mature manhood when the persecutions of Charles and James were at their height, and remember the general regret excited by the death of Renwick.[1] My eldest maternal aunt—the mother of Cousin George—remembered old John Feddes—turned of ninety at the time; and John's buccaneering expedition could not have dated later than the year 1687. I have known many who remembered the abolition of the hereditary jurisdictions;[2] and have listened to stories of executions which took place on the gallows-hills of burghs and sheriffdoms, and of witch-burnings perpetrated on town links and baronial laws. And I have felt a strange interest in these glimpses of a past so unlike the present, when thus presented to the mind as personal reminiscences, or as well-attested traditions, removed from the original witnesses by but a single stage. All, for instance, which I have yet read of witch-burnings has failed to impress me so strongly as the recollections of an old lady who in 1722 was carried in her nurse's

[1] James Renwick (1662-88), last of the covenanting martyrs. Having witnessed the execution of Donald Cargill in 1681 in Edinburgh, he suffered the same fate seven years later.
[2] In 1747.

arms—for she was almost an infant at the time—to witness a witch-execution in the neighbourhood of Dornoch—the last which took place in Scotland. The lady well remembered the awe-struck yet excited crowd, the lighting of the fire, and the miserable appearance of the poor fatuous creature whom it was kindled to consume, and who seemed to be so little aware of her situation, that she held out her thin shrivelled hands to warm them at the blaze. But what most impressed the narrator—for it must have been a frightful incident in a sad spectacle—was the circumstance that, when the charred remains of the victim were sputtering and boiling amid the intense heat of the flames, a cross gust of wind suddenly blew the smoke athwart the spectators, and she felt in her attendant's arms as if in danger of being suffocated by the horrible stench. I have heard described, too, by a man whose father had witnessed the scene, an execution which took place, after a brief and inadequate trial, on the burgh-gallows of Tain. The supposed culprit, a Strathcarron Highlander, had been found lurking about the place, noting, as was supposed, where the burghers kept their cattle, and was hung as a spy; but they all, after the execution, came to deem him innocent, from the circumstance that, when his dead body was dangling in the wind, a white pigeon had come flying the way, and, as it passed over, half-encircled the gibbet.

One of the two Culloden soldiers whom I remember was an old forester who lived in a picturesque cottage among the woods of the Cromarty Hill; and in his last illness, my uncles, whom I had always leave to accompany, used not unfrequently to visit him. He had lived at the time his full century, and a few months more: and I still vividly remember the large gaunt face that used to stare from the bed as they entered, and the huge, horny hand. He had been settled in life, previous to the year 1745, as the head gardener of a northern proprietor, and little dreamed of being engaged in war; but the rebellion broke out; and as his master, a staunch Whig, had volunteered to serve on behalf of his principles in the royal army, his gardener, a "mighty man of his hands," went with him. As his memory for the later events of his life was gone at this time, its preceding forty years seemed a blank, from which not a single recollection could be drawn; but well did he remember the battle, and more vividly still, the succeeding atrocities of the troops of Cumberland. He had accompanied the army, after its victory at Culloden, to the camp at Fort Augustus, and there witnessed scenes of cruelty and spoliation of which the recollection, after the lapse of seventy years, and in his extreme old age, had still power enough to set his Scotch blood aboil. While scores of cottages were flaming in the distance, and blood not unfrequently hissing on the embers, the men and women of the army used to be engaged in racing in sacks, or upon Highland ponies; and when the ponies were in request, the women, who must have sat for their portraits in Hogarth's "March to Finchley," took their seats astride like the men. Gold circulated and liquor flowed in abundance; and in a few weeks there were about twenty thousand head of cattle brought in by marauding parties of the soldiery from the crushed and impoverished Highlanders; and groups of drovers from Yorkshire and the south of Scotland—coarse vulgar men—used to come every day to share in the spoil, by making purchases at greatly less than half-price.

My grandfather's recollections of Culloden were merely those of an observant boy of fourteen, who had witnessed the battle from a distance. The day, he has told me, was drizzly and thick; and on reaching the brow of the Hill of Cromarty, where he found many of his townsfolk already assembled, he could scarce see the opposite land. But the fog gradually cleared away; first one hill-top came into view, and then another; till at length the long range of coast, from the opening of the great Caledonian valley to the promontory of Burghhead, was dimly visible through the haze. A little after noon there suddenly rose a round white cloud from the Moor of Culloden, and then a second round white cloud beside it. And then the two clouds mingled together, and went rolling slantways on the wind towards the west; and he could hear the rattle of the smaller fire-arms mingling with the roar of the artillery. And then, in what seemed an exceedingly brief space of time, the cloud dissipated and disappeared, the boom of the greater guns ceased, and a sharp intermittent patter of musketry passed on towards Inverness. But the battle was presented to the imagination, in these old personal narratives, in many a diverse form. I have been told by an ancient woman, who, on the day of the fight, was engaged in tending some sheep on a solitary common near Munlochy, separated from the Moor of Culloden by the Firth, and screened by a lofty hill, that she sat listening in terror to the boom of the cannon; but that she was still more scared by the continuous howling of her dog, who sat upright on his haunches all the time the firing lasted, with his neck stretched out towards the battle, and "looking as if he saw a spirit." Such are some of the recollections which link the memories of a man who has lived his half-century, to those of the preceding age, and which serve to remind him how one generation of men after another break and disappear on the shores of the eternal world, as wave after wave breaks in foam upon the beach, when storms are rising, and the ground-swell sets in heavily from the sea.

CHAPTER VII

SOME of the wealthier tradesmen of the town, dissatisfied with the small progress which their boys were making under the parish schoolmaster, clubbed together and got a schoolmaster of their own; but though a rather clever young man, he proved an unsteady one, and, regular in his irregularities, got diurnally drunk, on receiving the instalments of his salary at term-days, as long as his money lasted. Getting rid of him, they procured another—a licentiate of the Church—who for some time promised well. He seemed steady and thoughtful, and withal a painstaking teacher; but coming in contact with some zealous Baptists, they succeeded in conjuring up such a cloud of doubt around him regarding the propriety of infant baptism, that both his bodily and mental health became affected by his perplexities, and he had to resign his charge. And then, after a pause, during which the boys enjoyed a delightfully long vacation, they got yet a third schoolmaster, also a licentiate, and a person of a high, if not very consistent religious profession, who was always getting into pecuniary difficulties, and always courting, though with but little success, wealthy ladies, who, according to the poet, had "acres of charms." To the subscription school I was transferred, at the instance of Uncle James, who remained quite sure, notwithstanding the experience of the past, that I was destined to be a scholar. And, invariably fortunate in my opportunities of amusement, the transference took place only a few weeks ere the better schoolmaster, losing health and heart, in a labyrinth of perplexity resigned his charge. I had little more than time enough to look about me on the new forms, and to renew, on a firmer foundation than ever, my friendship with my old associate of the cave—who had been for the two previous years an inmate of the subscription school, and was now less under maternal control than before—when on came the long vacation; and for four happy months I had nothing to do.

My amusements had undergone very little change: I was even fonder of the shores and woods than ever, and better acquainted with the rocks and caves. A very considerable change, however, had taken place in the amusements of the school-fellows my contemporaries, who were now from two to three years older than when I had been associated with them in the parish school. Hyspy[1] had lost its charms; nor was there much of its old interest for them in French and English; whereas my rock excursions they came to regard as very interesting indeed. With the exception of my friend of the cave, they cared little about rocks or stones; but they all liked brambles, and sloes, and *craws-apples*, tolerably well, and took great delight in assisting me to kindle fires in the caverns of the old coast line, at which we used to broil shell-fish and crabs, taken among the crags and boulders of the ebb below, and roast potatoes, transferred from the fields of the hill above. There was one cave, an especial favourite with us, in which our fires used to blaze day after day for weeks together. It is deeply hollowed in the base of a steep ivy-mantled precipice of granitic gneiss, a full hundred feet in height; and bears on its smoothed sides and roof, and along its uneven bottom—fretted into pot-like cavities, with large rounded pebbles in them—unequivocal evidence that the excavating agent to which it owed its existence had been the wild surf of this exposed shore. But for more than two thousand years waves had never reached it: the last general elevation of the land had raised it beyond the reach of the highest stream-tides; and when my gang and I took possession of its twilight recesses, its stony sides were crusted with mosses and liverworts; and a crop of pale, attenuated, sickly-looking weeds, on which the sun had never looked in his strength, sprang thickly up over its floor. In the remote past it had been used as a sort of garner and thrashing-place by a farmer of the parish, named Marcus, who had succeeded

---

[1] I spy, hide-and-seek.

in rearing crops of bere and oats on two sloping plots at the foot of the cliffs in its immediate neighbourhood; and it was known, from this circumstance, to my uncles and the older inhabitants of the town, as Marcus's Cave. My companions, however, had been chiefly drawn to it by a much more recent association. A poor Highland pensioner—a sorely dilapidated relic of the French-American War, who had fought under General Wolfe in his day—had taken a great fancy to the cave, and would fain have made it his home. He was ill at ease in his family;—his wife was a termagant, and his daughter disreputable; and, desirous to quit their society altogether, and live as a hermit among the rocks, he had made application to the gentleman who tenanted the farm above, to be permitted to fit up the cave for himself as a dwelling. So bad was his English, however, that the gentleman failed to understand him; and his request was, as he believed, rejected, while it was in reality only not understood. Among the younger folk the cave came to be known, from the incident, as "Rory Shingles' Cave"; and my companions were delighted to believe that they were living in it as Rory would have lived, had his petition been granted. In the wild half-savage life which we led, we did contrive to provide for ourselves remarkably well. The rocky shores supplied us with limpets, periwinkles, and crabs, and now and then a lumpfish; the rugged slopes under the precipices, with hips, sloes, and brambles; the broken fragments of wreck along the beach, and the wood above, furnished abundance of fuel; and as there were fields not half a mile away, I fear the more solid part of our diet consisted often of potatoes which we had not planted, and of peas and beans which we had not sown. One of our number contrived to bring away a pot unobserved from his home; another succeeded in providing us with a pitcher; there was a good spring not two hundred yards from the cave mouth, which supplied us with water; and, thus possessed of not merely all that nature requires, but a good deal more, we contrived to fare sumptuously every day. It has been often remarked, that civilized man, when placed in circumstances at all favourable, soon learns to assume the savage. I shall not say that my companions or myself had been particularly civilized in our previous state; but nothing could be more certain, than that during our long vacation, we became very happy, and tolerably perfect savages. The class which we attended was of a kind not opened in any of our accredited schools, and it might be difficult to procure testimonials in its behalf, easily procurable as these usually are; and yet there were some of its lessons which might be conned with some little advantage, by one desirous of cultivating the noble sentiment of self-reliance, or the all-important habit of self-help. At the time, however, they appeared quite pointless enough; and the moral, as in the case of the continental apologue of Reynard the Fox, seemed always omitted

Our parties in these excursions used at times to swell out to ten or twelve—at times to contract to two or three; but what they gained in quantity they always lost in quality, and became mischievous with the addition of every new member, in greatly more than the arithmetical ratio. When most innocent, they consisted of only a brace of members—a warm-hearted, intelligent boy from the south of Scotland, who boarded with two elderly ladies of the place, and attended the subscription school; and the acknowledged leader of the band, who, belonging to the permanent irreducible staff of the establishment, was never off duty. We used to be very happy, and not altogether irrational, in these little skeleton parties. My new friend was a gentle, tasteful boy, fond of poetry, and a writer of soft, simple verses in the old-fashioned pastoral vein, which he never showed to any one save myself; and we learned to love one another all the more, from the circumstance that I was of a somewhat bold, self-relying temperament, and he of a clinging, timid one. Two of the stanzas of a little pastoral, which he addressed to me about a twelvemonth after this time, when permanently quitting the north country for Edinburgh, still remain fixed in my memory; and I must submit them to the reader, both as adequately representative of the many others, their fellows, which have been lost, and of that juvenile poetry in general which "is written," according to Sir Walter Scott, "rather from the recollection of what has pleased the author in others, than what has been suggested by his own imagination."

"To you my poor sheep I resign,
My colly, my crook, and my horn:
To leave you, indeed, I repine,
But I must away with the morn.
New scenes shall evolve on my sight,
The world and its follies be new;
But ah! can such scenes of delight
Ere arise, as I witnessed with you !"[1]

Timid as he naturally was, he soon learned to abide in my company terrors which most of my bolder companions shrank from encountering. I was fond of lingering in the caves until long after nightfall, especially in those seasons when the moon at full, or but a few days in her wane, rose out of the sea as the evening wore on, to light up the wild precipices of that solitary shore, and to render practicable our ascending path to the hill above. And Finlay was almost the only one of my band who dared to encounter with me the terrors of the darkness. Our fire has often startled the benighted boatman as he came rowing round some rocky promontory, and saw the red glare streaming seawards from the cavern mouth, and partially lighting up the angry tumbling of the surf beyond; and excise-cutters have oftener than once altered their tack in middle Firth, and come bearing towards the coast, to determine whether the wild rocks of Marcus were not becoming a haunt of smugglers.

Immediately beyond the granitic gneiss of the hill there is a subaqueous deposit of the Lias[2] formation, never yet explored by geologist, because never yet laid bare by the ebb; though every heavier storm from the sea tells of its existence, by tossing ashore fragments of its dark bituminous shale. I soon ascertained that the shale is so largely charged with inflammable matter as to burn

[1] Modelled on Shenstone's "Pastoral Ballads."
[2] A series of blue-black clays and thin limestones, rich in fossils; part of the system underlying the chalk.

with a strong flame, as if steeped in tar or oil, and that I could repeat with it the common experiment of producing gas by means of a tobacco-pipe luted with clay. And, having read in Shakespeare of a fuel termed "sea-coal," and unaware at the time that the poet merely meant coal brought to London by sea, I inferred that the inflammable shale cast up from the depths of the Firth by the waves could not be other than the veritable "sea-coal" which figured in the reminiscences of Dame Quickly; and so, assisted by Finlay, who shared in the interest which I felt in the substance, as at once classical and an original discovery, I used to collect it in large quantities and convert it into smoky and troubled fires, that ever filled our cavern with a horrible stench, and scented all the shore. Though unaware of the fact at the time, it owed its inflammability, not to vegetable, but to animal substance, the tar which used to boil in it to the heat, like resin in a fagot of moss-fir, was as strange a mixture as ever yet bubbled in witches' caldron—blood of pterodactyle[1] and grease of ichthyosaur[2]—eye of belemnite[3] and hood of nautilus[4]; and we learned to delight in its very smell, all oppressive as that was, as something wild, strange, and inexplicable. Once or twice I seemed on the eve of a discovery: in splitting the masses, I occasionally saw what appeared to be fragments of shells embedded in its substance; and at least once I laid open a mysterious-looking scroll or volute, existing on the dark surface as a cream-coloured film; but though these organisms raised a temporary wonder, it was not until a later period that I learned to comprehend their true import, as the half-effaced but still decipherable characters of a marvellous record of the grey, dream-encircled past.

With the docile Finlay as my companion, and left to work out my own will unchallenged, I was rarely or never mischievous. On the occasions, however, in which my band swelled out to ten or

[1] A winged reptile, which probably flew from tree to tree and shuffled along the ground.
[2] A fish-lizard, in shape like a large-sized porpoise.
[3] The fossil "pen" or straight internal shell of an extinct form of cuttle-fish.
[4] A family of cuttle-fish, still surviving in a few species.

a dozen, I often experienced the ordinary evils of leadership, as known in all gangs and parties, civil and ecclesiastical; and was sometimes led, in consequence, to engage in enterprises which my better judgment condemned. I fain wish that among the other "Confessions" with which our literature is charged, we had the *bona fide* "Confessions of a Leader," with examples of the cases in which, though he seems to overbear, he is in reality overborne, and actually follows, though he appears to lead. Honest Sir William Wallace, though seven feet high, and a hero, was at once candid and humble enough to confess to the canons of Hexham, that, his "soldiers being evil-disposed men," whom he could neither "justify nor punish," he was able to protect women and Churchmen only so long as they "abided in his sight." And, of course, other leaders, less tall and less heroic, must not unfrequently find themselves, had they but Wallace's magnanimity to confess the fact, in circumstances much akin to those of Wallace. When bee-masters get hold of queen bees, they are able, by controlling the movements of these natural leaders of hives, to control the movements of the hives themselves; and not unfrequently in Churches and States do there exist inconspicuous bee-masters, who, by influencing or controlling the leader-bees, in reality influence and control the movements of the entire body, politic or ecclesiastical, over which these natural monarchs seem to preside. But truce with apology. Partly in the character of leader— partly being myself led—I succeeded about this time in getting one of my larger parties into a tolerably serious scrape. We passed every day, on our way to the cave, a fine large orchard, attached to the manor-house of Cromarty estate; and in ascending an adjacent hill over which our path lay, and which commands a bird's-eye view of the trim-kept walks and well-laden trees, there used not infrequently to arise wild speculations among us regarding the possibility and propriety of getting a supply of the fruit, to serve as desserts to our meals of shell-fish and potatoes. Weeks elapsed, however, and autumn was drawing on to its close, ere we could quite make up our minds regarding the adventure, when at length I agreed to lead; and, after arranging the plan of the expedition, we broke into the orchard under the cloud of night, and carried away with us whole pocketfuls of apples. They were all intolerably bad—sour, hard, baking apples; for we had delayed the enterprise until the better fruit had been pulled: but though they set our teeth on edge, and we flung most of them into the sea, we had "snatched" in the foray, what Gray well terms "a fearful joy," and had some thought of repeating it, merely for the sake of the excitement induced and the risk encountered, when out came the astounding fact, that one of our number had "peached," and, in the character of king's evidence, betrayed his companions.

The factor of the Cromarty property had an orphan nephew, who formed at times a member of our gang, and who had taken a willing part in the orchard foray. He had also engaged, however, in a second enterprise of a similar kind wholly on his own account, of which we knew nothing. An out-house pertaining to the dwelling in which he lodged, though itself situated outside the orchard, was attached to another house inside the walls, which was employed by the gardener as a store-place for his apples; and finding an unsuspected crevice in the partition which divided the two buildings, somewhat resembling that through which Pyramus and Thisbe made love of old in the city of Babylon, our comrade, straightway availing himself of so fair an opening, fell a-courting the gardener's apples. Sharpening the end of a long stick, he began harpooning, through the hole, the apple-heap below; and though the hole was greatly too small for admitting the finer and larger specimens, and they, in consequence, fell back, disengaged from the harpoon, in the attempt to land them, he succeeded in getting a good many of the smaller ones. Old John Clark the gardener— far advanced in life at the time, and seeing too imperfectly to discover the crevice which opened high amid the obscurity of the loft—was in a perfect maze regarding the evil influence that was destroying his apples. The harpooned individuals lay scattered over the floor by scores; but the agent that had dispersed and perforated them remained for weeks together an inscrutable mystery to John. At length, however, there came a luckless morning, in which our quondam companion lost hold, when busy at work, of the pointed stick; and when John next entered his storehouse, the guilty harpoon lay stretched across the harpooned apples. The discovery was followed up; the culprit detected; and, on being closeted with his uncle the factor, he communicated not only the details of his own special adventure, but the particulars of ours also. And early next day there was a message sent us by a safe and secret messenger, to the effect that we would be all put in prison in the course of the week.

We were terribly frightened; so much so, that the strong point of our position—the double-dyed guilt of the factor's nephew—failed to occur to any of us; and we looked for only instant incarceration. I still remember the intense feeling of shame I used to experience every time I crossed my mother's door for the street—the agonizing, all-engrossing belief that every one was looking at and pointing me out—and the terror, when in my uncles'—akin to that of the culprit who hears from his box the footsteps of the returning jury—that, having learned of my offence, they were preparing to denounce me as a disgrace to an honest family, on which, in the memory of man, no stain had before rested. The discipline was eminently wholesome, and I never forgot it. It did seem somewhat strange, however, that no one appeared to know anything about our misdemeanour: the factor kept our secret remarkably well; but we inferred he was doing so in order to pounce upon us all the more effectually; and, holding a hasty council in the cave, we resolved that, quitting our homes for a few weeks, we should live among the rocks; till the storm that seemed rising should have blown by.

Marcus's Cave was too accessible and too well known; but my knowledge of the locality enabled me to recommend to my lads two other caves in which I thought we might be safe. The one opened in a thicket of furze, some forty feet above the shore; and, though large enough within to contain from fifteen to twenty men, it presented outside much the appearance of a fox-earth, and was not known to half-a-dozen people in the country. It was, however, damp and dark; and we found that we could not venture on lighting a fire in it without danger of suffocation. It was pronounced excellent, however, as a temporary place of conceal-ment, were the search for us to become very hot. The other cavern was wide and open; but it was a wild, ghostly-looking place, scarcely once visited from one twelvemonth's end to another: its floor was green with mould, and its ridgy walls and roof bristled over with slim pale stalactites, which looked like the pointed tags that roughen a dead-dress. It was certain, too, that it was haunted. Marks of a cloven foot might be seen freshly impressed on its floor, which had been produced either by a stray goat, or by something worse; and the few boys to whom its existence and character were known used to speak of it under their breath as "the Devil's Cave." My lads did at first look round them as we entered, with an awe-struck and disconsolate expression; but falling busily to work among the cliffs, we collected large quantities of withered grass and fern for bedding, and, selecting the drier and less exposed portions of the floor, soon piled up for ourselves a row of little lairs, formed in a sort of half-way style between that of the wild beast and the gipsy, on which it would have been possible enough to sleep. We selected, too, a place for our fire, gathered a little heap of fuel, and secreted in a recess, for ready use, our Marcus's Cave pot and pitcher, and the lethal weapons of the gang, which consisted of an old bayonet so corroded with rust that it somewhat resembled a three-edged saw, and an old horseman's pistol tied fast to the stock by cobbler's ends, and with lock and ramrod wanting. Evening surprised us in the middle of our preparations; and as the shadows fell dark and thick, my lads began to look most uncomfortably around them. At length they fairly struck work: there was no use, they said, for being in the Devil's Cave so late— no use, indeed, for being in it at all, until we were made sure the factor did actually intend to imprison us; and, after delivering themselves to this effect, they fairly bolted, leaving Finlay and myself to bring up the rear at our leisure. My well-laid plan was, in short, found unworkable, from the inferior quality of my materials. I returned home with a heavy heart, somewhat grieved that I had not confided my scheme to only Finlay, who could, I ascertained, do braver things, with all his timidity, than the bolder boys, our occasional associates. And yet, when in passing homewards through the dark lonely woods of the Hill, I bethought me of the still deeper solitude and gloom of the haunted cave far below, and thought further, that at that very moment the mysterious being with the cloven foot might be traversing its silent floor, I felt my blood run cold, and at once leaped to the conclusion that, save for the disgrace, a cave with an evil spirit in it could be not a great deal better than a prison. Of the prison, however, we heard no more; though I never forgot the grim but precious lesson read me by the factor's threat; and from that time till the present—save now and then, by inadvertently admitting into my newspaper a paragraph written in too terse a style by some good man in the provinces, against some very bad man his neighbour—I have not been fairly within wind of the law. I would, however, seriously advise such of my young friends as may cast a curious eye over these pages to avoid taking any such lesson as mine at first-hand. One half-hour of the mental anguish which I at this time experienced, when I thought of my mother and uncles, and the infamy of a prison, would have vastly more than counterbalanced all that could have been enjoyed from banqueting on apples, even had they been those of the Hesperides or of Eden, instead of being, what they were in this case, green masses of harsh acid, alike formidable to teeth and stomach. I must add, in justice to my friend of the Doocot Cave, that, though an occasional visitor at Marcus, he had prudently avoided getting into this scrape.

Our long vacation came at length to an end, by the appointment of a teacher to the subscription school; but the arrangement was not the most profitable possible for the pupils. It was an ominous circumstance, that we learned in a few days to designate the new master by a nickname, and that the name stuck—a misfortune which almost never befalls the truly superior man. He had, however, a certain dash of cleverness about him; and observing that I was of potent influence among my school-fellows, he set himself to determine the grounds on which my authority rested. Copy and arithmetic books, in schools in which there was liberty, used in those ancient times to be charged with curious revelations. In the parish school, for instance, which excelled, as I have said, every other school in the world in its knowledge of barques and carvels, it was not uncommon to find a book which, when opened at the right end, presented only copy-lines or arithmetical questions, that, when opened at the wrong one, presented only ships and boats. And there were cases on record in which, on the grand annual examination-day that heralded the vacation, the worthy parish minister, by beginning to turn over the leaves of some exhibited book at the reverse end, found himself engaged, when expecting only the questions of Cocker, or the slip-lines of Butterworth, amid whole fleets of smacks, frigates, and brigantines. My new master, professionally acquainted with this secret property of arithmetic and copy-books, laid hold of mine, and, bringing them to his desk, found them charged with very extraordinary revelations indeed. The blank spaces were occupied with deplorably scrabbled couplets and stanzas, blent with occasional remarks in rude prose, that dealt chiefly with natural phenomena. One note, for instance, which the master took the trouble of deciphering, referred to the supposed *fact*, familiar as a matter of sensation to boys located on the sea-coast, that during the bathing season the water is warmer on windy days, when the waves break high, than during dead calms; and accounted for it (I fear not very philosophically) on the hypothesis that the "waves, by slapping against each other, engender heat, as heat may be engendered by clapping the hands." The master read on, evidently with much difficulty, and apparently with considerable scepticism: he inferred that I had been borrowing, not inventing: though where such prose and such verse could have been borrowed, and, in especial, such grammar and such spelling, even cleverer men than he might well have despaired of ever finding out. And in order to test my powers, he proposed furnishing me with a theme on which to write. "Let us see," he said, "let us see: the dancing-school ball comes on here next week—bring me a poem on the dancing-school ball." The subject did not promise a great deal; but, setting myself to work in the evening, I produced half-a-dozen stanzas on the ball, which were received as good, in evidence that I actually could rhyme; and for some weeks after I was rather a favourite with the new master.

I had, however, ere now become a wild insubordinate boy, and the only school in which I could properly be taught was that world-wide school which awaited me, in which Toil and Hardship are the severe but noble teachers. I got into sad scrapes. Quarrelling, on one occasion, with a boy of my own standing, we exchanged blows across the form; and when called up for trial and punishment, the fault was found to attach so equally to both sides, that the same number of *palmies*, well laid on, were awarded to each. I bore mine, however, like a North American Indian, whereas my antagonist began to howl and cry; and I could not resist the temptation of saying to him in a whisper that unluckily reached the ear of the master, "Ye big blubbering blockhead, take that for a drubbing from me." I had of course to receive a few palmies additional for the speech; but then, "who cared for that?" The master, however, "cared" considerably more for the offence than I did for the punishment. And in a subsequent quarrel with another boy—a stout and somewhat desperate mulatto—I got into a worse scrape still, of which he thought still worse. The mulatto, in his battles, which were many, had a trick, when in danger of being over-matched, of drawing his knife; and in our affair—the necessities of the fight seeming to require it—he drew his knife upon me. To his horror and astonishment, however, instead of running off, I immediately drew mine, and, quick as lightning, stabbed him in the thigh. He roared out in fright and pain, and, though more alarmed than hurt, never after drew knife upon a combatant. But the value of the lesson which I gave, was like most other very valuable things, inadequately appreciated; and it merely procured for me the character of being a dangerous boy. I had certainly reached a dangerous stage; but it was mainly myself that was in jeopardy. There is a transition-time in which the strength and independence of the latent man begin to mingle with the wilfulness and indiscretion of the mere boy, which is more perilous than any other, in which many more downward careers of recklessness and folly begin, that end in wreck and ruin, than in all the other years of life which intervene between childhood and old age. The growing lad should be wisely and tenderly dealt with at this critical stage. The severity that would fain compel the implicit submission yielded at an earlier period, would probably succeed, if his character was a strong one, in insuring but his ruin. It is at this transition-stage that boys run off to sea from parents and masters, or, when tall enough, enlist in the army for soldiers. The strictly orthodox parent, if more severe than wise, succeeds occasionally in driving, during this crisis, his son into Popery or infidelity; and the sternly moral one, in landing *his* in utter profligacy. But, leniently and judiciously dealt with, the dangerous period passes: in a few years at most— in some instances in even a few months—the sobriety incidental to a further development of character ensues, and the wild boy settles down, into a rational young man.

It so chanced, however, that in what proved the closing scene in my term of school attendance, I was rather unfortunate than guilty. The class to which I now belonged read an English lesson every afternoon, and had its rounds of spelling; and in these last I acquitted myself but ill; partly from the circumstance that I spelt only indifferently, but still more from the further circumstance, that, retaining strongly fixed in my memory the broad Scotch pronunciation acquired at the dame's school, I had to carry on in my mind the double process of at once spelling the required word, and of translating the old sounds of the letters of which it was composed into the modern ones. Nor had I been taught to break the words into syllables; and so, when required one evening to spell the word "*awful*," with much deliberation—for I had to translate, as I went on, the letters *a-w* and *u*—I spelt it word for word, without break or pause, as a-w-f-u-l. "No," said the master, "a-w, *aw*, f-u-l, *awful*; spell again." This seemed preposterous spelling. It was sticking in an *a*, as I thought, into the middle of the word, where, I was sure, no *a* had a right to be; and so I spelt it as at first. The master recompensed my supposed contumacy with a sharp cut athwart the ears with his tawse; and again demanding the spelling of the word, I yet again spelt it as at first. But on receiving a second cut, I refused to spell it any more; and, determined on overcoming my obstinacy, he laid hold of me and attempted throwing me down. As wrestling, however, had been one of our favourite Marcus's Cave exercises, and as few lads of my inches wrestled better than I, the master, though a tall and tolerably robust fellow, found the feat considerably more difficult than he could have supposed. We swayed from side to side of the school-room, now backwards, now forward, and for a full minute it seemed to be rather a moot point on which side the victory was to incline. At length, however, I was tripped over a form; and as the master had to deal with me, not as master usually deals with pupil, but as one combatant deals with another, whom he has to beat into submission, I was mauled in a way that filled me with aches and bruises for a full month thereafter. I greatly fear that, had I met the fellow on a lonely road five years subsequent to our encounter, when I had become strong enough to raise breast-high the "great lifting stone of the Dropping Cave," he would have caught as sound a thrashing as he ever gave to little boy or girl in his life; but all I could do at this time was to take down my cap from off the pin, when the affair had ended, and march straight out of school. And thus terminated my school education. Before night I had avenged myself, in a copy of satiric verses, entitled "The Pedagogue," which—as they had some little cleverness in them, regarded as the work of a boy, and as the known eccentricities of their subject gave me large scope—

occasioned a good deal of merriment in the place; and of the verses a fair copy, written out by Finlay, was transmitted through the Post-office to the pedagogue himself. But the only notice he ever took of them was incidentally, in a short speech made to the copyist a few days after. "I *see*, Sir," he said—"I *see* you still associate with that fellow Miller; perhaps he will make you a poet!" "I thought, Sir," said Finlay very quietly, in reply, "that poets were born—not made."

As a specimen of the rhyme of this period, and as in some degree a set-off against my drubbing, which remains till this day an unsettled score, I submit my pasquinade to the reader;

THE PEDAGOGUE

WITH solemn mien and pious air,
S—k—r[1] attends each call of grace;
Loud eloquence bedecks his prayer,
And formal sanctity his face.

All good; but turn the other side,
And see the smirking beau displayed;
The pompous strut, exalted air,
And all that marks the fop, is there.

In character we seldom see
Traits so diverse meet and agree:
Can the affected mincing trip,
Exalted brow, and pride-pressed lip,
In strange incongruous union meet,
With all that stamps the hypocrite?
We see they do: but let us scan
Those secret springs which move the man.

Though now he wields the knotty birch,
His better hope lies in the Church:
For this the sable robe he wears,
For this in pious guise appears.

---

[1] Spanker (MS.).

But then, the weak will cannot hide
Th' inherent vanity and pride;
And thus he acts the coxcomb's part,
As dearer to his poor vain heart:
Nature's born fop! a saint by art!!
But hold! he wears no fopling's dress;
Each seam, each thread, the eye can trace,
His garb all o'er;—the dye, though true,
Time-blanch'd, displays a fainter hue:
Dress forms the fopling's better part;
Reconcile this, and prove your art.

"Chill penury represses pride;"—
A maxim by the wise denied;
For 'tis alone tame plodding souls,
Whose spirits bond when it controls,—
Whose lives run on in one dull same,
Plain honesty their highest aim.
With him it merely can repress—
Tailor o'er-cow'd—the pomp of dress;
His spirit, unrepressed, can soar
High as e'er folly rose before;
Can fly pale study, learn'd debate
And ape proud fashion's idle state;
Yet fails in that engaging grace
That lights the practised courtier's face.
His weak affected air we mark,
And, smiling, view the would-be spark;
Complete in every act and feature,—
An ill-bred, silly, awkward creature.

My school-days fairly over, a life of toil frowned full in front of me; but never yet was there a half-grown lad less willing to take up the man and lay down the boy. My set of companions was fast breaking up—my friend of the Doocot Cave was on the eve of proceeding to an academy in a neighbouring town; Finlay had received a call from the south, to finish his education in a seminary on the banks of the Tweed; one Marcus's Cave lad was preparing to go to sea; another to learn a trade; a third to enter a shop; the time of dispersal was too evidently at hand; and, taking counsel one day together, we resolved on constructing something—we at first knew not what—that might serve as a monument to recall to us in after years the memory of our early pastimes and enjoyments. The common school-book story of the Persian shepherd, who, when raised by his sovereign to high place in the empire, derived his chief pleasure from contemplating in a secret apartment, the pipe, crook, and rude habiliments of his happier days, suggested to me that we also should have our secret apartment, in which to store up, for future contemplation, our bayonet and pistol, pot and pitcher; and I recommended that we should set ourselves to dig a subterranean chamber for that purpose among the woods of the hill, accessible, like the mysterious vaults of our story-books, by a trap-door. The proposal was favourably received; and, selecting a solitary spot among the trees as a proper site, and procuring spade and mattock, we began to dig.

Soon passing through the thin crust of vegetable mould, we found the red boulder clay beneath exceedingly stiff and hard; but day after day saw us perseveringly at work; and we succeeded in digging a huge square pit about six feet in length and breadth, and fully seven feet deep. Fixing four upright posts in the corners, we lined our apartment with slender spars nailed closely together; and we had prepared for giving it a massive roof of beams formed of fallen trees, and strong enough to bear a layer of earth and turf from a foot to a foot and a half in depth, with a little opening for the trap-door; when we found, one morning, on pressing onwards to the scene of our labours, that we were doggedly tracked by a horde of boys considerably more numerous than our own party. Their curiosity had been excited, like that of the Princess Nekayah in "Rasselas", by the tools which we carried, and by "seeing that we had directed our walk every day to the same point;" and in vain, by running and doubling, by scolding and remonstrating, did we now attempt shaking them off. I saw that, were we to provoke a general *melée*, we could scarce expect to come off victors; but deeming myself fully a match for their stoutest boy, I stepped out and challenged him to come forward and fight me. He hesitated, looked foolish, and refused; but said he would readily fight with any of my party except myself. I immediately named my friend of the Doocot Cave, who leaped out with a bound to meet him; but the boy, as I had anticipated, refused to fight him also; and, observing the proper effect produced, I ordered my lads to march forward, and from an upper slope of the hill we had the satisfaction of seeing that our pursuers, after lingering for a little while on the spot on which we had left them, turned homewards, fairly cowed, and pursued us no more. But, alas! on reaching our secret chamber, we ascertained, by marks all too unequivocal, that it was to be secret no longer. Some rude hand had torn down the wooden lining, and cut two of the posts half through with a hatchet; and on returning disconsolately to the town, we ascertained that Johnstone the forester had just been there before us, declaring that some atrociously wicked persons—for whose apprehension a proclamation was to be instantly issued—had contrived a diabolical trap, which he had just discovered, for maiming the cattle of the gentleman, his employer, who farmed the Hill. Johnstone was an old Forty-Second man, who had followed Wellington over the larger part of the Peninsula; but though he had witnessed the storming and sack of San Sebastian, and a great many other bad things, nothing had he ever seen on the Peninsula, or anywhere else, he said, half so mischievous as the cattle-trap. We, of course, kept our own secret; and as we all returned under the cloud of night, and with heavy hearts filled up our excavation level with the soil, the threatened proclamation was never issued. Johnstone, however—who had been watching my motions for a considerable time before, and whom, as he was a formidable fellow, very unlike any of the other foresters, I had been sedulously watching in turn—had no hesitation in declaring that I, and I only, could be the designer of the cattle-trap. I had acquainted myself in books, he said, with the mode of entrapping by pitfalls wild beasts in the forests abroad; and my trap for the Colonel's cattle was, he was certain, a result of my book-acquired knowledge.

I was one day lounging in front of my mother's dwelling, when up came Johnstone to address me. As the evidence regarding the excavation had totally broken down, I was aware of no special offence at the time that could have secured for me such a piece of attention, and inferred that the old soldier was labouring under some mistake; but Johnstone's address soon evinced that he was not in the least mistaken. "He wished to be acquainted with me," he said. "It was all nonsense for us to be bothering one another, when we had no cause to quarrel." He used occasionally to eke out his pension, and his scanty allowance as forester, by catching a basket of fish for himself from off the rocks of the Hill; and he had just discovered a projecting rock at the foot of a tall precipice, which would prove, he was sure, one of the best fishing platforms in the Firth. But then, in the existing state, it was wholly inaccessible. He was, however, of opinion, that it was possible to lay it open by carrying a path adown the shelving face of the precipice. He had seen Wellington address himself to quite as desperate-looking matters in the Peninsula; and were I but to assist him, he was sure, he said, we could construct between us the necessary path. The undertaking was one wholly according to my own heart; and next morning Johnstone and I were hard at work on the giddy brow of the precipice. It was topped by a thick bed of boulder clay, itself—such was the steepness of the slope— almost a precipice; but a series of deeply-cut steps led us easily adown the bed of clay; and then a sloping shelf, which, with much labour, we deepened and flattened, conducted us not unsafely some five-and-twenty or thirty feet along the face of the precipice proper. A second series of steps, painfully scooped out of the living rock, and which passed within a few yards of a range of herons' nests perched on a hitherto inaccessible platform, brought us down some five-and-twenty or thirty feet more; but then we arrived at a sheer descent of about twenty feet, at which Johnstone looked rather blank, though, on my suggesting a ladder, he took heart again, and, cutting two slim taper trees in the wood above, we flung them over the precipice into the sea; and then fishing them up with a world of toil and trouble, we squared and bored them upwards, and, cutting tenons for them in the hard gneiss, we placed them against the rock front, and nailed over them a line of steps. The precipice beneath sloped easily on to the fishing rock, and so a few steps more completed our path. I never saw a man more delighted than Johnstone. As being lighter and more active than he—for though not greatly advanced in life, he was considerably debilitated by severe wounds—I had to take some of the more perilous parts of the work on myself. I had cut the tenons for the ladder with a rope round my waist, and had recovered the trees flung into the sea by some adroit swimming; and the old soldier became thoroughly impressed with the conviction that my proper sphere was the army. I was already five feet three, he said; in little more than a twelvemonth I would be five feet seven; and were I then but to enlist, and to keep from the "drop drink"— a thing which he never could do—I would, he was certain, rise to be a serjeant. In brief, such were the terms on which Johnstone and I learned to live ever after, that, had I constructed a *score* of traps for the Colonel's cattle, I believe he would have winked at them all. Poor fellow! he got into difficulties, a good many years after, and, on the accession of the Whigs to power, mortgaged his pension, and emigrated to Canada. Deeming the terms hard, however, as he well might, he first wrote a letter to his old commander, the Duke of Wellington—I holding the pen for him—in which, in the hope that their stringency might be relaxed in his behalf, he stated both his services and his case. And promptly did the Duke reply, in an essentially kind holograph epistle, in which, after stating that he had no influence at the time with the Ministers of the Crown, and no means of getting a relaxation of their terms in behalf of any one, he "earnestly recommended William Johnstone, *first*, not to seek a provision for himself in Canada, unless he were able-bodied, and fit to provide for himself in circumstances of extreme hardship; and, *second*, on no account to sell or mortgage his pension." But the advice was not taken— Johnstone did emigrate to Canada, and did mortgage his pension;

and I fear—though I failed to trace his after history—that he suffered in consequence.

CHAPTER VIII

"Now surely, thought I, there's enou'
To fill life's dusty way;
And who will miss a poet's feet,
Or wonder where he stray!
So to the woods and wastes I'll go
And I will build an ozier bower;
And sweetly there to me will flow
The meditative hour."—HENRY KIRKE WHITE

FINLAY was away; my friend of the Doocot Cave was away; my other companions were all scattered abroad; my mother, after a long widowhood of more than eleven years, had entered into a second marriage; and I found myself standing face to face with a life of labour and restraint. The prospect appeared dreary in the extreme. The necessity of ever toiling from morning to night, and from one week's end to another, and all for a little coarse food and homely raiment, seemed to be a dire one; and fain would I have avoided it. But there was no escape; and so I determined on being a mason. I remembered my cousin George's long winter holidays, and how delightfully he employed them; and, by making choice of Cousin George's profession, I trusted to find, like him, large compensation, in the amusements of one-half the year, for the toils of the other half. Labour shall not wield over me, I said, a rod entirely black, but a rod like one of Jacob's peeled wands, chequered white and black alternately.

I, however, did look, even at this time, notwithstanding the antecedents of a sadly mis-spent boyhood, to something higher than mere amusement; and, daring to believe that literature, and, mayhap, natural science, were, after all, my proper vocations, I resolved that much of my leisure time should be given to careful observation, and the study of our best English authors. Both my uncles, especially James, were sorely vexed by my determination

144

to be a mason; they had expected to see me rising in some one of the learned professions; yet there was I going to be a mere operative mechanic, like one of themselves! I spent with them a serious hour, in which they urged that, instead of entering as a mason's apprentice, I should devote myself anew to my education. Though the labour of their hands formed their only wealth, they would assist me, they said, in getting through college; nay, if I preferred it, I might meanwhile come and live with them: all they asked of me in return was that I should give myself as sedulously to my lessons as, in the event of my becoming a mason, I would have to give myself to my trade. I demurred. The lads of my acquaintance who were preparing for college had an eye, I said, to some profession; they were qualifying themselves to be lawyers, or medical men, or, in much larger part, were studying for the Church; whereas I had no wish, and no peculiar fitness to be either lawyer or doctor; and as for the Church, that was too serious a direction to look in for one's bread, unless one could honestly regard one's-self as *called* to the Church's proper work; and I could not. There, said my uncles, you are perfectly right; better be a poor mason—better be anything honest, however humble—than an *uncalled* minister. How very strong the hold taken of the mind in some cases by hereditary convictions of which the ordinary conduct shows little apparent trace! I had for the last few years been a wild boy—not without my share of respect for Donald Roy's religion, but possessed of none of Donald's seriousness; and yet here was his belief in this special matter lying so strongly entrenched in the recesses of my mind, that no consideration whatever could have induced me to outrage it by obtruding my unworthiness on the Church. Though, mayhap, overstrained in many of its older forms, I fain wish the conviction, in at least some of its better modifications, were more general now. It might be well for all the Protestant Churches practically to hold, with Uncles James and Sandy, that true ministers cannot be manufactured out of ordinary men—men ordinary in talent and character—in a given number of years, and then passed by the imposition of hands into the sacred office; but that, on the contrary, ministers, when real, are all special creations of the grace of God. I may add, that in a belief of this kind, deeply implanted in the popular mind of Scotland, the strength of our recent Church controversy mainly lay.

Slowly and unwillingly my uncles at length consented that I should make a trial of a life of manual labour. The husband of one of my maternal aunts was a mason,[1] who, contracting for jobs on a small scale, usually kept an apprentice or two, and employed a few journeymen. With him I agreed to serve for the term of three years; and, getting a suit of strong moleskin clothes, and a pair of heavy hob-nailed shoes, I waited only for the breaking up of the winter frosts, to begin work in the Cromarty quarries—jobbing masters in the north of Scotland usually combining the profession of the quarrier with that of the mason. In the beautiful poetic fragment from which I have chosen my motto, poor Kirke White fondly indulges in the dream of a hermit life—quiet, meditative, solitary, spent far away in deep woods or amid wide-spread wastes, where the very sounds that arose would be but the faint echoes of a loneliness in which man was not—a "voice of the desert, never dumb." The dream is that of a certain brief period of life between boyhood and comparatively mature youth; and we find more traces of it in the poetry of Kirke White than in that of almost any other poet; simply because he wrote at the age in which it is natural to indulge in it, and because, being less an imitator, and more original, than most juvenile poets, he gave it as portion of the internal experience from which he drew. But it is a dream not restricted to young poets: the ignorant, half-grown lad, who learns, for the first time, "about the great rich gentleman who advertises for a hermit," and wishes that he had but the necessary qualification of beard to offer himself as a candidate, indulges in it also; and I, too, in this transition stage, cherished it with all the strength of a passion. It seems to spring out of a latent timidity in the yet undeveloped mind, that shrinks from grappling with

[1] David Williamson.

146

the stern realities of life, amid the crowd and press of the busy world, and o'ershaded by the formidable competition of men already practised in the struggle. I have still before me the picture of the "lodge in some vast wilderness" to which I could have fain retired, to lead all alone a life quieter, but quite as wild, as my Marcus's Cave one; and the snugness and comfort of the humble interior of my hermitage, during some boisterous night of winter, when the gusty wind would be howling around the roof, and the rain beating on the casement, but when, in the calm within, the cheerful flame would roar in the chimney, and glance bright on rafter and wall, still impress me as if the recollection were in reality that of a scene witnessed, not of a mere vision conjured up by the fancy. But it was all the idle dream of a truant lad, who would fain now, as on former occasions, have avoided going to school—that best and noblest of all schools, save the Christian one, in which honest Labour is the teacher, in which the ability of being useful is imparted, and the spirit of independence communicated, and the habit of persevering effort acquired; and which is more moral than the schools in which only philosophy is taught, and greatly more happy than the schools which profess to teach only the art of enjoyment. Noble, upright, self-relying Toil! Who that knows thy solid worth and value would be ashamed of thy hard hands, and thy soiled vestments, and thy obscure tasks—thy humble cottage, and hard couch, and homely fare! Save for thee and thy lessons, man in society would everywhere sink into a sad compound of the fiend and the wild beast; and this fallen world would be as certainly a moral as a natural wilderness. But I little thought of the excellence of thy character and of thy teachings when, with a heavy heart, I set out about this time, on a morning of early spring, to take my first lesson from thee in a sandstone quarry.

I have elsewhere recorded the history of my few first days of toil;[1] but it is possible for two histories, of the same period and individual, to be at once true to fact, and unlike each other in the

---

[1] In the opening pages of *The Old Red Sandstone*.

scenes which they describe, and the events which they record. The quarry in which I commenced my life of labour was, as I have said, a sandstone one, and exhibited in the section of the furze-covered bank which it presented, a bar of deep red stone beneath, and a bar of pale red clay above. Both deposits belonged to formations equally unknown, at the time, to the geologist. The deep red stone formed part of an upper member of the Lower Old Red Sandstone; the pale red clay, which was much roughened by rounded pebbles, and much cracked and fissured by the recent frosts, was a bed of the boulder clay. Save for the wholesome restraint that confined me for day after day to this spot, I should perhaps have paid little attention to either. Mineralogy, in its first rudiments, had early awakened my curiosity, just as it never fails to awaken, with its gems and its metals, and its hard glittering rocks, of which tools may be made, the curiosity of infant tribes and nations. But in unsightly masses of mechanical origin, whether sandstone or clay, I could take no interest; just as infant societies take no interest in such masses, and so fail to know anything of geology; and it was not until I had learned to detect among the ancient sandstone strata of this quarry exactly the same phenomena as those which I used to witness in my walks with Uncle Sandy in the ebb, that I was fairly excited to examine and inquire. It was the necessity which made me a quarrier that taught me to be a geologist. Further, I soon found that there was much to be enjoyed in a life of labour. A taste for the beauties of natural scenery is of itself a never-failing spring of delight; and there was scarce a day in which I wrought in the open air, during this period, in which I did not experience its soothing and exhilarating influence. Well has it been said by the poet Keats, that "a thing of beauty is a joy for ever." I owed much to the upper reaches of the Cromarty Firth, as seen, when we sat down to our mid-day meal, from the gorge of the quarry, with their numerous rippling currents, that, in the calm, resembled streamlets winding through a meadow, and their distant grey promontories tipped with villages that brightened in the sunshine; while, pale in the background, the mighty hills, still streaked with snow, rose high over bay and promontory and gave dignity and power to the scene.

Still, however, with all my enjoyments, I had to suffer some of the evils of excessive toil. Though now seventeen, I was still seven inches short of my ultimate stature; and my frame, cast more at the time in the mould of my mother than in that of the robust sailor, whose "back" according to the description of one of his comrades, "no one had ever put to the ground," was slim and loosely knit; and I used to suffer much from wandering pains in the joints, and an oppressive feeling about the chest, as if crushed by some great weight. I became subject, too, to frequent fits of extreme depression of spirits, which took almost the form of a walking sleep—results, I believe, of excessive fatigue—and during which my absence of mind was so extreme, that I lacked the ability of protecting myself against accident, in cases the most simple and ordinary. Besides other injuries, I lost at different times during the first few months of my apprenticeship, when in these fits of partial somnambulism, no fewer than seven of my finger-nails. But as I gathered strength, my spirits became more equable; and not until many years after, when my health failed for a time under over-exertion of another kind, had I any renewed experience of the fits of walking sleep.

My master, an elderly man at the time—for, as he used not unfrequently to tell his apprentices, he had been born on the same day and year as George the Fourth, and so we could celebrate, if we pleased, both birthdays together—was a person of plodding, persevering industry, who wrought rather longer hours than was quite agreeable to one who wished to have some time to himself; but he was, in the main, a good master. As a builder, he made conscience of every stone he laid. It was remarked in the place, that the walls built by Uncle David never bulged or fell; and no apprentice or journeyman of his was permitted, on any plea, to make "slight wark." Though by no means a bold or daring man, he was, from sheer abstraction, when engrossed in his employment, more thoroughly insensible to personal danger than almost

149

any other individual I ever knew. On one occasion, when an overloaded boat, in which he was carrying stones from the quarry to the neighbouring town, was overtaken by a series of rippling seas, and suddenly sunk, leaving him standing on one of the thwarts submerged to the throat, he merely said to his partner, on seeing his favourite snuff-mull go floating past, "Od, Andro man, just rax out your han' and tak' in my snuff-box." On another, when a huge mass of the boulder clay came toppling down upon us in the quarry with such momentum, that it bent a massive iron lever like a bow, and crushed into minute fragments a strong wheelbarrow, Uncle David, who, older and less active than any of the others, had been entangled in the formidable debris, relieved all our minds by remarking, as we rushed back, expecting to find him crushed as flat as a botanical preparation, "Od, I draid, Andro man, we have lost our good barrow." He was at first of opinion that I would do him little credit as a workman: in my absent fits I was well-nigh as impervious to instruction as he himself was insensible to danger; and I laboured under the further disadvantage of knowing a little, as an amateur, of both hewing and building, from the circumstance, that when the undertakings of my schoolboy days involved, as they sometimes did, the erection of a house, I used always to be selected as the mason of the party. And all that I had learned on these occasions I had now to unlearn. In the course of a few months, however, I did unlearn it all; and then, acquiring in less than a fortnight a very considerable mastery over the mallet—for mine was one of the not unfrequent cases in which the mechanical knack seems, after many an abortive attempt, to be caught up at once—I astonished Uncle David one morning by setting myself to compete with him, and by hewing nearly two feet of pavement for his one. And on this occasion, my aunt, his wife, who had been no stranger to his previous complaints, was informed that her "stupid nephew" was to turn out "a grand workman after all."

A life of toil has, however its peculiar temptations. When overwrought, and in my depressed moods, I learned to regard the

150

ardent spirits of the dram-shop as high luxuries: they gave lightness and energy to both body and mind, and substituted for a state of dullness and gloom, one of exhilaration and enjoyment. Usquebaugh was simply happiness doled out by the glass, and sold by the gill. The drinking usages of the profession in which I laboured were at this time many: when a foundation was laid, the workmen were treated to drink; they were treated to drink when the walls were levelled for laying the joists; they were treated to drink when the building was finished; they were treated to drink when an apprentice joined the squad; treated to drink when his "apron was washed;" treated to drink when "his time was out;" and occasionally they learned to treat one another to drink. In laying down the foundation-stone of one of the larger houses built this year by Uncle David and his partner, the workmen had a royal "founding-pint," and two whole glasses of the whisky came to my share. A full-grown man would not have deemed a gill of usquebaugh an overdose, but it was considerably too much for me; and when the party broke up, and I got home to my books, I found, as I opened the pages of a favourite author, the letters dancing before my eyes, and that I could no longer master the sense. I have the volume at present before me—a small edition of the Essays of Bacon, a good deal worn at the corners by the friction of the pocket; for of Bacon I never tired. The condition into which I had brought myself was, I felt, one of degradation. I had sunk, by my own act, for the time, to a lower level of intelligence than that on which it was my privilege to be placed; and though the state could have been no very favourable one for forming a resolution, I in that hour determined that I should never again sacrifice my capacity of intellectual enjoyment to a drinking usage; and, with God's help, I was enabled to hold by the determination. Though never a strict abstainer, I have wrought as an operative mason for whole twelvemonths together, in which I did not consume half-a-dozen glasses of ardent spirits, or partake of half-a-dozen draughts of fermented liquor. But I do see, in looking back on this my first year of labour, a dangerous point, at which, in the attempt to escape from the sense of depression and fatigue, the craving appetite of the confirmed tippler might have been formed.

The ordinary, long-wrought quarries of my native town have been opened in the old coast-line along the southern shores of the Cromarty Firth, and they contain no organisms. The beds occasionally display their water-rippled surfaces, and occasionally their areas of ancient desiccation, in which the polygonal partings still remain as when they had cracked in the drying, untold ages before. But the rock contains neither fish nor shell; and the mere mechanical processes of which it gave evidence, though they served to raise strange questions in my mind, failed to interest me so deeply as the wonderful organisms of other creations would have done. We soon quitted these quarries, however, as they proved more than usually difficult in the working at this time, for a quarry situated on the northern shore of the Moray Firth, which had been recently opened in an inferior member of the Lower Old Red Sandstone, and which, as I subsequently ascertained, does in some of its beds contain fossils. It was, however, not to the quarry itself that my first-found organisms belonged. There lies, in the Firth beyond, an outlier of the Lias, which, like the Marcus's Cave one referred to in a preceding chapter, strews the beach with its fragments after every storm from the sea; and in a nodular mass of bluish-grey limestone derived from this subaqueous bed I laid open my first-found ammonite. It was a beautiful specimen, graceful in its curves as those of the Ionic volute, and greatly more delicate in its sculpturing; and its bright cream-coloured tint, dimly burnished by the prismatic hues of the original pearl, contrasted exquisitely with the dark grey of the matrix which enclosed it. I broke open many a similar nodule during our stay at this delightful quarry, and there were few of them in which I did not detect some organism of the ancient world—scales of fishes, groups of shells, bits of decayed wood, and fragments of fern. At the dinner hour I used to show my new-found specimens to the workmen; but though they always took the trouble of looking at them, and wondered at times how the shells and plants had "got into the stones," they seemed to regard them as a sort of natural toys, which a mere lad might amuse himself in looking after, but which were rather below the notice of grown-up people like themselves. One workman, however, informed me, that things of a kind I had not yet found—genuine thunderbolts— which in his father's time were much sought for the cure of bewitched cattle—were to be found in tolerable abundance on a reach of the beach about two miles further to the west; and as, on quitting the quarry for the piece of work on which we were to be next engaged, Uncle David gave us all a half-holiday, I made use of it in visiting the tract of shore indicated by the workman. And there, leaning against the granite gneiss and hornblend slate of the Hill of Eathie, I found a Liassic deposit, amazingly rich in its organisms—not buried under the waves, as at Marcus's shore, or as opposite our new quarry, but at one part underlying a little grass-covered plain, and at another exposed for several hundred yards together along the shore. Never yet did embryo geologist break ground on a more promising field; and memorable in my existence was this first of the many happy evenings that I have spent in exploring it.

The Hill of Eathie, like the Cromarty Sutors, belongs, as I have already had occasion to mention, to what De Beaumont would term the Ben Nevis system of hills—that latest of our Scottish mountain systems which, running from south-west to north-east, in the line of the great Caledonian valley, and in that of the valleys of the Nairn, Findhorn, and Spey, uptilted in its course, when it arose, the Oolites[1] of Sutherland, and the Lias of Cromarty and Ross. The deposit which the Hill of Eathie disturbed is exclusively a Liassic one. The upturned base of the formation rests immediately against the Hill; and we may trace the edges of the various overlying beds for several hundred feet outwards, until, apparently near the top of the deposit, we lose them in the sea. The various beds—all save the lowest, which consists of a blue adhesive clay— are composed of a dark shale, consisting of easily-separable

[1] A mainly granular limestone series above the Lias.

153

laminæ, thin as sheets of pasteboard; and they are curiously divided from each other by bands of fossiliferous limestone of but from one to two feet thick. These Liassic beds, with their separating bands, are a sort of boarded books; for as a series of volumes reclining against a granite pedestal in the geologic library of nature, I used to find pleasure in regarding them. The limestone bands, elaborately marbled with lignite, ichthyolite,[1] and shell, form the stiff boarding; the pasteboard-like laminæ between— tens and hundreds of thousands in number in even the slimmer volumes—compose the closely-written leaves. I say closely written; for never yet did signs or characters lie closer on page or scroll than do the organisms of the Lias on the surface of these leaf-like laminæ. I can scarce hope to communicate to the reader, after the lapse of so many years, an adequate idea of the feeling of wonder which the marvels of this deposit excited in my mind, wholly new as they were to me at the time. Even the fairy lore of my first-formed library—that of the birchen box—had impressed me less. The general tone of the colouring of these written leaves, though dimmed by the action of untold centuries, is still very striking. The ground is invariably of a deep neutral grey, verging on black; while the flattened organisms, which present about the same degree of relief as one sees in the figures of an embossed card, contrast with it in tints that vary from opaque to silvery white, and from pale yellow to an umbry or chestnut brown. Groups of ammonites[2] appear as if drawn in white chalk; clusters of a minute undescribed bivalve are still plated with thin films of the silvery nacre; the mytilaceæ[3] usually bear a warm tint of yellowish brown, and must have been brilliant shells in their day; gryphites[4] and oysters are always of a dark grey, and plagiostomæ[5] ordinarily of a bluish or neutral tint. On some of the

[1] Fossil fish.
[2] Fossilised shells, usually circular (like the horns of Jupiter-Ammon); an extinct family of molluscs allied to the cuttle-fish, and resembling the modern nautilus.
[3] Mussels.
[4] Shell-fish allied to the mussel, etc. (bivalve molluscs).
[5] A genus of molluscs still surviving.

leaves curious pieces of incident seem recorded. We see fleets of minute terebratulæ,[1] that appear to have been covered up by some sudden deposit from above, when riding at their anchors; and whole argosies of ammonites, that seem to have been wrecked at once by some untoward incident, and sent crushed and dead to the bottom. Assemblages of bright black plates, that shine like pieces of Japan work, with numerous parallelogrammical scales bristling with nail-like points, indicate where some armed fish of the old ganoid order[2] lay down and died; and groups of belemnites, that lie like heaps of boarding-pikes thrown carelessly on a vessel's deck on the surrender of the crew, tell where *skulls* of cuttle-fishes of the ancient type had ceased to trouble the waters. I need scarce add, that these spear-like belemnites formed the supposed thunderbolts of the deposit. Lying athwart some of the pages thus strangely inscribed we occasionally find, like the dark hawthorn leaf in Bewick's well-known vignette, slim-shaped leaves coloured in deep umber; and branches of extinct pines, and fragments of strangely-fashioned ferns, form their more ordinary garnishing. Page after page, for tens and hundreds of feet together, repeat the same wonderful story. The great Alexandrian library, with its tomes of ancient literature, the accumulation of long ages, was but a meagre collection—not less puny in bulk than recent in date— compared with this marvellous library of the Scotch Lias.

Who, after once spending even a few hours in such a school, could avoid being a geologist? I had formerly found much pleasure among rocks and in caves; but it was the wonders of the Eathie Lias that first gave direction and aim to my curiosity. From being a mere child, that had sought amusement in looking over the *pictures* of the stony volume of nature, I henceforth became a sober student desirous of reading and knowing it as a book. The extreme beauty, however, of the Liassic fossils made me pass over at this time, as of little interest, a discovery which, if duly followed up, would have probably landed me full in the midst of the Old Red

---

[1] Lamp shells.

[2] Fishes covered with scales or plates of enamelled bone, represented by the modern American gar-pike.

Sandstone ichthyolites fully ten years ere I learned to know them. In forming a temporary harbour, at which we boated the stones we had been quarrying, I struck my pick into a slaty sandstone bed, thickly mottled in the layers by carbonaceous markings. They consisted, I saw, of thin rectilinear stems or leaves, much broken and in a bad state of keeping, that at once suggested to me layers of comminuted *Zostera marina*,[1] such as I had often seen on the Cromarty beach thrown up from the submarine meadows of the Firth beyond. But then, with magnificent ammonites and belemnites, and large well-marked lignites,[2] to be had in abundance at Eathie just for the laying open and the picking up, how could I think of giving myself to disinter what seemed to be mere broken fragments of *Zostera*? Within, however, a few feet of these carbonaceous markings there occurred one of those platforms of violent death for which the Old Red Sandstone is so remarkable—a platform strewed over with fossil remains of the first-born ganoids of creation, many of which still bore in their contorted outlines evidence of sudden dissolution and the dying pang.

During the winter of this year—for winter at length came, and, my labours over, three happy months were all my own—I had an opportunity of seeing, deep in a wild Highland glen, the remains of one of our old Scotch forests of the native pine. My cousin George, finding his pretty Highland cottage on the birch-covered tomhan situated too far from his ordinary scenes of employment, had removed to Cromarty; and when his work had this year come to a close for the season, he made use of his first leisure in visiting his father-in-law, an aged shepherd who resided in the upper recesses of Strathcarron. He had invited me to accompany him; and of the invitation I gladly availed myself. We struck across the tract of wild hills which intervenes between the Cromarty and Dornoch Firths, a few miles to the west of the village of Invergordon; and after spending several hours in toiling across

[1] The grass-wrack.
[2] Fossil wood (brown-coal).

156

dreary moors, unopened at the time by any public road, we took our noon-day refreshment in an uninhabited valley, among broken cottage walls, with a few, furrowed patches stretching out around us, green amid the waste. One of the best swordsmen in Ross had once lived there; but both he and his race had been lost to Scotland in consequence of the compelled emigration so common in the Highlands during the last two ages; and Cousin George came strongly out against the lairds. The chill winter night had fallen on the dark hills and alder-skirted river of Strathcarron, as, turning from off the road that winds along the Kyle of Dornoch, we entered its bleak gorge; and as the shepherd's dwelling lay high up the valley, where the lofty sides approach so near, and rise so abruptly, that for the whole winter quarter the sun never falls on the stream below, we had still some ten or twelve miles of broken road before us. The moon, in her first quarter, hung on the edge of the hills, dimly revealing their rough outlines; while in a recess of the stream, far beneath, we could see the torch of some adventurous fisher, now gleaming red on rock and water, now suddenly disappearing, eclipsed by the overhanging brushwood. It was late ere we reached the shepherd's cottage—a dark-raftered, dimly-lighted erection of turf and stone. The weather for several weeks before had been rainy and close, and the flocks of the inmate had been thinned by the common scourge of the sheep-farmer at such seasons on damp, boggy farms. The beams were laden with skins besmeared with blood, that dangled overhead to catch the conservative influences of the smoke; and on a rude plank-table below, there rose two tall pyramids of braxy-mutton, heaped up each on a corn-riddle. The shepherd—a Highlander of large proportions, but hard, and thin, and worn by the cares and toils of at least sixty winters—sat moodily beside the fire. The state of his flocks was not cheering; and, besides, he had seen a vision of late, he said, that filled his mind with strange forebodings. He had gone out after nightfall on the previous evening to a dank hollow, in which many of his flock had died. The rain had ceased a few hours before, and a smart frost had set in, and filled the whole valley with a wreath of silvery vapour, dimly lighted by the thin fragment of a moon that appeared as if resting on the hill-top. The wreath stretched out its grey folds beneath him—for he had climbed half-way up the acclivity—when suddenly the figure of a man, formed as of heated metal—the figure of what seemed to be a brazen man brought to a red heat in a furnace—sprang up out of the darkness; and, after stalking over the surface of the fog for a few brief seconds, during which, however, it had traversed the greater part of the valley, it as suddenly disappeared, leaving an evanescent trail of flame behind it. There could be little doubt that the old shepherd had merely seen one of those shooting lights that in mountain districts so frequently startle the night traveller; but the apparition now filled his whole mind, as one vouchsafed from the spiritual world, and of strange and frightful portent:—

> "A meteor of the night of distant years,
> That flashed unnoticed, save by wrinkled eld,
> Musing at midnight upon prophecies."

I spent the greater part of the following day with my cousin in the forest of Corrybhalgan, and saw two large herds of red deer on the hills. The forest was but a shred of its former self; but the venerable trees still rose thick and tall in some of the more inaccessible hollows; and it was interesting to mark, where they encroached furthest on the open waste, how thoroughly they lost the ordinary character of the Scotch fir, and how, sending out from their short gnarled boles immense branches, some two or three feet over the soil, they somewhat resembled in their squat, dense proportions, and rounded contours, gigantic bee-hives. It was of itself worth while undertaking a journey to the Highlands, to witness these last remains of that arboreous condition of our country to which the youngest of our geological formations, the Peat Mosses, bear such significant witness; and which still, largely existing as the condition of the northern countries of continental Europe, "remains to attest," as Humboldt well remarks, "more than even the records of history, the youthfulness of our civilisation." I revisited at this time, before returning home, the Barony of Gruids; but winter had not improved it: its humble features, divested of their summer complexion, had assumed an expression of blank wretchedness; and hundreds of its people, appalled at the time by a summons of ejection, looked quite as depressed and miserable as its scenery.

Finlay and my friend of the Doocot Cave were no longer within reach; but during this winter I was much in the company of a young man about five years my senior, who was of the true stuff of which friends are made, and to whom I became much attached. I had formed some acquaintance with him about five years before, on his coming to the place from the neighbouring parish of Nigg, to be apprenticed to a house-painter, who lived a few doors from my mother's. But there was at first too great a disparity between us for friendship; he was a tall lad, and I a wild boy; and, though occasionally admitted into his sanctum—a damp little room in an outhouse in which he slept, and in his leisure hours made water-colour drawings and verses—it was but as an occasional visitor, who, having a rude taste for literature and the fine arts, was just worthy of being encouraged in this way. My year of toil had, however, wrought wonders for me: it had converted me into a sober young man; and William Ross now seemed to find scarce less pleasure in my company than I did in his. Poor William! his name must be wholly unfamiliar to the reader; and yet he had that in him which ought to have made it a known one. He was a lad of genius—drew truthfully, had a nice sense of the beautiful, and possessed the true poetic faculty; but he lacked health and spirits, and was naturally of a melancholy temperament, and diffident of himself. He was at this time a thin, pale lad, fair-haired, with a clear waxen complexion, flat chest, and stooping figure; and though he lasted considerably longer than could have been anticipated from his appearance, in seven years after he was in his grave. He was unfortunate in his parents; his mother, though of a devout family of the old Scottish type, was an aberrant specimen;—she had fallen in early youth, and had subsequently married an ignorant, half-imbecile labourer, with whom she passed a life of poverty and unhappiness; and of this unpromising marriage William was the eldest child. It was certainly not from either parent he derived his genius. His maternal grandmother and aunt were, however, excellent Christian women of superior intelligence, who supported themselves by keeping a girls' school in the parish; and William, who had been brought at an early age to live with them, and was naturally a gentle-spirited, docile boy, had the advantage, in consequence, of having that most important lesson of any education—the lesson of a good example at home— set well before him. His boyhood had been that of the poet: he had loved to indulge in his day-dreams in the solitude of a deep wood beside his grandmother's cottage; and had learned to write verses and draw landscapes in a rural locality in which no one had ever written verses or drawn landscapes before. And finally, as, in the north of Scotland, in those primitive times, the nearest approach to an artist was a house-painter, William was despatched to Cromarty, when he had grown tall enough for the work, to cultivate his natural taste for the fine arts, in papering rooms and lobbies, and in painting railings and wheelbarrows. There are, I believe, a few instances on record of house-painters rising to be artists; the history of the late Mr William Bonnar, of the Royal Academy of Edinburgh, furnishes one of these; but the fact that the cases are not more numerous serves, I fear, to show how much oftener a turn for drawing is a merely imitative, than an original, self-derived faculty. Almost all the apprentices of our neighbour the house-painter had their turn for drawing decided enough to influence their choice of a profession; and what was so repeatedly the case in Cromarty must, I should think, have been the case in many similar places; but of how few of these embryo limners have the works appeared in even a provincial exhibition-room!

At the time my intimacy with William became most close, both his grandmother and aunt were dead, and he was struggling with great difficulty through the last year of his apprenticeship. As his master supplied him with but food and lodging, his linen was becoming scant, and his Sabbath suit shabby; and he was looking forward to the time when he should be at liberty to work for himself, with all the anxiety of the voyager who fears that his meagre stock of provisions and water may wholly fail him ere he reaches port. I, of course, could not assist him. I was an apprentice like himself, and had not the command of a sixpence; nor, had the case been otherwise, would he in all probability have consented to accept of my help; but he lacked spirits as much as money, and in that particular my society did him good. We used to beat over all manner of subjects together, especially poetry and the fine arts; and though we often differed, our differences served only to knit us the more. He, for instance, deemed the "Minstrel" of Beattie the most perfect of English poems; but though he liked Dryden's "Virgil" well enough, he could find no poetry whatever in the "Absalom and Achitophel" of Dryden; whereas I liked both the "Minstrel" and the "Achitophel," and, indeed, could hardly say, unlike as they were in complexion and character, which of the two I read oftenest or admired most. Again, among the prose writers, Addison was his especial favourite, and Swift he detested; whereas I liked Addison and Swift almost equally well, and passed without sense of incongruity, from the Vision of Mirza, or the paper on Westminster Abbey, to the true account of the death of Partridge, or the "Tale of a Tub". If, however, he could wonder at the latitudinarian laxity of my taste, there was at least one special department in which I could marvel quite as much at the incomprehensible breadth of his. Nature had given me, in despite of the phrenologists, who find music indicated by two large protuberances on the corners of my forehead, a deplorably defective ear. My uncle Sandy, who was profoundly skilled in psalmody, had done his best to make a singer of me; but he was at length content to stop short, after a world of effort, when he had, as he thought, brought me to distinguish St. George's from any other psalm-tune. On the introduction, however, of a second tune into the parish church that repeated the line at the end of the stanza, even this poor fragment of ability deserted me; and to this day—though I rather like the strains of the bagpipe in general, and have no objection to drums in particular—doubts do occasionally come across me whether there be in reality any such thing as tune. My friend William Ross was, on the contrary, a born musician. When a little boy, he had constructed for himself a fife and clarionet of young shoots of elder, on which he succeeded in discoursing sweet music; and addressing himself at another and later period to both the principles and practice of the science, he became one of the best flute-players in the district. Notwithstanding my dimness of ear, I do cherish a pleasing recollection of the sweet sounds that used to issue from his little room in the outhouse, every milder evening as I approached, and of the soothed and tranquil state in which I ever found him on these occasions as I entered. I could not understand his music, but I saw that, mentally at least, though, I fear, not physically—for the respiratory organs were weak—it did him great good.

There was, however, one special province in which our tastes thoroughly harmonized. We were both of us, if not alike favoured, at least equally devoted, lovers of the wild and beautiful in nature; and many a moonlight walk did we take together this winter among the woods and rocks of the hill. It was once said of Thomson, by one who was himself not at all morbidly poetic in his feelings, that "he could not have viewed two candles burning but with a poetical eye." It might at least be said of my friend, that he never saw a piece of fine or striking scenery without being deeply moved by it. As for the mere candles, if placed on a deal dresser or shop-counter, they might have failed to touch him; but if burning in some *lyke*-wake beside the dead, or some vaulted crypt or lonely rock-cave, he also could not have looked other than poetically on them. I have seen him awed into deep solemnity, in our walks, by the rising moon, as it peered down upon us over the hill, red and broad, and cloud-encircled, through the interstices of some clump of dark firs; and have observed him become suddenly silent, as, emerging from the moonlight woods, we looked into a rugged dell, and saw far beneath, the slim rippling streamlet gleaming in the light, like a narrow strip of the aurora borealis shot athwart a dark sky, when the steep rough sides of the ravine, on either hand, were enveloped in gloom. My friend's opportunities of general reading had not been equal to my own, but he was acquainted with at least one class of books of which I knew scarce anything;—he had carefully studied Hogarth's "Analysis of Beauty," Fresnoy's "Art of Painting," Gessner's "Letters," the "Lectures of Sir Joshua Reynolds," and several other works of a similar kind; and in all the questions of criticism that related to external form, the effects of light and shade, and the influences of the meteoric media, I found him a high authority. He had a fine eye for detecting the peculiar features which gave individuality and character to a landscape—those features, as he used to say, which the artist or poet should seize and render prominent, while, at the same time, lest they should be lost as in a mob, he softened down the others; and, recognising him as a master in this department of characteristic selection, I delighted to learn in his school—by far the best of its kind I ever attended. I was able, however, in part to repay him, by introducing him to many an interesting spot among the rocks, or to retired dells and hollows in the woods, which, from his sedentary habits, he would scarce ever have discovered for himself. I taught him too, to light fires after nightfall in the caves, that we might watch the effects of the strong lights and deep shadows in scenes so wild; and I still vividly remember the delight he experienced, when, after kindling up in the day-time a strong blaze at the mouth of the Doocot Cave, which filled the recess within with smoke, we forced our way inwards through the cloud, to mark the appearance of the sea and the opposite land seen through a medium so dense, and saw, on turning round, the landscape strangely enwrapped "in the dun hues of earthquake and eclipse." We have visited, after nightfall, the glades of the surrounding woods together, to listen to the night breeze, as it swept solemnly along the pine-tops; and, after striking a light in the old burial vault of a solitary churchyard, we have watched the ray falling on the fissured walls and ropy damp and mould; or, on setting on fire a few withered leaves, have seen the smoke curling slowly upwards, through a square opening in the roof, into the dark sky. William's mind was not of the scientific cast. He had, however, acquired some knowledge of the mathematics, and some skill both in architecture and in the anatomy of the human skeleton and muscles; while of perspective he perhaps knew well-nigh as much as was known at the time. I remember he preferred the Treatise on this art of Ferguson[1] the astronomer and mechanician, to any other; and used to say that the twenty years spent by the philosopher as a painter were fully redeemed, though they had produced no good pictures, by his little work on Perspective alone. My friend had ere this time given up the writing of verses very much because he had learned to know what verses ought to be, and failed to satisfy himself with his own; and ere his death, I saw him resign in succession his flute and pencil, and yield up all the hopes he had once cherished of being known. But his weak health affected his spirits, and prostrated the energies of a mind originally rather delicate than strong.

[1] James Ferguson (1710-76). His collected miscellaneous writings on astronomy and mechanics were edited by Sir David Brewster and published in 1823.

CHAPTER IX

"Others apart sat on a hill retired,
In thoughts more elevate; and reasoned high
Of Providence, foreknowledge, will, and fate—
Fixed fate, freewill, foreknowledge absolute;
And found no end, in wandering mazes lost."—MILTON.

SPRING came on, and brought with it its round of labour—
quarrying, building, and stone-cutting; but labour had now no
terrors for me: I wrought hard during the hours allotted to toil,
and was content; and read, wrote, or walked, during the hours that
were properly my own, and was happy. Early in May, however,
we had finished all the work for which my master had previously
contracted; and as trade was unusually dull at the time, he could
procure no further contracts, and the squad was thrown out of
employment. I rushed to the woods and rocks, and got on with my
lessons in geology and natural science; but my master, who had
no lessons to learn, wearied sadly of doing nothing; and at length,
very unwillingly—for he had enacted the part of the employer,
though on a small scale, for a full quarter of a century—he set
himself to procure work as a journeyman. He had another
apprentice at the time; and he, availing himself of the opportunity
which the old man's inability of employing him furnished, quitted
his service, and commenced work on his own behalf—a step to
which, though the position of a journeyman's apprentice seemed
rather an anomalous one, I could not see my way. And so, as work
turned up for both master and apprentice at a place about twenty
miles distant from Cromarty, I set out with him, to make trial, for
the first time, of the sort of life that is spent in bothies and
barracks. Our work was to consist, I was informed, of building and
hewing at an extensive farm-steading on the banks of the river
Conon, which one of the wealthier proprietors of the district was

getting built for himself, not on contract, but by the old mode of employing operatives on day's wages; and my master was to be permitted to rate as a full journeyman, though now considerably in his decline as a workman, on condition that the services of his apprentice should be rated so much lower than their actual value as to render master and man regarded as one lot—a fair bargain to the employer, and somewhat more. The arrangement was not quite a flattering one for me; but I acquiesced in it without remark, and set out with my master for Conon-side.

The evening sun was gleaming delightfully as we neared the scene of our labours, on the broad reaches of the Conon, and lighting up the fine woods and noble hills beyond. It would, I knew, be happiness to toil for some ten hours or so per day in so sweet a district, and then to find the evening all my own; but on reaching the work, we were told that we would require to set out in the morning for a place about four miles further to the west, where there were a few workmen engaged in building a jointure-house for the lady of a Ross-shire proprietor lately dead, and which lay off the river in a rather unpromising direction. And so, a little after sunrise, we had to take the road with our tools slung across our backs, and before six o'clock we reached the rising jointure-house, and set to work. The country around was somewhat bare and dreary—a scene of bogs and moors, overlooked by a range of tame heathy hills; but in our immediate neighbourhood there was a picturesque little scene—rather a vignette than a picture—that in some degree redeemed the general deformity. Two meal-mills—the one small and old, the other larger and more modern—were placed beside each other, on ground so unequal, that, seen in front, the smaller seemed perched on the top of the larger; a group of tall graceful larches rose immediately beside the lower building, and hung their slim branches over the huge wheel; while a few aged ash-trees that encircled the mill pond, which, in sending its waters down the hill, supplied both wheels in succession, sprang up immediately beside the upper erection, and shot their branches over its roof. On closing our labours for the evening, we repaired to the old mansion-house, about half a mile away, in which the dowager lady for whom we wrought still continued to reside, and where we expected to be accommodated like the other workmen, with beds for the night. We had not been expected, however, and there were no beds provided for us; but as the Highland carpenter who had engaged to execute the woodwork of the new building had an entire bed to himself, we were told we might, if we pleased, lie three a-bed with him. But though the carpenter was, I daresay, a most respectable man, and a thorough Celt, I had observed during the day that he was miserably affected by a certain skin disease, which, as it was more prevalent in the past of Highland history than even at this time, must have rendered his ancestors of old very formidable, even without their broadswords; and so I determined on no account to sleep with him. I gave my master fair warning, by telling him what I had seen; but uncle David, always insensible to danger, conducted himself on the occasion as in the sinking boat or under the falling bank, and so went to bed with the carpenter; while I, stealing out, got into the upper story of an outhouse; and, flinging myself down in my clothes on the floor on a heap of straw, was soon fast asleep. I was, however, not much accustomed at the time to so rough a bed; every time I turned me in my lair, the strong, stiff straw rustled against my face; and about midnight I awoke.

I rose to a little window which opened upon a dreary moor, and commanded a view in the distance, of a ruinous chapel and solitary burying-ground, famous in the traditions of the district as the chapel and burying-ground of Gillie-christ. Dr Johnson relates, in his "Journey," that when eating, on one occasion, his dinner in Skye to the music of the bagpipe, he was informed by a gentleman, "that in some remote time, the Macdonalds of Glengarry having been injured or offended by the inhabitants of Culloden, and resolving to have justice, or vengeance, they came to Culloden on a Sunday, when, finding their enemies at worship, they shut them up in the church, which they set on fire; and this, said he, is the tune that the piper played while they were burning." Culloden, however, was not the scene of the atrocity: it was the Mackenzies of Ord that their fellow-Christians and brother-Churchmen, the Macdonalds of Glengarry, succeeded in converting into animal charcoal, when the poor people were engaged, like good Catholics, in attending mass; and in this old chapel of Gillie-christ was the experiment performed. The Macdonalds, after setting fire to the building, held fast the doors until the last of the Mackenzies of Ord had perished in the flames; and then, pursued by the Mackenzies of Brahan, they fled into their own country, to glory ever after in the greatness of the feat. The evening was calm and still, but dark for the season, for it was now near mid-summer; and every object had disappeared in the gloom, save the outlines of a ridge of low hills that rose beyond the moor; but I could determine where the chapel and churchyard lay; and great was my astonishment to see a light flickering amid the gravestones and the ruins. At one time seen, at another hid, like the revolving lantern of a lighthouse, it seemed to be passing round and round the building; and, as I listened, I could hear distinctly what appeared to be a continuous screaming of most unearthly sound, proceeding from evidently the same spot as the twinkle of the light. What could be the meaning of such an apparition, with such accompaniments—the time of its appearance midnight—the place a solitary burying-ground? I was in the Highlands: was there truth, after all, in the many floating Highland stories of spectral dead-lights and wild supernatural sounds, seen and heard by nights in lonely places of sepulture, when some sudden death was near? I did feel my blood run somewhat cold, for I had not yet passed the credulous time of life—and had some thoughts of stealing down to my master's bedside, to be within reach of the human voice, when I saw the light quitting the churchyard, and coming downwards across the moor in a straight line, though tossed about in the dead calm, in many a wave and flourish; and further, I could ascertain, that what I had deemed a persistent screaming was in reality a continuous singing, carried on at the pitch of a powerful though somewhat cracked voice. In a moment after, one of the servant girls of the mansion-house came rushing out half-dressed to the door of an outer-building in which the workmen and the farm-servant lay, and summoned them immediately to rise. Mad Bell had again broke out, she said, and would set them on fire a second time.

The men rose, and, as they appeared at the door, I joined them; but on striking out a few yards into the moor, we found the maniac already in the custody of two men, who had seized and were dragging her towards her cottage, a miserable hovel, about half a mile away. She never once spoke to us, but continued singing, though in a lower and more subdued tone of voice than before, a Gaelic song. We reached her hut, and, making use of her own light, we entered. A chain of considerable length, attached by a stopple in one of the Highland *couples* of the erection, showed that her neighbours had been compelled on former occasions to abridge her liberty; and one of the men, in now making use of it, so wound it round her person as to bind her down, instead of giving her the scope of the apartment, to the damp uneven floor. A very damp and uneven floor it was. There were crevices in the roof above, which gave free access to the elements; and the turf walls, perilously bulged by the leakage in several places, were green with mould. One of the masons and I simultaneously interfered. It would never do, we said, to pin down a human creature in that way to the damp earth. Why not give her what the length of the chain permitted—the full range of the room? If we did that, replied the man, she would be sure to set herself free before morning, and we would just have to rise and bind her again. But we resolved, we rejoined, whatever might happen, that she should *not* be tied down in that way to the filthy floor; and ultimately we succeeded in carrying our point. The song ceased for a moment: the maniac turned round, presenting full to the light the strongly-marked, energetic features of a woman of about fifty-five; and, surveying us with a keen, scrutinizing glance, altogether unlike that of the idiot, she emphatically repeated the sacred text, "Blessed are the merciful, for they shall obtain mercy." She then began singing, in a low, mournful tone, an old Scotch ballad; and, as we left the cottage, we could hear her voice gradually heightening as we retired, until it had at length attained to its former pitch and wildness of tone.

Before daybreak the maniac succeeded in setting herself free; but the paroxysm of the fit had meanwhile passed over; and when she visited me next morning at the place where I was hewing— a little apart from the other workmen, who were all engaged in building on the walls—save for the strongly-marked features, I would scarce have recognised her. She was neatly dressed, though her gown was neither fine nor new; her clean white cap was nicely arranged; and her air seemed to be rather that of the respectable tradesman's wife or daughter, than of the ordinary country woman. For some little time she stood beside me without speaking, and then somewhat abruptly asked—"What makes *you* work as a mason?" I made some commonplace reply; but it failed to satisfy her. "All your fellows are real masons," she said; "but you are merely in the disguise of a mason; and I have come to consult you about the deep matters of the soul." The matters she had come to inquire regarding were really very deep indeed; she had, I found, carefully read Flavel's "Treatise on the Soul of Man"—a volume which, fortunately for my credit, I also had perused; and we were soon deep together in the rather bad metaphysics promulgated on the subject by the Schoolmen, and republished by the divine. It seemed clear, she said, that every human soul was created—not transmitted—created, mayhap, at the time when it began to be; but if so, how, or on what principle did it come under the influence of the Fall? I merely remarked, in reply, that she was of course acquainted with the views of the old theologians—*such as Flavel*—men who really knew as much about such things as could be known, and perhaps a little more: was she not satisfied with them? Not dissatisfied, she said; but she wanted more light. Could a soul not derived from our first parents be rendered vile simply by being put into a body derived from them? One of the passages in Flavel, on this special point, had luckily struck me, from its odd obscurity of expression, and I was able to quote it in nearly the original words. You know, I remarked, that a great authority on the question "declined confidently to affirm that the moral infection came by way of physical agency, as a rusty scabbard infects and defiles a bright sword when sheathed therein: it might be," he thought, "by way of natural concomitancy, as Estius will have it; or, to speak as Dr Reynolds doth, by way of ineffable resultancy and emanation." As this was perfectly unintelligible, it seemed to satisfy my new friend. I added, however, that, like herself, I was waiting for more light on the difficulty, and might set myself to it in right earnest, when I found it fully demonstrated that the Creator could not, or did not, make man equally the descendant in soul as in body of the original progenitors of the race. I believed, with the great Mr Looke, that he could do it; nor was I aware he had anywhere said that what he could do in the matter he had not done. Such was the first of many strange conversations with the maniac, who, with all her sad brokenness of mind, was one of the most intellectual women I ever knew. Humble as were the circumstances in which I found her, her brother, who was at this time about two years dead, had been one of the best-known Ministers of the Scottish Church in the northern Highlands. To quote from an affectionate notice by the editor of a little volume of his sermons, published a few years ago—the Rev. Mr Mackenzie of North Leith—"he was a profound divine, an eloquent preacher, a deeply-experienced Christian, and, withal, a classical scholar, a popular poet, a man of original genius, and eminently a man of prayer." And his poor sister Isabel, though grievously vexed at times by a dire insanity, seemed to have received from nature powers mayhap not inferior to his.

We were not always engaged with the old divines; Isabel's tenacious memory was stored with the traditions of the district; and many an anecdote could she tell of old chieftains, forgotten on the lands which had once been their own, and of Highland poets, whose songs had been sung for the last time. The story of

171

the "Raid of Gillie-christ" has been repeatedly in print since I first heard it from her; it forms the basis of the late Sir Thomas Dick Lauder's[1] powerful tale of "Allan with the Red Jacket;" and I have seen it in its more ordinary traditionary dress, in the columns of the *Inverness Courier*. But at this time it was new to me; and on no occasion could it have lost less by the narrator. She was herself a Mackenzie; and her eyes flashed a wild fire when she spoke of the barbarous and brutal Macdonalds, and of the measured march and unfaltering notes of their piper outside the burning chapel, when her perishing ancestors were shrieking in their agony within. She was acquainted also with the resembling story of that cave of Eigg, in which a body of the Macdonalds themselves, consisting of men, women, and children—the entire population of the island—had been suffocated wholesale by the Macleods of Skye; and I have heard from her more good sense on the subject of the Highland character "ere the gospel changed it," as illustrated by these passages in their history, than from some Highlanders sane enough on other matters, but carried away by a too indiscriminating respect for the wild courage and half-instinctive fidelity of the old race. The ancient Highlanders were bold, faithful dogs, she has said, ready to die for their masters, and prepared to do, at their bidding, like other dogs, the most cruel and wicked actions; and as dogs often were they treated; nay, even still, after religion had made them men (as if condemned to suffer for the sins of their parents), they were frequently treated as dogs. The pious martyrs of the south had contended in God's behalf; whereas the poor Highlanders of the north had but contended in behalf of their chiefs; and so, while God had been kind to the descendants of *His* servants, the chiefs had been very unkind to the descendants of theirs. From excellent sense, however, in these conversations, my new companion used often to wander into deplorable insanity. Her midnight visits to the old chapel of Gillie-christ were made, she said, in order that she might consult her

[1] Sir Thomas Dick Lauder of Grange (1784-1848), one of Miller's early patrons to whom his *Scenes and Legends of the North of Scotland* was dedicated, was himself a researcher and author of folklore, local history, natural history etc.

father in her difficulties; and the good man, though often silent for nights together, rarely failed to soothe and counsel her from the depths of his quiet grave, on every occasion when her unhappiness became extreme. It was acting on his advice, however, that she had set fire to a door that had for a time excluded her from the burying-ground, and burnt it down. She had been married in early life; and I have rarely heard anything wilder or more ingenious than the account she gave of a quarrel with her husband, that terminated in their separation.

After living happily with him for several years, she all at once, she said, became most miserable, and everything in their household went on ill. But though her husband seemed to have no true conception of the cause of their new-born misery, she had. He used, from motives of economy, to keep a pig, which, when converted into bacon, was always useful in the family; and an occasional ham of the animal now and then found its way to her brother's manse, as a sort of friendly acknowledgment of the many good things received from him. One wretched pig, however—a little black thing, only a few weeks old—which her husband had purchased at a fair, was, she soon discovered, possessed by an evil spirit, that had a strange power of quitting the animal to do mischief in her dwelling, and an ability of not only rendering her fearfully unhappy, but even of getting at times into her husband. The husband himself, poor blinded man! could see nothing of all this; nor would he believe *her*, who could and did see it; nor yet could she convince him that it was decidedly his duty to get rid of the pig. She was not satisfied that she herself had a clear right to kill the creature: it was undoubtedly her husband's property, not hers; but could she only succeed in placing it in circumstances in which it might be free either to kill itself or not, and were it, in these circumstances, to destroy itself, she was sure all the better divines would acquit her of aught approaching to moral guilt in the transaction; and the relieved household would be free from both the evil spirit and the little pig. The mill-pond was situated immediately beside her dwelling: its steep sides, which were walled with stone, were unscaleable by at least little pigs; and among the aged ashes which sprang up immediately at its edge, there was one that shot out a huge bough, like a bent arm, directly over it, far beyond the stonework, so that the boys of the neighbourhood used to take their seat on it, and fish for little trout that some times found their way into the pond. On the projecting branch one day, when her husband's back was turned, and there was no one to see or interfere, she placed the pig. It stood for a while: there was no doubt, therefore, it *could* stand; but, unwilling to stand any longer, it sprawled—slipped—fell—dropped into the water, in short—and ultimately, as it could not make its way up the bank, was drowned. And thus ended the pig. It would seem, however, as if the evil spirit had got into her husband instead— so extreme was his indignation at the transaction. He would accept of neither apology nor explanation; and, unable of course to live any longer under the same roof with a man so unreasonable, she took the opportunity, when he was quitting that part of the country for employment at a distance, to remain behind in her old cottage—the same in which she at that time resided. Such was the maniac's account of her quarrel with her husband; and, when listening to men chopping little familiar logic on one of the profoundest mysteries of Revelation—a mystery which, once received as an article of faith, serves to unlock many a difficulty, but which is itself wholly irreducible by the human intellect— I have been sometimes involuntarily led to think of her ingenious but not very sound argumentation on the fall of the pig. It is dangerous to attempt explaining, in the theological province, what in reality cannot be explained. Some weak abortion of the human reason is always substituted, in the attempt, for some profound mystery in the moral government of God; and men ill-grounded in the faith are led to confound the palpable abortion with the inscrutable mystery, and are injured in consequence.

I succeeded in getting a bed in the mansion-house, without, like Marsyas of old, perilling my skin; and though there was but little of interest in the immediate neighbourhood, and not much to be enjoyed within doors—for I could procure neither books nor congenial companionship—with the assistance of my pencil and sketch-book I got over my leisure hours tolerably well. My new friend Isabel would have given me as much of her conversation as I liked; for there was many a point on which she had to consult me, and many a mystery to state, and secret to communicate; but, though always interested in her company, I was also always pained, and invariably quitted her, after each lengthened *tête-à-tête*, in a state of low spirits, which I found it difficult to shake off. There seems to be something peculiarly unwholesome in the society of a strong-minded maniac; and so I contrived as much as possible—not a little, at times, to her mortification—to avoid her. For hours together, however, I have seen her perfectly sane; and, on these occasions, she used to speak much about her brother, for whom she entertained a high reverence, and gave me many anecdotes regarding him, not uninteresting in themselves, which she told remarkably well. Some of these my memory still retains.

"There were two classes of men," she has said, "for whom he had a special regard—Christian men of consistent character; and men who, though they made no profession of religion, were honest in their dealings, and of kindly dispositions. And with people of this latter kind he used to have a great deal of kindly intercourse, cheerful enough at times—for he could both make a joke and take one—but which usually did his friends good in the end. So long as my father and my mother lived, he used to travel across the country once every year to pay them a visit; and he was accompanied, on one of these journeys, by one of this less religious class of his parishioners, who had, however, a great regard for him, and whom he liked, in turn, for his blunt honesty, and obliging disposition. They had baited for some time at a house in the outer skirts of my brother's parish, where there was a child to baptise, and where, I fear, Donald must have got an extra dram; for he was very argumentative all the evening after; and finding he could not agree with my brother on any one subject, he suffered him to shoot ahead for a few hundred yards, and did not again come up with him, until, in passing through a thick clump of natural wood, he found him standing, lost in thought, before a singularly-shaped tree. Donald had never seen such a strange-looking tree in all his days before. The lower part of it was twisted in and out, and backwards and forwards, like an ill-made cork-screw; while the higher shot straight upwards, direct as a line; and its taper top seemed like a finger pointing at the sky. 'Come, tell me, Donald,' said my brother, 'what you think this tree is like?' 'Indeed, I kenna, Mr Lachlan,' replied Donald; 'but if you let me take that straight bit aff the tap o't, it will be gey an' like the worm o' a whisky still.' 'But I cannot want the straight bit,' said my brother; 'the very pith and point of my comparison lies in the straight bit. One of the old fathers would perhaps have said, Donald, that that tree resembled the course of the Christian. His early progress has turns and twists in it, just like the lower part of that tree; one temptation draws him to the left—another to the right: his upward course is a crooked one; but it is an upward course for all that; for he has, like the tree, the principle of sky-directed growth within him: the disturbing influences weaken as grace strengthens, and appetite and passion decay; and so the early part of his career is not more like the warped and twisted trunk of that tree, than his latter years resemble its taper top. He shoots off heavenward in a straight line.'" Such is a specimen of the anecdotes of this poor woman. I saw her once afterwards, though for only a short time; when she told me that, though people could not understand *us*, there was meaning in both her thoughts and in mine; and some years subsequently, when I was engaged as a journeyman mason in the south of Scotland, she walked twenty miles to pay my mother a visit, and stayed with her for several days. Her death was a melancholy one. When fording the river Conon in one of her wilder moods, she was swept away by the stream and drowned, and her body cast upon the bank a day or two after.

Our work finished at this place, my master and I returned on a Saturday evening to Conon-side, where we found twenty-four workmen crowded in a rusty corn-kiln, open from gable to gable, and not above thirty feet in length. A row of rude beds, formed of undressed slabs, ran along the sides; and against one of the gables there blazed a line of fires, with what are known as masons' setting-irons stuck into the stonework behind, for suspending over them the pots used in cooking the food of the squad. The scene, as we entered, was one of wild confusion. A few of the soberer workmen were engaged in "baking and firing" oaten cakes, and a few more occupied, with equal sobriety, in cooking their evening porridge; but in front of the building there was a wild party of apprentices, who were riotously endeavouring to prevent a Highland shepherd from driving his flock past them, by shaking their aprons at the affrighted animals; and a party equally bent on amusement inside were joining with burlesque vehemence in a song which one of the men, justly proud of his musical talents, had just struck up. Suddenly the song ceased, and with wild uproar a bevy of some eight or ten workmen burst out into the green in full pursuit of a squat little fellow, who had, they said, insulted the singer. The cry rose wild and high, "A ramming! a ramming!" The little fellow was seized and thrown down; and five men—one holding his head, and one stationed at each arm and leg—proceeded to execute on his body the stern behests of barrack-law. He was poised like an ancient battering-ram, and driven endlong against the wall of the kiln—that important part of his person coming in violent contact with the masonry, "where," according to Butler, "a kick hurts honour" very much. After the third blow, however, he was released, and the interrupted song went on as before. I was astonished, and somewhat dismayed, by this specimen of barrack-life; but, getting quietly inside the building, I succeeded in cooking for my uncle and myself some porridge over one of the unoccupied fires, and then stole off, as early as I could, to my lair in a solitary hay-loft—for there was no room for us in the barrack—where, by the judicious use of a little sulphur and mercury, I succeeded in freeing my master from the effects of the strange bed-fellowship which our recent misery had made, and preserving myself from infection. The following Sabbath was a day of quiet rest; and I commenced the labours of the week, disposed to think that my lot, though rather a rough one, was not altogether unendurable; and that, even were it worse than it was, it would be at once wise and manly, seeing that winter would certainly come, cheerfully to acquiesce in and bear up under it.

I had, in truth, entered a school altogether new—at times, as I have just shown, a singularly noisy and uproarious one, for it was a school without master or monitor; but its occasional lessons were, notwithstanding, eminently worthy of being scanned. All know that there exists such a thing as professional character. On some men, indeed, nature imprints so strongly the stamp of individuality, that the feebler stamp of circumstance and position fails to impress them. Such cases, however, must always be regarded as exceptional. On the average masses of mankind, the special employments which they pursue, or the kinds of business which they transact, have the effect of moulding them into distinct classes, each of which bears an artificially induced character peculiarly its own. Clergymen, as such, differ from merchants and soldiers, and all three from lawyers and physicians. Each of these professions has long borne in our literature, and in common opinion, a character so clearly appreciable by the public generally, that, when truthfully reproduced in some new work of fiction, or exemplified by some transaction in real life, it is at once recognised as marked by the genuine class-traits and peculiarities. But the professional characteristics descend much lower in the scale than is usually supposed. There is scarce a trade or department of manual labour that does not induce its own set of peculiarities— peculiarities which, though less within the range of the observation of men in the habit of recording what they remark, are not less real than those of the man of physic or of law. The barber is as unlike the weaver, and the tailor as unlike both, as the farmer is unlike the soldier, or as either farmer or soldier is unlike the merchant, lawyer, or minister. And it is only on the same sort of principle that all men, when seen from the top of a lofty tower, whether they be tall or short, seem of the same stature, that these differences escape the notice of men in the higher walks.

Between the workmen that pass sedentary lives within doors, such as weavers and tailors, and those who labour in the open air, such as masons and ploughmen, there exists a grand generic difference. Sedentary mechanics are usually less contented than laborious ones; and as they almost always work in parties, and as their comparatively light, though often long and wearily-plied employments, do not so much strain their respiratory organs but that they can keep up an interchange of ideas when at their toils, they are generally much better able to state their grievances, and much more fluent in speculating on their causes. They develop more freely than the laborious out-of-door workers of the country, and present, as a class, a more intelligent aspect. On the other hand, when the open-air worker does so overcome his difficulties as to get fairly developed, he is usually of a fresher or more vigorous type than the sedentary one. Burns, Hogg, Allan Cunningham, are the literary representatives of the order; and it will be found that they stand considerably in advance of the Thoms, Bloomfields, and Tannahills, that represent the sedentary workmen. The silent, solitary, hard-toiled men, if nature has put no better stuff in them than that of which stump-orators and Chartist lecturers are made, remain silent, repressed by their circumstances; but if of a higher grade, and if they once do get their mouths fairly opened, they speak with power, and bear with them into our literature the freshness of the green earth and the freedom of the open sky.

The specific peculiarities induced by particular professions are not less marked than the generic ones. How different, for instance, the character of a sedentary tailor, as such, from that of the equally sedentary barber! Two imperfectly-taught young lads, of not more than the average intellect, are apprenticed, the one to the hair-dresser, the other to the fashionable clothes-maker of a large village. The barber has to entertain his familiar round of customers, when operating upon their heads and beards. He must have no controversies with them; that might be disagreeable, and might affect his command of the scissors or razor; but he is expected to communicate to them all he knows of the gossip of the place; and as each customer supplies him with a little, he of course comes to know more than anybody else. And as his light and easy work lays no stress on his respiration, in course of time he learns to be a fast and fluent talker, with a great appetite for news, but little given to dispute. He acquires, too, if his round of customers be good, a courteous manner; and if they be in large proportion Conservatives, he becomes, in all probability, a Conservative too. The young tailor goes through an entirely different process. He learns to regard dress as the most important of all earthly things—becomes knowing in cuts and fashions—is taught to appreciate, in a way no other individual can, the aspect of a button, or the pattern of a vest; and as his work is cleanly, and does not soil his clothes, and as he can get them more cheaply, and more perfectly in the fashion, than other mechanics, the chances are ten to one that he turns out a beau. He becomes great in that which he regards as of all things greatest—dress. A young tailor may be known by the cut of his coat and the merits of his pantaloons, among all other workmen; and as even fine clothes are not enough of themselves, it is necessary that he should also have fine manners; and not having such advantages of seeing polite society as his neighbour the barber, his gentlemanly manners are always less fine than grotesque. Hence more ridicule of tailors among working men than of any other class of mechanics. And such—if nature has sent them from her hand ordinary men, for the extraordinary rise above all the modifying influences of profession—are the processes through which tailors and hair-dressers put on their distinctive characters as such. A village smith hears well-nigh as much gossip as a village barber; but he develops into an entirely different sort of man. He is not bound to please his customers by his talk; nor does his profession leave his breath free enough to talk fluently or much; and so he listens in grim and swarthy independence—strikes his iron while it is hot—and when, after thrusting it into the fire, he bends himself to the bellows, he drops, in rude phrase, a brief judicial remark, and again falls sturdily to work. Again, the shoemaker may be deemed, in the merely mechanical character of his profession, near of kin to the tailor. But such is not the case. He has to work amid paste, wax, oil, and blacking, and contracts a smell of leather. He cannot keep himself particularly clean; and although a nicely-finished shoe be all well enough in its way, there is not much about it on which conceit can build. No man can set up as a beau on the strength of a prettily-shaped shoe; and so a beau the shoemaker is not, but, on the contrary, a careless, manly fellow, who, when not overmuch devoted to Saint Monday, gains usually, in his course through life, a considerable amount of sense. Shoemakers are often in large proportion intelligent men; and Bloomfield, the poet, Gifford the critic and satirist, and Carey the missionary, must certainly be regarded as thoroughly respectable contributions from the profession, to the worlds of poetry, criticism, and religion.

The professional character of the mason varies a good deal in the several provinces of Scotland, according to the various circumstances in which he is placed. He is in general a blunt, manly, taciturn fellow, who, without much of the Radical or Chartist about him, especially if wages be good and employment abundant, rarely touches his hat to a gentleman. His employment is less purely mechanical than many others: he is not like a man ceaselessly engaged in pointing needles or fashioning pin-heads. On the contrary, every stone he lays or hews demands the exercise of a certain amount of judgment for itself; and so he cannot wholly suffer his mind to fall asleep over his work. When engaged, too, in erecting some fine building, he always experiences a degree of interest in marking the effect of the design developing itself piecemeal, and growing up under his hands; and so he rarely wearies of what he is doing. Further, his profession has this advantage, that it educates his sense of sight. Accustomed to ascertain the straightness of lines at a glance, and to cast his eye along plane walls, or the mouldings of entablatures or architraves, in order to determine the rectitude of the masonry, he acquires a sort of mathematical precision in determining the true bearings and position of objects, and is usually found, when admitted into a rifle club, to equal without previous practice, its second-rate shots. He only falls short of its first-rate ones, because, uninitiated by the experience of his profession in the mystery of the parabolic curve, he fails, in taking aim, to make the proper allowance for it. The mason is almost always a silent man: the strain on his respiration is too great, when he is actively employed, to leave the necessary freedom to the organs of speech; and so at least the provincial builder or stone-cutter rarely or never becomes a democratic orator. I have met with exceptional cases in the larger towns; but they were the result of individual idiosyncrasies, developed in clubs and taverns, and were not professional.

It is, however, with the character of our north-country masons that I have at present chiefly to do. Living in small villages, or in cottages in the country, they can very rarely procure employment in the neighbourhood of their dwellings, and so they are usually content to regard these as simply their homes for the winter and earlier spring months, when they have nothing to do, and to remove for work to other parts of the country, where bridges, or harbours, or farm-steadings are in the course of building—to be subjected there to the influences of what is known as the barrack or rather bothy life. These barracks or bothies are almost always of the most miserable description. I have lived in hovels that were invariably flooded in wet weather by the overflowings of neighbouring swamps, and through whose roofs I could tell the hour at night, by marking from my bed the stars that were passing over the openings along the ridge: I have resided in other dwellings of rather higher pretensions, in which I have been awakened during every heavier night-shower by the rain-drops splashing upon my face where I lay a-bed. I remember that Uncle James, in urging me not to become a mason, told me that a neighbouring laird, when asked why he left a crazy old building standing behind a group of neat modern offices, informed the querist that it was not altogether through bad taste the hovel was spared, but from the circumstance that he found it of great convenience every time his speculations brought a *drove of pigs* or a *squad of masons* the way. And my after experience showed me that the story might not be in the least apocryphal, and that masons had reason at times for not touching their hats to gentlemen.

In these barracks the food is of the plainest and coarsest description: oatmeal forms its staple, with milk, when milk can be had, which is not always; and as the men have to cook by turns, with only half an hour or so given them in which to light a fire, and prepare the meal for a dozen or twenty associates, the cooking is invariably an exceedingly rough and simple affair. I have known mason-parties engaged in the central Highlands in building bridges, not unfrequently reduced, by a tract of wet weather, that soaked their only fuel the turf, and rendered it incombustible, to the extremity of eating their oatmeal raw, and merely moistened by a little water, scooped by the hand from a neighbouring brook. I have oftener than once seen our own supply of salt fail us; and after relief had been afforded by a Highland smuggler—for there was much smuggling in salt in those days, ere the repeal of the duties—I have heard a complaint from a young fellow, regarding the hardness of our fare, at once checked by a comrade's asking him whether he was not an ungrateful dog to grumble in that way, seeing that, after living on fresh poultices for a week, we had actually that morning got porridge with salt in it. One marked effect of the annual change which the north-country mason has to undergo, from a life of domestic comfort to a life of hardship in the bothy, if he has not passed middle life, is a great apparent increase in his animal spirits. At home he is in all probability a quiet, rather dull-looking personage, not much given to laugh or joke; whereas in the bothy, if the squad be a large one, he becomes wild, and a humorist—laughs much, and grows ingenious in playing off pranks on his fellows. As in all other communities, there are certain laws recognised in the barrack as useful for controlling at least its younger members, the apprentices; but in the general tone of merriment, even these lose their character, and, ceasing to be a terror to evil-doers, become in the execution mere occasions of mirth. I never, in all my experience, saw a serious punishment inflicted. Shortly after our arrival at Cononside, my master, chancing to remark that he had not wrought as a journeyman for twenty-five years before, was voted a "ramming," for taking, as was said, such high ground with his brother workmen; but, though sentence was immediately executed, they dealt gently with the old man, who had good sense enough to acquiesce in the whole as a joke. And yet, amid all this wild merriment and license, there was not a workman who did not regret the comforts of his quiet home, and long for the happiness which was, he felt, to be enjoyed only there. It has been long known that gaiety is not solid enjoyment; but that the gaiety should indicate little else than the want of solid enjoyment, is a circumstance not always suspected. My experience of barrack-life has enabled me to receive without hesitation what has been said of the occasional merriment of slaves in America and elsewhere, and fully to credit the often-repeated statement, that the abject serfs of despotic Governments laugh more than the subjects of a free country. Poor fellows! If the British people were as unhappy as slaves or serfs, they would, I daresay, learn in time to be quite as merry. There are, however, two circumstances that serve to prevent the bothy life of the north-country mason from essentially injuring his character in the way it almost never fails to injure that of the farm-servant. As he has to calculate on being part of every winter, and almost every spring, unemployed, he is compelled to practise a self-denying economy, the effect of which, when not carried to the extreme of a miserly narrowness, is always good; and Hallow-day returns him every season to the humanizing influences of his home.

CHAPTER X

"The muse, nae poet ever fand her,
Till by himsel' he learned to wander
Adown some trottin' burn's meander,
An' no think lang:
Oh, sweet to muse, and pensive ponder
A heartfelt sang!"—BURNS.

THERE are delightful walks in the immediate neighbourhood of Conon-side; and as the workmen—engaged, as I have said, on day's wages—immediately ceased working as the hour of six arrived, I had, during the summer months, from three to four hours to myself every evening, in which to enjoy them. The great hollow occupied by the waters of the Cromarty Firth divides into two valleys at its upper end, just where the sea ceases to flow. There is the valley of the Peffer, and the valley of the Conon; and a tract of broken hills lies between, formed of the Great Conglomerate base of the Old Red System. The conglomerate, always a picturesque deposit, terminates some four or five miles higher up the valley, in a range of rough precipices, as bold and abrupt, though they front the interior of the country, as if they formed the terminal barrier of some exposed sea-coast. A few straggling pines crest their summits; and the noble woods of Brahan Castle, the ancient seat of the Earls of Seaforth, sweep downwards from their base to the margin of the Conon. On our own side of the river, the more immature but fresh and thickly-clustered woods of Conon House rose along the banks; and I was delighted to find among them a ruinous chapel and ancient burying-ground, occupying, in a profoundly solitary corner, a little green hillock, once an island of the river, but now left dry by the gradual wear of the channel, and the consequent fall of the water to a lower level. A few broken walls rose on the highest peak of

185

the eminence; the slope was occupied by the little mossy hillocks and sorely lichened tombstones that mark the ancient grave-yard; and among the tombs immediately beside the ruin there stood a rustic dial, with its iron gnomon worn to an oxydized film, and green with weather-stains and moss. And around this little lonely yard sprang the young wood, thick as a hedge, but just open enough towards the west to admit, in slant lines along the tombstones and the ruins, the red light of the setting sun.

I greatly enjoyed those evening walks. From Conon-side as a centre, a radius of six miles commands many objects of interest; Strathpeffer, with its mineral springs—Castle Leod, with its ancient trees, among the rest, one of the largest Spanish chestnuts in Scotland—Knockferrel, with its vitrified fort—the old tower of Fairburn—the old though somewhat modernized tower of Kinkell— the Brahan policies, with the old Castle of the Seaforths—the old Castle of Kilcoy—and the Druidic circles of the moor of Redcastle. In succession I visited them all, with many a sweet scene besides; but I found that my four hours, when the visit involved, as it sometimes did, twelve miles' walking, left me little enough time to examine and enjoy. A half-holiday every week would be a mighty boon to the working man who has acquired a taste for the quiet pleasures of intellect, and either cultivates an affection for natural objects, or, according to the antiquary, "loves to look upon what is old." My recollections of this rich tract of country, with its woods, and towers, and noble river, seem as if bathed in the red light of gorgeous sunsets. Its uneven plain of Old Red Sandstone leans, at a few miles' distance, against dark Highland hills of schistose gneiss, that, at the line where they join on to the green Lowlands, are low and tame, but sweep upwards into an alpine region, where the old Scandinavian flora of the country— that flora which alone flourished in the times of its boulder clay— still maintains its place against the Germanic invaders which cover the lower grounds, as the Celt of old used to maintain exactly the same ground against the Saxon. And at the top of a swelling moor, just beneath where the hills rise rugged and black, stands the pale tall tower of Fairburn, that, seen in the gloamin', as I have often seen it, seems a ghastly spectre of the past, looking from out its solitude at the changes of the present. The freebooter, its founder, had at first built it, for greater security, without a door, and used to climb into it through the window of an upper story by a ladder. But now unbroken peace brooded over its shattered ivy-bound walls, and ploughed fields crept up year by year along the moory slope on which it stood, until at length all became green, and the dark heath disappeared. There is a poetic age in the life of most individuals, as certainly as in the history of most nations; and a very happy age it is. I had now fully entered on it; and enjoyed in my lonely walks along the Conon, a happiness ample enough to compensate for many a long hour of toil, and many a privation. I have quoted, as the motto of this chapter, an exquisite verse from Burns. There is scarce another stanza in the wide round of British literature that so faithfully describes the mood which, regularly as the evening came, and after I had buried myself in the thick woods, or reached some bosky recess of the river bank, used to come stealing over me, and in which I have felt my heart and intellect as thoroughly in keeping with the scene and hour as the still woodland pool beside me, whose surface reflected in the calm every tree and rock that rose around it, and every hue of the heavens above. And yet the mood, though sweet, was also, as the poet expresses it, a pensive one: it was steeped in the happy melancholy sung so truthfully by an elder bard, who also must have entered deeply into the feeling.

> "When I goe musing all alone,
> Thinking of divers things foreknowne—
> When I builde castles in the air,
> Voide of sorrow and voide of care,
> Pleasing myself with phantasms sweet—
> Methinks the time runs very fleet;
> All my joyes to this are follie;—
> None soe sweet as melanchollie.

When to myself I sit and smile,
With pleasing thoughts the time beguile,
By a brook-side or wood soe green,
Unheard, unsought for, or unseen,
A thousand pleasures doe me blesse,
And crowne my soul with happiness,
All my joyes to this are follie;—
None soe sweet as melanchollie."

When I remember how my happiness was enhanced by every little bird that burst out into sudden song among the trees, and then as suddenly became silent, or by every bright-scaled fish that went darting through the topaz-coloured depths of the water, or rose for a moment over its calm surface—how the blue sheets of hyacinths that carpeted the openings in the wood delighted me, and every golden-tinted cloud that gleamed over the setting sun, and threw its bright flush on the river, seemed to inform the heart of a heaven beyond—I marvel, in looking over the scraps of verse produced at the time, to find how little of the sentiment in which I so luxuriated, or of the nature which I so enjoyed, found their way into them. But what Wordsworth well terms "the accomplishment of verse," given to but few, is as distinct from the poetic faculty vouchsafed to many as the ability of relishing exquisite music is distinct from the power of producing it. Nay, there are cases in which the "faculty" may be very high, and yet the "accomplishment" comparatively low, or altogether wanting. I have been told by the late Dr Chalmers, whose "Astronomical Discourses" form one of the finest philosophical poems in any language, that he never succeeded in achieving a readable stanza; and Dr Thomas Brown, whose metaphysics glow with poetry, might, though he produced whole volumes of verse, have said nearly the same thing of himself. But, like the Metaphysician, who would scarce have published his verses unless he had thought them good ones, my rhymes pleased me at this period, and for some time after, wonderfully well: they came to be so associated in my mind with the scenery amid which they were composed, and the mood which it rarely failed of inducing, that though they neither breathed the mood nor reflected the scenery, they always suggested both; on the principle, I suppose, that a pewter spoon, bearing the London stamp, suggested to a crew of poor weather-beaten sailors in one of the islands of the Pacific, their far-distant home and its enjoyments. One of the pieces suggested at this time I shall, however, venture on submitting to the reader. The few simple thoughts which it embodies arose in the solitary church-yard among the woods, beside the aged, lichen-incrusted dial-stone.

ON SEEING A SUN-DIAL IN A CHURCHYARD

GREY dial-stone, I fain would know
What motive placed thee here,
Where darkly opes the frequent grave,
And rests the frequent bier.
Ah! bootless creeps the dusky shade
Slow o'er thy figured plain:
When mortal life has passed away,
Time counts his hours in vain.

As sweeps the clouds o'er ocean's breast,
When shrieks the wintry wind,
So doubtful thoughts, grey dial-stone,
Come sweeping o'er my mind.
I think of what could place thee here,
Of those beneath thee laid,
And ponder if thou wert not raised
In mockery o'er the dead.

Nay, man, when on life's stage they fret,
May mock his fellow-men!
In sooth, their soberest freaks afford
Rare food for mockery then.
But ah! when passed their brief sojourn—
When Heaven's dread doom is said—
Beats there the human heart could pour
Like mockeries o'er the dead?

The fiend unblest, who still to harm
Directs his felon power,
May ope the book of grace to him
Whose day of grace is o'er;
But never sure could mortal man,
Whate'er his age or clime,
Thus raise, in mockery o'er the dead,
The stone that measures time.

Grey dial-stone, I fain would know
What motive placed thee here,
Where sadness heaves the frequent sigh,
And drops the frequent tear.
Like thy carved plain, grey dial-stone,
Grief's weary mourners be:
Dark sorrow metes out time to them—
Dark shade marks time on thee.

I know it now: wert thou not placed
To catch the eye of him
To whom, through glistening tears, earth's gauds
Worthless appear, and dim?
We think of time when time has fled,
The friend our tears deplore;
The God whom pride-swollen hearts deny,
Grief-humbled hearts adore.

Grey stone, o'er thee the lazy night
Passes untold away;
Nor were it thine at noon to teach,
If failed the solar ray.
In death's dark night, grey dial-stone,
Cease all the works of men;
In life, if Heaven withhold its aid,
Bootless these works and vain.

Grey dial-stone, while yet thy shade
Points out those hours are mine—
While yet at early morn I rise,
And rest at day's decline—
Would that the SUN that formed thine,
His bright rays beamed on me,
That I, wise for the final day,
Might measure time, like thee!

These were happy evenings—all the more happy from the circumstance that I was still in heart and appetite a boy, and could relish as much as ever, when their season came on, the wild raspberries of the Conon woods—a very abundant fruit in that part of the country—and climb as lightly as ever, to strip the guean-trees of their wild cherries. When the river was low, I used to wade into its fords in quest of its pearl mussels (*Unio Margaritiferus*); and, though not very successful in my pearl-fishing, it was at least something to see how thickly the individuals of this greatest of British fresh-water molluscs lay scattered among the pebbles of the fords, or to mark them creeping slowly along the bottom—when, in consequence of prolonged droughts, the current had so moderated that they were in no danger of being swept away—each on its large white foot, with its valves elevated over its back, like the carapace of some tall tortoise. I found occasion at this time to conclude that the *Unio* of our river-fords secretes pearls so much more frequently than the *Unionidæ* and *Anadonta* of our still pools and lakes, not from any specific peculiarity in the constitution of the creature, but from the effects of the habitat which it is its nature to choose. It receives in the fords and shallows of a rapid river many a rough blow from sticks and pebbles carried down in times of flood, and occasionally from the feet of the men and animals that cross the stream during droughts; and the blows induce the morbid secretions of which pearls are the result. There seems to exist no inherent cause why *Anadon Cygnea*, with its beautiful silvery nacre—as bright often, and always more delicate than that of *Unio Margaritiferus*—should not be equally productive of pearls; but, secure from violence in its still pools and lakes, and unexposed to the circumstances that provoke abnormal secretions, it does not produce a single pearl for every hundred that are ripened into value and beauty by the exposed current-tossed *Unionadæ* of our rapid mountain rivers. Would that hardship and suffering bore always in a creature of a greatly higher family similar results, and that the hard buffets dealt him by fortune in the rough stream of life could be transmuted, by some blessed internal predisposition of his nature, into pearls of great price.

It formed one of my standing enjoyments at this time to bathe, as the sun was sinking behind the woods, in the deeper pools of the Conon—a pleasure which, like all the more exciting pleasures of youth, bordered on terror. Like that of the poet, when he "wantoned with the breakers," and the "freshening sea made them a terror," "'twas a pleasing fear." But it was not current nor freshening eddy that rendered it such: I had acquired, long before, a complete mastery over all my motions in the water, and, setting out from the shores of the Bay of Cromarty, have swam round vessels in the roadstead, when, among the many boys of a seaport town, not more than one or two would venture to accompany me; but the poetic age is ever a credulous one, as certainly in individuals as in nations: the old fears of the supernatural may be modified and etherealised, but they continue to influence it; and at this period the Conon still took its place among the haunted streams of Scotland. There was not a river in the Highlands that used, ere the erection of the stately bridge in our neighbourhood, to sport more wantonly with human life—an evidence, the ethnographer might perhaps say, of its purely Celtic origin; and as Superstition has her figures as certainly as Poesy, the perils of a wild mountain-born stream, flowing between thinly-inhabited banks, were personified in the beliefs of the people by a frightful goblin, that took a malignant delight in luring into its pools, or overpowering in its fords, the benighted traveller. Its goblin, the "water-wraith," used to appear as a tall woman dressed in green, but distinguished chiefly by her withered, meagre countenance, ever distorted by a malignant scowl. I knew all the various fords—always dangerous ones—where of old she used to start, it was said, out of the river, before the terrified traveller, to point at him, as in derision, with her skinny finger, or to beckon him invitingly on; and I was shown the very tree to which a poor Highlander had clung, when, in crossing the river by night, he was seized by the goblin, and from which, despite of his utmost exertions, though

192

assisted by a young lad, his companion, he was dragged into the middle of the current, where he perished. And when, in swimming at sunset over some dark pool, where the eye failed to mark or the foot to sound the distant bottom, the twig of some sunken bush or tree has struck against me as I passed, I have felt, with sudden start, as if touched by the cold, bloodless fingers of the goblin.

The old chapel among the woods formed the scene, says tradition, of an incident similar to that which Sir Walter Scott relates in his "Heart of Mid-Lothian," when borrowing, as the motto of the chapter in which he describes the preparations for the execution of Porteous, from an author rarely quoted—the Kelpie. "The hour's come," so runs the extract, "but not the man;"—nearly the same words which the same author employs in his "Guy Mannering," in the cave scene between Meg Merrilies and Dirk Hatteraick. "There is a tradition," he adds, in the accompanying note, "that while a little stream was swollen into a torrent by recent showers, the discontented voice of the water-spirit was heard to pronounce these words. At the same moment, a man urged on by his fate, or, in Scottish language, *fey*, arrived at a gallop, and prepared to cross the water. No remonstrance from the bystanders was of power to stop him; he plunged into the stream, and perished." So far Sir Walter. The Ross-shire story is fuller, and somewhat different in its details. On a field in the near neighbourhood of the chapel, now laid out into the gardens of Conon House, there was a party of Highlanders engaged in an autumnal day at noon, some two or three centuries ago, in cutting down their corn, when the boding voice of the wraith was heard rising from the Conon beneath—"The hour's come, but not the man." Immediately after, a courier on horseback was seen spurring down the hill in hot haste, making directly for what is known as a "fause ford," that lies across the stream just opposite the old building, in the form of a rippling bar, which, indicating apparently, though very falsely, little depth of water, is flanked by a deep black pool above and below. The Highlanders sprang forward to warn him of his danger, and keep him back; but he was unbelieving and in haste, and rode express, he said, on business that would brook no delay; and as for the "fause ford," if it could not be ridden, it could be swam; and, whether by riding or swimming, he was resolved on getting across. Determined, however, on saving him in his own despite, the Highlanders forced him from his horse, and, thrusting him into the little chapel, locked him in; and then, throwing open the door when the fatal hour had passed, they called to him that he might now pursue his journey. But there was no reply, and no one came forth; and on going in they found him lying cold and stiff, with his face buried in the water of a small stone font. He had fallen, apparently, in a fit, athwart the wall; and his predestined hour having come, he was suffocated by the few pints of water in the projecting font. At this time the stone font of the tradition—a rude trough, little more than a foot in diameter either way—was still to be seen among the ruins; and, like the veritable cannon in the Castle of Udolpho, beside which, according to Annette, the ghost used to take its stand, it imparted by its solid reality a degree of authenticity to the story in this part of the country, which, if unfurnished with a "local habitation," as in Sir Walter's note, it would have wanted. Such was one of the many stories of the Conon with which I became acquainted at a time when the beliefs they exemplified were by no means quite dead, and of which I could think as tolerably serious realities, when, lying a-bed all alone at midnight, the solitary inmate of a dreary barrack, listening to the roar of the Conon.

Besides the long evenings, we had an hour to breakfast, and another to dinner. Much of the breakfast hour was spent in cooking our food; but as a bit of oaten cake and a draught of milk usually served us for the mid-day meal, the greater part of the hour assigned to *it* was available for purposes of rest or amusement. And when the day was fine, I used to spend it by the side of a mossy stream, within a few minutes' walk of the work-shed, or in a neighbouring planting, beside a little irregular lochan, fringed round with flags and rushes. The mossy stream, black in its deeper pools, as if it were a rivulet of tar, contained a good many trout, which had acquired a hue nearly as deep as its own, and formed the very negroes of their race. They were usually of small size—for the stream itself was small; and, though little countries sometimes produce great men, little streams rarely produce great fish. But on one occasion, towards the close of autumn, when a party of the younger workmen set themselves, in a frolic, to sweep it with torch and spear, they succeeded in capturing, in a dark alder-o'ershaded pool, a monstrous individual, nearly three feet in length, and proportionally bulky, with a snout bent over the lower jaw at its symphysis, like the beak of a hawk, and as deeply tinged (though with more of brown in its complexion) as the blackest coal-fish I ever saw. It must have been a bull-trout, a visitor from the neighbouring river; but we all concluded at the time, from the extreme dinginess of its coat, that it had lived for years in its dark pool, a hermit apart from its fellows. I am not now, however, altogether certain that the inference was a sound one. Some fishes, like some men, have a wonderful ability of assuming the colours that best suit their interests for the time. I have been unable to determine whether the trout be one of these conformists; but it used to strike me at this period as at least curious, that the fishes in even the lower reaches of the dark little rivulet should differ so entirely in hue from those of the greatly clearer Conon, into which its peaty waters fall, and whose scaly denizens are of silvery brightness. No fish seems to possess a more complete power over its dingy coat than a very abundant one in the estuary of the Conon—the common flounder. Standing on the bank, I have startled these creatures from off the patch of bottom on which they lay—visible to only a very sharp eye—by pitching a very small pebble right over them. Was the patch a pale one—for a minute or so they carried its pale colour along with them into some darker tract, where they remained distinctly visible from the contrast, until, gradually acquiring the deeper hue, they again became inconspicuous. But if startled back to the same pale patch from which they had set out, I have then seen them visible for a minute or so, from their over-dark tint, until, gradually losing it in turn, they paled down, as at first, to the colour of the lighter ground. An old Highlander, whose suit of tartan conformed to the general hue of the heather, was invisible at a little distance, when traversing a moor, but came full into view in crossing a green field or meadow: the suit given by nature to the flounder, tinted apparently on the same principle of concealment, exhibits a degree of adaptation to its varying circumstances, which the tartan wanted. And it is certainly curious enough to find, in one of our commonest fishes, a property which used to be regarded as one of the standing marvels of the zoology of those remote countries of which the chameleon is a native.

The pond in the piece of planting, though as unsightly a little patch of water as might be, was, I found, a greatly richer study than the dark rivulet. Mean and small as it was—not larger in area inside its fringe of rushes than a fashionable drawing-room—its natural history would have formed an interesting volume; and many a half-hour have I spent beside it in the heat of the day, watching its numerous inhabitants—insect, reptilian, and vermiferous. There were two—apparently *three*—different species of libellula that used to come and deposit their eggs in it— one of the two, that large kind of dragon-fly (*Eshna grandis*), scarce smaller than one's middle-finger—which is so beautifully coloured black and yellow, as if adorned by the same taste one sees displayed in the chariots and liveries of the fashionable world. The other fly was a greatly more slender and smaller species or genus rather, *Agrion*; and it seemed two, not one, from the circumstance, that about one-half the individuals were beautifully variegated black and sky-blue, the other half black and bright crimson. But the peculiarity was merely a sexual one; as if in illustration of those fine analogies with which all nature is charged, the sexes put on the *complementary* colours, and are mutually fascinating, not by resembling, but by *corresponding* to, each other. I learned in time to distinguish the disagreeable-looking larvæ of these flies, both larger and smaller, with their six hairy legs, and their grotesque formidable vizors, and found that they were the very pirates of the water, as the splendid insects into which they were ultimately developed were the very tyrants of the lower air. It was strange to see the beautiful winged creature that sprang out of the pupa into which the repulsive-looking pirate had been transformed, launch forth into its new element, changed in everything save its nature, but still unchanged in that, and rendering itself as formidable to the moth and the butterfly as it had been before to the newt and the tadpole. There is, I daresay, an analogy here also. It is in the first state of our own species, as certainly as in that of the dragon-fly, that the character is fixed. Further, I used to experience much interest in watching the progress of the frog, in its earlier stages from the egg to the fish; then from the fish to the reptile fish, with its fringed tail, and ventral and pectoral *limbs*; and, last of all, from the reptile fish to the complete reptile. I had not yet learned—nor was it anywhere known at the time— that the history of the individual frog, through these successive transformations, is a history in small of the animal creation itself in its earlier stages—that in order of time the egg-like mollusc had taken precedence of the fish, and the fish of the reptile; and that an intermediate order of creatures had once abounded, in which, as in the half-developed frog, the natures of both fish and reptile were united. But, though unacquainted with this strange analogy, the transformations were of themselves wonderful enough to fill for a time my whole mind. I remember being struck one afternoon, after spending my customary spare half hour beside the pond, and marking the peculiar style of colouring in the yellow and black *libellulidæ* in the common wasp, and in a yellow and black species of ichneumon fly, to detect in some half-dozen gentlemen's carriages that were standing opposite our work-shed—for the good old knight of Conon House had a dinner-party that evening—exactly the same style of ornamental colouring. The greater number of the vehicles were yellow and black—just as these were the prevailing colours among the wasps and *libellulidæ*; but there was a slight admixture of other colours among them too; there was at least one that was black and green, or black and blue, I forget which; and another black and brown. And so it was among the insects also: the same sort of taste, both in colour and the arrangements of colour, and even in the proportions of the various colours, seemed to have regulated the style of ornament manifested in the carriages of the dinner party, and of the insect visitors of the pond. Further, I thought I could detect a considerable degree of resemblance in form between a chariot and an insect. There was a great *abdominal* body separated by a narrow isthmus from a *thoracic* coach-box, where the directing power was stationed; while the wheels, poles, springs, and general framework on which the vehicle rested, corresponded to the wings, limbs, and antennæ of the insect. There was at least sufficient resemblance of form to justify resemblance of colour; and here *was* the actual resemblance of colour which the resemblance of form justified. I remember that, in musing over the coincidence, I learned to suspect, for the first time, that it might be no mere coincidence after all; and that the fact embodied in the remarkable text which informs us that the Creator made man in his own image, might in reality lie at its foundation as the proper solution. Man, spurred by his necessities, has discovered for himself mechanical contrivances, which he has afterwards found anticipated as contrivances of the Divine Mind, in some organism, animal or vegetable. In the same way his sense of beauty in form or colour originates some pleasing combination of lines or tints; and then he discovers that *it* also has been anticipated. He gets his chariot tastefully painted black and yellow, and lo! the wasp that settles on its wheel, or the dragon-fly that darts over it, he finds painted in exactly the same style. His neighbour, indulging in a different taste, gets *his* vehicle painted black and blue, and lo! some lesser libellula or ichneumon fly comes whizzing past, to justify his style of ornament also, but at the same time to show that it, too, had existed ages before.

The evenings gradually closed in as the season waned—at first abridging, and at length wholly interdicting, my evening walks;

and having no other place to which to retire, save the dark, gousty hay-loft, into which a light was never admitted, I had to seek the shelter of the barrack, and succeeded usually in finding a seat within at least *sight* of the fire. The place was greatly over-crowded; and, as in all over-large companies, it had commonly its four or five groups of talkers; each group furnished with a topic of its own. The elderly men spoke about the state of the markets, and speculated, in especial, on the price of oatmeal; the apprentices talked about lassies; while knots of intermediate age discussed occasionally both markets and lassies too, or spoke of old companions, their peculiarities and history, or expatiated on the adventures of former work seasons, and the characters of the neighbouring lairds. Politics proper I never heard. During the whole season a newspaper never once entered the barrack door. At times a song or story secured the attention of the whole barrack; and there was in especial one story-teller whose powers of commanding attention were very great. He was a middle-aged Highlander, not very skilful as a workman, and but indifferently provided with English; and as there usually attaches a nickname to persons in the humbler walks that are marked by any eccentricity of character, he was better known among his brother workmen as Jock Mo-ghoal, *i.e.* John my Darling, than by his proper name. Of all Jock Mo-ghoal's stories Jock Mo-ghoal was himself the hero; and certainly most wonderful was the invention of the man. As recorded in his narratives, his life was one long epic poem, filled with strange and startling adventure, and furnished with an extraordinary machinery of the wild and supernatural; and though all knew that Jock made imagination supply, in his histories, the place of memory, not even Ulysses or Æneas—men who, unless very much indebted to their poets, must have been of a similar turn—could have attracted more notice at the courts of Alcinous or Dido, than Jock in the barrack. The workmen used, on the mornings after his greater narratives, to look one another full in the face, and ask, with a smile rather incipient than fully manifest, whether "Jock wasna perfectly wonderfu' last nicht?"

He had several times visited the south of Scotland, as one of a band of Highland reapers, for employment in his proper profession very often failed poor Jock; and these journeys formed the grand occasions of his adventures. One of his narratives commenced, I remember, with a frightful midnight scene in a solitary churchyard. Jock had lost his way in the darkness; and, after stumbling among burial-mounds and tombstones, he had toppled into an open grave, which was of a depth so profound, that for some time he failed to escape from it, and merely pulled down upon himself, in his attempts to climb its loose sides, musty skulls, and great thigh-bones, and pieces of decayed coffins. At length, however, he did succeed in getting out, just as a party of unscrupulous resurrectionists were in the act of entering the burying-ground; and they, naturally enough preferring an undecayed subject that had the life in it to preserve it fresh, to dead corpses the worse for the keeping, gave him chase; and it was with the extremest difficulty that, after scudding over wild moors and through dark woods, he at length escaped them by derning[1] himself in a fox-earth. The season of autumnal labour over, he visited Edinburgh on his way north; and was passing along the High Street, when, seeing a Highland girl on the opposite side with whom he was intimate and whom he afterwards married, he strode across to address her, and, a chariot coming whirling along the street at the time at full speed, he was struck by the pole and knocked down. The blow had taken him full on the chest; but though the bone seemed injured, and the integuments became frightfully swollen and livid, he was able to get up; and, on asking to be shown the way to a surgeon's shop, his acquaintance the girl brought him to an underground room in one of the narrow lanes off the street, which, save for the light of a great fire, would have been pitch dark at mid-day, and in which he found a little, wrinkled old woman, as yellow as the smoke that filled the apartment. "Choose," said the hag, as she looked at the injured part, "one of two things—a cure slow but sure, or sudden but

---

[1] Concealing. Old Scots, found also in Shakespeare.

imperfect. Or shall I put back the hurt altogether till you get home?" "That, that," said Jock; "if I were ance hame I could bear it well enouch." The hag began to pass her hand over the injured part, and to mutter under her breath some potent charm; and as she muttered and manipulated, the swelling gradually subsided, and the livid tints blanched, till at length nought remained to tell of the recent accident save a pale spot in the middle of the breast, surrounded by a thread-like circle of blue. "And now," she said, "you are well for three weeks; but be prepared for the fourth." Jock prosecuted his northward journey, and encountered the usual amount of adventure by the way. He was attacked by robbers, but, assistance coming up, he succeeded in beating them off. He lost his way in a thick mist, but found shelter, after many hours' wandering far among the hills, in a deserted shepherd's shielin'. He was nearly buried in a sudden snow-storm that broke out by night, but, getting into the middle of a cooped-up flock of sheep, they kept him warm and comfortable amid the vast drift-wreaths, till the light of morning enabled him to prosecute his journey. At length he reached home, and was prosecuting his ordinary avocations, when the third week came to a close; and he was on a lonely moor at the very hour he had met with the accident on the High Street, when he suddenly heard the distant rattle of a chariot, though not a shadow of the vehicle was to be seen; the sounds came bearing down upon him, heightening as they approached, and, when at the loudest, a violent blow on the breast prostrated him on the moor. The stroke of the High Street "had come back," just as the wise woman had said it would, though with accompaniments that Jock had not anticipated. It was with difficulty he reached his cottage that evening; and there elapsed fully six weeks ere he was able to quit it again. Such, in its outlines, was one of the marvellous narratives of Jock Mo-ghoal. He belonged to a curious class, known by specimen in, I suppose, almost every locality, especially in the more primitive ones—for the smart ridicule common in the artificial states of society greatly stunt their growth; and in our literature—as represented by the

Bobadils, Young Wildings, Caleb Balderstones, and Baron Munchausens—they hold a prominent place. The class is to be found of very general development among the vagabond tribes. I have listened to wonderful personal narratives that had not a word of truth in them, "from gipsies brown in summer glades that bask," as I took my seat beside their fire, in a wild rock-cave in the neighbourhood of Rosemarkie, or at a later period in the cave of Marcus; and in getting into conversation with individuals of the more thoroughly lapsed classes of our large towns, I have found that a faculty of extemporary fabrication was almost the only one which I could calculate on finding among them in a state of vigorous activity. That in some cases the propensity should be found co-existing with superior calibre and acquirement, and even a sense of honour by no means very obtuse, must be regarded as one of the strange anomalies which so often surprise and perplex the student of human character. As a misdirected toe-nail, injured by pressure, sometimes turns round, and, re-entering the flesh, vexes it into a sore, it would seem as if that noble inventive faculty to which we owe the parable and the epic poem, were liable, when constrained by self-love, to similar misdirections; and certainly, when turned inwards upon its possessor, the moral character festers or grows callous around it.

There was no one in the barrack with whom I cared much to converse, or who, in turn, cared much to converse with me; and so I learned, on the occasions when the company got dull, and broke up into groups, to retire to the hay-loft where I slept, and pass there whole hours seated on my chest. The loft was a vast apartment some fifty or sixty feet in length, with its naked rafters raised little more than a man's height over the floor; but in the starlit nights, when the openings in the wall assumed the character of square patches of darkness-visible stamped upon utter darkness, it looked quite as well as any other unlighted place that could not be seen; and in nights brightened by the moon, the pale beams, which found access at openings and crevices, rendered its wide area quite picturesque enough for ghosts to walk in. But I never saw any; and the only sounds I heard were those made by the horses in the stable below, champing and snorting over their food. They were, I doubt not, happy enough in their dark stalls, because they were horses, and had plenty to eat; and I was at times quite happy enough in the dark loft above, because I was a man, and could think and imagine. It is, I believe, Addison who remarks, that if all the thoughts which pass through men's minds were to be made public, the great difference which seems to exist between the thinking of the wise and of the unwise would be a good deal reduced; seeing that it is a difference which does not consist in their not having the same weak thoughts in common, but merely in the prudence through which the wise suppress their foolish ones. I still possess notes of the cogitations of these solitary evenings, ample enough to show that they were extraordinary combinations of the false and the true; but I at the same time hold them sufficiently in memory to remember, that I scarce, if at all, distinguished between what was false and true in them at the time. The literature of almost every people has a corresponding early stage, in which fresh thinking is mingled with little conceits, and in which the taste is usually false, but the feeling true.

Let me present my young readers, from my notes, with the variously compounded cogitations of one of these quiet evenings. What formed so long ago one of my exercises may now form one of theirs, if they but set themselves to separate the solid from the unsolid thinking contained in my abstract.

MUSINGS

"I stood last summer on the summit of Tor-Achilty [a pyramidal hill about six miles from Conon-side], and occupied, when there, the centre of a wide circle, about fifty miles in diameter. I can still call up its rough-edged sea of hills, with the clear blue firmament arching over, and the slant rays of the setting sun gleaming athwart. Yes, over that circular field, fifty miles across, the firmament closed all around at the horizon, as a watch-glass closes round the dial-plate of the watch. Sky and earth seemed co-extensive; and yet how incalculably vast their difference of area! Thousands of systems seemed but commensurate, to the eye, with a small district of earth fifty miles each way. But capacious as the human imagination has been deemed, can it conceive of an area of wider field? Mine cannot. My mind cannot take in more at a glance, if I may so speak, than is taken in by the eye. I cannot conceive of a wider area than that which the sight commands from the summit of a lofty eminence. I can pass in imagination through many such areas. I can add field to field *ad infinitum*; and thus conceive of infinite space, by conceiving of a space which can be infinitely added to; but all of space that I can take in at one process, is an area commensurate with that embraced at a glance by the eye. How, then, have I my conception of the earth as a whole—of the solar system as a whole—nay, of many systems as a whole? Just as I have my conceptions of a school-globe or of an Orrery—by diminution. It is through the diminution induced by distance that the sidereal heavens only co-extend, as seen from the top of Tor-Achilty, with a portion of the counties of Ross and Inverness. The apparent area is the same, but the colouring is different. Our ideas of greatness, then, are much less dependent on actual area than on what painters term aerial perspective. The dimness of distance, and the diminution of parts, are essential to right conceptions of great magnitude.

"Of the various figures presented to me here, I seize strong hold of but one. I brood over the picture of the solar system conjured up. I conceive of the satellites as light shallops that continually sail round heavier vessels, and consider how much more of space they must traverse than the orbs to which they are attached. The entire system is presented to me as an Orrery of the apparent size of the area of landscape seen from the hill-top; but dimness and darkness prevent the diminution from communicating that appearance of littleness to the whole which would attach to it, were it, like an actual Orrery, sharply defined and clear. As the picture rises before me, the entire system seems to possess, what I suspect it wants, its atmosphere like that of the earth, which reflects the light of the sun in the different degrees of excessive brightness—noon-tide splendour, the fainter shades of evening, and grey twilight obscurity. This veil of light is thickest towards the centre of the system; for when the glance rests on its edges, the suns of other systems may be seen peeping through. I see Mercury sparkling to the sun, with its oceans of molten glass, and its fountains of liquid gold. I see the ice-mountains of Saturn, hoar through the twilight. I behold the earth rolling upon itself, from darkness to light, and from light to darkness. I see the clouds of winter settling over one part of it, with the nether mantle of snow shining through them; I see in another a brown, dusky waste (of sand lighted up by the glow of summer. One ocean appears smooth as a mirror—another is black with tempest. I see the pyramid of shade which each of the planets casts from its darkened side into the space behind; and I perceive the stars twinkling through each opening, as through the angular doors of a pavilion.

"Such is the scene seen at right angles with the plane in which the planets move; but what would be its aspect if I saw it in the line of the plane? What would be its appearance if I saw it edgewise? There arises in my mind one of those uncertainties which so frequently convince me that I am ignorant. I cannot complete my picture, for I do not know whether all the planets move in one plane. How determine the point? A ray of light breaks in. Huzza! I have found it. If the courses of the planets as seen in the heavens form parallel lines, then must they all move in one plane; and *vice versa*. But hold! That would be as seen from the sun—if the planets *could* be seen from the sun. The earth is but one of their own number, and from it the point of view must be disadvantageous. The diurnal motion must perplex. But no. The apparent motion of the heavens need not disturb the observation. Let the course of the planets through the fixed stars be marked, and though, from the peculiarity of the point of observation, their motion may at one time seem more rapid, and at another more slow, yet, if their plane be, as a workman would say, *out of twist*, their lines will seem parallel. Still in some doubt, however: I long for a glance at an Orrery, to determine the point; and then I remember that Ferguson, an untaught man like myself, had made more Orreries than any one else, and that mechanical contrivances of the kind were the natural recourse of a man unskilled in the higher geometry. But it would be better to be a mathematician than skilful in contriving Orreries. A man of the Newtonian cast of mind, and accomplished in the Newtonian learning, could solve the problem where I sat, without an Orrery.

"From the thing contemplated, I pass to the consideration of the mind that contemplates. Oh! that wonderful Newton, respecting whom the Frenchman inquired whether he ate and slept like other men! I consider how one mind excels another; nay, how one man excels a thousand; and, by way of illustration, I bethink me of the mode of valuing diamonds. A single diamond that weighs fifty carats is deemed more valuable than two thousand diamonds, each of which only weighs one. My illustration refers exclusively to the native powers; but may it not, I ask, bear also on the acquisition of knowledge? Every new idea added to the stock already collected is a carat added to the diamond; for it is not only valuable in itself, but it also increases the value of all the others, by giving to each of them a new link of association.

"The thought links itself on to another, mayhap less sound:—Do not the minds of men of exalted genius, such as Homer, Milton, Shakspere, seem to partake of some of the qualities of infinitude? Add a great many bricks together, and they form a pyramid as huge as the peak off Tenerife. Add all the common minds together that the world ever produced, and the mind of a Shakspere towers over the whole, in all the grandeur of unapproachable infinity. That which is infinite admits of neither increase nor diminution. Is it not so with genius of a certain altitude? Homer, Milton, Shakspere, were perhaps men of equal powers. Homer was, it is said, a beggar; Shakspere an illiterate wool-comber; Milton skilled in all human learning. But they have all risen to an equal height. Learning has added nothing to the *illimitable* genius of the one; nor has the want of it detracted from the *infinite* powers of the others. But it is time that I go and prepare supper."

I visited the policies of Conon House a full quarter of a century after this time—walked round the kiln, once our barrack—scaled the outside stone-stair of the hay-loft, to stand for half a minute on the spot where I used to spend whole hours seated on my chest, so long before; and then enjoyed a quiet stroll among the woods of the Conon. The river was big in flood: it was exactly such a river Conon as I had lost sight of in the winter of 1821, and eddied past dark and heavy, sweeping over bulwark and bank. The low-stemmed alders that rose on islet and mound seemed shorn of half their trunks in the tide; here and there an elastic branch bent to the current, and rose and bent again; and now a tuft of withered heath came floating down, and now a soiled wreath of foam. How vividly the past rose up before me!—boyish day-dreams, forgotten for twenty years—the fossils of an early formation of mind, produced at a period when the atmosphere of feeling was warmer than now, and the immaturities of the mental kingdom grew rank and large, like the ancient *cryptogamia*,[1] and bore no specific resemblance to the productions of a riper time. The season I had passed in the neighbourhood so long before—the first I had anywhere spent among strangers—belonged to an age when home is not a country, nor a province even, but simply a little spot of earth, inhabited by friends and relatives; and the verses, long forgotten, in which my joy had found vent when on the eve of returning to that home, came chiming as freshly into my memory as if scarce a month had passed since I had composed them beside the Conon. Here they are, with all the green juvenility of the home-sickness still about them—a true petrifaction of an extinct feeling:—

TO THE CONON

Conon, fair flowed thy mountain stream,
Through blossom'd heath and ripening field,
When, shrunk by summer's fervid beam,
Thy peaceful waves I first beheld.

---

[1] A flowerless order of plants.

Calmly they swept thy winding shore,
When harvest's mirthful feast was nigh—
When, breeze-borne, with thy hoarser roar
Came mingling sweet the reapers' cry.

But now I mark thy angry wave
Rush headlong to the stormy sea;
Wildly the blasts of winter rave,
Sad rustling through the leafless tree.
Loose on its spray the alder leaf
Hangs wavering, trembling, sear and brown;
And dark thy eddies whirl beneath,
And white thy foam comes floating down.

Thy banks with withered shrubs are spread;
Thy fields confess stern winter's reign;
And gleams yon thorn with berries red,
Like banner on a ravaged plain.
Hark! ceaseless groans the leafless wood;
Hark! ceaseless roars thy stream below;
Ben-Vaichard's peaks are dark with cloud;
Ben-Weavis' crest is white with snow.

And yet, though red thy stream comes down—
Though bleak th' encircling hills appear—
Though field be bare, and forest brown,
And winter rule the waning year—
Unmoved I see each charm decay,
Unmourn'd the sweets of autumn die;
And fading flower and leafless spray
Court all in vain the thoughtful sigh.

Not that dull grief delights to see
Vex'd Nature wear a kindred gloom;
Not that she smiled in vain to me,
When gaily prank'd in summer's bloom.
Nay, much I loved, at even-tide,
Through Brahan's lonely woods to stray,
To mark thy peaceful billows glide,
And watch the sun's declining ray.

But yet, though roll'd thy billows fair,
As e'er roll'd those of classic stream—
Though green thy woods, now dark and bare,
Bask'd beauteous in the western beam;
To mark a scene that childhood loved,
The anxious eye was turned in vain;
Nor could I find the friend approved,
That shared my joy or soothed my pain.

Now winter reigns: these hills no more
Shall sternly bound my anxious view;
Soon, bent my course to Croma's shore,
Shall I yon winding path pursue.
Fairer than *here* gay summer's glow
To me *there* wintry storms shall seem:
Then blow, ye bitter breezes, blow,
And lash the Conon's mountain stream.

CHAPTER XI

"The bounding pulse, the languid limb,
The changing spirit's rise and fall—
We know that these were felt by him,
For these are felt by all."—MONTGOMERY.

THE apprenticeship of my friend William Ross had expired during the working season of this year, when I was engaged at Conon-side; and he was now living in his mother's cottage in the parish of Nigg, on the Ross-shire side of the Cromarty Firth. And so, with the sea between us, we could no longer meet every evening as before, or take long night-walks among the woods. I crossed the Firth, however, and spent one happy day in his society, in a little, low-roofed domicile, with a furze-roughened ravine on the one side, and a dark fir-wood on the other; and which, though picturesque and interesting as a cottage, must, I fear, have been a very uncomfortable home. His father, whom I had not before seen, was sitting beside the fire as I entered. In all except expression he was wonderfully like my friend; and yet he was one of the most vapid men I ever knew—a man literally without an idea, and almost without a recollection or a fact. And my friend's mother, though she showed a certain kindliness of disposition which her husband wanted, was loquacious and weak. Had my quondam acquaintance, the vigorous-minded maniac of Ord, seen William and his parents, she would have triumphantly referred to them in evidence that Flavel and the Schoolmen were wholly in the right in holding that souls are not "derived through parental traduction."

My friend had much to show me: he had made an interesting series of water-colour sketches of the old castles of the neighbourhood, and a very elaborate set of drawings of what are known as the Runic obelisks of Ross: he had made some first attempts, too, in oil-painting; but though his drawing was, as usual, correct, there was a deadness and want of transparency about his colouring, which characterized all his after attempts in the same department, and which was, I suspect, the result of some such deficiency in his perceptions of the harmonies of colour as that which, in another department of sense, made me so insensible to the harmonies of sound. His drawings of the obelisks were of singular interest. Not only have the thirty years which have since elapsed exerted their dilapidating effect on all the originals from which he drew, but one of the number—the most entire of the group at that time— has been since almost wholly destroyed; and so, what he was then able to do, there can be no such opportunity of doing again. Further, his representations of the sculptured ornaments, instead of being (what those of artists too often are) mere picturesque approximations, were true in every curve and line. He told me he had spent a fortnight in tracing out the involved mathematical figures, curves, circles, and right lines—on which the intricate fretwork of one of the obelisks was formed, and in making separate drawings of each compartment, before commencing his draught of the entire stone. And, looking with the eye of the stone-cutter at his preliminary sketches, from the first meagre lines that formed the groundwork of some involved and difficult knot, to the elaborate knot itself, I saw that, with such a series of drawings before me, I myself could learn to cut Runic obelisks, in all the integrity of the complex ancient style, in less than a fortnight. My friend had formed some striking and original views regarding the theology represented by symbol on these ancient stones—at that time regarded as Runic, but now held to be rather of Celtic origin. In the centre of each obelisk, on the more important and strongly relieved side, there always occurs a large cross, rather of the Greek than of the Roman type, and usually elaborately wrought into a fretwork, composed of myriads of snakes, raised in some of the compartments over half-spheres resembling apples. In one of the Ross-shire obelisks—that of Shadwick, in the parish of Nigg—the cross is entirely composed of these apple-like, snake-covered protuberances; and it was the belief of my friend, that the original idea of the whole, and, indeed, the fundamental idea of this school of sculpture, was exactly that so emphatically laid down by Milton in the opening argument of his poem—man's fall symbolized by the serpents and the apples, and the great sign of his restoration, by the cross. But in order to indicate that to the divine Man, the Restorer, the cross itself was a consequence of the Fall, even it was covered over with symbols of the event, and, in one curious specimen, built up of them. It was the snakes and apples that had reared, i.e., rendered imperative, the cross. My friend further remarked, that from this main idea a sort of fretwork had originated, which seemed more modern in some of its specimens than the elaborately-carved snakes, and strongly-relieved apples, but in which the twistings of the one, and the circular outlines of the others might be distinctly traced; and that it seemed ultimately to have passed from a symbol into a mere ornament; as, in earlier instances, hieroglyphic pictures had passed into mere arbitrary signs or characters. I know not what may be thought of the theory of William Ross; but when, in visiting, several years ago, the ancient ruins of Iona, I marked, on the more ancient crosses, the snakes and apparent apples, and then saw how the same combination of figures appeared as mere ornamental fretwork on some of the later tombs, I regarded it as more probably the right one than any of the others I have yet seen broached on the subject. I dined with my friend this day on potatoes and salt, flanked by a jug of water; nor were the potatoes by any means very good ones; but they formed the only article of food in the household at the time. He had now dined and breakfasted upon them, he said, for several weeks together; but though not very strengthening, they kept in the spark of life; and he had saved up money enough to carry him to the south of Scotland in the spring, where he trusted to find employment. A poor friendless lad of genius, diluting his thin consumptive blood on bad potatoes and water, and, at the same time, anticipating the labours of our antiquarian societies by his elaborate and truthful drawings of an interesting class of

211

national antiquities, must be regarded as a melancholy object of contemplation; but such hapless geniuses there are in every age in which art is cultivated and literature has its admirers; and, shrinkingly modest and retiring in their natures, the world rarely finds them out in time.

I found employment enough for my leisure during this winter in my books and walks, and in my Uncle James's workshop, which, now that Uncle James had no longer to lecture me about my Latin, and my carelessness as a scholar in general, was a very pleasant place, where a great deal of sound remark and excellent information were always to be had. There was another dwelling in the neighbourhood in which I sometimes spent a not unpleasant hour. It was a damp underground room, inhabited by a poor old woman, who had come to the town from a country parish in the previous year, bringing with her a miserably deformed lad, her son, who, though now turned of twenty, more resembled, save in his head and face, a boy of ten, and who was so helpless a cripple, that he could not move from off his seat. "Poor lame Danie," as he was termed, was, notwithstanding the hard measure dealt him by nature, an even-tempered, kindly-dispositioned lad, and was, in consequence, a great favourite with the young people in the neighbourhood, especially with the humbly taught young women, who—regarding him simply as an intelligence, coupled with sympathies, that could write letters—used to find him employment, which he liked not a little, as a sort of amanuensis and adviser-general in their affairs of the heart. Richardson tells that he learned to write his Pamela by the practice he acquired in writing love-letters when a very young lad, for half a score love-sick females, who trusted and employed him. "Poor Danie," though he bore on a skeleton body, wholly unfurnished with muscle, a brain of the average size and activity, was not born to be a novelist; but he had the necessary materials in abundance; and though secret enough to all his other acquaintance, I, who cared not a great deal about the matter, might, I found, have as many of his experiences as I pleased. I enjoyed among my companions the reputation of being what they termed "close-minded;" and Danie, satisfied, in some sort, that I deserved the character, seemed to find it a relief to roll over upon my shoulders the great weight of confidence which, rather liberally, as would seem, for his comfort, had been laid upon his own. It is recorded of himself by Burns, that he "felt as much pleasure in being in the secret of half the loves of the parish of Tarbolton, as ever did statesman in knowing the intrigues of half the Courts of Europe." And, writing to Dr Moore, he adds, that it was "with difficulty" his pen was "restrained from giving him a couple of paragraphs on the love-adventures of his compeers, the humble inmates of the farm-house and cottage." I, on the other hand, bore my confidences soberly enough, and kept them safe and very close—regarding myself as merely a sort of back-yard of mind, in which Danie might store up at pleasure the precious commodities entrusted to his charge, which, from want of stowage, it cumbered him to keep, but which were his property, not mine. And though, I daresay, I could fill more than "a couple of paragraphs" with the love-affairs of townswomen, some of whose daughters were courted and married ten years ago, I feel no inclination whatever, after having kept their secrets so long, to begin blabbing them now. Danie kept a draft-board, and used to take a pride in beating all his neighbours; but in a short time he taught me—too palpably to his chagrin—to beat himself; and finding the game a rather engrossing one besides, and not caring to look on the woe-begone expression that used to cloud the meek pale face of my poor acquaintance, every time he found his men swept off the board or cooped up into a corner, I gave up drafts, the only game of the kind of which I ever knew anything, and in the course of a few years succeeded in unlearning pretty completely all the moves. It appeared wonderful that the processes essential to life could have been carried on in so miserable a piece of framework as the person of poor Danie: it was simply a human skeleton bent double, and covered with a sallow skin. But they were not carried on in it long. About eighteen months after the first commencement of our acquaintance, when I was many miles away, he was seized by a sudden illness, and died in a few hours. I have seen, in even our better works of fiction, less interesting characters portrayed than poor gentle-spirited Danie, the love-depository of the young dames of the village; and I learned a thing or two in his school.

It was not until after several weeks of the working season had passed that my master's great repugnance to doing nothing overcame his almost equally great repugnance again to seek work as a journeyman. At length, however, a life of inactivity became wholly intolerable to him; and, applying to his former employer, he was engaged on the previous terms—full wages for himself, and a very small allowance for his apprentice, who was now, however, recognised as the readier and more skilful stone-cutter of the two. In cutting mouldings of the more difficult kinds, I had sometimes to take the old man under charge, and give him lessons in the art, from which, however, he had become rather too rigid in both mind and body greatly to profit. We both returned to Conon-side, where there was a tall dome of hewn work to be erected over the main archway of the steading at which we had been engaged during the previous year; and, as few of the workmen had yet assembled on the spot, we succeeded in establishing ourselves as inmates of the barrack, leaving the hay-loft, with its inferior accommodation, to the later comers. We constructed for ourselves a bed-frame of rough slabs, and filled it with hay; placed our chests in front of it; and, as the rats mustered by thousands in the place, suspended our sack of oatmeal by a rope, from one of the naked rafters, at rather more than a man's height over the floor. And, having both pot and pitcher, our household was complete. Though resolved not to forego my evening walks, I had determined to conform also to every practice of the barrack; and as the workmen, drafted from various parts of the country, gradually increased around us, and the place became crowded, I soon found myself engaged in the rollicking barrack-life of the north-country mason. The rats were somewhat troublesome. A comrade who slept in the bed immediately beside ours had one of his ears bitten through one night as he lay asleep, and remarked that he supposed it would be his weasand they would attack next time; and, on rising one morning, I found that the four brightly plated jack-buttons to which my braces had been fastened had been fairly cut from off my trousers, and carried away, to form, I doubt not, a portion of some miser-hoard in the wall. But even the rats themselves became a source of amusement to us, and imparted to our rude domicile, in some little degree, the dignity of danger. It was not likely that they would succeed in eating us all up, as they had done wicked Bishop Hatto of old; but it was at least something that they had begun to try.

The dwellers in the hay-loft had not been admitted in the previous season to the full privileges of the barrack, nor had they been required to share in all its toils and duties. They had to provide their quota of wood for the fire, and of water for general household purposes; but they had not to take their turn of cooking and baking for the entire mess, but were permitted, as convenience served, to cook and bake for themselves. And so, till now, I had made cakes and porridge, with at times an occasional mess of brose or *brochan*, for only my master and myself—a happy arrangement, which, I daresay, saved me a few *rammings*; seeing that, in at least my earlier efforts, I had been rather unlucky as a cook, and not very fortunate as a baker. My experience in the Cromarty caves had rendered me skilful in both boiling and roasting potatoes, and in preparing shell-fish for the table, whether molluscous or crustacean, according to the most approved methods; but the exigencies of our wild life had never brought me fairly in contact with the cerealia; and I had now to spoil a meal or two, in each instance, ere my porridge became palatable, or my cakes crisp, or my brose free and knotty, or my *brochan* sufficiently smooth and void of knots. My master, poor man, did grumble a little at first; but there was a general disposition in the barrack to take part rather with his apprentice than with himself; and after finding that the cases were to be given against him, he ceased making complaints. My porridge was at times, I must confess, very like leaven; but then, it was a standing recipe in the barrack, that the cook should continue stirring the mess and adding meal, until, from its first wild ebullitions in full boil it became silent over the fire; and so I could show that I had made my porridge like leaven quite according to rule. And as for my *brochan*, I succeeded in proving that I had actually failed to satisfy, though I had made two kinds of it at once in the same pot. I preferred this viand when of a thicker consistency than usual, whereas my master liked it thin enough to be drunk out of the bowl; but as it was I who had the making of it, I used more instead of less meal than ordinary, and unluckily, in my first experiment, mixed up the meal in a very small bowl. It became a dense dough-like mass; and on emptying it into the pot, instead of incorporating with the boiling water, it sank in a solid cake to the bottom. In vain I stirred, and manipulated, and kept up the fire. The stubborn mass refused to separate or dilute, and at length burnt brown against the bottom of the pot—a hue which the gruel-like fluid which floated over also assumed; and at length, in utter despair of securing aught approaching to an average consistency for the whole, and hearing my master's foot at the door, I took the pot from off the fire, and dished up for supper a portion of the thinner mixture which it contained, and which, in at least colour and consistency, not a little resembled chocolate. The poor man ladled the stuff in utter dismay. "Od, laddie," he said, "what ca' ye this? Ca' ye this *brochan*?" "Onything ye like, master," I replied; "but there are two kinds in the pot, and it will go hard if none of them please you." I then dished him a piece of the cake, somewhat resembling in size and consistency a small brown dumpling, which he of course found wholly inedible, and became angry. But this bad earth of ours "is filled," according to Cowper, "with wrongs and outrage"; and the barrack laughed and took part with the defaulter. Experience, however, that does so much for all, did a little for me. I at length became a tolerably fair plain cook, and not a very bad baker; and now, when the exigencies required that I should take my full share in the duties of the barrack, I was found adequate to their proper fulfilment. I made cakes and porridge of fully the average excellence; and my brose and *brochan* enjoyed at least the negative happiness of escaping animadversion and comment.

Some of the inmates, however, who were exceedingly nice in their eating, were great connoisseurs in porridge, and it was no easy matter to please them. There existed unsettled differences— the results of a diversity of tastes—regarding the time that should be given to the boiling of the mess, respecting the proportion of salt that should be allotted to each individual, and as to whether the process of "mealing," as it was termed, should be a slow or a hasty one; and, of course, as in all controversies of all kinds, the more the matters in dispute were discussed, the more did they grow in importance. Occasionally the disputants had their porridge made at the same time in the same pot: there were, in especial, two of the workmen who differed upon the degree-of-salt question, whose bickers were supplied from the same general preparation; and as these had usually opposite complaints to urge against the cooking, their objections served so completely to neutralize each other, that they in no degree told against the cook. One morning the cook—a wag and a favourite—in making porridge for both the controversialists, made it so exceedingly fresh as to be but little removed from a poultice; and, filling with the preparation in this state the bicker of the salt-loving connoisseur, he then took a handful of salt, and mixing it with the portion which remained in the pot, poured into the bicker of the fresh man, porridge very much akin to a pickle. Both entered the barrack sharply set for breakfast, and sat down each to his meal; and both at the first spoonfuls dropped their spoons. "A ramming to the cook!" cried the one—"he has given me porridge without salt!" "A ramming to the cook!" roared out the other—"he has given me porridge like brine!" "You see, lads," said the cook, stepping out into the middle of the floor, with the air of a much-injured orator—"you see, lads, what matters have come to at last: there is the very pot in which I made in one mess the porridge in both their bickers. I don't think we should bear this any longer; we have all had our turn of it, though mine happens to be the worst; and I now move that these two fellows be rammed." No sooner said than done. There was a terrible struggling, and a burning sense of injustice; but no single man in the barrack was match for half-a-dozen of the others. The disputants, too, instead of making common cause together, were prepared to assist in ramming each the other; and so rammed they both were. And at length, when the details of the stratagem came out, the cook— by escaping for half an hour into the neighbouring wood, and concealing himself there, like some political exile under ban of the Government—succeeded in escaping the merited punishment.

The cause of justice was never, I found, in greater danger in our little community, than when a culprit succeeded in getting the laughers on his side. I have said that I became a not very bad baker. Still less and less sorely, as I improved in this useful art, did my cakes try the failing teeth of my master, until at length they became crisp and nice; and he began to find that my new accomplishment was working serious effects upon the contents of his meal-chest. With a keenly whetted appetite, and in vigorous health, I was eating a great deal of bread; and, after a good deal of grumbling, he at length laid it down as law that I should restrict myself for the future to two cakes per week. I at once agreed; but the general barrack, to whose ears some of my master's remonstrances had found their way, was dissatisfied; and it would probably have overturned in conclave our agreement, and punished the old man, my master, for the niggardly stringency of his terms, had I not craved, by way of special favour, to be permitted to give them a week's trial. One evening early in the week, when the old man had gone out, I mixed up the better part of a peck of meal in a pot, and placing two of the larger chests together in the same plane, kneaded it out into an enormous cake, at least equal in area to an ordinary-sized Newcastle grindstone. I then cut it up into about twenty pieces, and, forming a vast semi-circle of stone round the fire, raised the pieces to the heat in a continuous row, some five or six feet in length. I had ample and ready assistance vouchsafed me in the "firing"—half the barrack were engaged in the work when my master entered, and after scanning our employment in utter astonishment—now glancing at the ring of meal which still remained on the united chests, to testify to the huge proportions of the disparted bannock, and now at the cones, squares, rhombs, and trapeziums of cake that hardened to the heat in front of the fire, he abruptly asked— "What's this, laddie?—are ye baking for a wadding?" "Just baking one of the two cakes, master," I replied; "I don't think we'll need the other one before Saturday night." A roar of laughter from every corner of the barrack precluded reply; and in the laughter, after an embarrassed pause, the poor man had the good sense to join. And during the rest of the season I baked as often and as much as I pleased. It is, I believe, Goldsmith who remarks, that "wit generally succeeds more from being happily addressed, than from its native poignancy," and that "a jest calculated to spread at a gaming table, may be received with perfect indifference should it happen to drop in a mackerel-boat." On Goldsmith's principle, the joke of what was termed, from the well known fairy tale, "the big bannock wi' the malison," could have perhaps succeeded in only a mason's barrack; but never there at least could joke have been more successful.

As I had not yet ascertained that the Old Red Sandstone of the north of Scotland is richly fossiliferous, Conon-side and its neighbourhood furnished me with no very favourable field for geologic exploration. It enabled me, however, to extend my acquaintance with the great conglomerate base of the system, which forms here, as I have already said, a sort of miniature Highlands, extending between the valleys of the Conon and the Peffer, and which—remarkable for its picturesque cliffs, abrupt eminences and narrow steep-sided dells—bears in its centre a pretty wood-skirted loch, into which the old Celtic prophet Kenneth Ore, when, like Prospero, he relinquished his art, buried "deep beyond plummet sound" the magic stone in which he was wont to see both the distant and the future. Immediately over the pleasure-grounds of Brahan, the rock forms exactly such cliffs as the landscape gardener would make, if he could—cliffs with their rude prominent pebbles breaking the light over every square foot of surface, and furnishing footing, by their innumerable projections, to many a green tuft of moss, and many a sweet little flower; while far below, among the deep woods, there stand up enormous fragments of the same rock, that must have rolled down in some remote age from the precipices above, and which, mossy and hoar, and many of them ivy-bound, resemble artificial ruins—obnoxious, however, to none of the disparaging associations which the make-believe ruin is sure always to awaken. It was inexpressibly pleasant to spend a quiet evening hour among these wild cliffs, and imagine a time when the far distant sea beat against their bases; but though their enclosed pebbles evidently owed their rounded form to the attrition of water, the imagination seemed paralyzed when it attempted calling up a still earlier time, when these solid rocks existed as but loose sand and pebbles, tossed by waves or scattered by currents; and when, for hundreds and thousands of square miles, the wild tract around existed as an ancient ocean, skirted by unknown lands. I had not yet collected enough of geologic fact to enable me to grapple with the difficulties of a restoration of the more ancient time. There was a later period, also, represented in the immediate neighbourhood by a thick deposit of stratified sand, of which I knew as little as of the conglomerate. We dug into it, in founding a thrashing-mill, for about ten feet, but came to no bottom; and I could see that it formed the subsoil of the valley all around the policies of Cononside, and underlay most of its fields and woods. It was white and pure, as if it had been washed by the sea only a few weeks previous; but in vain did I search its beds and layers for a fragment of shell by which to determine its age. I can now, however, entertain little doubt that it belonged to the boulder clay period of submergence, and that the fauna with which it was associated bore the ordinary subarctic character. When this stratified sand was deposited, the waves must have broken against the conglomerate precipices of Brahan, and the sea have occupied, as firths and sounds, the deep Highland valleys of the interior. And on such of the hills of the country as had their heads above water at the time, that interesting but somewhat meagre Alpine Flora must have flourished, which we now find restricted to our higher mountain summits.

Once every six weeks I was permitted to visit Cromarty, and pass a Sabbath there; but as my master usually accompanied me, and as the way proved sufficiently long and weary to press upon his failing strength and stiffening limbs, we had to restrict ourselves to the beaten road, and saw but little. On, however, one occasion this season, I journeyed alone, and spent so happy a day in finding my homeward road along blind paths—that ran now along the rocky shores of the Cromarty Firth in its upper reaches, now through brown, lonely moors, mottled with Danish encampments, and now beside quiet, tomb-besprinkled burying-grounds, and the broken walls of deserted churches—that its memory still lives freshly in my mind, as one of the happiest of my life. I passed whole hours among the ruins of Craighouse—a grey fantastic rag of a castle, consisting of four heavily-arched storeys of time-eaten stone, piled over each other, and still bearing a-top its stone roof and its ornate turrets and bartizans—

> "A ghastly prison, that eternally
> Hangs its blind visage out to the lone sea."

It was said in these days to be haunted by its goblin—a miserable-looking, grey-headed, grey-bearded, little old man, that might be occasionally seen late in the evening, or early in the morning, peering out through some arrow-slit or shot-hole at the chance passenger. I remember getting the whole history of the goblin this day from a sunburnt herd-boy, whom I found tending his cattle under the shadow of the old castle-wall. I began by asking him whose *apparition* he thought it was that could continue to haunt a building, the very name of whose last inhabitant had been long since forgotten. "*Oh, they're saying,*" was the reply, "it's the spirit of the man that was killed on the foundation-stone, just after it was laid, and then built intil the wa' by the masons, that he might *keep* the castle by coming back again; and *they're saying* that a' the verra auld houses in the kintra had murderit men built intil them in that way, and that they have a' o' them their bogle." I recognised in the boy's account of the matter an old and widely-spread tradition, which, whatever may have been its original basis of truth, seems to have so far influenced the buccaneers of the 17th century, as to have become a reality in their hands. "If time," says Sir Walter Scott, "did not permit the buccaneer to lavish away their plunder in their usual debaucheries, they were wont to hide it, with many superstitious solemnities, in the desert islands and *keys* which they frequented, and where much treasure, whose lawless owners perished without reclaiming it, is still supposed to be concealed. The most cruel of mankind are often the most superstitious; and those pirates are said to have had recourse to a horrid ritual, in order to secure an unearthly guardian to their treasures. They killed a negro or Spaniard, and buried him with the treasure, believing that his spirit would haunt the spot, and terrify away all intruders." There is a figurative peculiarity in the language in which Joshua denounced the man who should dare rebuild Jericho, that seems to point at some ancient pagan rite of this kind. Nor does it seem improbable that a practice which existed in times so little remote as those of the buccaneers, may have first begun in the dark and cruel ages of human sacrifices. "Cursed be the man before the Lord," said Joshua, "that riseth up and buildeth this city of Jericho: *he shall lay the foundation thereof in his first-born, and on his youngest son shall he set up the gates of it.*"

The large-farm system had been already introduced into the part of the country in which I at this time resided, on the richer and more levels lands; but many a Gaelic-speaking cottar and small tenant still lived on the neighbouring moors and hill-sides. Though Highland in their surnames and language, they bore a character considerably different from that of the simpler Highlanders of the interior of Sutherland, or of a class I had shortly afterwards an opportunity of studying—the Highlanders of the western coast of Ross-shire. Doors were not left unbarred at night in the neighbourhood; and there were wretched hovels among the moors, very zealously watched and guarded indeed. There was much illicit distillation and smuggling at this time among the Gaelic-speaking people of the district; and it told upon their character with the usual deteriorating effect. Many of the Highlanders, too, had wrought as labourers at the Caledonian Canal, where they had come in contact with south-country workmen, and brought back with them a confident, loquacious smartness, that, based on a ground-work of ignorance, which it rendered active and obtrusive, had a bizarre and disagreeable effect, and formed but an indifferent substitute for the diffident and taciturn simplicity which it had supplanted. But I have ever found the people of those border districts of the Highlands which join on to the low country, or that inhabit districts much traversed by tourists, of a comparatively inferior cast: the finer qualities of the Highland character seem easily injured: the hospitality, the simplicity, the unsuspecting honesty, disappear; and we find, instead, a people rapacious, suspicious and unscrupulous, considerably beneath the Lowland average. In all the unopened districts of the remote Highlands into which I have penetrated, I have found the people strongly engage my sympathies and affections— much more strongly than in any part of the Lowlands; whereas, on the contrary, in the deteriorated districts I have been sensible of an involuntary revulsion of feeling, when in contact with the altered race, of which, among the low-country Scotch or the English, I have had no experience. I remember being impressed, in reading, many years ago, one of Miss Ferrier's novels, with the truth of a stroke that brought out very practically the ready susceptibility of injury manifested by the Celtic character. Some visitors of condition from the Highlands are represented as seeking out in one of our larger towns of the south, a simple Highland lad, who had quitted a remote northern district only a few months before; and when they find him, it is as a prisoner in Bridewell.

Towards the end of September, my master, who had wholly failed in overcoming his repugnance to labour as a mere journey-man, succeeded in procuring a piece of work by contract, in a locality about fourteen miles nearer our home than Conon-side, and I accompanied him to assist in its completion. Our employment in our new scene of labour was of the most disagreeable kind. Burns, who must have had a tolerably extensive experience of the evils of hard work, specifies in his "Twa Dogs" three kinds of labour in especial that give poor "cot-folk" "fash eneugh."

> "Trowth, Cæsar, whiles they're fash'd eneugh;
> A cottar howkin' in a sheugh,
> Wi' dirty stanes biggin' a dyke,
> Baring a quarry, and sic like."

All very disagreeable employments, as I also can testify; and our work here unfortunately combined the whole three. We were engaged in rebuilding one of those old-fashioned walls of gentlemen's pleasure-grounds known as "*ha has*," that line the sides of deep ditches, and raise their tops to but the level of the sward; and as the ditch in this special instance was a wet one, and as we had to clear it of the old fallen materials, and to dig it out for our new line of foundation, while at the same time we had to furnish ourselves with additional materials from a neighbouring quarry, we had at once the "baring of the quarry," the "howkin' in the sheugh," and the "biggin' of the dyke wi' dirty stanes," to "fash" us. The last-named employment is by far the most painful and trying. In most kinds of severe labour the skin thickens, and the hand hardens, through a natural provision, to suit the requirements of the task imposed, and yield the necessary protection to the integuments below; but the "dirty stanes" of the dyke-builder, when wet as well as dirty, try the reproductive powers of the cuticle too severely, and wear it off, so that under the rough friction the quick is laid bare. On this occasion, and on at least one other, when engaged in building in a wet season in the Western Highlands, I had all my fingers oozing blood at once; and those who think that in such circumstances labour protracted throughout a long day can be other than torture, would do well to try. How these poor hands of mine burnt and beat at night at this time, as if an unhappy heart had been stationed in every finger! and what cold chills used to run, sudden as electric shocks, through the feverish frame!

My general health, too, had become far from strong. As I had been almost entirely engaged in hewing for the two previous seasons, the dust of the stone, inhaled at every breath, had exerted the usual weakening effects on the lungs—those effects under which the life of the stone-cutter is restricted to about forty-five years; but it was only now, when working day after day with wet feet in a water-logged ditch, that I began to be sensibly informed, by a dull, depressing pain in the chest, and a blood-stained mucoidal substance, expectorated with difficulty, that I had already caught harm from my employment, and that my term of life might fall far short of the average one. I resolved, however, as the last year of my apprenticeship was fast drawing to its close, to complete, at all hazards, my engagement with my master. It had been merely a verbal engagement, and I might have broken it without blame, when, unable to furnish me with work in his character as a master-mason, he had to transfer my labour to another; but I determined not to break it, all the more doggedly from the circumstance that my uncle James, in a moment of irritation, had said at its commencement that he feared I would no more persist in being a mason that I had done in being a scholar; and so I wrought perseveringly on; and slowly and painfully, rood after rood, the wall grew up under our hands. My poor master, who suffered even more from chopped hands and bleeding fingers than I did, was cross and fretful, and sometimes sought relief in finding fault with his apprentice; but, sobered by my forebodings of an early death, I used to make no reply; and the hasty, ill-tempered expressions in which he gave vent virtually to but his sense of pain and discomfort, were almost always followed by some conciliatory remark. Superstition takes a strong hold of the mind in circumstances such as those in which I was at this time placed. One day when on the top of a tall building, part of which we were throwing down to supply us with materials for our work, I raised up a broad slab of red micaceous sandstone, thin as a roofing slate, and exceedingly fragile, and, holding it out at arm's length, dropped it over the wall. I had been worse than usual all that morning and much depressed; and, ere the slab parted from my hand, I said— looking forward to but a few months of life—I shall break up like that sandstone slab, and perish as little known. But the sandstone slab did not break up: a sudden breeze blew it aslant as it fell; it cleared the rough heap of stones below, where I had anticipated it would have been shivered to fragments; and, lighting on its edge, stuck upright like a miniature obelisk, in the soft green sward beyond. None of the Philosophies or the Logics would have sanctioned the inference which I immediately drew; but that curious chapter in the history of human belief which treats of signs and omens abounds in such postulates and such conclusions. I at once inferred that recovery awaited me: I was "to live and not die;" and felt lighter, during the few weeks I afterwards toiled at this place, under the cheering influence of the conviction.

The tenant of the farm on which our work was situated, and who had been both a great distiller and considerable farmer in his day, had become bankrupt shortly before, and was on the eve of quitting the place, a broken man. And his forlorn circumstances seemed stamped on almost every field and outhouse of his farm. The stone fences were ruinous; the hedges gapped by the almost untended cattle; a considerable sprinkling of corn-ears lay rotting on the lea; and here and there an entire sheaf, that had fallen from the "leading-cart" at the close of harvest, might be seen still lying among the stubble, fastened to the earth by the germination of its grains. Some of the outhouses were miserable beyond description. There was a square of modern offices, in which the cattle and horses of the farm—appropriated by the landlord, at the time under the law of hypothec—were tolerably well lodged; but the hovel in which three of the farm-servants lived, and in which, for want of a better, my master and I had to cook and sleep, was one of the most miserable tumble-down erections I ever saw inhabited. It had formed part of an ancient set of offices that had been condemned about fourteen years before; but the proprietor of the place becoming insolvent, it had been spared, in lack of a better, to accommodate the servants who wrought on the farm; and it had now become not only a comfortless, but also a very unsafe dwelling. It would have formed no bad subject, with its bulging walls and gapped roof, that showed the bare ribs through the breaches, for the pencil of my friend William Ross; but the cow or horse that had no better shelter than that which it afforded could not be regarded as other than indifferently lodged. Every heavier shower found its way through the roof in torrents: I could even tell the hour of the night by the stars which passed over the long opening that ran along the ridge from gable to gable; and in stormy evenings I have paused at every ruder blast, in the expectation of hearing the rafters crack and give way over my head. The distiller had introduced upon his farm, on a small scale, what has since been extensively known as the bothy system; and this hovel was the bothy. There were, as I have said, but three farm-servants who lived in it at the time—young, unmarried lads, extremely ignorant, and of gay, reckless dispositions, whose care for their master's interests might be read in the germinating sheaves that lay upon his fields, and who usually spoke of him, when out of his hearing, as "the old sinner." He too evidently cared nothing for them; and they detested him, and regarded the ruin which had overtaken him, and which their own recklessness and indifference to his welfare must have at least assisted to secure, with open satisfaction. "It was ae comfort, anyhow," they said, "that the blastit old sinner, after a' his near-goingness wi' them, was now but a dyvour, bankrupt." Bad enough certainly; and yet natural enough, and, in a sense, proper enough too. The Christian divine would have urged these men to return their master good for evil. Cobbett, on the contrary, would have advised them to go out at nights a rick-burning. The better advice will to a certainty not be taken by ninety-nine out of every hundred of our bothy-men; for it is one of the grand evils of the system, that it removes its victims beyond the ennobling influences of religion; and, on the other hand, at least this much may be said for the worse counsel, that the system costs the country every year the price of a great many corn-ricks.

The three lads lived chiefly on brose, as the viand at all edible into which their oatmeal could be most readily converted; and never baked or made for themselves a dish of porridge or gruel, apparently to avoid trouble, and that they might be as little as possible in the hated bothy. I always lost sight of them in the evening; but towards midnight their talk frequently awoke me as they were going to bed; and I heard them tell of incidents that had befallen them at the neighbouring farm-houses, or refer to blackguard bits of scandal which they had picked up. Sometimes a fourth voice mingled in the dialogue. It was that of a reckless poacher, who used to come in, always long after nightfall, and fling himself down on a lair of straw in a corner of the bothy; and usually ere day broke he was up and away. The grand enjoyment of the three farm-lads—the enjoyment which seemed to counter-balance, with its concentrated delights, the comfortless monotony of weeks—was a rustic ball which took place once every month, and sometimes oftener, at a public-house in the neighbouring village, and at which they used to meet some of the farm-lassies of the locality, and dance and drink whisky till morning. I know not how their money stood such frequent carousals; but they were, I saw, bare of every necessary article of clothing, especially of underclothing and linen; and I learned from their occasional talk about justice-of-peace summonses, that the previous term-day had left in the hands of their shoemakers and drapers unsettled bills. But such matters were taken very lightly: the three lads, if not happy, were at least merry; and the monthly ball, for which they sacrificed so much, furnished not only its hours of pleasure while it lasted, but also a week's talking in anticipation ere it came, and another week's talking over its various incidents after it had passed. And such was my experience of the bothy system in its first beginnings. It has since so greatly increased, that there are now single counties in Scotland in which there are from five to eight hundred farm-servants exposed to its deteriorating influences; and the rustic population bids fair in those districts fully to rival that of our large towns in profligacy, and greatly to outrival them in coarseness. Were I a statesman, I would, I think, be bold enough to try the efficacy of a tax on bothies. It is long since Goldsmith wrote regarding a state of society in which "wealth accumulates and men decay," and since Burns looked with his accustomed sagacity on that change for the worse in the character of our rural people which the large-farm system has introduced. "A fertile improved country is West Lothian," we find the latter poet remarking in one of his journals, "but the more elegance and luxury among the farmers, I always observe in equal proportion the rudeness and stupidity of the peasantry. This remark I have made all over the Lothians, Merse, Roxburgh, etc.; and for this, among other reasons, I think that a man of romantic taste—'a man of feeling'—will be better pleased with the poverty but intelligent minds of the peasantry of Ayrshire (peasantry they all are, below the Justice of Peace), than the opulence of a club of Merse farmers, when he at the same time considers the Vandalism of their plough-folks." The deteriorating effect of the large-farm system, remarked by the poet, is inevitable. It is impossible that the modern farm-servant, in his comparatively irresponsible situation, and with his fixed wages of meagre amount, can be rendered as thoughtful and provident a person as the small farmer of the last age, who, thrown on his own resources, had to cultivate his fields and drive his bargains with his Martinmas and Whitsunday settlement with the landlord full before him; and who often succeeded in saving money, and in giving a classical education to some promising son or nephew, which enabled the young man to rise to a higher sphere of life. Farm-servants, as a class, *must* be lower in the scale than the old tenant-farmers, who wrought their little farms with their own hands; but it is possible to elevate them far above the degraded level of the bothy; and unless means be taken to check the spread of the ruinous process of brute-making which the system involves, the Scottish people will sink, to a certainty, in the agricultural districts, from being one of the most provident, intelligent, and moral in Europe, to be one of the most licentious, reckless, and ignorant.

Candlelight is a luxury in which no one ever thinks of indulging in a barrack; and in a barrack such as ours at this time, riddled with gaps and breaches, and filled with all manner of cold draughts, it was not every night in which a candle would have burnt. And as our fuel, which consisted of sorely decayed wood— the roofing of a dilapidated outhouse which we were pulling down—formed but a dull fire, it was with difficulty I could read by its light. By spreading out my book, however, within a foot or so of the embers, I was enabled, though sometimes at the expense of a headache, to prosecute a new tract of reading which had just opened to me, and in which, for a time, I found much amusement. There was a vagabond pedlar who travelled at this time the northern counties, widely known as Jack from Dover, but whose true name was Alexander Knox, and who used to affirm that he was of the same family as the great Reformer. The pedlar himself was, however, no reformer. Once every six weeks or two months he got madly drunk, and not only "perished the pack," as he used to say, but sometimes got into prison to boot. There were, however, some kind relations in the south, who always set him up again; and Jack from Dover, after a fortnight of misery, used to appear with the ordinary bulk of merchandise at his back, and continue thriving until he again got drunk. He had a turn for buying and reading curious books, which, after mastering their contents, he always sold again; and he learned to bring them, when of a kind which no one else would purchase, to my mother, and recommend them as suitable for me. Poor Jack was always conscientious in his recommendations. I know not how he contrived to take the exact measure of my tastes in the matter, but suitable for me they invariably were; and as his price rarely exceeded a shilling per volume, and sometimes fell below a sixpence, my mother always purchased, when she could, upon his judgment. I owed to his discrimination my first copy of Bacon's "Wisdom of the Ancients: done into English by Sir Arthur Gorges," and a book to which I had long after occasion to refer in my geological writings— Maillet's "Telliamed"—one of the earlier treatises on the development hypothesis; and he had now procured for me a selection, in one volume, of the poems of Gavin Douglas and Will Dunbar, and another collection in a larger volume, of "Ancient Scottish Poems," from the MSS of George Bannatyne. I had been previously almost wholly unacquainted with the elder Scotch poets. My Uncle James had introduced me, at a very early age, to Burns and Ramsay, and I had found out Fergusson and Tannahill for myself; but that school of Scotch literature which flourished between the reigns of David the Second and James the Sixth had remained to me, until now, well-nigh a *terra incognita*, and I found no little pleasure in exploring the antique recesses which it opened up. Shortly after, I read Ramsay's "Evergreen," the "King's Quair," and the true "Actes and Deides of ye illuster and vailyeand campioun Shyr Wilham Wallace," not modernized, as in my first copy, but in the tongue in which they had been recited of old by Henry the Minstrel: I had previously gloated over Barbour's Bruce; and thus my acquaintance with the old Scots poets, if not very profound, became at least so respectable, that not until many years after did I meet with an individual who knew them equally well.

The strange picturesque allegories of Douglas, and the terse sense and racy humour of Dunbar, delighted me much. As I had to con my way slowly amid the difficulties of a language which was no longer that spoken by my country-folk, I felt as if I were creating the sense which I found; it came gradually out like some fossil of the rock, from which I had laboriously to chip away the enveloping matrix; and in hanging admiringly over it, I thought I perceived how it was that some of my old schoolfellows, who were prosecuting their education at college, were always insisting on the great superiority of the old Greek and Roman writers over the writers of our own country. I could not give them credit for much critical discernment: they were indifferent enough, some of them, to both verse and prose, and hardly knew in what poetry consisted; and yet I believed them to be true to their perceptions when they insisted on what they termed the high excellence of the ancients. With my old schoolfellows, I now said, the process of perusal, when reading an English work of classical standing, is so sudden, compared with the slowness with which they imagine or understand, that they slide over the surface of their author's numbers, or of his periods, without acquiring a due sense of what lies beneath; whereas, in perusing the works of a Greek or Latin author, they have just to do what I am doing in deciphering the "Palice of Honour" or the "Goldin Terge"—they have to proceed slowly, and to render the language of their author into the language of their own thinking. And so, losing scarce any of its meaning in consequence, and not reflecting on the process through which they have entered into it, they contrast the little which they gain from a hurried perusal of a good English book, with the much which they gain from the very leisurely perusal of a good Latin or Greek one; and term *the little* the poverty of modern writers, and *the much* the fertility of the ancients. Such was my theory, and it was at least not an uncharitable one to my acquaintance. I was, however, arrested in the middle of my studies by a day of soaking rain, which so saturated with moisture the decayed spongy wood, our fuel, that, though I succeeded in making with some difficulty such fires of it as sufficed to cook our victuals, it defied my skill to make one by which I could read. At length, however, this dreary season of labour—by far the gloomiest I ever spent— came to a close, and I returned with my master to Cromarty about Martinmas, our heavy job of work completed, and my term of apprenticeship at a close.

CHAPTER XII

"Far let me wander down thy craggy shore,
With rocks and trees bestrewn, dark Loch Maree."—SMALL.

THE restorative powers of a constitution which at this time it took much hard usage to injure, came vigorously into operation on my removal from the wet ditch and the ruinous hovel; and ere the close of winter I had got once more into my ordinary state of robust health. I read, wrote, drew, corresponded with my friend William Ross (who had removed to Edinburgh), re-examined the Eathie Lias, and re-explored the Eathie Burn—a noble Old Red Sandstone ravine, remarkable for the wild picturesqueness of its cliffs and the beauty of its cataracts. I spent, too, many an evening in Uncle James's workshop, on better terms with both my uncles than almost ever before—a consequence, in part, of the sober complexion which, as the seasons passed, my mind was gradually assuming, and in part, of the manner in which I had completed my engagement with my master. "Act always," said Uncle James, "as you have done in this matter. In all your dealings, give your neighbour the *cast of the bauk*—'good measure, heaped up and running over'—and you will not lose by it in the end." I certainly did not lose by faithfully serving out my term of apprenticeship. It is not uninstructive to observe how strangely the public are led at times to attach paramount importance to what is in reality only subordinately important, and to pass over the really paramount without thought or notice. The destiny in life of the skilled mechanic is much more influenced, for instance, by his second education—that of his apprenticeship—than by his first—that of the school; and yet it is to the education of the school that the importance is generally regarded as attaching, and we never hear of the other. The careless, incompetent scholar has many opportunities of recovering himself; the careless, incompetent apprentice, who either fails to serve out his regular time, or who, though he fulfils his term, is discharged an inferior workman, has very few; and further, nothing can be more certain than that inferiority as a workman bears much more disastrously on the condition of the mechanic than inferiority as a scholar. Unable to maintain his place among brother journeymen, or to render himself worthy of the average wages of his craft, the ill-taught mechanic falls out of regular employment, subsists precariously for a time on occasional jobs, and either, forming idle habits, becomes a vagabond *tramper*, or, getting into the toils of some rapacious task-master, becomes an enslaved *sweater*. For one workman injured by neglect of his school-education, there are scores ruined by neglect of their apprenticeship-education. Three-fourths of the distress of the country's mechanics (of course not reckoning that of the unhappy class who have to compete with machinery), and nine-tenths of their vagabondism, will be found restricted to inferior workmen, who, like Hogarth's "careless apprentice," neglected the opportunities of their second term of education. The sagacious painter had a truer insight into this matter than most of our modern educationists.

My friend of the Doocot Cave had been serving a short apprenticeship to a grocer in London during the latter years in which I had been working out mine as a stone-mason in the north country; and I now learned that he had just returned to his native place, with the intention of setting up in business for himself. To those who move in the upper walks, the superiority in status of the village shop-keeper over the journeyman mason may not be very perceptible; but, surveyed from the lower levels of society, it is quite considerable enough to be seen; even Gulliver could determine that the Emperor of Lilliput was taller by almost the breadth of a nail than any of his Court; and, though extremely desirous of renewing my acquaintanceship with my old friend, I was sensible enough of his advantage over me in point of position, to feel that the necessary advances should be made on his part, not on mine. I, however, threw myself in his way, though after a manner so fastidiously proud and jealous, that even yet, every time the recollection crosses me, it provokes me to a smile. On learning that he was engaged at the quay in superintending the landing of some goods, for, I suppose, his future shop, I assumed the leathern apron, which I had thrown aside for the winter at Martinmas, and stalked past him in my working dress—a veritable operative mason—eyeing him steadfastly as I passed. He looked at me for a moment; and then, without sign of recognition, turned indifferently away. I failed taking into account that he had never seen me girt with a leathern apron before—that, since we had last parted, I had grown more than half a foot—and that a young man of nearly five feet eleven inches, with an incipient whisker palpably visible on his cheek, might be a different-looking sort of person from a smooth-chinned stripling of little more than five feet three. And certainly my friend, as I learned from him nearly three years after, failed on this occasion to recognise me. But believing that he did, and that he did not choose to reckon among his friends a humble working man, I returned to my home very sad, and I am afraid, not a little angry; and, locking up the supposed slight in my breast, as of too delicate a nature to be communicated to any one, for more than two years from this time I did not again cross his path.

I was now my own master, and commenced work as a journeyman on behalf of one of my maternal aunts—the aunt who had gone so many years before to live with her aged relative, the cousin of my father and the mother of his first wife. Aunt Jenny had resided for many years after this time with an aged widow lady, who had lived apart in quiet gentility on very small means; and now that she was dead, my aunt saw her vocation gone, and wished that she too could live apart, a life of humble independency, supporting herself by her spinning-wheel, and by now and then knitting a stocking. She feared, however, to encounter the formidable drain on her means of a half-yearly room-rent; and, as there was a little bit of ground at the head of the strip of garden left me by my father, which bordered on a road that, communicating between town and country, bore, as is common in the north of Scotland, the French name of the *Pays*, it occurred to me that I might try my hand, as a skilled mechanic, in erecting upon it a cottage for Aunt Jenny. Masons have, of course, more in their power in the way of house-building than any other class of mechanics. It was necessary, however, that there should be money provided for the purchase of wood for the roof, and for the carting of the necessary stones and mortar; and I had none. But aunt Jenny had saved a few pounds, and a very few proved sufficient; and so I built a cottage in the *Pays*, of a single room and a closet, as my first job, which, if not very elegant, or of large accommodation, came fully up to Aunt Jenny's ideas of comfort, and which, for at least a quarter of a century, has served her as a home. It was complete before Whitsunday, and then I deliberated on setting myself to seek after employment of a more remunerative kind, with just a little of the feeling to which we owe one of the best-known elegiac poems in the language—the "Man was made to mourn" of Burns. "There is nothing that gives me a more mortifying picture of human life," said the poet, "than a man seeking work." The required work, however, came direct in my way without solicitation, and exactly at the proper time. I was engaged to assist in hewing a Gothic gateway among the woods of my old haunt, Conon-side; and was then despatched, when the work was on the eve of being finished, to provide materials for building a house on the western coast of Ross-shire. My new master had found me engaged in the previous season amid the wild turmoil of the barrack, in studying practical geometry, and had glanced approvingly over a series of architectural drawings which I had just completed; and he now sought me out in consequence, and placed me in charge of a small party which he despatched in advance of his other workmen, and which I was instructed to increase, by employing a labourer or two on arriving at the scene of our future employment.

We were to be accompanied by a carter from a neighbouring

town; and on the morning fixed for the commencement of our journey, his cart and horse were early at Conon-side, to carry across the country the tools required at our new job; but of himself we saw no trace; and about ten o'clock we set off without him. Ascertaining, however, when about two miles on our way, that we had left behind us a lever useful in the setting of large stones, I bade my companion wait for me at the village of Contin, where we expected meeting the carter; and, returning for the tool, I quitted the high road on finding it, and, to save time, and avoid a detour of about three miles, struck across the country direct on the village. My way was, however, a very rough one; and in coming upon the Conon, which it was necessary I should ford— for by avoiding the detour I had missed the bridge—I found it tolerably heavy in flood. Save for the iron lever which I carried, I would have selected, as my point of crossing, one of the still deep pools, as much safer to a vigorous swimmer than any of the apparent fords, with their powerful currents, whirling eddies, and rough bottoms. But though the heroes of antiquity—men such as Julius Caesar and Horatius Cocles—could swim across rivers and seas in heavy armour, the specific gravity of the human subject in these latter ages of the world forbids such feats; and, concluding that I had not levity enough in my framework to float across the lever, I selected, with some hesitation, one of the better-looking fords, and, with my trousers dangling from the iron beam on my shoulder, entered the river. Such was the arrowy swiftness of the current, however, that the water had scarce reached my middle when it began to hollow out the stones and gravel from under my feet, and to bear me down per force in a slanting direction. There was a foaming rapid just at hand; and immediately beyond, a deep, dark pool, in which the chafed current whirled around, as if exhausting the wrath aroused by its recent treatment among rocks and stones, ere recovering its ordinary temper; and had I lost footing, or been carried a little further down, I know not how it might have fared with me in the wild foaming descent that lay between the ford and the pool. Curiously enough, however, the one idea which, in the excitement of the moment, filled my mind, was an intensely ludicrous one. I would, of course, lose not only the lever in the torrent, but my trousers also; and how was I ever to get home without them? Where, in the name of wonder, should I get a kilt to borrow? I have oftener than once experienced this strange sensation of the ludicrous in circumstances with which a different feeling would have harmonized better. Byron represents it as rising in extreme grief: it is, however, I suspect, greatly more common in extreme danger; and all the instances which the poet himself gives in his note—Sir Thomas More on the scaffold, Anne Boleyn in the Tower, and those victims of the French Revolution "with whom it became a fashion to leave some *mot* as a legacy"— were all jokes rather in circumstances of desperate and hopeless peril than of sorrow. It is, however, in danger, as certainly as in grief, a joyless sort of mirth.

> "That playfulness of sorrow ne'er beguiles;
> It smiles in bitterness; but still it smiles,
> And sometimes with the wisest and the best,
> Till even the scaffold echoes with their jest."

The feeling, however, though an inharmoniously toned, is not a weakening one. I laughed in the stream, but I did not yield to it; and, making a violent effort, when just on the edge of the rapid, I got into stiller water, and succeeded in making my way to the opposite bank, drenched to the arm-pits. It was in nearly the same reach of the Conon that my poor friend the maniac of Ord lost her life a few days after.

I found my companion in charge of the cart with our tools, baiting at an inn a little beyond Contin; but there was no sign of the carter; and we were informed by the innkeeper, to whom he was well known, that we might have to wait for him all day, and perhaps not see him at night. Click-Clack—a name expressive of the carter's fluency as a talker, by which he was oftener designated than by the one in the parish register—might no doubt have purposed in the morning joining us at an early hour, but that was when he was sober; and what his intention might be now, said the innkeeper, when in all probability he was drunk, no living man could say. This was rather startling intelligence to men who had a long journey through a rough country before them; and my comrade—a lad a year or two older than myself, but still an apprentice—added to my dismay by telling me he had been sure from the first there was something wrong with Click-Clack, and that his master had secured his services, not from choice, but simply because, having thoughtlessly become surety for him at a sale for the price of a horse, and being left to pay for the animal, he had now employed him, in the hope of getting himself reimbursed. I resolved, however, on waiting for the carter until the last moment after which it would be possible for us to reach our ultimate stage without perilously encroaching on the night; and, taking it for granted that he would not very soon join us, I set out for a neighbouring hill, which commands an extensive view, to take note of the main features of a district with which I had formed, during the two previous years, not a few interesting associations, and to dry my wetted clothes in the breeze and the sun. The old tower of Fairburn formed one of the most striking objects in the prospect; and the eye expatiated beyond from where the gneiss region begins, on a tract of broken hill and brown moor, uncheered by a single green field or human dwelling. There are traditions that, in their very peculiarity, and remoteness from the tract of ordinary invention, give evidence of their truth; and I now called up a tradition, which I owed to my friend the maniac, respecting the manner in which the Mackenzies of Fairburn and the Chisholms of Strathglass had divided this barren tract between them. It had lain, from the first settlement of the country, an unappropriated waste, and neither proprietor could tell where his own lands terminated, or those of his neighbour began; but finding that the want of a proper line of demarcation led to quarrels between their herdsmen when baiting in their summer shielings[1] with their cattle, they agreed to have the tract divided. The age

[1] Temporary dwellings on the hill pastures where the cattle are fed for about two months in the summer.

of land-surveyors had not yet come; but, selecting two old women of seventy-five, they sent them out at the same hour, to meet among the hills, the one from Fairburn Tower, and the other from Erchless Castle, after first binding themselves to accept their place of meeting as the point at which to set up the boundary-stone of the two properties. The women, attended by a bevy of competent witnesses, journeyed as if for life and death; but the Fairburn woman, who was the laird's foster-mother, either more zealous or more active than the Chisholm one, travelled nearly two miles for her one; and when they came in sight of each other in the waste, it was far from the fields of Fairburn, and comparatively at no great distance from those of the Chisholm. It is not easy knowing why they should have regarded one another in the light of enemies; but at a mile's distance their flagging pace quickened into a run, and, meeting at a narrow rivulet, they would fain have fought; but lacking, in their utter exhaustion, strength for fighting and breath for scolding, they could only seat themselves on the opposite banks, and *girn* at one another across the stream. George Cruikshank has had at times worse subjects for his pencil. It is, I believe, Landor, in one of his "imaginary conversations," who makes a Highland laird inform Adam Smith that, desirous to ascertain, in some sort of conceivable degree, the size of his property, he had placed a line of pipers around it, each at such a distance from his nearest neighbour that he could barely catch the sound of his bagpipe; and that from the number of pipers required he was able to form an approximate estimate of the extent of his estate. And here, in a Highland tradition, genuine at least as such, are we introduced to an expedient of the kind scarce less ludicrous or inadequate than that which Landor must, in one of his humorous moods, have merely imagined.

I returned to the inn at the hour from which, as I have said, it would be possible for us, and not more than possible, to complete our day's journey; and finding, as I had anticipated, no trace of Click-Clack, we set off without him. Our way led us through long moory straths, with here and there a blue lake and birch wood, and here and there a group of dingy cottages and of irregular fields; but the general scenery was that of the prevailing schistose gneiss of the Scotch Highlands, in which rounded confluent hills stand up over long withdrawing valleys, and imposing rather from its bare and lonely expansiveness, than from aught bold or striking in its features. The district had been opened up only a few seasons previous by the Parliamentary road over which we travelled, and was at that time little known to the tourist; and the thirty years which have since passed have in some respects considerably changed it, as they have done the Highlands generally. Most of the cottages, when I last journeyed the way, were represented by but broken ruins, and the fields by mossy patches that remained green amid the waste. I marked at one spot an extraordinary group of oak-trees, in the last stage of decay, which would have attracted notice from their great bulk and size in even the forests of England. The largest of the group lay rotting upon the ground—a black, doddered shell, fully six feet in diameter, but hollow as a tar-barrel; while the others, some four or five in number, stood up around it, totally divested of all their larger boughs, but green with leaves, that, from the minuteness of the twigs on which they grew, wrapped them around like close-fitting mantles. Their period of "tree-ship"—to borrow a phrase from Cowper—must have extended far into the obscure past of Highland history—to a time, I doubt not, when not a few of the adjacent peat mosses still lived as forests, and when some of the neighbouring clans—Frasers, Bissets, and Chisholms—had, at least under the existing names (French and Saxon in their derivation), not yet begun to be. Ere we reached the solitary inn of Auchen-nasheen—a true Highland clachan of the ancient type—the night had fallen dark and stormy for a night in June; and a grey mist which had been descending for hours along the hills—blotting off their brown summits bit by bit, as an artist might his pencilled hills with a piece of India rubber, but which, methodical in its encroachments, had preserved in its advances a perfect horizontality of line—had broken into a heavy, continuous rain. As, however, the fair weather had lasted us till we were within a mile of our journey's end, we were only partially wet on our arrival, and soon succeeded in drying ourselves in front of a noble turf fire. My comrade would fain have solaced himself, after our weary journey, with something nice. He held that a Highland inn should be able to furnish at least a bit of mutton-ham or a cut of dried salmon, and ordered a few slices first of ham, and then of salmon; but his orders served merely to perplex the landlord and his wife, whose stores seemed to consist of only oatmeal and whisky; and, coming down in his expectations and demands, and intimating that he was very hungry, and that anything edible would do, we heard the landlady inform, with evident satisfaction, a red-armed wench, dressed in blue plaiding, that "the lads would take porridge." The porridge was accordingly prepared; and, when engaged in discussing this familiar viand, a little before midnight—for we had arrived late—a tall Highlander entered the inn, dripping like a mill-wheel. He was charged, he said, with messages to the landlord, and to two mason lads in the inn, from a forlorn carter with whom he had travelled about twenty miles, but who, knocked up by the "drap drink" and a pair of bad shoes, had been compelled to shelter for the night in a cottage about seven miles short of Auchennasheen. The carter's message to the landlord was simply to the effect that the two mason lads having stolen his horse and cart, he instructed him to detain his property for him until he himself should come up in the morning. As for his message to the lads, said the Highlander, "it was no meikle worth gaun o'er again; but if we liked to buckle on a' the Gaelic curses to a' the English ones, it would be something like that."

We were awakened next morning by a tremendous hubbub in the adjoining apartment. "It is Click-Clack the carter," said my comrade: "Oh, what shall we do?" We leaped up; and getting into our clothes in doubly-quick time, set ourselves to reconnoitre through the crannies of a deal partition, and saw the carter standing in the middle of the next room, storming furiously, and the landlord, a smooth-spoken, little old man, striving hard to conciliate him. Click-Clack was a rough-looking fellow, turned of forty, of about five feet ten, with a black unshaven beard, like a shoe-brush stuck under his nose, which was red as a coal, and attired in a sadly-breached suit of Aberdeen grey, topped by a brimless hat, that had been borrowed, apparently, from some obliging scarecrow. I measured him in person and expression; and, deeming myself his match, even unassisted by my comrade, on whose discretion I could calculate with more certainty than on his valour, I entered the apartment and taxed him with gross dereliction of duty. He had left us to drive his horse and cart for a whole day, and had broken, for the sake of his wretched indulgence in the public-house, his engagement with our master; and I would report him to a certainty. The carter turned upon me with the fierceness of a wild beast; but, first catching his eye, as I would that of a maniac, I set my face very near his, and he calmed down in a moment. He could not help being late, he said; he had reached the inn at Contin not an hour after we had left it; and it was really very hard to have to travel a long day's journey in such bad shoes. We accepted his apology; and, ordering the landlord to bring in half a mutchkin of whisky, the storm blew by. The morning, like the previous night, had been thick and rainy; but it gradually cleared up as the day rose; and after breakfast we set out together along a broken footpath, never before traversed by horse and cart. We passed a solitary lake, on whose shores the only human dwelling was a dark turf shieling, at which, however, Click-Clack ascertained there was whisky to be sold; and then entered upon a tract of scenery wholly different in its composition and character from that through which our journey had previously lain.

There runs along the west coast of Scotland, from the island of Rum to the immediate neighbourhood of Cape Wrath, a formation, laid down by Macculloch, in his Geological Map of the Kingdom, as Old Red Sandstone[1] but which underlies formations

---

[1] The Cambrian Sandstones, etc., of the West coast are in fact vastly older than the "Old Red" of the East. John Macculloch's (1773-1835) *Geological Map of Scotland* appeared posthumously in 1836.

deemed primary—two of these of quartz rock, and a third of that unfossiliferous limestone in which the huge Cave of Smoo is hollowed, and to which the Assynt marbles belong. The system, which taken as a whole—quartz-rock, lime, and sandstone—corresponds bed for bed with the Lower Old Red of the east coast, and is probably a highly metamorphic example of that great deposit, exhibits its fullest development in Assynt, where all its four component beds are present. In the tract on which we now entered, it presents only two of these—the lower quartz-rock, and the underlying red sandstone; but wherever any of its members appear, they present unique features—marks of enormous denudation, and a bold style of landscape altogether its own; and, in now entering upon it for the first time, I was much impressed by its extraordinary character. Loch Maree, one of the wildest of our Highland lakes, and at this time scarce at all known to the tourist, owes to it all that is peculiar in its appearance—its tall pyramidal quartz mountains, that rise at one stride, steep, and well-nigh as naked as the old Pyramids, from nearly the level of the sea, to heights on which at midsummer snows of the winter gleam white in streaks and patches; and a picturesque sandstone tract of precipitous hills, which flanks its western shore, and bore at this period the remains of one of the old pine forests. A continuous wall of gneiss mountains, that runs along the eastern side of the lake, sinks sheer into its brown depths, save at one point, where a level tract, half-encircled by precipices, is occupied by fields and copsewood, and bears in the midst a white mansion-house; the blue expanse of the lake greatly broadens in its lower reaches; and a group of partially submerged hillocks, that resemble the forest-covered ones on its western shores, but are of lower altitude, rise over its waters, and form a miniature archipelago, grey with lichened stone, and bosky with birch and hazel. Finding at the head of the loch that no horse and cart had ever forced their way along its sides, we had to hire a boat for the transport of at least cart and baggage; and when the boatmen were getting ready for the voyage, which was, with the characteristic dilatoriness of the

district, a work of hours, we baited at the clachan of Kinlochewe—
a humble Highland inn, like that in which we had passed the
night. The name—that of an old farm which stretches out along
the *head* or upper end of the Loch Maree—has a remarkable
etymology: it means simply the *head* of Loch Ewe—the salt-water
loch into which the waters of Loch Maree empty themselves by
a river little more than a mile in length, and whose present *head*
is some sixteen or twenty miles distant from the farm which bears
its name. Ere that last elevation of the land, however, to which
our country owes the level marginal strip that stretches between
the present coast-line and the ancient one, the sea must have found
its way to the old farm. Loch Maree (Mary's Loch),[1] a name
evidently of mediaeval origin, would then have existed as a
prolongation of the marine Loch Ewe, and *Kinlochewe* would have
actually been what the compound words signify—the head of
Loch Ewe. There seems to be reason for holding that, ere the latest
elevation of the land took place in our island, it had received its
first human inhabitants—rude savages, who employed tools and
weapons of stone, and fashioned canoes out of single logs of wood.
Are we to accept etymologies such as the instanced one—and there
are several such in the Highlands—as good, in evidence that these
aboriginal savages were of the Celtic race, and that Gaelic was
spoken in Scotland at a time when its strips of grassy links, and
the sites of many of its seaport towns, such as Leith, Greenock,
Musselburgh, and Cromarty, existed as oozy sea-beaches, covered
twice every day by the waters of the ocean?

It was a delightful evening—still, breathless, clear—as we
swept slowly across the broad breast of Loch Maree; and the red
light of the sinking sun fell on many a sweet wild recess, amid
the labyrinth of islands purple with heath, and overhung by the
birch and mountain-ash; or slanted along the broken glades of the
ancient forest; or lighted up into a blush the pale stony faces of
the tall pyramidal hills. A boat bearing a wedding party was
crossing the lake to the white house on the opposite side, and a

[1] No: Maree is a form of "Malruba," an ancient Ross-shire saint.

piper stationed in the bows, was discoursing sweet music, that, softened by distance, and caught up by the echoes of the rocks, resembled no strain I had ever heard from the bagpipe before. Even the boatmen rested on their oars, and I had just enough of Gaelic to know that they were remarking how very beautiful it was. "I wish," said my comrade, "you understood these men: they have a great many curious stories about the loch, that I am sure you would like. See you that large island? It is Island-Maree. There is, they tell me, an old burying-ground on it, in which the Danes used to bury long ages ago, and whose ancient tomb-stones no man can read. And yon other island beside it is famous as the place in which the *good* people meet every year to make submission to their queen. There is, they say, a little loch in the island, and another little island in the loch; and it is under a tree on that inner island that the queen sits and gathers kain[1] for the Evil One. They tell me that, for certain, the fairies have not left this part of the country yet." We landed, a little after sunset, at the point from which our road led across the hills to the sea-side, but found that the carter had not yet come up; and at length, despairing of his appearance, and unable to carry off his cart and the luggage with us, as we had succeeded in bringing off cart, horse, and luggage on the previous day, we were preparing to take up our night's lodging under the shelter of an overhanging crag, when we heard him coming soliloquizing through the wood, in a manner worthy of his name, as if he were not one, but twenty carters. "What a perfect shame of a country!" he exclaimed—"perfect shame! Road for a horse, forsooth!—more like a turnpike stair. And not a feed of corn for the poor beast; and not a public-house atween this and Kinlochewe; and not a drop of whisky: perfect, perfect shame of a country!" On his coming up, in apparently very bad humour, we found him disposed to transfer the shame of the country to our shoulders. What sort of people were we, he asked, to travel in such a land without whisky! Whisky, however, there was none to produce: there was no whisky nearer, we told him, than the public-

[1] An ancient Celtic form of rent or tax paid from the produce of a farm.

house at the sea-side, where we proposed spending the night; and, of course, the sooner we got there the better. And after assisting him to harness his horse, we set off in the darkening twilight, amid the hills. Rough grey rocks, and little blue lochans, edged with flags, and mottled in their season with water-lilies, glimmered dim and uncertain in the imperfect light as we passed; but ere we reached the inn of Flowerdale in Gairloch, every object stood out clear, though cold, in the increscent light of morning; and a few light streaks of cloud, poised in the east over the unrisen sun, were gradually exchanging their gleam of pale bronze for a deep flush of mingled blood and fire.

After the refreshment of a few hours' sleep and a tolerable breakfast, we set out for the scene of our labours, which lay on the sea-shore, about two miles further to the north and west; and were shown an outhouse—one of a square of dilapidated offices—which we might fit up, we were told, for our barrack. The building had been originally what is known on the northwestern coast of Scotland, with its ever-weeping climate, as a hay-barn; but it was now merely a roof-covered tank of green stagnant water, about three-quarters of a foot in depth, which had oozed through the walls from an over-gorged pond in the adjacent court, that in a tract of recent rains had overflowed its banks, and not yet subsided. Our new house did look exceedingly like a beaver-dam, with this disadvantageous difference, that no expedient of diving could bring us to better chambers on the other side of the wall. My comrade, setting himself to sound the abyss with his stick, sung out in sailor style, "three feet water in the hold." Click-Clack broke into a rage: "That a dwelling for human creatures!" he said. "If I was to put my horse intil't, poor beast! the very hoofs would rot off him in less than a week. Are we eels or puddocks,[1] that we are sent to live in a loch?" Marking, however, a narrow portion of the ridge which dammed up the waters of the neighbouring pool, whence our domicile derived its supply, I set myself to cut it across, and had soon the satisfaction of seeing the general surface lowered

[1] Frogs or toads.

fully a foot, and the floor of our future dwelling laid bare. Click-Clack, gathering courage as he saw the waters ebbing away, seized a shovel, and soon showed us the value of his many years' practice in the labours of the stable; and then, despatching him for a few cart-loads of a dry shell-sand from the shore, which I had marked by the way as suitable for mixing with our lime, we had soon for our tank of green water a fine white floor. "Man wants but little here below," especially in a mason's barrack. There were two square openings in the apartment, neither of them furnished with frame or glass; but the one we filled up with stone, and an old unglazed frame, which, with the assistance of a base and border of turf, I succeeded in fitting into the other, gave at least an air of respectability to the place. Boulder stones, capped with pieces of mossy turf, served us for seats; and we had soon a comfortable peat fire blazing against the gable; but we were still sadly in want of a bed; the fundamental damp of the floor was, we saw, fast gaining on the sand; and it would be neither comfortable nor safe to spread our dried grass and blankets over *it*. My comrade went out to see whether the place did not furnish materials enough of any kind to make a bedstead, and soon returned in triumph, dragging after him a pair of harrows, which he placed side by side in a snug corner beside the fire, with of course the teeth downwards. A good Catholic, prepared to win heaven for himself by a judicious use of sharp points, might have preferred having them turned the other way; but my comrade was an enlightened Protestant; and besides, like Goldsmith's sailor, he loved to lie soft. The second piece of luck was mine. I found lying unclaimed in the yard an old barn-door, which a recent gale had blown from off its hinges; and by placing it above the harrows, and driving a row of stakes around it into the floor, to keep the outer sleeper from rolling off—for the wall served to secure the position of the inner one—we succeeded in constructing, by our joint efforts, a luxurious bed. There was but one serious drawback on its comforts: the roof overhead was bad, and there was an obstinate drop, that used, during every shower which fell in the season of sleep, to

248

make a dead set at my face, and try me at times with the water torture of the old story, mayhap half a dozen times in the course of a single night.

Our barrack fairly fitted up, I set out with my comrade, whose knowledge of Gaelic enabled him to act as my interpreter, to a neighbouring group of cottages, to secure a labourer for the work of the morrow. The evening was now beginning to darken; but there was still light enough to show me that the little fields I passed though on my way resembled very much those of Lilliput, as described by Gulliver. They were, however, though equally small, greatly more irregular, and had peculiarities, too, altogether their own. The land had originally been stony; and as it showed, according to the Highland phrase, its "bare bones through its skin"—large bosses of the rock beneath coming here and there to the surface—the Highlanders had gathered the stones in great pyramidal heaps on the bare bosses; and so very numerous were these in some of the fields, that they looked as if some malignant sorcerer had, in the time of harvest, converted all their shocks into stone. On approaching the cottage of our future labourer, I was attracted by a door of very peculiar construction that lay against the wall. It had been brought from the ancient pine forest on the western bank of Loch Maree, and was formed of the roots of trees so curiously interlaced by nature, that when cut out of the soil, which it had covered over like a piece of network, it remained firmly together, and now formed a door which the mere imitator of the rustic might in vain attempt to rival. We entered the cottage, and plunging downwards two feet or so, found ourselves upon the dunghill of the establishment, which in this part of the country usually occupied at the time an ante-chamber which corresponded to that occupied by the cattle a few years earlier, in the midland districts of Sutherland. Groping in this foul outer chamber though a stifling atmosphere of smoke, we came to an inner door raised to the level of the soil outside, through which a red umbry gleam escaped into the darkness; and, climbing into the inner apartment, we found ourselves in the presence of the inmates of the mansion. The fire, as in the cottage of my Sutherlandshire relative, was placed in the middle of the floor: the master of the mansion, a red-haired, strongly-built Highlander, of the middle size and age, with his son, a boy of twelve, sat on the one side; his wife, who, though not much turned of thirty, had the haggard, drooping cheeks, hollow eyes, and pale, sallow complexion of old age, sat on the other. We broke our business to the Highlander through my companion—for, save a few words caught up at school by the boy, there was no English in the household—and found him disposed to entertain it favourably. A large pot of potatoes hung suspended over the fire, under a dense ceiling of smoke; and he hospitably invited us to wait supper, which, as our dinner had consisted of but a piece of dry oaten cake, we willingly did. As the conversation went on, I became conscious that it turned upon myself, and that I was an object of profound commiseration to the inmates of the cottage. "What," I inquired of my companion, "are these kind people pitying me so very much for?" "For your want of Gaelic, to be sure. How can a man get on in the world that wants Gaelic?" "But do not they themselves," I asked, "want English?" "O yes," he said, "but what does that signify? What is the use of English in Gairloch?" The potatoes, with a little ground salt, and much unbroken hunger as sauce, ate remarkably well. Our host regretted that he had no fish to offer us; but a tract of rough weather had kept him from sea, and he had just exhausted his previous supply; and as for bread, he had used up the last of his grain crop a little after Christmas, and had been living, with his family, on potatoes, with fish when he could get them, ever since.

Thirty years have now passed since I shared in the Highlander's evening meal, and during the first twenty of these, the use of the potato—unknown in the Highlands a century before—greatly increased. I have been told by my maternal grandfather, that about the year 1740, when he was a boy of about eight or nine years of age, the head-gardener at Balnagown Castle used, in his occasional visits to Cromarty, to bring him in his pocket, as great rarities, some three or four potatoes; and that it was not until some fifteen or twenty years after this time that he saw potatoes reared in fields in any part of the Northern Highlands. But, once fairly employed as food, every season saw a greater breadth of them laid down. In the North-western Highlands, in especial, the use of these roots increased from the year 1801 to the year 1846 nearly a hundredfold, and came at length to form, as in Ireland, not merely the staple, but in some localities almost the only food of the people; and when destroyed by disease in the latter year, famine immediately ensued in both Ireland and the Highlands. A writer in the *Witness*, whose letter had the effect of bring that respectable paper under the eye of Mr Punch, represented the Irish famine as a direct judgment on the Maynooth Endowment; while another writer, a member of the Peace Association—whose letter did not find its way into the *Witness*, though it reached the editor—challenged the decision on the ground that the Scotch Highlanders, who were greatly opposed to Maynooth, suffered from the infliction nearly as much as the Irish themselves, and that the offence punished must have been surely some one of which both Highlanders and Irish had been guilty in common. He, however, had found out, he said, what the crime visited actually was. Both the Irish and Highland famines were judgments upon the people for their great homicidal efficiency as soldiers in the wars of the empire—an efficiency which, as he truly remarked, was almost equally characteristic of both nations. For my own part, I have been unable hitherto to see the steps which conduct to such profound conclusions; and am content simply to hold, that the superintending Providence who communicated to man a calculating, foreseeing nature, does occasionally get angry with him, and inflict judgments upon him, when, instead of exercising his faculties, he sinks to a level lower than his own, and becomes content, like some of the inferior animals, to live on a single root.

There are two periods favourable to observation—an early and a late one. A fresh eye detects external traits and peculiarities among a people, seen for the first time, which disappear as they become familiar; but it is not until after repeated opportunities of study, and a prolonged acquaintanceship, that internal characteristics and conditions begin to be rightly known. During the first fortnight of my residence in this remote district, I was more impressed than at a later stage by certain peculiarities of manner and appearance in the inhabitants. Dr Johnson remarked that he found fewer very tall or very short men among the people of the Hebrides than in England: I was now struck by a similar mediocrity of size among the Highlanders of Western Ross; five-sixths of the grown men seemed to average between five feet seven and five feet nine inches in height and either tall or short men I found comparatively rare. The Highlanders of the eastern coast were, on the contrary, at that period, mayhap still, very various of stature—some of them exceedingly diminutive, others of great bulk and height; and, as might be seen in the congregations of the parish churches removed by but a few miles, there were marked differences in this respect between the people of contiguous districts—certain tracts of plain or valley producing larger races than others. I was inclined to believe at the time that; the middle-sized Highlanders of the west coast were a less mixed race than the unequally-sized Highlanders of the east: I at least found corresponding inequalities among the higher-born Highland families, that, as shown by their genealogies, blended the Norman and Saxon with the Celtic blood; and as the unequally-sized Highland race bordered on that Scandinavian one which fringes the greater part of the eastern coast of Scotland, I inferred that there had been a similar blending of blood amongst *them*. I have since seen, in Gustav Kombst's Ethnographic Map of the British Islands, the difference which I at this time but inferred, indicated by a different shade of colour, and a different name. The Highlanders of the east coast Kombst terms "Scandinavian-Gaelic;" those of the west, "Gaelic-Scandinavian-Gaelic"—names indicative, of course, of the proportions in which he holds that they possess the Celtic blood. Disparity of bulk and size appears to be one of the consequences of a mixture of races; nor does the induced inequality seem restricted to the physical framework. Minds of large calibre, and possessed of the kingly faculty, come first into view, in our history, among the fused tribes, just as of old it was the mixed marriages that first produced the giants. The difference in size which I remarked in particular districts of the Scandinavian-Gaelic region, separated, in some instances, by but a ridge of hills or an expanse of moor, must have been a result of the old clan divisions, and is said to have marked the clans themselves very strongly. Some of them were of a greatly more robust and some of a slimmer type, than others.

I was struck by another peculiarity in the west coast Highlanders. I found the men in general greatly better-looking than the women, and that in middle life they bore their years much more lightly. The females seemed old and haggard at a period when the males were still comparatively fresh and robust. I am not sure whether the remark may not in some degree apply to Highlanders generally. The "rugged form" and "harsher features," which, according to Sir Walter, "mark the mountain band," accord worse with the female than with the male countenance and figure. But I at least found this discrepancy in the appearance of the sexes greatly more marked on the west than on the eastern coast; and saw only too much reason to conclude, that it was owing in great part to the disproportionately large share of crushing labour laid, in the district, in accordance with the practice of a barbarous time, on the weaker frame of the female. There is, however, a style of female loveliness, occasionally though rarely exemplified in the Highlands, which far transcends the Saxon or Scandinavian type. It is manifested usually in extreme youth—at least between the fourteenth and eighteenth year; and its effect we find happily indicated by Wordsworth—who seems to have met with a characteristic specimen—in his lines to a Highland girl. He describes her as possessing as her "dower," "a very *shower* of beauty." Further, however, he describes her as very young.

> "Twice seven consenting years had shed
> Their utmost bounty on her head."

I was, besides, struck at this time by finding, that while almost all the young lads under twenty with whom I came in contact had at least a smattering of English, I found only a single Highlander turned of forty with whom I could exchange a word. The exceptional Highlander was, however, a curiosity in his way. He seemed to have a natural turn for acquiring languages, and had derived his English, not from conversation, but, in the midst of a Gaelic-speaking people, from the study of the Scriptures in our common English version. His application of Bible language to ordinary subjects told at times with rather ludicrous effect. Upon inquiring of him, on one occasion, regarding a young man whom we wished to employ as an extra labourer, he described him in exactly the words in which David is described in the chapter that records the combat with Goliath, as "but a youth, and ruddy, and of a fair countenance;" and on asking where he thought we could get a few loads of water-rolled pebbles for causewaying a floor, he directed us to the bed of a neighbouring rivulet, where we might "choose us," he said, "smooth stones out of the brook." He spoke with great deliberation, translating evidently his Gaelic thinking, as he went on, into scriptural English.

CHAPTER XIII

"A man of glee
With hair of glittering grey,
As blythe a man as you could see
On a spring holiday."—WORDSWORTH.

THERE existed at this time no geological map of Scotland. Macculloch's did not appear until about six or seven years after (in 1829 or 1830), and Sedgwick and Murchison's interesting sketch of the northern formations[1] not until at least five years after (1828). And so, on setting out on the morning after that of my arrival, to provide stones for our future erection, I found myself in a *terra incognita*, new to the quarrier, and unknown to the geologist. Most of the stratified primary rocks make but indifferent building materials; and in the immediate neighbourhood of our work I could find only one of the worst of the class—the schistose gneiss. On consulting, however, the scenery of the district, I marked that at a certain point both shores of the open sea-loch on whose margin we were situated suddenly changed their character. The abrupt rugged hills of gneiss that, viewed from an eminence, resembled a tumbling sea, suddenly sank into low brown promontories, unbroken by ravines, and whose eminences were mere flat swellings; and in the hope of finding some change of formation coincident with the change of scenery, I set out with my comrade for the nearest point at which the broken outline passed into the rectilinear or merely undulatory one. But though I did expect a change, it was not without some degree of surprise that, immediately after passing the point of junction, I found myself in a district of red sandstone. It was a hard, compact, dark-coloured stone, but dressed readily to pick and

[1] Appended to their joint paper on the "Deposits contained between the Scottish Primary Rocks and Oolitic series," and interesting, as the first published geological map of Scotland to the north of the Firths of Forth and Clyde (Miller).

255

hammer, and made excellent corner-stones and ashlar; and it would have furnished us with even hewn work for our building, had not our employer, unacquainted, like every one else at the time, with the mineral capabilities of the locality, brought his hewing stone in a sloop, at no small expense, through the Caledonian Canal, from one of the quarries of Moray—a circuitous voyage of more than two hundred miles.

Immediately beside where we opened our quarry, there was a little solitary shieling: it was well-nigh such an edifice as I used to erect when a boy—some eight or ten feet in length, and of so humble an altitude, that, when standing erect in the midst, I could lay my hand on the roof-tree. A heath-bed occupied one of the corners; a few grey embers were smouldering in the middle of the floor; a pot lay beside them, ready for use, half-filled with cockles and razor-fish, the spoils of the morning ebb; and a cog of milk occupied a small shelf that projected from the gable above. Such were the contents of the shieling. Its only inmate, a lively little old man, sat outside, at once tending a few cows grouped on the moor, and employed in stripping with a pocket-knife, long slender filaments from off a piece of moss fir; and as he wrought and watched, he crooned a Gaelic song, not very musically mayhap, but, like the happy song of the humble-bee, there was perfect content in every tone. He had a great many curious questions to ask in his native Gaelic, of my comrade, regarding our employment and our employer; and when satisfied, he began, I perceived, like the Highlander of the previous evening, to express very profound commiseration for me. "Is that man also pitying me?" I asked. "O yes, very much ," was the reply: "he does not at all see how you are to live in Gairloch without Gaelic." I was reminded by the shieling and its happy inmate of one of my father's experiences, as communicated to me by Uncle James. In the course of a protracted kelp voyage among the Hebrides, he had landed in his boat, before entering one of the sounds of the Long Island, to procure a pilot, but found in the fisherman's cottage, on which he had directed his course, only the fisherman's wife—a young creature of not more than eighteen—engaged in nursing her child, and singing a Gaelic song, in tones expressive of a light heart, till the rocks rang again. A heath-bed, a pot of baked clay, of native manufacture, fashioned by the hand, and a heap of fish newly caught, seemed to constitute the only wealth of the cottage; but its mistress was, notwithstanding, one of the happiest of women; and deeply did she commiserate the poor sailors, and earnestly wish for the return of her husband, that he might assist them in their perplexity. The husband at length appeared. "Oh," he asked, after the first greeting, "have you any salt?" "Plenty," said the master; "and you, I see, from your supply of fresh fish, want it very much; but come, pilot us through the sound, and you shall have as much salt as you require." And so the vessel got a pilot, and the fisherman got salt; but never did my father forget the light-hearted song of the happy mistress of that poor Highland cottage. It was one of the palpable characteristics of our Scottish Highlanders, for at least the first thirty years of the century, that they were contented enough, as a people, to find more to pity than to envy in the condition of their neighbours; and I remember that at this time, and for years after, I used to deem the trait a good one. I have now, however, my doubts on the subject, and am not quite sure whether a content so general as to be national may not, in certain circumstances, be rather a vice than a virtue. It is certainly no virtue when it has the effect of arresting either individuals or peoples in their course of development; and is perilously allied to great suffering, when the men who exemplify it are so thoroughly happy amid the mediocrities of the present, that they fail to make provision for the contingencies of the future.

We were joined in about a fortnight by the other workmen from the Low country, and I resigned my temporary charge (save that I still retained the time-book in my master's behalf) into the hands of an ancient mason, remarkable over the north of Scotland for his skill as an operative, and who, though he was now turned of sixty, was still able to build and hew considerably more than the youngest and most active man in the squad. He was at this time the only survivor of three brothers, all masons, and all not merely first-class workmen, but of a class to which, at least to the north of the Grampians, only they themselves belonged, and very considerably in advance of the first. And on the removal of the second of the three brothers to the south of Scotland, it was found that, amid the stonecutters of Glasgow, David Fraser held relatively the same place that he had done among those of the north. I have been told by Mr Kenneth Matheson—a gentleman well known as a master-builder in the west of Scotland—that in erecting some hanging stairs of polished stone, ornamented in front and at the outer edge by the common fillet and torus, his ordinary workmen used to complete for him their one step a-piece per day and David Fraser his *three* steps, finished equally well. It is easily conceivable how, in the higher walks of arts, one man should excel a thousand—nay, how he should have neither competitor when living, nor successor when dead. The English gentleman, who, after the death of Canova, asked a surviving brother of the sculptor whether he purposed carrying on Canova's *business*, found that he had achieved in the query an unintentional joke. But in the commoner avocations there appear no such differences between man and man; and it may seem strange how, in ordinary stone-cutting, one man could thus perform the work of three. My acquaintance with old John Fraser showed me how very much the ability depended on a natural faculty. John's strength had never been above the average of that of Scotchmen, and it was now considerably reduced; nor did his mallet deal more or heavier blows than that of the common workman. He had, however, an extraordinary power of conceiving of the finished piece of work, as lying within the rude stone from which it was his business to disinter it; and while ordinary stone-cutters had to repeat and re-repeat their lines and draughts, and had in this way virtually to give to their work several surfaces in detail ere they reached the true one, old John cut upon the true figure at once, and made one surface serve for all. In building, too, he exercised a similar power: he hammer-dressed his stones with fewer strokes than other workmen, and in fitting the interspaces between stones already laid, always picked from out of the heap at his feet the stone that exactly fitted the place; while other operatives busied themselves in picking up stones that were too small or too large; or, if they set themselves to reduce the too large ones, reduced them too little or too much, and had to fit and fit again. Whether building or hewing, John never seemed in a hurry. He has been seen, when far advanced in life, working very leisurely, as became his years, on the one side of a wall, and two stout young fellows building against him on the other side—toiling, apparently, twice harder than he, but the old man always contriving to keep a little ahead of them both.

David Fraser I never saw; but as a hewer he was said considerably to excel even his brother John. On hearing that it had been remarked among a party of Edinburgh masons, that, though regarded as the first of Glasgow stone-cutters, he would find in the eastern capital at least his equals, he attired himself most uncouthly, in a long-tailed coat of tartan, and, looking to the life the untamed, untaught, conceited little Celt, he presented himself on Monday morning, armed with a letter of introduction from a Glasgow builder, before the foreman of an Edinburgh squad of masons engaged upon one of the finer buildings at that time in the course of erection. The letter specified neither his qualifications nor his name: it had been written merely to secure for him the necessary employment, and the necessary employment it did secure. The better workmen of the party were engaged, on his arrival, in hewing columns, each of which was deemed sufficient work for a week; and David was asked, somewhat incredulously, by the foreman, "if he could hew?" "O yes, *he thought* he could hew." "Could he hew columns such as these?" "O yes, *he thought* he could hew columns such as these." A mass of stone in which a possible column lay hid, was accordingly placed before David, not under cover of the shed, which was already occupied by workmen, but, agreeably to David's own request, directly in front of it, where he might be seen by all, and where he straightway commenced a most extraordinary course of antics. Buttoning his long tartan coat fast around him, he would first look along the stone from the one end, anon from the other, and then examine it in front and rear; or, quitting it altogether for the time, he would take up his stand beside the other workmen, and, after looking at them with great attention, return and give it a few taps with the mallet, in a style evidently imitative of theirs, but monstrously a caricature. The shed all that day resounded with roars of laughter; and the only thoroughly grave man on the ground was he who occasioned the mirth of all the others. Next morning David again buttoned his coat; but he got on much better this day than the former: he was less awkward and less idle, though not less observant than before: and he succeeded ere evening in tracing, in workman-like fashion, a few draughts along the future column. He was evidently greatly improving. On the morning of Wednesday he threw off his coat; and it was seen that, though by no means in a hurry, he was seriously at work. There were no more jokes or laughter; and it was whispered in the evening that the strange Highlander had made astonishing progress during the day. By the middle of Thursday he had made up for his two days' trifling, and was abreast of the other workmen; before night he was far ahead of them; and ere the evening of Friday, when they had still a full day's work on each of their columns, David's was completed in a style that defied criticism; and, his tartan coat again buttoned around him, he sat resting himself beside it. The foreman went out and greeted him. "Well," he said, "you have beaten us all: you certainly *can* hew!" "Yes," said David; "I thought I could hew columns. Did the other men take much more than a week to learn?" "Come, come, *David Fraser*," replied the foreman; "we all guess who you are: you have had your joke out; and now, I suppose, we must give you your week's wages, and let you away." "Yes," said David; "work waits for me in Glasgow; but I just thought it might be well to know how you hewed on this east side of the country."

John Fraser was a shrewd, sarcastic old man, much liked,

however, by his brother workmen; though his severe sayings—
which, never accompanied by any ill-nature, were always tolerated in the barrack—did both himself and them occasional harm
when repeated outside. To men who have to live for months
together on oatmeal and salt, the difference between porridge
with and porridge without milk is a very great difference indeed,
both in point of salutariness and comfort; and I had succeeded in
securing, on the ordinary terms, ere the arrival of John, what was
termed a *set*[1] of skimmed milk from the wife of the gentleman
at whose dwelling-house we were engaged in working. The
skimmed milk was, however, by no means good: it was thin, blue,
and sour; and we received it without complaint only because we
knew that, according to the poet, it was "better just than want
aye," and that there was no other dairy in that part of the country.
But old John was less prudent; and, taking the dairy-maid to task
in his quiet ironical style, he began by expressing wonder and
regret that a grand lady like her mistress should be unable to
distinguish the difference between milk and wine. The maid
indignantly denied the fact *in toto*: her mistress, she said, did know
the difference. "Oh, no," replied John; "wine always gets better
the longer it is kept, and milk always the worse; but your mistress,
not knowing the difference, keeps her milk very long, in order to
make it better, and makes it so very bad in consequence, that there
are some days we can scarce eat it at all." The dairy-maid bridled
up, and, communicating the remark to her mistress, we were told
next morning that we might go for our milk to the next dairy, if
we pleased, but that we would get none from her. And so, for four
months thereafter, we had to do penance for the joke, on that not
very luxurious viand "dry porridge." The pleasures of the table
had occupied but small space amid the very scanty enjoyments of
our barrack even before, and they were now so considerably
reduced that I could have almost wished at meal-times that—like
the inhabitants of the moon, as described by Baron Munchausen—
I could open up a port-hole in my side, and lay in at once provisions

---

[1] A regular supply.

enough for a fortnight; but the infliction told considerably more on our constitutions than on our appetites; and we all became subject to small but very painful boils in the muscular parts of the body—a species of disease which seems to be scarce less certainly attendant on the exclusive use of oatmeal, than sea-scurvy on the exclusive use of salt meat. Old John, however, though in a certain sense the author of our calamity, escaped all censure, while a double portion fell to the share of the gentleman's wife.

I never met a man possessed of a more thoroughly mathematical head than this ancient mason. I know not that he ever saw a copy of Euclid; but the principles of the work seemed to lie as self-evident truths in his mind. In the ability, too, of drawing shrewd inferences from natural phenomena, old John Fraser excelled all the other untaught men I ever knew. Until my acquaintance with him commenced, I had been accustomed to hear the removal of what was widely known in the north of Scotland as "the travelled stone of Petty,"[1] attributed to supernatural agency. An enormous boulder had been carried in the night-time by the fairies, it was said, from its resting place on the sea beach, into the middle of a little bay—a journey of several hundred feet; but old John, though he had not been on the spot at the time, at once inferred that it had been carried, not by the fairies, but by a thick cake of ice, considerable enough, when firmly clasped round it, to float it away. He had seen, he told me, stones of considerable size floated off by ice on the shore opposite his cottage, in the upper reaches of the Cromarty Firth: ice was an agent that sometimes "walked off with great stones;" whereas he had no evidence whatever that the fairies had any powers that way; and so he accepted the agent which he knew, as the true one in the removal of the travelled stone, and not the hypothetical agents of which he knew nothing. Such was the natural philosophy of old John; and in this special instance geologic science has since fully confirmed his decision. He was chiefly a favourite among us, however, from his even and cheerful temper, and his ability of telling humorous stories, that

[1] A village near Inverness.

used to set the barrack in a roar, and in which he never spared himself, if the exhibition of a weakness or absurdity gave but point to the fun. His narrative of a visit to Inverness, which he had made when an apprentice lad, to see a sheep-stealer hung, and his description of the terrors of a night-journey back, in which he fancied he saw men waving in the wind on almost every tree, till on reaching his solitary barrack he was utterly prostrated by the apparition of his own great-coat suspended from a pin, has oftener than once convulsed us with laughter. But John's humorous confessions, based as they always were on a strong good sense, that always saw the early folly in its most ludicrous aspect, never lowered him in our eyes. Of his wonderful skill as a workman, much was incommunicable; but it was at least something to know the principles on which he directed the operations of what a phrenologist would perhaps term his extraordinary faculties of *form* and *size*; and so I recognised old John as one of not the least useful or able of my many teachers. Some of his professional lessons were of a kind which the south and east country masons would be the better for knowing. In that rainy district of Scotland of which we at this time occupied the central tract, rubble walls built in the ordinary style leak like the bad roofs of other parts of the country; and mansion-houses constructed within its precincts by qualified workmen from Edinburgh and Glasgow have been found to admit the water in such torrents as to be uninhabitable, until their more exposed walls had been slated over like their roofs. Old John, however, always succeeded in building water-tight walls. Departing from the ordinary rule of the builder elsewhere, and which on the east coast of Scotland he himself always respected, he slightly elevated the under beds of his stones, instead of laying them, as usual, on the dead level; while along the edges of their upper beds he struck off a small rude chamfer; and by these simple contrivances, the rain, though driven with violence against his work, coursed in streams along its face, without entering into the interior and soaking through.

For about six weeks we had magnificent weather—clear, sunny

skies, and calm seas; and I greatly enjoyed my evening rambles amid the hills, or along the sea-shore. I was struck, in these walks, by the amazing abundance of the wild flowers which covered the natural meadows and lower hill-slopes—an abundance, as I have since remarked, equally characteristic of both the northern and western islands of Scotland. The lower slopes of Gairloch, of western Sutherland, of Orkney, and of the northern Hebrides generally—though, for the purposes of the agriculturalist, vegetation languishes, and wheat is never reared—are by many degrees richer in wild flowers than the fat, loamy meadows of England. They resemble gaudy pieces of carpeting, as abundant in petals as in leaves. Little of the rare is to be detected in these meadows, save, perhaps, that in those of western Sutherland a few Alpine plants may be found at a greatly lower level than elsewhere in Britain; but the vast profusion of blossoms borne by species common to almost every other part of the kingdom, imparts to them an apparently novel character. We may detect, I am inclined to think, in this singular floral profusion, the operation of a law not less influential in the animal than the vegetable world, which, when hardship presses upon the life of the individual shrub or quadruped, so as to threaten its vitality, renders it fruitful on behalf of its species. I have seen the principle strikingly exemplified in the common tobacco plant, when reared in a northern country, in the open air. Year after year it continued to degenerate, and to exhibit a smaller leaf and shorter stem, until the successors of what in the first year of trial had been vigorous plants, of some three to four feet in height, had in the sixth or eighth become mere weeds, of scarce as many inches. But while the as yet undegenerate plant had merely borne atop a few florets, which produced a small quantity of exceedingly minute seeds, the stunted weed, its descendant, was so thickly covered over in its season with its pale yellow bells, as to present the appearance of a nosegay; and the seeds produced were not only bulkier in the mass, but also individually of much greater size. The tobacco had grown productive in proportion as it had degenerated. In the common scurvy-grass, too—remarkable, with some other plants, for taking its place among both the productions of our Alpine heights and of our sea-shores—it will be found that, in proportion as its habitat proves ungenial, and its leaves and stems become dwarfish and thin, its little white cruciform flowers increase, till, in localities where it barely exists, as if on the edge of extinction, we find the entire plant forming a dense bundle of seed vessels, each charged to the full with seed. And in the gay meadows of Gairloch and Orkney, crowded with a vegetation that approaches its northern limit of production, we detect what seems to be the same principle chronically operative; and hence, it would seem, their extraordinary gaiety. Their richly blossoming plants are the poor productive *Irish* of the vegetable world; for Doubleday[1] seems quite in the right in holding that the law extends to not only the inferior animals, but to our own species also. The lean, ill-fed sow and rabbit rear, it has been long known, a greatly more numerous progeny than the same animals when well cared for and fat; and every horse and cattle breeder knows that to over-feed his animals proves a sure mode of rendering them sterile. The sheep, if tolerably well pastured, brings forth only a single lamb at a birth; but if half-starved and lean, the chances are that it may bring forth two or three. And so it is also with the greatly higher human race. Place them in circumstances of degradation and hardship so extreme as almost to threaten their existence as individuals, and they increase, as if in behalf of the species, with a rapidity without precedent in circumstances of greater comfort. The aristocratic families of a country are continually running out; and it requires frequent creations to keep up the House of Lords; whereas our poorer people seem increasing in more than arithmetical ratio. In Skye, though fully two-thirds of the population emigrated early in the latter half of the last century, a single generation had scarce passed ere the gap was completely filled; a miserable Ireland, as it existed ere the famine, would have been of itself sufficient, had the human family no other breeding-place, to people in a few ages

[1] A reference to either Henry (1808-75) or Edward (1811-49), brothers and both naturalists from Epping in Essex.

the world. Here, too, in close neighbourhood with the flower-covered meadows, were there miserable cottages that were swarming with children—cottages in which, for nearly the half of every twelvemonth, the cereals were unknown as food, and whose over-toiled female inmates did all the domestic work, and more than half the work of the little fields outside.

How exquisitely the sun sets in a clear, calm, summer evening over the blue Hebrides! Within less than a mile of our barrack, there rose a tall hill, whose bold summit commanded all the Western Isles, from Sleat in Skye, to the Butt of the Lewis. To the south lay the trap[1] islands; to the north and west, the gneiss ones. They formed, however, seen from this hill, one great group, which, just as the sun had sunk, and sea and sky were so equally bathed in gold as to exhibit on the horizon no dividing line, seemed in their transparent purple—darker or lighter according to the distance—a group of lovely clouds, that, though moveless in the calm, the first light breeze might sweep away. Even the flat promontories of sandstone, which, like outstretched arms, enclosed the outer reaches of the foreground—promontories edged with low red cliffs, and covered with brown heath—used to borrow at these times, from the soft yellow beam, a beauty not their own. Amid the inequalities of the gneiss region within—a region more broken and precipitous, but of humbler altitude, than the great gneiss tract of the midland Highlands—the chequered light and shade lay, as the sun declined, in strongly contrasted patches, that betrayed the abrupt inequalities of the ground, and bore, when all around was warm, tinted, and bright, a hue of cold neutral grey; while immediately over and beyond this rough sombre base there rose two noble pyramids of red sandstone, about two thousand feet in height, that used to flare to the setting sun in bright crimson, and whose nearly horizontal strata, deeply scored along the lines, like courses of ashlar in an ancient wall, added to the mural effect communicated by their bare fronts and steep rectilinear outlines. These tall pyramids form the terminal members, towards the

---

[1] Lava of geologic age.

south, of an extraordinary group of sandstone hills, of denudation unique in the British islands, to which I have already referred, and which extends from the northern boundary of Assynt to near Applecross. But though I formed at this time my first acquaintance with the group, it was not until many years after that I had an opportunity of determining the relations of their component beds to each other, and to the fundamental rocks of the country.

At times my walks were directed along the sea-shore. Naturalists well know how much the western coasts of Scotland differ in their productions from its eastern ones; but it was a difference wholly new to me at this time; and though my limited knowledge enabled me to detect it in but comparatively few particulars, I found it no uninteresting task to trace it for myself in even these few. I was first attracted by one of the larger sea-weeds, *Himanthalia lorea*[1]—with its cup-shaped disc and long thong-like receptacles—which I found very abundant on the rocks here, but which I had never seen in the upper reaches of the Moray Firth, and which is by no means very common on any portion of the east coast. From the sea-weeds I passed to the shells, among which I detected not only a difference in the proportions in which the various species occurred, but also species that were new to me— such as a shell, not rare in Gairloch, *Nassa reticulata*,[2] but rarely if ever seen in the Moray or Cromarty Firths; and three other shells which I saw here for the first time, *Trochus umbilicatus*, *Trochus magus*[3] and *Pecten niveus*.[4] I found, too, that the common edible oyster, *ostrea edulis*, which on the east coast lies always in comparatively deep water, is sometimes found in the Gairloch, as, for instance, in the little bay opposite the Flowerdale, in beds laid

[1] The Sea-thongs.
[2] The Netted Dog whelk.
[3] Species of Top-shells.
[4] A species of Scallop. There are only two of these exclusively west coast shells—*Trochus umbilicatus* and *Pecten niveus*. As neither of them has yet been detected in any Tertiary formation, they are in all probability shells of comparatively recent origin, that came into existence in some western centre of creation; whereas specimens of *Trochus magus* and *Nassa reticulata*, which occasionally occur on the eastern coasts of the kingdom, I have also found in a Pleistocene deposit. Thus the more widely-spread shells seem to be also the shells of more ancient standing (Miller).

bare by the ebb of stream-tides. It is always interesting to come unexpectedly either upon a new species or a striking peculiarity in an old one; and I deemed it a curious and suggestive fact that there should be British shells still restricted to our western shores, and that have not yet made their way into the German Ocean, along the coasts of either extremity of the island. Are we to infer that they are shells of more recent origin than the widely-diffused ones? or are they merely feebler in their reproductive powers? and is the German Ocean, as some of our geologists hold, a comparatively modern sea, into which only the hardier mollusca of rapid increase have yet made their way? Further, I found that the true fishes differ considerably in the group on the opposite sides of the island. The haddock and whiting are greatly more common on the east coast: the hake and horse mackerel very much more abundant on the west. Even where the species are the same on both sides, the varieties are different. The herring of the west coast is a short, thick, richly-flavoured fish, greatly superior to the large lean variety so abundant on the east; whereas the west-coast cod are large-headed, thin-bodied, pale-coloured fishes, inferior, even in their best season, to the darker-coloured, small-headed variety of the east. In no respect do the two coasts differ more, or at least to the north of the Grampians, than in the transparency of the water. The bottom is rarely seen on the east coast at a depth of more than twenty feet, and not often at more than twelve; whereas on the west I have seen it very distinctly, during a tract of dry weather, at a depth of sixty or seventy feet. The handles of the spears used in Gairloch in spearing flat fish and the common edible crab (*Cancer Pagurus*), are sometimes five-and-twenty feet in length—a length which might in vain be given to spear-handles upon the east coast, seeing that there, at such a depth of water, flat fish or crab was never yet seen from the surface.

Deceived by this transparency, I have plunged oftener than once over head and ears when bathing among the rocks, in pools where I had confidently expected to find footing. From a rock that rose abrupt as a wall from the low-water level of stream-tides to a little above the line of flood, I occasionally amused myself, when the evenings were calm, in practising the Indian method of diving—that in which the diver carries a weight with him, to facilitate his sinking, and keep him steadily at the bottom. I used to select an oblong-shaped stone, of sixteen or eighteen pounds' weight, but thin enough to be easily held in one hand; and after grasping it fast, and quitting the rock edge, I would in a second or two find myself on the grey pebble-strewed ooze beneath, some twelve or fifteen feet from the surface, where I found I could steadily remain, picking up any small objects I chanced to select, until, breath failing, I quitted my hold of the stone. And then two or three seconds more were always sufficient to bring me to the surface again. There are many descriptions, in the works of the poets, of submarine scenery, but it is always scenery such as may be seen by an eye looking down into the water—not by an eye enveloped in it—and very different from that with which I now became acquainted. I found that in these hasty trips to the bottom I could distinguish masses and colours, but that I always failed to determine outlines. The minuter objects—pebbles, shells, and the smaller bunches of sea-weed—always assumed the circular form; the larger, such as detached rocks, and patches of sand, appeared as if described by irregular curves, The dingy gneiss rock rose behind and over me like a dark cloud, thickly dotted with minute circular spots of soiled white—the aspect assumed, as seen through the water, by the numerous specimens of univalve shells (*Purpura lapillus*[1] and *Patella vulgata*[2]) with which it was speckled; beneath, the irregular floor seemed covered by a carpet that somewhat resembled in the pattern a piece of marbled paper, save that the circular or oval patches of which it was composed, and which had as their nuclei, stones, rocks, shell-fish, bunches of fuci, and fronds of laminaria, were greatly larger. There spread around a misty groundwork of green intensely deep along its horizon, but comparatively light overhead, in its middle sky, which had always its prodigy—wonderful circlets of light, that went widening

[1] The Dog Winkle. [2] The Common Limpet.

outwards, and with whose delicate green there mingled occasional flashes of pale crimson. Such was the striking though somewhat meagre scenery of a sea-bottom in Gairloch, as seen by a human eye submerged in from two to three fathoms of water.

There still continued to linger in this primitive district, at the time, several curious arts and implements, that had long become obsolete in most other parts of the Highlands, and of which the remains, if found in England or the Low country, would have been regarded by the antiquary as belonging to very remote periods. During the previous winter I had read a little work descriptive of an ancient ship, supposed to be Danish, which had been dug out of the silt of an English river, and which, among other marks of antiquity, exhibited seams caulked with moss—a peculiarity which had set at fault, it was said, the modern ship-carpenter, in the chronology of his art, as he was unaware that there had ever been a time when moss was used for such a purpose. On visiting, however, a boat-yard at Gairloch, I found the Highland builder engaged in laying a layer of dried moss, steeped in tar, along one of his seams, and learned that such had been the practice of boat-carpenters in that locality from time immemorial. I have said that the little old Highlander of the solitary shieling, whom we met on first commencing our quarrying labours beside his hut, was engaged in stripping with a pocket-knife long slender filaments from off a piece of moss-fir. He was employed in preparing these ligneous fibres for the manufacture of a primitive kind of cordage, in large use among the fishermen, and which possessed a strength and flexibility that could scarce have been expected from materials of such venerable age and rigidity as the roots and trunks of ancient trees, that had been locked up in the peat-mosses of the district for mayhap a thousand years. Like the ordinary cordage of the rope-maker, it consisted of three strands, and was employed for haulsers, the cork-bauks of herring-nets, and the lacing of sails. Most of the sails themselves were made, not of canvas, but of a woollen stuff, the thread of which, greatly harder and stouter than that of common plaid, had been spun on the distaff and spindle.

As hemp and flax must have been as rare commodities of old in the western Highlands, and the Hebrides generally, as they both were thirty years ago in Gairloch, whereas moss-fir must have been abundant, and sheep, however coarse their fleeces, common enough, it seems not improbable that the old Highland fleets that fought in the "Battle of the Bloody Bay,"[1] or that, in troublous times, when Donald quarrelled with the king, ravaged the coasts of Arran and Ayrshire, may have been equipped with similar sails and cordage. Scott describes the fleet of the "Lord of the Isles," in the days of the Bruce, as consisting of "proud galleys," "streamered with silk and tricked with gold." I suspect he would have approved himself a truer antiquary, though mayhap worse poet, had he described it as composed of very rude carvels, caulked with moss, furnished with sails of dun-coloured woollen stuff still redolent of the oil, and rigged out with brown cordage formed of the twisted fibres of moss-fir. The distaff and spindle was still, as I have said, in extensive use in the district. In a scattered village in the neighbourhood of our barrack, in which all the adult females were ceaselessly engaged in the manufacture of yarn, there was not a single spinning-wheel. Nor, though all its cottages had their little pieces of tillage, did it boast its horse or plough. The cottars turned up the soil with the old Highland implement, the *cass-chron*;[2] and the necessary manure was carried to the fields in spring, and the produce brought home in autumn, on the backs of the women, in square wickerwork panniers with slip-bottoms. How these poor Highland women did toil! I have paused amid my labours under the hot sun, to watch them as they pressed, bending under their load of peat or manure, and at the same time twirling the spindle as they crept long, and drawing out the never-ending thread from the distaff stuck in their girdles. Their appearance in most cases betrayed their life of hardship. I scarce saw a Gairloch woman of the humbler class turned of thirty, who was not thin,

[1] Near Tobermory in Mull, scene of a famous sea-fight between two West Highland factions towards the end of the fifteenth century.

[2] The cas-crom (Gaelic, "bent-foot") or plough-foot, having a small plough-like share pressed by the foot, and a long handle.

sallow, and prematurely old. The men, their husbands and brothers, were by no means worn out with hard work. I have seen them, time after time, sunning themselves on a mossy bank, when the females were thus engaged; and used, with my brother-workmen—who were themselves Celts, but of the industrious hard-working type—to feel sufficiently indignant at the lazy fellows. But the arrangement which gave them rest, and their wives and sisters hard labour, seemed to be as much the off-spring of a remote age as the woollen sails and the moss-fir cordage. Several other ancient practices and implements had at this time just disappeared from the district. A good meal-mill of the modern construction had superseded, not a generation before, several small mills with horizontal water-wheels, of that rude antique type which first supplanted the still more ancient handmill. These horizontal mills still exist, however—at least they did so only two years ago—in the gneiss region of Assynt. The antiquary sometimes forgets that, tested by his special rules for determining periods, several ages may be found contemporary in contiguous districts of the same country. I am old enough to have seen the handmill at work in the north of Scotland; and the traveller into the Highlands of western Sutherland might have witnessed the horizontal mill in action only two years ago. But to the remains of either, if dug out of the mosses or sand-hills of the southern counties, we would assign an antiquity of centuries. In the same way, the unglazed earthen pipkin, fashioned by the hand without the assistance of the potter's wheel, is held to belong to the "bronze and stone periods" of the antiquary; and yet my friend of the Doocot Cave, when minister of Small Isles, found the remains of one of these pipkins in the famous charnel cave[1] of Eigg, which belonged to an age not earlier than that of Mary, and more probably pertained to that of her son James; and I have since learned, that in the southern portions of the Long Island, this same hand-moulded pottery of the bronze period has been fashioned for domestic use during the early part of the present century. A

[1] In which a party of MacLeods smoked to death the MacDonalds of Eigg in 1577.

272

chapter devoted to these lingering, or only recently departed, arts of the primitive ages, would be a curious one; but I fear the time for writing it is now well-nigh past. My few facts on the subject may serve to show that, even as late as the year 1823, some three days' journey into the Highlands might be regarded as analogous in some respects to a journey into the past of some three or four centuries. But even since that comparatively recent period the Highlands have greatly changed.

After some six or eight weeks of warm sunny days and lovely evenings, there came on a dreary tract of rainy weather, with strong westerly gales; and for three months together, while there was scarce a day that had not its shower, some days had half-a-dozen. Gairloch occupies, as I have said, exactly the focus of that great curve of annual rain which, impinging on our western shores from the Atlantic, extends from the north of Assynt to the south of Mull, and exhibits on the rain-gauge an average of thirty-five yearly inches—an average very considerably above the medium quantity that falls in any other part of Great Britain, save a small tract at the Land's End, included in a southern curve of equal fall. The rain-fall of this year, however, must have stood very considerably above even this high average; and the corn crops of the poor Highlanders soon began to testify to the fact. There had been a larger than ordinary promise during the fine weather; but in the danker hollows the lodged oats and barley now lay rotting on the ground, or, on the more exposed heights, stood up, shorn of the ears, as mere naked spikes of straw. The potatoes, too, had become soft and watery, and must have formed but indifferent food to the poor Highlanders, condemned, even in better seasons, to feed upon them during the greater part of the year, and now thrown upon them almost exclusively by the failure of the corn crop. The cottars of the neighbouring village were on other accounts in more than usually depressed circumstances at the time. Each family paid to the laird for its patch of cornland, and the pasturage of a wide upland moor, on which each kept three cows a-piece, a small yearly rent of three pounds. The males were all fishermen as well as crofters; and, small as the rent was, they derived their only means of paying it from the sea—chiefly, indeed, from the herring fishery—which, everywhere an uncertain and precarious source of supply, is more so here than in most other places on the north-western coasts of Scotland. And as for three years together the herring fishing had failed in the Loch, they had been unable, term after term, to meet with the laird, and were now three years in arrears. Fortunately for them, he was a humane, sensible man, comfortable enough in his circumstances to have, what Highland proprietors often have not, the complete command of his own affairs; but they all felt that their cattle were their own only by sufferance, and so long as he forbore urging his claims against them; and they entertained but little hope of ultimate extrication. I saw among these poor men much of that indolence of which the country has heard not a little; and could not doubt, from the peculiar aspects in which it presented itself, that it was, as I have said, a long derived hereditary indolence, in which their fathers and grandfathers had indulged for centuries. But there was certainly little in their circumstances to lead to the formation of new habits of industry. Even a previously industrious people, were they to be located within the great north-western curve of thirty-five inch rain, to raise corn and potatoes for the autumnal storms to blast, and to fish in the laird's behalf herrings that year after year refused to come to be caught, would, I suspect, in a short time get nearly as indolent as themselves. And certainly, judging from the contrast which my brother-workmen presented to these Highlanders of the west coast, the indolence which we saw, and for which my comrades had no tolerance whatever, could scarce be described as inherently Celtic. I myself was the only genuine Lowlander of our party. John Fraser, who, though turned of sixty, would have laid or hewn stone for stone with the most diligent Saxon mason in Britain or elsewhere, was a true Celt of the Scandinavian-Gaelic-variety; and all our other masons— Macdonalds, M'Leods, and Mackays, hard-working men, who were content to toil from season to season, and all day long—were

274

true Celts also. But they had been bred on the eastern border of the Highlands, in a sandstone district, where they had the opportunity of acquiring a trade, and of securing in the working season regular well-remunerated employment; and so they had developed into industrious, skilled mechanics, of at least the ordinary efficiency. There are other things much more deeply in fault as producing causes of the indolence of the west-coat Highlander than his Celtic blood.

On finishing the dwelling-house upon which we had been engaged, nearly one-half the workmen quitted the squad for the low country, and the remainder removed to the neighbourhood of the inn at which we had spent our first night, or rather morning, in the place, to build a kitchen and store-room for the inn-keeper. Among the others, we lost the society of Click-Clack, who had been a continual source of amusement and annoyance to us in the barrack all the season long. We soon found that he was regarded by the Highlanders in our neighbourhood with feelings of the intensest horror and dread: they had learned somehow that he used to be seen in the low country flitting suspiciously at night about churchyards, and was suspected of being a resurrectionist; and not one of the ghouls or vampires of eastern story could have been more feared or hated in the regions which they were believed to infest, than a resurrectionist in the Western Highlands. Click-Clack had certainly a trick of wandering about at nights and not unfrequently did he bring, on his return from some nocturnal ramble, dead bodies with him into the barrack; but they were invariably the dead bodies of cod, gurnard, and hake. I know not where his fishing-bank lay, or what bait he employed, but I observed that almost all the fish which he caught were ready dried and salted. Old John Fraser was not without suspicion that there were occasional interferences on the part of the carter with the integrity of our meal-barrel; and I have seen the old man smoothing the surface of the meal just before quitting the barrack for his work, and inscribing upon it with his knife-point the important moral injunction, "thou shalt not steal," in such a way as to render it impossible to break the commandment within the precincts of the barrel, without, at the same time, effacing some of its characters. And these once effaced, Click-Clack, as he was no writer himself, and had no assistant or confidant, could not have re-inscribed. Ere quitting us for the low country, I bargained with him that he should carry my blanket in his cart to Conon-side, and gave him a shilling and a dram in advance, as pay for the service. He carried it, however, no further than the next inn, where, pledging it for a second shilling and second dram, he left me to relieve it as I passed. Poor Click-Clack, though one of the cleverest of his class, was decidedly half-witted; and I may remark, as at least curious, that though I have known idiocy in its unmixed state united to great honesty, and capable of disinterested attachment, I never yet knew one of the half-witted caste who was not selfish and a rogue.

We were unlucky in our barracks this season. Ere completing our first piece of work, we had to quit the hay-barn, our earliest dwelling, to make way for the proprietor's hay, and to shelter in a cow-house, where, as the place had no chimney, we were nearly suffocated by smoke; and we now found the inn-keeper, our new employer, speculating, like the magistrates in Joe Miller, on the practicability of lodging us in a building, the materials of which were to be used in erecting the one which we were engaged to build. We did our best to solve the problem, by hanging up at the end of the doomed hovel—which had been a salt-store in its day, and was in damp weather ever sweating salt-water—a hanging partition of mats, that somewhat resembled the curtain of a barn-theatre; and, making our beds within, we began pulling down piecemeal, as the materials were required, that part of the erection which lay outside. We had very nearly unhoused ourselves ere our work was finished; and the chill blasts of October, especially when they blew in at the open end of our dwelling, rendered it as uncomfortable as a shallow cave in an exposed rock front. My boyish experiences, however, among the rocks of Cromarty, constituted no bad preparation for such a life, and I roughed it out at least as well as any of my comrades. The day had so contracted, that night always fell upon our unfinished labours, and I had no evening walks; but there was a delightful gneiss island, of about thirty acres in extent, and nearly two miles away, to which I used to be occasionally despatched to quarry lintels and corner stones, and where work had all the charms of play; and the quiet Sabbaths were all my own. So long as the laird and his family were at the mansion-house of Flowerdale—at least four months of every year—there was an English service in the parish church; but I had come to the place this season before the laird, and now remained in it after he had gone away, and there was no English service for me. And so I usually spent my Sabbaths all alone, in the noble Flowerdale woods, now bright, under their dark hillsides, in the autumnal tints, and remarkable for the great height and bulk of their ash trees, and of a few detached firs, that spoke, in their venerable massiveness, of former centuries. The clear, calm mornings, when the gossamer went sailing in long grey films along the retired glades of the wood, and the straggling sunlight fell on the crimson and orange mushroom, as it sprang up amid the dank grass, and under thickly-leaved boughs of scarlet and gold, I deemed peculiarly delightful. For one who had neither home nor church, the autumnal woods formed by much a preferable Sabbath haunt to a shallow cave, dropping brine, unprovided with chair or table, and whose only furniture consisted of two rude bedsteads of undressed slabs, that bore atop two blankets a-piece, and a heap of straw. Sabbath-walking in parties, and especially in the neighbourhood of our large towns, is always a frivolous, and often a very bad thing; but lonely Sabbath-walks in a rural district—walks such as the poet Grahame describes— are not necessarily bad; and the Sabbatarians who urge that in all cases, men, when not in the church on Sabbath, ought to be in their dwellings, must know very little indeed of the "huts where poor men lie." In the mason's barrack, or the farm-servant's bothy, it is often impossible to enjoy the quiet of the Sabbath: the circumstances necessary to its enjoyment must be sought in the open air, amid the recesses of some thick wood, or along the banks of some unfrequented river, or on the brown wastes of some solitary moor.

We had completed all our work ere Hallow-day, and, after a journey of nearly three days, I found myself once more at home, with the leisure of the long happy winter before me. I still look back on the experiences of this year with a feeling of interest. I had seen in my boyhood, in the interior of Sutherland, the Highlanders living in that condition of comparative comfort which they enjoyed from shortly after the suppression of the rebellion of 1745, and the abolition of the hereditary jurisdictions, till the beginning of the present century, and in some localities for ten or twelve years later. And here again I saw them in a condition—the effect mainly of the introduction of the extensive sheep-farm system into the interior of the country—which has since become general over almost the entire Highlands, and of which the result may be seen in the annual famines. The population, formerly spread pretty equally over the country, now exists as a miserable selvage stretched along its shores, dependent in most cases on precarious fisheries, that prove remunerative for a year or two, and disastrous for mayhap half-a-dozen; and, able barely to subsist when most successful, a failure in the potato crop or in the expected return of the herring shoals, at once reduces them to starvation. The grand difference between the circumstances of the people of the Highlands in the better time and the worse may be summed up in the one important vocable—*capital*. The Highlander was never wealthy: the inhabitants of a wild mountainous district, formed of the primary rocks, never are. But he possessed, on the average, his six, or eight, or ten head of cattle, and his small flock of sheep; and when, as sometimes happened in the high-lying districts, the corn-crop turned out a failure, the sale of a few cattle or sheep more than served to clear scores with the landlord, and enabled him to purchase his winter and spring supply of meal in the Lowlands. He was thus a capitalist, and possessed the capitalist's peculiar advantage of not "living from hand to mouth," but on an accumulated fund, which always stood between him and absolute want, though not between him and positive hardship, and which enabled him to rest, during a year of scarcity, on his own resources, instead of throwing himself on the charity of his Lowland neighbours. Nay, in what were emphatically termed "the dear years" of the beginning of the present and latter half of the past century, the humble people of the Lowlands, especially our Lowland mechanics and labourers, suffered more than the crofters and *small* farmers of the Highlands, and this mainly from the circumstance, that as the failure of the crops which induced the scarcity was a corn failure, not a failure of grass and pasture, the humbler Highlanders had sheep and cattle, which continued to supply them with food and raiment; while the humbler Lowlanders, depending on corn almost exclusively, and accustomed to deal with the draper for their articles of clothing, were reduced by the high price of provisions to great straits. There took place, however, about the beginning of the century, a mighty change, coincident with, and, to a certain extent, an effect of, the wars of the first French Revolution. The price of provisions rose in England and the Lowlands, and, with the price of provisions, the rent of land. The Highland proprietor naturally enough set himself to determine how his rental also was to be increased; and, as a consequence of the conclusion at which he arrived, the sheep-farm and clearance system began. Many thousand Highlanders, ejected from their snug holdings, employed their little capital in emigrating to Canada and the States; and there, in most cases, the little capital increased, and a rude plenty continues to be enjoyed by their descendants. Many thousands more, however, fell down upon the coasts of the country, and, on moss-covered moors or bare promontories, ill suited to repay the labours of the agriculturist, commenced a sort of amphibious life as crofters and fishermen. And, located on an ungenial soil, and prosecuting with but indifferent skill a precarious trade, their little capital dribbled out of their hands, and they became the poorest of men. Meanwhile, in some parts of the Highlands and Islands a busy commerce sprang up, which employed—much to the profit of the land-lords—many thousands of the inhabitants. The kelp manufacture rendered inhospitable islets and tracts of bleak rocky shore, rich in sea-weed, of as much value to the proprietors as the best land in Scotland; and, under the impetus given by full employment, and, if not ample, at least remunerative pay, population increased. Suddenly, however, Free Trade, in its first approaches, destroyed the trade in kelp; and then the discovery of a cheap mode of manufacturing soda out of common salt secured its ruin beyond the power of legislation to retrieve. Both the people and landlords experienced in the kelp districts the evils which a ruined commerce always leaves behind it. Old Highland families disappeared from amid the aristocracy and landowners of Scot-land; and the population of extensive islands and sea-boards of the country, from being no more than adequate, suddenly became oppressively redundant. It required, however, another drop to make the full cup run over. The potatoes had become, as I have shown, the staple food of the Highlands; and when, in 1846 the potato-blight came on, the people, most of them previously stripped of their little capitals, and divested of their employment, were deprived of their food, and ruined at a blow. The same stroke which did little more than slightly impinge on the comforts of the people of the Lowlands, utterly prostrated the Highlanders; and ever since, the sufferings of famine have become chronic along the bleak shores and rugged islands of at least the north-western portion of our country. Nor is it perhaps the worst part of the evil that takes the form of clamorous want: so heavily have the famines borne on a class which were not absolutely the poor when they came on, that they are absolutely the poor now;—they have dissipated the last remains of capital possessed by the *people* of the Highlands.

CHAPTER XIV

"Edina! Scotia's darling seat!
All hail thy palaces and towers!" BURNS

THERE had occurred a sad accident among the Cromarty rocks this season, when I was labouring in Gairloch, which, from the circumstance that it had nearly taken place in my own person about five years before, a good deal impressed me on my return. A few hundred yards from the very bad road which I had assisted old Johnstone of the Forty-Second in constructing, there is a tall inaccessible precipice of ferruginous gneiss, that from time immemorial down to this period had furnished a secure nestling-place to a pair of ravens—the only birds of their species that frequented the rocks of the Hill. Year after year, regularly as the breeding season came round, the ravens used to make their appearance, and enter on possession of their hereditary home: they had done so for a hundred years, to a certainty—some said, for a much longer time; and as there existed a tradition in the place that the nest had once been robbed of its young birds by a bold climber, I paid it a visit one morning, in order to determine whether I could not rob it too. There was no getting up to it from below: the precipice, more inaccessible for about a hundred feet from its base than a castle wall, overhung the shore; but it seemed not impracticable from above; and, coming gradually down upon it, availing myself, as I crept along, of every little protuberance and hollow, I at length stood within seven or eight feet of the young birds. From that point, however, a smooth shelf, without projection or cavity, descended at an angle of about forty to the nest, and terminated abruptly, without ledge or margin, in the overhanging precipice. Have I not, I asked, crept along a roof of even a steeper slope than that of the shelf? Why not, in like manner, creep along it to the nest, where there is firm footing? I had actually stretched out my naked foot to take the first step when I observed, as the sun suddenly broke out from behind a cloud, that the light glistened on the smooth surface. It was incrusted over by a thin layer of chlorite,[1] slippery as the mixture of soap and grease that the ship-carpenter spreads over his slips on the morning of a launch. I at once saw there was an element of danger in the way, on which I had at first failed to calculate; and so, relinquishing the attempt as hopeless, I returned by the path I had come, and thought no more of robbing the raven's nest. It was, however, again attempted this season, but with tragic results, by a young lad from Sutherland, named Mackay, who had previously approved his skill as a cragsman in his native county, and several times secured the reward given by an Agricultural Society for the destruction of young birds of prey. As the incident was related to me, he had approached the nest by the path which I had selected; he had paused where I had paused, and even for a longer time; and then, venturing forward, he no sooner committed himself to the treacherous chlorite, than, losing footing as if on a steep sheet of ice, he shot right over the precipice. Falling sheer for the first fifty feet or so without touching the rock, he was then turned full round by a protuberance against which he had glanced, and, descending for the lower half of the way head foremost, and dashing with tremendous force among the smooth sea-stones below, his brains were scattered over an area of from ten to twelve square yards in extent. His only companion—an ignorant Irish lad—had to gather up the fragments of his head in a napkin.

I now felt that, save for the gleam of the sun on the glistening chlorite—seen not a moment too soon—I should probably have been substituted as the victim for poor Mackay, and that he, warned by my fate, would in all likelihood have escaped. And though I knew it might be asked, Why the interposition of a Providence to save *you*, when he was left to perish? I *did* feel that

---

[1] As a "hydrous" mineral it is greasy to the touch.

I did not owe my escape merely to my acquaintance with chlorite and its properties. For the full development of the moral instincts of our nature, one may lead a life by much too quiet and too secure: a sprinkling in one's lot of sudden perils and hair-breadth escapes is, I am convinced, more wholesome, if positive superstition be avoided, than a total absence of danger. For my own part, though I have, I trust, ever believed in the doctrine of a particular Providence, it has been always some narrow escape that has given me my best evidences of the vitality and strength of the belief within. It has ever been the touch of danger that has rendered it emotional. A few years after this time, when stooping forward to examine an opening fissure in a rock front, at which I was engaged in quarrying, a stone, detached from above by a sudden gust of wind, brushed so closely past my head as to beat down the projecting front of my bonnet, and then dented into a deep hollow the sward at my feet. There was nothing that was not perfectly natural in the occurrence; but the gush of acknowledgement that burst spontaneously from my heart would have set at nought the scepticism which would have held that there was no Providence in it. On another occasion, I paused for some time, when examining a cave of the old coast line, directly under its low-browed roof of Old Red conglomerate, as little aware of the presence of danger as if I had been standing under the dome of St. Paul's; but when I next passed the way, the roof had fallen, and a mass, huge enough to have given me at once death and burial, cumbered the spot which I had occupied. On yet another occasion, I clambered a few yards down a precipice, to examine some crab-apple trees, which, springing from a turret-like projection of the rock, far from gardens and nurseries, had every mark of being indigenous; and then, climbing up among the branches, I shook them in a manner that must have exerted no small leverage power on the outjet beneath, to possess myself of some of the fruit, as the native apples of Scotland. On my descent, I marked, without much thinking of the matter, an apparently recent crack running between the outjet and the body of the precipice. I found, however, cause enough to think of it on my return, scarce a month after; for then both outjet and trees lay broken and fractured on the beach more than a hundred feet below. With such momentum had even the slimmer twigs been dashed against the sea-pebbles, that they stuck out from under more than a hundred tons of fallen rock, divested of the bark on their under sides, as if peeled by the hand. And what I felt on all these occasions was, I believe, not more in accordance with the nature of man as an instinct of the moral faculty, than in agreement with that provision of the Divine Government under which a sparrow falleth not without permission. There perhaps never was a time in which the doctrine of a particular Providence was more questioned and doubted than in the present; and yet the scepticism which obtains regarding it seems to be very much a scepticism of effort, conjured up by toiling intellects, in a quiet age, and among the easy classes; while the belief which, partially and for the time, it overshadows, lies safely entrenched all the while amid the fastnesses of the unalterable nature of man. When danger comes to touch it, it will spring up in its old proportions; nay, so indigenous is it to the human heart, that if it will not take its *cultivated* form as a belief in Providence, it will to a certainty take to its *wild* form as a belief in Fate or Destiny. Of a doctrine so fundamentally important that there can be no religion without it, God himself seems to have taken care when he moulded the human heart.

The raven no longer builds among the rocks of the Hill of Cromarty; and I saw many years ago its last pair of eagles. This last noble bird was a not unfrequent visitor at the Sutors early in the present century. I still remember scaring it from its perch on the southern side of the hill, as day was drawing to a close, when the tall precipices amid which it had lodged lay deep in the shade; and vividly recollect how picturesquely it used to catch the red gleam of evening on its plumage of warm brown, as, sailing outwards over the calm sea many hundred feet below, it emerged from under the shadow of the cliffs into the sunshine. Uncle James once shot a very large eagle beneath one of the loftiest precipices of the southern Sutor: and, swimming out through the surf to recover its body—for it had dropped dead into the sea—he kept its skin for many years as a trophy.[1] But eagles are now no longer to be seen or shot on the Sutors or their neighbourhood. The badger, too—one of perhaps the oldest inhabitants of the country, for it seems to have been contemporary with the extinct elephants and hyænas of the Pleistocene[2] periods—has become greatly less common on their steep sides than in the days of my boyhood; and both the fox and otter are less frequently seen. It is not uninteresting to mark with the eye of the geologist, how palpably in the course of a single lifetime—still nearly twenty years short of the term fixed by the Psalmist—these wild animals have been posting on in Scotland to that extinction which overtook, within its precincts, during the human period, the bear, the beaver and the wolf, and of which the past history of the globe, as inscribed on its rocks, furnishes so strong a record.

Winter passed in the usual pursuits; and I commenced the working season of a new year by assisting my old master to enclose with a stone wall a little bit of ground, which he had bought on speculation, but had failed in getting feued out for buildings. My services, however, were gratuitous—given merely to eke out the

[1] Uncle James would scarce have sanctioned, had he been consulted in the matter, the use to which the carcase of his dead eagle was applied. There lived in the place an eccentric, half-witted old woman, who, for the small sum of one halfpenny, used to fall a-dancing on the street to amuse children, and rejoice in the euphonious though somewhat obscure appellation of "Dribble Drone." Some young fellows, on seeing the eagle divested of its skin, and looking remarkably clean and well-conditioned, suggested that it should be sent to "Dribble"; and accordingly, in the character of a "great goose, the gift of a gentleman," it was landed at her door. The gift was thankfully accepted. Dribble's cottage proved odoriferous at dinner-time for the several following days; and when asked, after a week had gone by, how she had relished the great goose which the gentleman had sent, she replied that it was "Unco sweet, but oh! teuch, teuch!" For years after, the reply continued to be proverbial in the place; and many a piece of over-hard stock-fish, and over-fresh steak, used to be characterised as, "Like Dribble Drone's eagle, unco sweet, but oh! teuch, teuch!" (Miller.)

[2] The latest of the geological periods, often called the Ice Age.

rather indifferent bargain that the old man had been able to drive in his own behalf for my labours as an apprentice; and when our job was finished, it became necessary that I should look out for employment of a more profitable character. There was not much doing in the north; but work promised to be abundant in the great towns of the south: the disastrous building mania of 1824-25 had just begun, and, after some little hesitation I resolved on trying whether I could not make my way as a mechanic among the stone-cutters of Edinburgh—perhaps the most skilful in their profession in the world. I was, besides, desirous to get rid of a little property in Leith, which had cost the family great annoyance, and not a little money, but from which, so long as the nominal proprietor was a minor, we could not shake ourselves loose. It was a house on the Coal-hill, or rather the self-contained ground-floor of a house, which had fallen to my father through the death of a relative, so immediately before his own death that he had not entered upon possession. It was burdened with legacies to the amount of nearly two hundred pounds; but then the yearly rent amounted to twenty-four pounds; and my mother, acting on the advice of friends, and deeming the investment a good one, had no sooner recovered the insurance money of my father's vessel from the underwriter, than she handed the greater part of it to the legatees, and took possession of the property in my behalf. Alas! never was there a more unfortunate inheritance or worse investment. It had been let as a public-house and tap-room, and been the scene of a somewhat rough, and, I daresay, not very respectable, but yet profitable trade; but no sooner had it become mine than, in consequence of some alterations in the harbour, the greater part of the shipping that used to lie at the Coal-hill removed to a lower reach; the tap-room business suddenly fell off; and the rent sank, during the course of one twelvemonth, from twenty-four to twelve pounds. And then in its sear and wintry state, the unhappy house came to be inhabited by a series of miserable tenants, who, though they sanguinely engaged to pay the twelve pounds, never paid them. I still remember the brief, curt letters from our agent, the late Mr Veitch, town-clerk of Leith, that never failed to fill my mother with terror and dismay, and very much resembled, in at least the narrative parts, jottings by the poet Crabbe, for some projected poem on the profligate poor. Two of our tenants made moonlight flittings just on the eve of the term; and though the little furniture which they left behind them was duly rouped at the cross, such was the inevitable expense of the transaction, that none of the proceeds of the sale reached Cromarty. The house was next inhabited by a stout female, who kept a certain description of lady-lodgers; and for the first half-year she paid the rent most conscientiously, but the authorities interfering, there was another house found for her and her ladies in the neighbourhood of the Calton, and the rent of the second half-year remained unpaid. And as the house lost, in consequence of her occupation, the modicum of character which it had previously retained, it lay for five years wholly untenanted, save by a mischievous spirit—the ghost, it was said, of a murdered gentleman, whose throat had been cut in an inner apartment by the ladies, and his body flung by night into the deep mud of the harbour. The ghost was, however, at length detected by the police, couching, in the form of one of the ladies themselves, on a lair of straw in the corner of one of the rooms, and exorcised into Bridewell; and then the house came to be inhabited by a tenant who had both the will and the ability to pay. One year's rent, however, had to be expended in repairs; and ere the next year passed, the heritors of the parish were rated for the erection of the magnificent parish church of North Leith, then in course of building, with its tall and graceful spire and classic portico; and as we had no one to state our case, our house was rated, not according to its reduced, but according to its original value. And so the entire rental of the second year, with several pounds additional which I had to subtract from my hard-earned savings as a mason, were appropriated in behalf of the ecclesiastical Establishment of the country, by the builders of the church and spire. I had attained my majority when lodging in the fragment of a salt storehouse in Gairloch; and, competent in the eye of the law to dispose of the house on the Coal-hill, I now hoped to find, if not a purchaser, at least some one foolish enough to take it off my hands for nothing. I have since heard and read a good deal about the atrocious landlords of the poorer and less reputable sort of houses in our large towns, and have seen it asserted that, being a bad and selfish kind of people, they ought to be rigorously dealt with. And so, I daresay, they ought; but at the same time I cannot forget, that I myself was one of these atrocious landlords from my fifth till nearly my twenty-second year, and that I could not possibly help it, and was very sorry for it.

On the fourth day after losing sight of the Hill of Cromarty, the Leith smack in which I sailed was slowly threading her way, in a morning of light airs and huge broken fog-wreaths, through the lower tracts of the Firth of Forth. The islands and distant land looked dim and grey through the haze, like objects in an unfinished drawing; and at times some vast low-browed cloud from the sea applied the sponge as it rolled past, and blotted out half a county at a time; but the sun occasionally broke forth in partial glimpses of great beauty, and brought out into bold relief little bits of the landscape—now a town, and now an islet, and anon the blue summit of a hill. A sunlit wreath rose from around the abrupt and rugged Bass as we passed, and my heart leaped within me as I saw, for the first time, that stern Patmos of the devout and brave of another age looming dark and high through the diluted mist, and enveloped for a moment, as the cloud parted, in an amber-tinted glory. There had been a little Presbyterian oasis of old in the neighbourhood of Cromarty, which, in the midst of the Highland and *Moderate* indifferency that characterized the greater part of the north of Scotland during the seventeenth century, had furnished the Bass with not a few of its most devoted victims.[1] Mackilligen of Alness, Hogg of Kiltearn, and the Rosses of Tain and Kincardine, had been incarcerated in its dungeons; and, when labouring in the Cromarty quarries in early spring, I

[1] Presbyterian ministers who refused to recognise the jurisdiction of bishops in the Church of Scotland.

used to know that it was time to gather up my tools for the evening, when I saw the sun resting over the high-lying farm which formed the patrimony of another of its better-known victims—young Fraser of Brea. And so I looked with a double interest on the bold sea-girt rock, and the sun-gilt cloud that rose over its scarred forehead, like that still brighter halo which glorifies it in the memories of the Scottish people. Many a long-cherished association drew my thoughts to Edinburgh. I was acquainted with Ramsay, and Fergusson, and the "Humphrey Clinker" of Smollett, and had read a description of the place in the "Marmion" and the earlier novels of Scott; and I was not yet too old to feel as if I were approaching a great magical city—like some of those in the "Arabian Nights"—that was even more intensely poetical than Nature itself. I did somewhat chide the tantalizing mist, that, like a capricious showman, now raised one corner of its curtain, and anon another, and showed me the place at once very indistinctly, and only by bits at a time; and yet I know not that I could in reality have seen it to greater advantage, or after a mode more in harmony with my previous conceptions. The water in the harbour was too low, during the first hour or two after our arrival, to float our vessel, and we remained tacking in the roadstead, watching for the signal from the pier-head which was to intimate to us when the tide had risen high enough for our admission; and so I had sufficient time given me to con over the features of the scene, as presented in detail. At one time a flat reach of the New Town came full into view, along which, in the general dimness, the multitudinous chimneys stood up like stacks of corn in a field newly reaped; at another, the Castle loomed out dark in the cloud; then, as if suspended over the earth, the rugged summit of Arthur's Seat came strongly out, while its base still remained invisible in the wreath; and anon I caught a glimpse of the distant Pentlands, enveloped by a clear blue sky, and lighted up by the sun. Leith, with its thicket of masts, and its tall round Tower, lay deep in shade in the foreground—a cold, dingy, ragged town, but, so strongly relieved against the pale smoky grey of the background, that it seemed another little city of Zoar, entire in front of the burning. And such was the strangely picturesque countenance with which I was favoured by the Scottish capital, when forming my earliest acquaintance with it, twenty-nine years ago.

It was evening ere I reached it. The fog of the early part of the day had rolled off, and every object stood out in clear light and shade under a bright sunshiny sky. The workmen of the place— their labours just closed for the day—were passing in groups along the streets to their respective homes; but I was too much engaged in looking at the buildings and shops to look very discriminately at them; and it was not without some surprise that I found myself suddenly laid hold of by one of their number, a slim lad, in pale moleskin a good deal bespattered with paint. My friend William Ross stood before me; and his welcome on the occasion was a very hearty one. I had previously taken a hasty survey of my unlucky house in Leith, accompanied by a sharp, keen-looking, one-handed man of middle age, who kept the key, and acted, under the town-clerk, as general manager; and who, as I afterwards ascertained, was the immortal Peter M'Craw. But I had seen nothing suited to put me greatly in conceit with my patrimony. It formed the lowermost floor of an old black building, four stories in height, flanked by a damp narrow court along one of its sides, and that turned to the street its sharp-peaked, many-windowed gable. The lower window were covered up by dilapidated, weather-bleached shutters; in the upper, the comparatively fresh appearance of the rags that stuffed up holes where panes ought to have been, and a few very pale-coloured petticoats and very dark-coloured shirts fluttering in the wind, gave evident signs of habitation. It cost my conductor's one hand an arduous wrench to lay open the lock of the outer door, in front of which he had first to dislodge a very dingy female, attired in an earth-coloured gown, that seemed as if starched with ashes; and as the rusty hinges creaked, and the door fell against the wall, we became sensible of a damp, unwholesome smell, like the breath of a charnel-house, which issued from the interior. The place had been shut up for nearly two years; and so foul had the stagnant atmosphere become, that the candle which we brought with us to explore burned dim and yellow like a miner's lamp. The floors, broken up in fifty different places, were littered with rotten straw; and in one of the corners there lay a damp heap, gathered up like the lair of some wild beast, on which someone seemed to have slept, mayhap months before. The partitions were crazed and tottering; the walls blackened with smoke; broad patches of plaster had fallen from the ceilings, or still dangled from them, suspended by single hairs; and the bars of the grates, crusted with rust, had become red as fox-tails. Mr M'Craw nodded his head over the gathered heap of straw. "Ah," he said—"got in again, I see! The shutters must be looked to." "I daresay," I remarked, looking disconsolately round me, "you don't find it very easy to get tenants for houses of this kind." "*Very* easy!" said Mr M'Craw with somewhat of a Highland twang, and, as I thought, with also a good deal of Highland *hauteur*—as was of course quite natural in so shrewd and extensive a house-agent, when dealing with the owner of a domicile that would not let, and who made foolish remarks—"No, not easy at all, or it would not be locked up in this way: but if we took off the shutters you would soon get tenants enough." "Oh, I suppose so; and I daresay it is as difficult to sell as to let such houses." "Ay, and more," said Mr M'Craw: "it's all sellers, and no buyers, when we get this low." "But do you not think," I perseveringly asked, "that some kind, charitable person might be found in the neighbourhood disposed to take it off my hands as a free gift! It's terrible to be married for life to a baggage of a house like this, and made liable, like other husbands, for all its debts. Is there no way of getting a divorce?" "Don't know," he emphatically replied, with somewhat of a nasal snort; and we so parted; and I saw or heard no more of Peter M'Craw until many years after, when I found him celebrated in the well known song by poor Gilfillan.[1] And in the society of my friend I soon forgot my miserable house, and all the liabilities which it entailed.

---

[1] See next page for note.

I was as entirely unacquainted with great towns at this time as the shepherd in Virgil; and, excited by what I saw, I sadly tasked my friend's peripatetic abilities, and, I fear, his patience also, in taking an admiring survey of all the more characteristic streets, and then in setting out for the top of Arthur's Seat—from which, this evening, I watched the sun set behind the distant Lomonds— that I might acquaint myself with the features of the surrounding country, and the effect of the city as a whole. And amid much confused and imperfect recollection of picturesque groups of ancient buildings, and magnificent assemblages of elegant modern ones, I carried away with me two vividly distinct ideas—first results, as a painter might perhaps say, of a "fresh eye," which no after survey has served to freshen or intensify. I felt that I had seen, not one, but two cities—a city of the past and a city of the

[1] Robert Gilfillan (1798-1850) author of "Oh why I Left my Hame," for some time collector of Poor Rates in Leith.

Well known as Gilfillan's song is among ourselves, it is much less so to the south of the Border, and I present it to my English readers, as a worthy representative, in these latter days, of those ludicrous songs of our country in the olden time which are so admirably suited to show, notwithstanding the gibe of Goldsmith,

"That a Scot may have humour, I almost said wit" (Miller).

THE TAX-GATHERER.

Oh! do you ken Peter, the taxman an' writer?
Ye're well aff wha ken naething 'bout him ava:
They ca' him Inspector, or Poor's Rate Collector—
My faith! he's weel kent in Leith, Peter M'Craw!
He ca's and he comes again—haws, and he hums again—
He's only ae hand, but it's as good as twa:
He pu's't out and raxes, an' draws in the taxes,
An' pouches the siller—shame! Peter M'Craw!

He'll be at your door by daylight on a Monday,
On Tyesday ye're favoured again wi' a ca':
E'en a slee look he gied me at kirk the last Sunday,
Whilk meant—"*Mind the preachin' an' Peter M'Craw.*"
He glowers at my auld door as if he had made it,
He keeks through the keyhole when I am awa':
He'll syne read the auld stane, that tells a' wha read it,
To "*Blisse God for a' giftes,*"[2]—but Peter M'Craw!

[2] A devout legend, common in the seventeenth century above the entrance of houses (Miller).

present—set down side by side as if for purposes of comparison, with a picturesque valley drawn like a deep score between them, to mark off the line of division. And such in reality seems to be the grand peculiarity of the Scottish capital—its distinguishing trait among the cities of the empire; though, of course, during the twenty-nine years that have elapsed since I first saw it, the more ancient of its two cities—greatly modernised in many parts—has become less uniformly and consistently antique in its aspect. Regarded simply as matters of taste, I have found little to admire in the improvements that have so materially changed its aspect. Of its older portions I used never to tire: I found I could walk among them as purely for the pleasure which accrued, as among the wild and picturesque of nature itself; whereas, one visit to the elegant streets and ample squares of the new city always proved sufficient to satisfy; and I certainly never felt the desire to return to any of them to saunter in quest of pleasure along the smooth, well kept pavements. I of course except Princes Street. There the

His sma' papers neatly are 'ranged a' completely,
That yours, for a wonder, 's the first on the raw!
There's nae jinkin' Peter, nae antelope's fleeter,
Nae *cuttin'* acquaintance wi' Peter M'Craw!
'Twas just Friday e'enin', Auld Reekie I'd been in,
I'd gatten a shillin'—I maybe gat twa;
I thought to be happy wi' friends ower a drappie,
When wha suld come pap in—but Peter M'Craw?

There's houp o' a ship though she's sair pressed wi' dangers,
An' roun' her frail timmers the angry winds blaw;
I've aften gat kindness unlooked for frae strangers,
But wha need houp kindness frae Peter M'Craw?
I've kent a man pardoned when just at the gallows—
I've kent a chiel honest whase trade was the law!
I've kent fortune's smile even fa' on gude fallows;
But I ne'er kent exception wi' Peter M'Craw!

Our toun, yince sae cheerie, is dowie an' eerie;
Our shippies hae left us, our trade is awa';
There's nae fair maids strayin', nae wee bairnies playin';
Ye've muckle to answer for, Peter M'Craw!
But what gude o' greevin' as lang's we are leevin'?
My banes I'll soon lay within yon kirkyard wa';
There's nae care shall press me, nae taxes distress me,
For there I'll be free frae thee—Peter M'Craw!

two cities stand ranged side by side, as if for comparison; and the eye falls on the features of a natural scenery that would of itself be singularly pleasing even were both the cities away.

Next day I waited on the town-clerk, Mr Veitch, to see whether he could not suggest to me some way in which I might shake myself loose from my unfortunate property on the Coal-hill. He received me civilly—told me that the property was not quite so desperate an investment as I seemed to think it, as at least the site, in which I had an interest with the other proprietors, was worth something, and as the little courtyard was exclusively my own; and that he thought he could get the whole disposed of for me, if I was prepared to accept of a small price. And I was, of course, as I told him, prepared to accept of a very small one. Further, on learning that I was a stone-cutter, and unemployed, he kindly introduced me to one of his friends, a master-builder, by whom I was engaged to work at a manor-house a few miles to the south of Edinburgh. And procuring "lodgings" in a small cottage of but a single apartment, near the village of Niddry Mill, I commenced my labours as a hewer under the shade of the Niddry woods.

There was a party of sixteen masons employed at Niddry, besides apprentice and labourers. They were accomplished stone-cutters—skilful, especially in the cutting of mouldings, far above the average of the masons of the north country; and it was with some little solicitude that I set myself to labour beside them on mullions, and transoms, and labels, for our work was in the old English style—a style in which I had no previous practice. I was diligent, however, and kept old John Fraser's principle in view (though, as Nature had been less liberal in imparting the necessary faculties, I could not cut so directly as he used to do on the required planes and curves enclosed in the stones); and I had the satisfaction of finding, when pay night came round, that the foreman, who had frequently stood beside me during the week to observe my modes of working, and the progress which I made, estimated my services at the same rate as he did those of the others. I was by and by intrusted, too, like the best of them, with all the more difficult kinds of work required in the erection, and was at one time engaged for six weeks together in fashioning long, slim, deeply-moulded mullions, not one of which broke in my hand, though the stone on which I wrought was brittle and gritty, and but indifferently suited for the nicer purposes of the architect. I soon found, however, that most of my brother workmen regarded me with undisguised hostility and dislike, and would have been better pleased had I, as they seemed to expect, from the northern locality in which I had been reared, broken down in the trial. I was, they said, "a Highlander newly come to Scotland," and, if not chased northwards again, would carry home with me half the money of the country. Some of the builders used to criticize very unfairly the workmanship of the stones which I hewed: they could not lay them, they said: and the hewers sometimes refused to assist me in carrying in or in turning the weightier blocks on which I wrought. The foreman, however, a worthy, pious man, a member of a Secession congregation, stood my friend, and encouraged me to persevere. "Do not," he said "suffer yourself to be driven from the work, and they will soon tire out, and leave you to pursue your own course. I know exactly the nature of your offence: you do not drink with them or treat them; but they will soon cease to expect that you should; and when once they find that you are not to be coerced or driven off, they will let you alone." As, however, from the abundance of employment—a consequence of the building mania—the men were masters and more at the time, the foreman could not take my part openly in opposition to them; but I was grateful for his kindness, and felt too thoroughly indignant at the mean fellows who could take such odds against an inoffensive stranger, to be much in danger of yielding to the combination. It is only a weak man whom the wind deprives of his cloak: a man of the average strength is more in danger of losing it when assailed by the genial beams of a too kindly sun.

I threw myself, as usual, for the compensatory pleasures, on my evening walks, but found the enclosed state of the district, and the fence of a rigorously-administered trespass-law, serious drawbacks; and ceased to wonder that a thoroughly cultivated country is, in most instances, so much less beloved by its people than a wild and open one. Rights of proprietorship may exist equally in both; but there is an important sense in which the open country belongs to the proprietors and to the people too. All that the heart and the intellect can derive from it may be alike free to peasant and aristocrat; whereas the cultivated and strictly fenced country belongs usually, in every sense, to only the proprietor; and as it is a much simpler and more obvious matter to love one's country as a scene of hills, and streams, and green fields, amid which Nature has often been enjoyed, than as a definite locality, in which certain laws and constitutional privileges exist, it is rather to be regretted than ordered at that there should be often less true patriotism in a country of just institutions and equal laws, whose soil has been so exclusively appropriated as to leave only the dusty high-roads to its people, than in wild open countries, in which the popular mind and affections are left free to embrace the soil, but whose institutions are partial and defective. Were our beloved Monarch to regard such of the gentlemen of her court as taboo their Glen Tilts, and shut up the passes of the Grampians, as a sort of disloyal Destructives of a peculiar type, who make it their vocation to divest her people of their patriotism, and who virtually teach them that a country no longer theirs is not worth the fighting for, it might be very safely concluded that she was but manifesting, in one other direction, the strong good sense which has ever distinguished her. Though shut out, however, from the neighbouring fields and policies, the Niddry woods were open to me; and I have enjoyed many an agreeable saunter along a broad planted belt, with a grassy path in the midst that forms their southern boundary, and through whose long vista I could see the sun sink over the picturesque ruins of Craigmillar Castle. A few peculiarities in the natural history of the district showed me, that the two degrees of latitude which lay between me and the former scenes of my studies were not without their influence on both the animal and vegetable kingdoms. The group of land-shells was different, in at least its proportions; and one well-marked mollusc—the large tortoise-shell helix[1] (*helix aspersa*), very abundant in this neighbourhood—I had never seen in the north at all. I formed, too, my first acquaintance in this woody, bush-skirted walk, with the hedgehog[2] in its wild state—an animal which does not occur to the north of the Moray Firth. I saw, besides, though the summer was of but the average warmth, the oak ripening its acorns—a rare occurrence among the Cromarty woods where in at least nine out of every ten seasons, the fruit merely forms and then drops off. But my researches this season lay rather among fossils than among recent plants and animals. I was now for the first time located on the Carboniferous System:[3] the stone at which I wrought was intercalated among the working coal-seams, and abounded in well-marked impressions of the more robust vegetables of the period—stigmaria,[4] sigillaria,[5] calamites,[6] and lepidodendra;[7] and as they greatly excited my curiosity, I spent many an evening hour in the quarry in which they occurred, in tracing their forms in the rock; or, extending my walks to the neighbouring coal pits, I laid open with my hammer, in quest of organisms, the blocks of shale or stratified clay raised from beneath by the miner. There existed at the time none of those popular digests of geological science which are now so common; and so I had to grope my way without guide or assistant, and wholly unfurnished with a vocabulary. At length, however, by dint of patient labour, I came to form not very erroneous, though of course inadequate, conceptions of the ancient Coal Measure Flora: it was impossible to doubt that its numerous ferns were really such; and though I at first failed to trace the supposed

[1] A genus of land-snails.
[2] This animal is now common in the neighbourhood of Cromarty, where it does not seem to have existed in Miller's time.
[3] The principal geological division in which Coal Measures occur.
[4] The roots of Sigillaria, not an independent "vegetable" as was long believed.
[5] A common tree of the Coal Measures, the trunk of which is marked by vertical lines enclosing parallel rows of leaf-scars like seals (*sigilla*).
[6] Tall reed-like plants resembling exaggerated horsetails that grew in thick brakes along the lagoon borders of the Sigillarian jungle.
[7] "Scaly" (*lepis*) trees of the Coal rising to fifty feet or more, resembling the lowly club-moss on a gigantic scale.

analogies of its lepidodendra and calamites, it was at least evident that they were the bole-like stems of great plants, that had stood erect like trees. A certain amount of fact, too, once acquired, enabled me to assimilate to the mass little snatches of information, derived from chance paragraphs and occasional articles in magazines and reviews, that, save for my previous acquaintance with the organisms to which they referred, would have told me nothing. And so the vegetation of the Coal Measures began gradually to form within my mind's eye, where all had been blank before, as I had seen the spires and columns of Edinburgh forming amid the fog, on the morning of my arrival.

I found, however, one of the earliest dreams of my youth curiously mingling with my restorations, or rather forming their groundwork. I had read Gulliver at the proper age; and my imagination had become filled with the little men and women, and retained strong hold of at least one scene laid in the country of the very tall men—that in which the traveller, after wandering amid grass that rose twenty feet over his head, lost himself in a vast thicket of barley forty feet high. I became the owner, in fancy, of a colony of Lilliputians, that manned my eighteen-inch canoe, or tilled my apron-breadth of a garden; and, coupling with the men of Lilliput the scene in Brobdingnag, I had often set myself to imagine, when playing truant on the green slopes of the Hill, or among the swamps of the "Willows," how some of the vignette-like scenes by which I was surrounded would have appeared to creatures so minute. I have imagined them threading their way through dark forests of bracken forty feet high—or admiring on the hill-side some enormous club-moss that stretched out its green hairy arms for whole roods—or arrested at the edge of some dangerous morass, by hedges of gigantic horse-tail, that bore a-top, high over the bog, their many-windowed, club-like cones, and at every point shot forth their green verticillate leaves, huge as coach-wheels divested of the rim. And while I thus dreamed for my Lilliputian companions, I became for the time a Lilliputian myself, examined the minute in Nature as if through a magnifying-glass, roamed in fancy under ferns that had shot up into trees, and saw the dark club-like heads of the equisetaceæ[1] stand up over the spiky branches, some six yards or so above head. And now, strange to tell, I found I had just to fall back on my old juvenile imaginings, and to form my first approximate conceptions of the forests of the Coal Measures, by learning to look at our ferns, club-mosses, and equisetaceæ, with the eye of some wandering traveller of Lilliput lost amid their entanglements. When sauntering at sunset along the edge of a wood-embosomed stream that ran through the grounds, and beside which the horse-tail rose thick and rank in the danker hollows, and the bracken shot out its fronds from the drier banks, I had to sink in fancy, as of old, into a manikin of a few inches, and to see intertropical jungles in the tangled grasses and thickly-interlaced equisetaceæ, and tall trees in the brake and the lady-fern. But many a wanting feature had to be supplied, and many an existing one altered. Amid forests of arboraceous ferns, and of horse-tails tall as the masts of pinnaces, there stood up gigantic club-mosses, thicker than the body of a man, and from sixty to eighty feet in height, that mingled their foliage with strange monsters of the vegetable world, of types no longer recognisable among the existing forms— sculptured ullodendra,[2] bearing rectilinear stripes of sessile[3] cones along their sides—and ornately tattooed sigillaria, fluted like columns, and with vertical rows of leaves bristling over their stems and larger branches. Such were some of the dreams in which I began at this period for the first time to indulge; nor have they, like the other dreams of youth, passed away. The aged poet has not unfrequently to complain that, as he rises in years, his "visions float less palpably before him." Those, on the contrary, which science conjures up, grow in distinctness, as, in the process of slow acquirement, form after form is evoked from out the obscurity of the past, and one restoration added to another.

[1] Horse-tail.
[2] The fertile or cone-bearing branches of *Lepidodendron*, long supposed to be an independent species.
[3] Directly attached, not supported on a stalk.

There were at this time several collier villages in the neighbourhood of Edinburgh, which have since disappeared. They were situated on what were called the "edge-coals"—those steep seams of the Mid-Lothian Coal Basin which, lying low in the system, have got a more vertical tilt against the trap eminences of the south and west than the upper seams in the middle of the field, and which, as they could not be followed in their abrupt descent beyond a certain depth, are now regarded, for at least the practical purposes of the miner, and until the value of coal shall have risen considerably, as wrought out. One of these villages, whose foundations can no longer be traced, occurred in the immediate vicinity of Niddry Mill. It was a wretched assemblage of dingy, low-roofed, tile-covered hovels, each of which perfectly resembled all the others, and was inhabited by a rude and ignorant race of men, that still bore about them the soil and stain of recent slavery. Curious as the fact may seem, all the older men of the village, though situated little more than four miles from Edinburgh, had been born slaves. Nay, eighteen years later (in 1842), when Parliament issued a commission to inquire into the nature and results of female labour in the coal-pits of Scotland, there was a collier still living that had never been twenty miles from the Scottish capital, who could state to the Commissioners that both his father and grandfather had been slaves—that he himself had been born a slave—and that he had wrought for years in a pit in the neighbourhood of Musselburgh ere the colliers got their freedom. Father and grandfather had been parishioners of the late Dr Carlyle of Inveresk. They were contemporary with Chatham and Cowper, and Burke and Fox; and at a time when Granville Sharpe could have stepped forward and effectually protected the runaway negro who had taken refuge from the tyranny of his master in a British port, no man could have protected *them* from the Inveresk laird, their proprietor, had they dared to exercise the right, common to all Britons besides, of removing to some other locality, or of making choice of some other employment. Strange enough, surely, that so entire a fragment of the barbarous past should have been thus dovetailed into the age not yet wholly passed away! I regard it as one of the more singular circumstances of my life, that I should have conversed with Scotchmen who had been born slaves. The collier women of this village—poor over-toiled creatures, who carried up all the coal from underground on their backs, by a long turnpike stair inserted in one of the shafts—continued to bear more of the marks of serfdom still about them than even the men. How these poor women did labour, and how thoroughly, even at this time, were they characterized by the slave nature! It has been estimated by a man who knew them well—Mr Robert Bald—that one of their ordinary day's work was equal to the carrying of a hundred weight from the level of the sea to the top of Ben Lomond. They were marked by a peculiar type of mouth, by which I learned to distinguish them from all the other females of the country. It was wide, open, thick-lipped, projecting equally above and below, and exactly resembled that which we find in the prints given of savages in their lowest and most degraded state, in such narratives of our modern voyagers as, for instance, the "Narrative of Captain Fitzroy's Second Voyage of the Beagle." During, however, the lapse of the last twenty years this type of mouth seems to have disappeared in Scotland. It was accompanied by traits of almost infantile weakness. I have seen these collier women crying like children, when toiling under their load along the upper rounds of the wooden stair that traversed the shaft; and then returning, scarce a minute after, with the empty creel, singing with glee. The collier houses were chiefly remarkable for being all alike, outside and in; all were equally dingy, dirty, naked, and uncomfortable. I first learned to suspect, in this rude village, that the democratic watchword, "Liberty and Equality," is somewhat faulty in its philosophy. "Slavery and Equality" would be nearer the mark. Wherever there is liberty, the original differences between man and man begin to manifest themselves in their external circumstances, and the equality straightway ceases. It is through slavery that equality, among at least the masses, is to be fully attained.[1]

I found but little intelligence in the neighbourhood, among even the villagers and country people, that stood on a higher platform than the colliers. The fact may be variously accounted for; but so it is, that though there is almost always more than the average amount of knowledge and acquirement amongst the mechanics of large towns, the little hamlets and villages by which they are surrounded are usually inhabited by a class considerably below the average. In M. Quetelet's interesting "Treatise on Man," we find a series of maps given, which, based on extensive statistical tables, exhibit by darker and lighter shadings the moral and intellectual character of the people in the various districts of the countries which they represent. In one map, for instance, representative of the state of education in France, while certain well-taught provinces are represented by a bright tint, as if enjoying the light, there are others, in which great ignorance obtains, that exhibit a deep shade of blackness, as if a cloud rested over them; and the general aspect of the whole is that of a

[1] The act for manumitting our Scotch colliers was passed in the year 1775, forty-nine years prior to the date of my acquaintance with the class at Niddry. But though it was only such colliers of the village as were in their fiftieth year when I knew them (with, of course, all the older ones), who had been born slaves, even its men of thirty had actually, though not nominally, come into the world in a state of bondage, in consequence of certain penalties attached to the emancipating act, of which the poor ignorant workers underground were both too improvident and too little ingenious to keep clear. They were set free, however, by a second act passed in 1799. The language of both these acts, regarded as British ones of the latter half of the last century, and as bearing reference to British subjects living within the limits of the island, strikes with startling effect. "Whereas," says the preamble of the older act—that of 1775— "by the statute law of Scotland, as explained by the judges of the courts of law there, many colliers, and coal-bearers, and salters, are in a state of *slavery or bondage*, bound to the collieries or saltworks where they work *for life, transferable with the collieries and saltworks;* and whereas the emancipating," &c. &c. A passage in the preamble of the act of 1799 is scarce less striking: it declares that, notwithstanding the former act, "many colliers and coal bearers *still continue in a state of bondage*" in Scotland. The history of our Scotch colliers will be found a curious and instructive one. Their slavery seems not to have been derived from the ancient times of general serfship, but to have originated in comparatively modern acts of the Scottish Parliament, and in decisions of the Court of Session— in acts of Parliament in which the poor ignorant subterranean men of the country were, of course, wholly unrepresented, and in decisions of a Court in which no agent of theirs ever made appearance in their behalf. (Miller)

landscape seen from a hill-top in a day of dappled light and shadow. There are certain minuter shadings, however, by which certain curious facts might be strikingly represented to the eye in this manner, for which statistical tables furnish no adequate basis, but which men who have seen a good deal of the people of a country might be able to give in a manner at least approximately correct. In a shaded map representative of the intelligence of Scotland, I would be disposed—sinking the lapsed classes, or representing them merely by a few such dark spots as mottle the sun—to represent the large towns as centres of focal brightness; but each of these focal centres I would encircle with a halo of darkness considerably deeper in shade than the medium spaces beyond. I found that in the tenebrious halo of the Scottish capital there existed, independently of the ignorance of the poor colliers, three distinct elements. A considerable proportion of the villagers were farm-servants in the decline of life, who, unable any longer to procure, as in their days of unbroken strength, regular engagements from the farmers of the district, supported them-selves as occasional labourers. And they, of course, were charac-terized by the ignorance of their class. Another portion of the people were carters—employed mainly, in these times, ere the railways began, in supplying the Edinburgh coal-market, and in driving building materials into the city from the various quarries. And carters as a class, like all who live much in the society of horses, are invariably ignorant and unintellectual. A third, but greatly smaller portion than either of the other two, consisted of mechanics; but it was only mechanics of an inferior order, that remained outside the city to work for carters and labourers; the better skilled, and, as to a certain extent the terms are convertible, the more intelligent mechanics found employment and a home in Edinburgh. The cottage in which I lodged was inhabited by an old farm-servant—a tall, large-bodied, small-headed man, who, in his journey through life, seemed to have picked up scarce an idea; and his wife, a woman turned of sixty, though a fine enough *body* in the main, and a careful manager, was not more intellectual.

They had but a single apartment in their humble dwelling, fenced off by a little bit of partition from the outer door—and I could fain have wished that they had two—but there was no choice of lodgings in the village, and I had just to content myself, as the working man always must in such circumstances, with the shelter I could get. My bed was situated in the one end of the room, and my landlady's and her husband's in the other, with the passage by which we entered between; but decent old Peggy Russel had been accustomed to such arrangements all her life long, and seemed never once to think of the matter, and—as she had reached that period of life at which women of the humbler class assume the characteristics of the other sex, somewhat, I suppose, on the principle on which very ancient female birds put on male plumage—I in a short time ceased to think of it also. It is not the less true, however, that the purposes of decency demand that much should be done, especially in the southern and midland districts of Scotland, for the dwellings of the poor.

CHAPTER XV

"See Inebriety, her wand she waves,
And lo! her pale; and lo! her purple slaves."—CRABBE.

I WAS joined in the course of a few weeks, in Peggy Russel's one-roomed cottage, by another lodger—lodgers of the humbler class usually consociating together in pairs. My new companion had lived for some time, ere my arrival at Niddry, in a neighbouring domicile, which, as he was what was termed a "quiet-living man," and as the inmates were turbulent and unsteady, he had, after bearing a good deal, been compelled to quit. Like our foreman, he was a strict Seceder,[1] in full communion with his church. Though merely a common labourer, with not more than half the wages of our skilled workmen, I had observed, ere our acquaintance began, that no mason in the squad was more comfortably attired on week-days than he, or wore a better suit on Sunday; and so I had set him down, from the circumstance, as a decent man. I now found that, like my uncle Sandy, he was a great reader of good books—an admirer even of the same old authors—deeply read like him, in Durham and Rutherford—and entertaining, too, a high respect for Baxter, Boston, old John Brown, and the Erskines. In one respect, however, he differed from both my uncles: he had begun to question the excellence of religious Establishments; nay, to hold that the country might be none the worse were its Ecclesiastical endowments taken away—a view which our foreman also entertained; whereas both Uncles Sandy and James were as little averse as the old divines themselves to a State-paid ministry, and desiderated only that it should be a good

---

[1] A supporter of the Secession Church which hived off from the Establishment in 1733 mainly in protest against forcing a minister on a parish against the will of the congregation. It was the nucleus of the later United Presbyterian Church, which united with the Free Church in 1900. The leader of the Secession was the Rev. Ebenezer Erskine. Later he was joined by his brother, the Rev. Ralph.

one. There were two other Seceders engaged as masons at the work—more of the polemical and less of the devout type than the foreman or my new comrade the labourer; and they also used occasionally to speak, not merely of the doubtful usefulness, but—as they were stronger in their language than their more self-denying and more consistent co-religionists—of the positive worthlessness of Establishments. The Voluntary controversy[1] did not break out until about nine years after this time, when the Reform Bill gave vent to many a pent-up opinion and humour among that class to which it extended the franchise; but the materials of the war were evidently already accumulating among the intelligent Dissenters of Scotland; and from what I now saw, its first appearance in a somewhat formidable aspect failed to take me by surprise. I must in justice add, that all the religion of our party was to be found among its Seceders. Our other workmen were really wild fellows, most of whom never entered a church. A decided reaction had already commenced within the Establishment, on the cold, elegant, unpopular Moderatism of the previous period—that Moderatism which had been so adequately represented in the Scottish capital by the theology of Blair and the ecclesiastical policy of Robertson; but it was chiefly among the middle and upper classes that the reaction had begun; and scarce any portion of the humbler people, lost to the Church during the course of the two preceding generations, had yet been recovered. And so the working men of Edinburgh and its neighbourhood at this time, were in large part either non-religious, or included within the Independent or Secession pale.

John Wilson—for such was the name of my new comrade—was a truly good man—devout, conscientious, friendly—not highly intellectual, but a person of plain good sense, and by no means devoid of general information. There was another labourer at the work, an unhappy little man, with whom I have often seen John engaged in mixing mortar, or carrying materials to the builders, but never without being struck by the contrast which

---

[1] See note at start of Chapter XXV.

they presented in character and appearance. John was a plain, somewhat rustic-looking personage; and an injury which he had received from gunpowder in a quarry, that had destroyed the sight of one of his eyes, and considerably dimmed that of the other, had, of course, not served to improve his looks; but he always wore a cheerful, contented air; and, with all his homeliness, was a person pleasant to the sight. His companion was a really handsome man—grey-haired, silvery-whiskered, with an aristocratic cast of countenance, that would have done no discredit to a royal drawing-room, and an erect though somewhat petit figure, cast in a mould that, if set off more to advantage, would have been recognised as elegant. But John Lindsay—for so he was called—bore always the stamp of misery on his striking features. There lay between the poor little man and the Crawford peerage only a narrow chasm, represented by a missing marriage certificate; but he was never able to bridge the gulf across; and he had to toil on in unhappiness, in consequence, as a mason's labourer. I have heard the call resounding from the walls twenty times a day—"John, Yearl Crafurd, bring us anither hod o' lime."

I found religion occupying a much humbler place among these workmen of the south of Scotland than that which I had used to see assigned to it in the north. In my native district and the neighbouring counties, it still spoke with authority; and a man who stood up in its behalf in any society, unless very foolish or very inconsistent, always succeeded in silencing opposition, and making good its claims. Here, however, the irreligious asserted their power as the majority, and carried matters with a high hand; and religion itself, existing as but *dissent*, not as an *establishment*, had to content itself with bare toleration. Remonstrance, or even advice, was not permitted. "Johnnie, boy," I have heard one of the rougher mechanics say, half in jest, half in earnest, to my companion, "if you set yourself to convert me, I'll brak your face;" and I have known another of them remark, with a patronizing air, that "kirks werena very bad things, after a';" that he "aye liked to be in a kirk, for the sake of decency, once a twelvemonth;" and that, as he "hadna been kirked for the last ten months, he was just only waiting for a rainy Sabbath, to lay in his stock o' divinity for the year." Our new lodger, aware how little any interference with the religious concerns of others was tolerated in the place, seemed unable for some time to muster up resolution enough to broach in the family his favourite subject. He retired every night, before going to bed, to his closet—the blue vault with all its stars—often the only closet of the devout lodger in a south-country cottage; but I saw that each evening, ere he went out, he used to look uneasily at the landlord and me, as if there lay some weight on his mind regarding us, of which he was afraid to rid himself, and which yet rendered him very uncomfortable. "Well, John," I asked one evening, speaking direct, to his evident embarrassment, "what is it?" John looked at old William the landlord, and then at me. "Did we not think it right," he said, "that there should be evening worship in the family?" Old William had not idea enough for conversation; he either signified acquiescence in whatever was said that pleased him, by an ever-recurring ay, ay, ay; or he grumbled out his dissent in a few explosive sounds, that conveyed his meaning rather in their character as tones than as vocables. But there now mingled with the ordinary explosions the distinct enunciation, given with, for him, unwonted emphasis, that he "wasna for *that*." I struck in, however, on the other side, and appealed to Peggy. "I was sure," I said, "that Mrs Russel would see the propriety of John's proposal." And Mrs Russel, as most women would have done in the circumstances, unless, indeed, very bad ones, did see the propriety of it; and from that evening forward the cottage had its family worship. John's prayers were always very earnest and excellent, but sometimes just a little too long; and old William, who, I fear, did not greatly profit by them, used not unfrequently to fall asleep on his knees. But though he sometimes stole to his bed when John chanced to be a little later in taking the book than usual, and got into a profound slumber ere the prayer began, he deferred to the majority, and gave us no active opposition. He was not a vicious man: his intellect had slept through life, and he had as little religion as an old horse or dog; but he was quiet and honest, and, to the measure of his failing ability, a faithful worker in his humble employments. His religious training, like that of his brother villagers, seemed to have been sadly neglected. Had he gone to the parish church on Sunday, he would have heard a respectable moral essay read from the pulpit, and would, of course, have slept under it; but William, like most of his neighbours, preferred sleeping out the day at home, and never did go to the church; and as certainly as he went not to the teacher of religion, the teacher of religion never came to him. During the ten months which I spent in the neighbourhood of Niddry Mill, I saw neither minister nor missionary. But if the village furnished no advantageous ground on which to fight the battle of religious Establishments—seeing that the Establishment was of no manner of use there—it furnished ground quite as unsuitable for the class of Voluntaries who hold that the supply of religious instruction should, as in the case of all other commodities, be regulated by the demand. Demand and supply were admirably well balanced in the village of Niddry: there was no religious instruction, and no wish or desire for it.

The masons at Niddry House were paid fortnightly, on a Saturday night. Wages were high—we received two pounds eight shillings for our two weeks' work; but scarce half-a-dozen in the squad could claim at settlement the full tale, as the Monday and Tuesday after pay-night were usually blank days, devoted by two-thirds of the whole to drinking and debauchery. Not often have wages been more sadly mis-spent than by my poor work-fellows at Niddry, during this period of abundant and largely-remuner-ated employment. On receiving their money, they set straightway off to Edinburgh, in parties of threes and fours; and until the evening of the following Monday or Tuesday I saw no more of them. They would then come dropping in, pale, dirty, disconso-late-looking—almost always in the reactionary state of unhappiness which succeeds intoxication—(they themselves used to term it "*the horrors*")—and with their nervous system so shaken, that rarely until a day or two after did they recover their ordinary working ability. Narratives of their adventures, however, would then begin to circulate through the squad—adventures commonly of the "Tom and Jerry" type; and always, the more extravagant they were, the greater was the admiration which they excited. On one occasion, I remember (for it was much spoken about as a manifestation of high spirit) that three of them, hiring a coach, drove out on the Sunday to visit Roslin and Hawthornden, and in this way spent their six pounds so much in the style of gentlemen, that they were able to get back to the mallet without a farthing on the evening of Monday. And, as they were at work on Tuesday in consequence, they succeeded, as they said, in saving the wages of a day usually lost, just by doing the thing so genteelly. Edinburgh had in those times a not very efficient police, and, in some of its less reputable localities, must have been dangerous. Burke found its West Port a fitting scene for his horrid trade a good many years after; and from the stories of some of our bolder spirits, which, though mayhap exaggerated, had evidently their nucleus of truth, there was not a little of the violent and the lawless perpetrated in its viler haunts during the years of the speculation mania. Four of our masons found, one Saturday evening, a country lad bound hand and foot on the floor of a dark inner room in one of the dens of the High Street; and such was the state of exhaustion to which he was reduced mainly through the compression of an old apron wrapped tightly round his face, that though they set him loose, it was some time ere he could muster strength enough to crawl away. He had been robbed by a bevy of women whom he had been foolish enough to treat; and on threatening to call in the watchman, they had fallen upon a way of keeping him quiet, which, save for the interference of my wild fellow-workmen, would soon have rendered him permanently so. And such was but one of many stories of the kind.

There was of course a considerable diversity of talent and acquirement among my more reckless associates at the work; and it was curious enough to mark their very various views regarding what constituted spirit or the want of it. One weak lad used to tell us about a singularly spirited brother apprentice of his, who not only drank, kept loose company, and played all sorts of very mischievous practical jokes, but even occasionally stole out of warehouses; which was of course a very dauntless thing, seeing that it brought him within wind of the gallows; whereas another of our wild workmen—a man of sense and intelligence—not unfrequently cut short the narratives of the weaker brother, by characterizing his spirited apprentice as a mean, graceless scamp, who, had he got his deservings, would have been hung like a dog. I found that the intelligence which results from a fair school education, sharpened by a subsequent taste for reading, very much heightened in certain items the standard by which my comrades regulated their conduct. Mere intelligence formed no guard amongst them against intemperance or licentiousness; but it did form a not ineffectual protection against what are peculiarly the mean vices—such as theft, and the grosser and more creeping forms of untruthfulness and dishonesty. Of course, exceptional cases occur in all grades of society: there have been accomplished ladies of wealth and rank who have indulged in a propensity for stealing out of drapers' shops; and gentlemen of birth and education who could not be trusted in a library or a bookseller's back-room; and what sometimes occurs in the higher walks must be occasionally exemplified in the lower also; but, judging from what I have seen, I must hold it as a general rule, that a good intellectual education is a not inefficient protection against the meaner felonies, though not in any degree against the "pleasant vices." The only adequate protection against both, equally, is the sort of education which my friend John Wilson the labourer exemplified—a kind of education not often acquired in schools, and not much more frequently possessed by schoolmasters than by any other class of professional men.

The most remarkable man in our party was a young fellow of three-and-twenty—at least as much a blackguard as any of his companions, but possessed of great strength of character and

311

intellect, and, with all his wildness, marked by very noble traits. He was a strongly and not inelegantly formed man, of about six feet—dark-complexioned, and of a sullen cast of countenance, which, however, though he could, I doubt not, become quite as formidable as he looked, concealed in his ordinary moods much placidity of temper, and a rich vein of humour. Charles was the recognised hero of the squad; but he differed considerably from the men who admired him most. Burns tells us that he "often courted the acquaintance of the part of mankind commonly known by the ordinary phrase of *blackguards*;" and that, "though disgraced by follies, nay, sometimes stained with guilt, he had yet found among them, in not a few instances, some of the noblest virtues—magnanimity, generosity, disinterested friendship, and even modesty." I cannot say with the poet that I ever courted the acquaintance of blackguards; but though the labouring man may select his friends, he cannot choose his work-fellows; and so I have not unfrequently *come in contact* with blackguards, and have had opportunities of pretty thoroughly knowing them. And my experience of the class has been very much the reverse of that of Burns. I have usually found their virtues of a merely theatric cast, and their vices real: much assumed generosity in some instances, but a callousness of feeling, and meanness of spirit, lying concealed beneath. In this poor fellow, however, I certainly did find a sample of the nobler variety of the *genus*. Poor Charles did too decidedly belong to it. He it was that projected the Sunday party to Roslin; and he it was that, pressing his way into the recesses of a disreputable house in the High Street, found the fast-bound wight choking in an apron, and, unloosing the cords, let him go. No man of the party squandered his gains more recklessly than Charles, or had looser notions regarding the legitimacy of the uses to which he too often applied them. And yet, notwithstanding, he was a generous-hearted fellow; and, under the influence of religious principle, would, like Burns himself, have made a very noble man.

In gradually forming my acquaintance with him, I was at first struck by the circumstance that he never joined in the clumsy ridicule with which I used to be assailed by the other workmen. When left, too, on one occasion, in consequence of a tacit combination against me, to roll up a large stone to the sort of block-bench, or *siege*, as it is technically termed, on which the mass had to be hewn, and as I was slowly succeeding in doing, through dint of very violent effort, what some two or three men usually united to do, Charles stepped out to assist me; and the combination at once broke down. Unlike the others, too, who, while they never scrupled to take odds against me, seemed sufficiently chary of coming in contact with me singly, he learned to seek me out in our intervals of labour, and to converse on subjects upon which we felt a common interest. He was not only an excellent operative mechanic, but possessed also of considerable architectural skill; and in this special province we found an interchange of idea not unprofitable. He had a turn, too, for reading, though he was by no means extensively read; and liked to converse about books. Nor, though the faculty had been but little cultivated, was he devoid of an eye for the curious in nature. On directing his attention, one morning, to a well-marked impression of lepidodendron, which delicately fretted with its lozenge-shaped network one of the planes of the stone before me, he began to describe, with a minuteness of observation not common among working men, certain strange forms which had attracted his notice when employed among the grey flagstones of Forfarshire. I long after recognised in his description that strange crustacean of the Middle Old Red Sandstone of Scotland, the *Pterygotus*[1]—an organism which was wholly unknown at this time to geologists, and which is but partially known still; and I saw in 1838, on the publication, in its first edition, of the "Elements" of Sir Charles Lyell, what he meant to indicate, by a rude sketch which he drew on the stone before us, and which, to the base of a semi-ellipsis, somewhat resembling a horseshoe, united an angular prolongation not very

[1] A genus of Eurypterids or "Water-Scorpions" now extinct. The "Middle O. R." here should be the "Lower O. R." A genus closely allied to Pterygotus discovered in the United States (*Upper Silurian*, New York State) has been named *Hughmilleria*.

313

unlike the iron stem of a pointing trowel drawn from the handle. He had evidently seen, long ere it had been detected by the scientific eye, that strange ichthyolite of the Old Red system, the *Cephalaspis*.[1] His story, though he used to tell it with great humour, and no little dramatic effect, was in reality a very sad one. He had quarrelled, when quite a lad, with one of his fellow-workmen, and was unfortunate enough, in the pugilistic encounter which followed, to break his jawbone, and otherwise so severely to injure him, that for some time his recovery seemed doubtful. Flying, pursued by the officers of the law, he was, after a few days' hiding, apprehended, lodged in jail, tried at the High Court of Justiciary, and ultimately sentenced to three months' imprisonment. And these three months he had to spend—for such was the wretched arrangement of the time—in the worst society in the world. In sketching, as he sometimes did, for the general amusement, the characters of the various prisoners with whom he had associated—from the sneaking pick-pocket and the murderous ruffian, to the simple Highland smuggler, who had converted his grain into whisky, with scarce intelligence enough to see that there was aught morally wrong in the transaction—he sought only to be as graphic and humorous as he could, and always with complete success. But there attached to his narratives an unintentional moral; and I cannot yet call them up without feeling indignant at that detestable practice of promiscuous imprisonment which so long obtained in our country, and which had the effect of converting its jails into such complete criminal-manufacturing institutions, that, had the honest men of the community risen and dealt by them as the Lord George Gordon mob dealt with Newgate, I hardly think they would have been acting out of character. Poor Charles had a nobility in his nature which saved him from being contaminated by what was worst in his meaner associates; but he was none the better for his imprisonment, and he quitted jail, of course, a marked man; and his after career was, I fear, all the more reckless in consequence of the stain imparted

[1] A "buckler-headed" fish.

314

at this time to his character. He was as decidedly a leader among his brother workmen as I myself had been, when sowing my wild oats, among my schoolfellows; but society in its resettled state, and in a country such as ours, allows no such scope to the man as it does to the boy; and so his leadership, dangerous both to himself and his associates, had chiefly as the scene of its trophies the grosser and more lawless haunts of vice and dissipation. His course through life was a sad, and, I fear, a brief one. When that sudden crash in the commercial world took place, in which the speculation mania of 1824-25 terminated, he was, with thousands more, thrown out of employment, and, having saved not a farthing of his earnings, he was compelled, under the pressure of actual want, to enlist as a soldier into one of the regiments of the line, bound for one of the intertropical colonies. And there, as his old comrades lost all trace of him, he too probably fell a victim, in an insalubrious climate, to old habits and new rum.

Finding me incorrigible, I was at length left by my brother operatives to be as peculiar as I pleased; and the working portion of the autumnal months passed off pleasantly enough in hewing great stones under the branching foliage of the elm and chestnut trees of Niddry Park. From the circumstance, however, that the stones were so great, the previous trial had been an embarrassing one; and, though too proud to confess that I cared aught about the matter, I was now glad enough that it was fairly over. Our modern Temperance Societies—institutions which at this time had not begun to exist—had done much to shield sober working men from combinations of the trying character to which, in the generation well-nigh passed away, they were too often exposed. There are few working parties which have not now their groups of enthusiastic Teetotallers, that always band together against the drinkers, and mutually assist and keep one another in countenance: and a breakwater is thus formed in the middle of the stream, to protect from that grinding oppression of the poor by the poor which, let popular agitators declaim on the other side as they may, is at once more trying and more general than the oppression which they experience from the great and wealthy. According to the striking figure of the wise old king, "it is like a sweeping rain, which leaveth no food." Fanaticism in itself is not a good thing; nor are there many quiet people who do not dislike enthusiasm; and the members of new sects, whether they be religious sects or no, are almost always enthusiasts, and in some degree fanatical. A man can scarce become a vegetarian even without also becoming in some measure intolerant of the still large and not very disreputable class that eat beef with their greens, and herrings with their potatoes; and the drinkers of water do say rather strong things of the men who, had they been guests at the marriage in Cana of Galilee, would have seen no great harm in partaking in moderation of the wine. There is a somewhat intolerant fanaticism among the Teetotallers, just as there is fanaticism amongst most other new sects; and yet, recognising it simply as strength, and knowing what it has to contend with, I am much disposed to tolerate it, whether *it* tolerate me or no. Human nature, with all its defects, is a wiser thing than the mere common sense of the creatures whose nature it is; and we find in it special provisions, as in the instincts of the humbler animals, for overmastering the special difficulties with which it is its destiny to contend. And the sort of fanaticism to which I refer seems to be one of those provisions. A few Teetotallers of the average calibre and strength, who take their stand against the majority in a party of wild dissipated mechanics, would require a considerable amount of vigorous fanaticism to make good their position; nor do I see in ordinary men, as society at present exists, aught at once sufficiently potent in its nature, and sufficiently general in its existence, to take its place and do its work. It seems to subsist in the present imperfect state as a wise provision, though, like other wise provisions, such as the horns of the bull or the sting of the bee, it is misdirected at times, and does harm.

Winter came on, and our weekly wages were lowered, immediately after Hallow-day, from twenty-four to fifteen shillings per week. This was deemed too large a reduction; and, reckoning by the weekly hours during which, on the average, we were still able to work—forty-two, as nearly as I could calculate, instead of sixty—it *was* too great a reduction by about one shilling and ninepence. I would, however, in the circumstances, have taken particular care not to strike work for an advance. I knew that three-fourths of the masons about town—quite as improvident as the masons of our own party—could not live on their resources for a fortnight, and had no general fund to sustain them: and further, that many of the master-builders were not very urgently desirous to press on their work throughout the winter. And so, when, on coming to the work-shed on the Monday morning after the close of our first fortnight on the reduced scale, I found my comrades gathered in front of it in a group, and learned that there was a grand strike all over the district, I received the intelligence with as little of the enthusiasm of the "independent associated mechanic" as possibly may be. "You are in the right in your claims," I said to Charles; "but you have taken a bad time for urging them, and will be beaten to a certainty. The masters are much better prepared for a strike than you are. How, may I ask, are you yourself provided with the sinews of war?" "Very ill indeed," said Charles, scratching his head; "if the masters don't give in before Saturday, it's all up with me; but never mind, let us have one day's fun: there's to be a grand meeting at Bruntsfield Links; let us go in as a deputation from the country masons, and make a speech about our rights and duties; and then, if we see matters going very far wrong, we can just step back again, and begin work to-morrow." "Bravely resolved," I said: "I shall go with you by all means, and take notes of your speech." We marched into town, about sixteen in number; and, on joining the crowd already assembled on the Links, were recognised, by the deep red hue of our clothes and aprons, which differed considerably from that borne by workers in the paler Edinburgh stone, as a reinforcement from a distance, and were received with loud cheers. Charles, however, did not make his speech: the meeting which was about eight hundred strong, seemed fully in the possession of a few crack orators, who spoke with a fluency to which he could make no pretensions; and so he replied to the various calls from among his comrades of "Cha, Cha," by assuring them that he could not catch the eye of the gentleman in the chair. The meeting had, of course, neither chair nor chairman; and after a good deal of idle speech-making which seemed to satisfy the speakers themselves remarkably well, but which at least some of their auditory regarded as nonsense, we found that the only motion on which we could harmoniously agree was a motion for an adjournment. And so we adjourned till the evening, fixing as our place of meeting one of the humbler halls of the city.

My comrades proposed that we should pass the time until the hour of meeting in a public-house, and, desirous of securing a glimpse of the sort of enjoyment for which they sacrificed so much, I accompanied them. Passing not a few more inviting-looking places, we entered a low tavern in the upper part of the Canongate, kept in an old half-ruinous building, which has since disappeared. We passed on through a narrow passage to a low-roofed room in the centre of the erection, into which the light of day never penetrated, and in which the gas was burning dimly in a close, sluggish atmosphere, rendered still more stifling by tobacco-smoke, and a strong smell of ardent spirits. In the middle of the crazy floor there was a trap-door which lay open at the time; and a wild combination of sounds, in which the yelping of a dog, and a few gruff voices that seemed cheering him on, were most noticeable, rose from the apartment below. It was customary at this time for dram-shops to keep badgers housed in long narrow boxes, and for working men to keep dogs; and it was part of the ordinary sport of such places to set the dogs to unhouse the badgers. The wild sport which Scott describes in his "Guy Mannering," as pursued by Dandy Dinmont and his associates among the Cheviots, was extensively practised twenty-nine years ago amid the dingier haunts of the High Street and the Canongate. Our party, like most others, had its dog—a repulsive-looking brute, with an earth-directed eye, as if he carried about with him an evil conscience; and my companions were desirous of getting his earthing ability tested upon the badger of the establishment; but on summoning the tavern-keeper, we were told that the party below had got the start of us: their dog was as we might hear, "just drawing the badger; and before our dog could be permitted to draw him, the poor brute would require to get an hour's rest." I need scarce say that the hour was spent in hard drinking in that stagnant atmosphere; and we then all descended through the trap-door, by means of a ladder, into a bare-walled dungeon, dark and damp, and where the pestiferous air smelt like that of a burial vault. The scene which followed was exceedingly repulsive and brutal—nearly as much so as some of the scenes furnished by those other hunts in which the aristocracy of the country delight occasionally to indulge. Amid shouts and yells, the badger, with the blood of his recent conflict still fresh upon him, was again drawn to the box mouth; and the party returning satisfied to the apartment above, again betook themselves to hard drinking. In a short time the liquor began to tell, not first, as might be supposed, on our younger men, who were mostly tall, vigorous fellows, in the first flush of their full strength, but on a few of the middle-aged workmen, whose constitutions seemed undermined by a previous course of dissipation and debauchery. The conversation became very loud, very involved, and, though highly seasoned with emphatic oaths, very insipid; and, leaving with Cha—who seemed somewhat uneasy that my eye should be upon their meeting in its hour of weakness—money enough to clear off my share of the reckoning, I stole out to the King's Park, and passed an hour to better purpose among the trap rocks than I could possibly have spent it beside the trap-door. Of that tavern party, I am not aware that a single individual save the writer is now living—its very dog did not live out half his days. His owner was alarmed one morning, shortly after this time, by the intelligence that a dozen of sheep had been worried during the night on a neighbouring farm, and that a dog very like his had been seen prowling about the fold; but in order to determine the point, he would be visited, it was added, in the course of the day, by the shepherd and a law-officer. The dog meanwhile, however, conscious of guilt—for dogs do seem to have consciences in such matters—was nowhere to be found, though, after the lapse of nearly a week, he again appeared at the work; and his master, slipping a rope round his neck, brought him to a deserted coal-pit half-filled with water, that opened in an adjacent field, and flinging him in, left the authorities no clue by which to establish his identity with the robber and assassin of the fold.

I had now quite enough of the strike; and, instead of attending the evening meeting, passed the night with my friend William Ross. Curious to know, however, whether my absence had been observed by my brother workmen, I asked Cha, when we next met, "what he thought of *our* meeting?" "Gudesake!" he replied, "let that flee stick to the wa'! We got upon the *skuff* [1] after you left us, and grew deaf to time, and so not one of us has seen the meeting yet." I learned, however, that, though somewhat reduced in numbers, it had been very spirited and energetic, and had resolved on nailing the colours to the mast; but in a few mornings subsequent, several of the squads returned to work on their master's terms, and all broke down in about a week after. Contrary to what I should have expected from my previous knowledge of him, I found that my friend William Ross took a warm interest in strikes and combinations, and was much surprised at the apathy which I manifested on this occasion; nay, that he himself, as he told me, actually officiated as clerk for a combined society of house-painters, and entertained sanguine hopes regarding the happy influence which the principle of union was yet to exercise on the status and comfort of the working man. There are no problems more difficult than those which speculative men sometimes attempt solving, when they set themselves to predict how certain given characters would act in certain given circumstances. In what spirit, it has been asked, would Socrates have listened to the address of Paul on Mars Hill, had he lived a few

[1] State of intoxication.

ages later? and what sort of a statesman would Robert Burns have made? I cannot answer either question; but this I know, that from my intimate acquaintance with the retiring, unobtrusive character of my friend in early life, I should have predicted that he would have taken no interest whatever in strikes or combinations; and I was now surprised to find the case otherwise. And he, on the other hand, equally intimate with my comparatively wild boyhood, and my influence among my schoolfellows, would have predicted that I should have taken a very warm interest in such combinations, mayhap as a ringleader; at all events, as an energetic, influential member; and he was now not a little astonished to see me keeping aloof from them, as things of no account or value. I believe, however, we were both acting in character. Lacking my obstinacy, he had in some degree yielded, on first coming to the capital, to the tyranny of his brother workmen; and, becoming one of themselves, and identifying his interest with theirs, his talents and acquirements had recommended him to an office of trust among them; whereas I, stubbornly battling, like Harry of the Wynd, "for my own hand,"[1] would not stir a finger in assertion of the alleged rights of fellows who had no respect for the rights which were indisputably mine.

I may here mention, that this first year of the building mania was also the first, in the present century, of those great strikes among workmen of which the public has since heard and seen so much. Up till this time, combination among operatives for the purpose of raising the rate of wages had been a crime punishable by law; and though several combinations and trade unions did exist, open strikes, which would have been a too palpable manifestation of them to be tolerated, could scarce be said ever to take place. I saw enough at the period to convince me, that though the *right* of combination, abstractly considered, is just and proper, the strikes which would result from it as consequences would be productive of much evil, and little good; and in an argument with my friend William on the subject, I ventured to

---

[1] In Scott's *The Fair Maid of Perth.*

assure him that his house-painter's union would never benefit the operative house-painters as a class, and urged him to give up his clerkship. "There is a want," I said, "of true leadership among our operatives in these combinations. It is the wilder spirits that dictate the conditions; and, pitching their demands high, they begin usually by enforcing acquiescence in them on the quieter and more moderate among their companions. They are tyrants to their fellows ere they come into collision with their masters, and have thus an enemy in the camp, not unwilling to take advantage of their seasons of weakness, and prepared to rejoice, though secretly mayhap, in their defeats and reverses. And further, their discomfiture will be always quite certain enough when seasons of depression come, from the circumstance that, fixing their terms in prosperous times, they will fix them with reference rather to their present power of enforcing them, than to that medium line of fair and equal adjustment on which a conscientious man could plant his foot and make a firm stand. Men such as you, able and ready to work in behalf of these combinations, will of course get the work to do, but you will have little or no power given you in their direction; the direction will be apparently in the hands of a few fluent *gabbers*; and yet even they will not be the actual directors—they will be but the exponents and voices of the general mediocre sentiment and inferior sense of the mass as a whole, and acceptable only so long as they give utterance to that; and so, ultimately, exceedingly little will be won in this way for working men. It is well that they should be allowed to combine, seeing that combination is permitted to those who employ them; but until the majority of our working men of the south become very different from what they now are—greatly wiser and greatly better—there will be more lost than gained by their combinations. According to the circumstances of the time and season, the current will be at one period running in their favour against the masters, and at another in favour of the masters against them; there will be a continual ebb and flow, like that of the sea, but no general advance; and the sooner that the like of you and I get out of the rough conflict and jostle of the tideway, and set ourselves to labour apart on our own internal resources, it will be all the better for us." William, however, did not give up his clerkship; and I daresay the sort of treatment which I had received at the hands of my fellow-workmen made me express myself rather strongly on the subject; but the actual history of the numerous strikes and combinations which have taken place during the quarter of a century and more which has since intervened, is of a kind not in the least suited to modify my views. There *is* a want of judicious leadership among our working men; and such of the autobiographies of the class as are able and interesting enough to obtain a hearing for their authors show, I am inclined to think, how this takes place. Combination is first brought to bear among them against the men, their fellows, who have vigour enough of intellect to think and act for themselves; and such always is the character of the born leader; these true leaders are almost always forced into the opposition; and thus separating between themselves and the men fitted by nature to render them formidable, they fall under the direction of mere chatterers and stump orators, which is in reality no direction at all. The author of the "Working Man's Way in the World"—evidently a very superior man—had, he tells us, to quit at one time his employment, overborne by the senseless ridicule of his brother workmen. Somerville[1] states in his Autobiography, that, both as a labouring man and a soldier, it was from the hands of his comrades that—save in one memorable instance—he had experienced all the tyranny and oppression of which he had been the victim. Nay, Benjamin Franklin himself was deemed a much more ordinary man in the Printing-house in Bartholomew Close, where he was teased and laughed at as the *Water-American*, than in the House of Representatives, the Royal Society, or the Court of France. The great Printer, though recognised by accomplished politicians as a profound statesman, and by men of solid science as "the most rational of the philosophers," was regarded by his poor brother compositors as

[1] Alexander Somerville (1811-85), a reformer born in East Lothian, published, among other works, his *Autobiography of a Working Man* in 1848.

merely an odd fellow, who did not conform to their drinking usages, and whom it was therefore fair to tease and annoy as a contemner of the *sacrament* of the *chapel*.[1]

The life of my friend was, however, pitched on a better and higher tone than that of most of his brother unionists. It was intellectual and moral, and its happier hours were its hours of quiet self-improvement, when, throwing himself on the resources within, he forgot for the time the unions and combinations that entailed upon him much troublesome occupation, but never did him any service. I regretted, however, to find that a distrust of his own powers was still growing upon him, and narrowing his circle of enjoyment. On asking him whether he still amused himself with his flute, he turned, after replying with a brief "O no!", to a comrade with whom he had lived for years, and quietly said to him, by way of explaining the question, "Robert, I suppose you don't know I was once a grand flute-player!" And sure enough Robert did not know. He had given up, too, his water-colour drawing, in which his taste was decidedly fine; and even in oils, with which he still occasionally engaged himself, instead of casting himself full on nature, as at an earlier period, he had become a copyist of the late Rev. Mr Thomson of Duddingstone, at that time in the full glow of his artistic reputation; nor could I see that he copied him well. I urged and remonstrated, but to no effect. "Ah, Miller," he has said, "what matters it how I amuse myself? You have stamina in you, and will force your way; but I want strength: the world will never hear of me." That overween-

---

[1] The kind of club into which the compositors of a printing house always form themselves has from time immemorial been termed a *chapel*; and the petty tricks by which Franklin was annoyed were said to be played him by the chapel ghost. "My employer desiring," he says, "after some weeks to have me in the composing-room, I left the pressmen. A new *bien-venu* for drink, being five shillings, was demanded of me by the compositors. I thought it an imposition, as I had paid one to the pressmen. The master thought so too, and forbade my paying it. I stood out two or three weeks, was accordingly considered an *excommunicate*, and had so many little pieces of private malice practised on me by mixing my sorts, transposing and breaking my matter, &c. &c., if ever I stepped out of the room, and all ascribed to the *chapel ghost*, which they said, ever haunted those not regularly admitted, that, notwithstanding my master's protection, I found myself obliged to comply and pay the money." (Miller)

ing conceit which seems but natural to the young man, as a playful disposition to the kitten, or a soft and timid one to the puppy, often assumes a ridiculous, and oftener still an unamiable, aspect. And yet, though it originates many very foolish things, it seems to be in itself, like the fanaticism of the Teetotaller, a wise provision, which, were it not made by nature, would leave most minds without spring enough to effect, with the required energy, the movements necessary to launch them fairly into busy or studious life. The sobered man of mature age who has learned pretty correctly to take the measure of himself, has usually acquired both habits and knowledge that assist him in urging his onward way, and the moving force of necessity always presses him onward from behind; but the exhilarating conviction of being born to superior parts, and to do something astonishingly clever, seems necessary to the young man; and when I see it manifesting itself, if not very foolishly or very offensively, I usually think of my poor friend William Ross, who was unfortunate enough wholly to want it; and extend to it a pretty ample toleration. Ultimately my friend gave up painting, and restricted himself to the ornamental parts of his profession, of which he became very much a master. In finishing a ceiling in oils, upon which he had represented in bold relief some of the ornately sculptured foliage of the architect, the gentleman for whom he wrought (the son-in-law of a distinguished artist, and himself an amateur), called on his wife to admire the truthful and delicate shading of the house-painter. It was astonishing, he said, and perhaps somewhat humiliating, to see the mere mechanic trenching so decidedly on the province of the artist. Poor William Ross, however, was no mere mechanic; and even artists might have regarded his encroachments on their proper domain with more of complacency than humiliation. One of the last pieces of work upon which he was engaged was a gorgeously painted ceiling in the palace of some Irish Bishop, which he had been sent all the way from Glasgow to finish.

Every society, however homely, has its picturesque points, nor did even that of the rather commonplace hamlet in which I resided at this time wholly want them. There was a decaying cottage a few doors away, that had for its inmate a cross-tempered old crone, who strove hard to set up as a witch, but broke down from sheer want of the necessary capital. She had been one of the underground workers at Niddry in her time; and, being as little intelligent as most of the other collier-women of the neighbourhood, she had not the necessary witch-lore to adapt her pretensions to the capacity of belief which obtained in the district. And so the general estimate formed regarding her was that to which our landlady occasionally gave expression. "Donnart auld bodie," Peggy used to say; "though she threaps hersel' a witch she's nae mair witch than I am: she's only just trying in her feckless auld age, to make folk stand in her reverence." Old Alie was, however, a curiosity in her way—quite malignant enough to be a real witch, and fitted, if, with a few more advantages of acquirement, she had been antedated an age or two, to become as hopeful a candidate for a tar-barrel as most of her class. Her next-door neighbour was also an old woman, and well-nigh as poor as the crone; but she was an easy-tempered, genial sort of person, who wished harm to no one; and the expression of content that dwelt on her round fresh face, which, after the wear of more than seventy winters, still retained its modicum of colour, contrasted strongly with the fierce wretchedness that gleamed from the sharp and sallow features of the witch. It was evident that the two old women, though placed externally in almost the same circumstances, had essentially a very different lot assigned to them, and enjoyed existence in a very unequal degree. The placid old woman kept a solitary lodger— "Davie the apprentice"—a wayward, eccentric lad, much about my own age, though in but the second "year of his time," who used to fret even her temper, and who, after making trial of I know not how many other professions, now began to find that his genius did not lie to the mallet. Davie was stage-mad; but for the stage Nature seemed to have fitted him rather indifferently: she had given him a squat ungainly figure, an inexpressive face, a voice that in its intonations somewhat resembled the grating of a carpenter's saw; and, withal, no very nice conception of either comic or serious character; but he could recite in the "big bow-wow-style," and think and dream of only plays and play-actors. To Davie the world and its concerns seemed unworthy of a moment's care, and the stage appeared the only great reality. He was engaged, when I first made his acquaintance, in writing a play, with which he had already filled a whole quire of foolscap, without, however, having quite entered upon the plot; and he read to me some of the scenes in tones of such energy that the whole village heard. Though written in the kind of verse which Dr Young believed to be the language of angels, his play was sad stuff; and when he paused for my approbation, I ventured to suggest an alteration in one of the speeches. "There, Sir," said Davie, in the vein of Cambyses, "take the pen; let me see, Sir, how *you* would turn it." I accordingly took the pen, and re-wrote the speech. "Hum," said Davie, as he ran his eye along the lines, "that, Sir, is mere poetry. What, think you, could the great Kean make of feeble stuff like that? Let me tell you, Sir, you have no notion whatever of stage effect." I, of course, at once acquiesced; and Davie, mollified by my submission, read to me yet another scene. Cha, however, of whom he stood a good deal in awe, used to tease him not a little about his play. I have heard him inquire sedulously about the development of the story and the management of the characters, and whether he was writing the several parts with a due eye to the capabilities of the leading actors of the day; and Davie, not quite sure, apparently, whether Cha was in joke or earnest, was usually on these occasions very chary of reply.

Davie, had he but the means of securing access, would have walked in every night to the city to attend the playhouse; and it quite astonished him, he used to say, that I, who really knew something of the drama, and had four shillings a day, did not nightly at least devote one of the four to purchase perfect happiness and a seat in the shilling gallery. On some two, or at most three occasions, I did attend the playhouse, accompanied by Cha and a few of the other workmen; but though I had been greatly delighted, when a boy, by the acting of a company of strollers that had visited Cromarty, and converted the Council House Hall into a theatre, the greatly better acting of the Edinburgh company failed to satisfy me now. The few plays, however, which I saw enacted chanced to be of a rather mediocre character, and gave no scope for the exhibition of nice histrionic talent; nor were any of the great actors of the south on the Edinburgh boards at the time. The stage scenery, too, though quite fine enough of its kind, had, I found, altogether a different effect upon me from the one which it had been elaborated to produce. In perusing our fine old dramas, it was the truth of nature that the vividly-drawn scenes and figures, and the happily-portrayed characters, always suggested; whereas the painted canvas, and the respectable but yet too palpable acting, served but to unrealize what I saw, and to remind me that I was merely in a theatre. Further, I deemed it too large a price to devote a whole evening to see some play acted which, mayhap, as a composition I would not have deemed worth the reading; and so the temptation of play-going failed to tempt me; and latterly, when my comrades set out for the playhouse, I stayed at home. Whatever the nature of the process through which they have gone, a considerable proportion of the more intelligent mechanics of the present generation seem to have landed in conclusions similar to the one at which I at this time arrived. At least, for every dozen of the class that frequented the theatre thirty years ago, there is scarce one that frequents it now. I have said that the scenery of the stage made no very favourable impression upon me. Some parts of it must, however, have made a considerably stronger one than I could have supposed at the time. Fourteen years after, when the whole seemed to have passed out of memory, I was lying ill of smallpox, which, though a good deal modified apparently by the vaccination of a long anterior period, was accompanied by such a degree of fever, that for two days together one delirious image continued to succeed another in the troubled sensorium, as scene succeeds scene in the box of an itinerant showman. As is not uncommon, however, in such cases, though ill enough to be haunted by the images, I was yet well enough to know that they were idle unrealities, the mere effects of indisposition; and even sufficiently collected to take an interest in watching them as they arose, and in striving to determine whether they were linked together by the ordinary associative ties. I found, however, that they were wholly independent of each other. Curious to know whether the will exerted any power over them, I set myself to try whether I could not conjure up a death's-head as one of the series; but what rose instead was a cheerful parlour fire, bearing atop a tea-kettle, and as the picture faded and then vanished, it was succeeded by a gorgeous cataract, in which the white foam, at first strongly relieved against the dark rock over which it fell, soon exhibited a deep tinge of sulphurous blue, and then came dashing down in one frightful sheet of blood. The great singularity of the vision served to freshen recollection, and I detected in the strange cataract every line and tint of the waterfall in the incantation scene in "Der Freischütz", which I had witnessed in the Theatre Royal of Edinburgh, with certainly no very particular interest, so long before. There are, I suspect, provinces in the philosophy of mind into which the metaphysicians have not yet entered. Of that accessible store-house in which the memories of past events lie arranged and taped up, they appear to know a good deal; but of a mysterious cabinet of daguerreotype pictures, of which, though fast locked up on ordinary occasions, disease sometimes flings the door ajar, they seem to know nothing.

CHAPTER XVI

"Let not this weak, unknowing hand,
Presume thy bolts to throw."—POPE.

THE great fires of the Parliament Close and the High Street were events of this winter. A countryman, who had left town when the old spire of the Tron Church was blazing like a torch, and the large group of buildings nearly opposite the Cross still enveloped in flame from ground-floor to roof-tree, passed our work-shed, a little after two o'clock, and, telling us what he had seen, remarked that if the conflagration went on as it was doing, we would have, as our next season's employment, the Old Town of Edinburgh to rebuild. And as the evening closed over our labours, we went in to town in a body, to see the fires that promised to do so much for us. The spire had burnt out, and we could but catch between us and the darkened sky, the square abrupt outline of the masonry a-top that had supported the wooden broach, whence, only a few hours before, Fergusson's bell had descended in a molten shower. The flames, too, in the upper group of buildings, were restricted to the lower storeys, and flared fitfully on the tall forms and bright swords of the dragoons, drawn from the neighbouring barracks, as they rode up and down the middle space, or gleamed athwart the street on groups of wretched-looking women and ruffian men, who seemed scanning with greedy eyes the still unremoved heaps of household goods rescued from the burning tenements. The first figure that caught my eye was a singularly ludicrous one. Removed from the burning mass by but the thickness of a wall, there was a barber's shop brilliantly lighted with gas, the uncurtained window of which permitted the spectators outside to see whatever was going on in the interior. The barber was as busily at work as if he were a hundred miles from the scene of danger, though the engines at the time were playing against the outside of his gable wall; and the immediate subject under his hands, as my eye rested upon him, was an immensely fat old fellow, on whose round bald forehead and ruddy cheeks the perspiration, occasioned by the oven-like heat of the place, was standing out in huge drops, and whose vast mouth, widely opened to accommodate the man of the razor, gave to his countenance such an expression as I have sometimes seen in grotesque Gothic heads of that age of art in which the ecclesiastical architect began to make sport of his religion. The next object that presented itself was, however, of a more sobering description. A poor working man, laden with his favourite piece of furniture, a glass-fronted press or cupboard, which he had succeeded in rescuing from his burning dwelling, was emerging from one of the lanes, followed by his wife, when, striking his foot against some obstacle in the way, or staggering from the too great weight of his load, he tottered against a projecting corner, and the glazed door was driven in with a crash. There was hopeless misery in the wailing cry of his wife— "Oh, ruin, ruin!—*it's* lost too!" Nor was his own despairing response less sad—"Ay, ay, puir lassie, its a' at an end noo." Curious as it may seem, the wild excitement of the scene had at first rather exhilarated than depressed my spirits; but the incident of the glass cupboard served to awaken the proper feeling; and as I came more into contact with the misery of the catastrophe, and marked the groups of shivering houseless creatures that watched beside the broken fragments of their stuff, I saw what a dire calamity a great fire really is. Nearly two hundred families were already at this time cast homeless into the streets. Shortly before quitting the scene of the conflagration for the country, I passed along a common stair, which led from the Parliament Close towards the Cowgate, through a tall old domicile, eleven storeys in height, and I afterwards remembered that the passage was occupied by a smouldering oppressive vapour, which, from the direction of the wind, could scarce have been derived from the adjacent conflagration, though at the time, without thinking much of the circumstances, I concluded it might have come creeping westwards on some low cross current along the narrow lanes. In less than an hour after, that lofty tenement was wrapped in flames, from the ground storey to more than a hundred feet over its tallest chimneys, and about sixty additional families, its tenants, were cast into the streets with the others. My friend William Ross afterwards assured me, that never had he witnessed anything equal in grandeur to this last of the conflagrations. Directly over the sea of fire below, the low-browed clouds above seemed as if charged with a sea of blood, that lightened and darkened by fits as the flames rose and fell; and far and wide, tower and spire, and tall house-top, glared out against a background of darkness, as if they had been brought to a red heat by some great subterranean, earth-born fire, that was fast rising to wrap the entire city in destruction. The old church of St Giles, he said, with the fantastic masonry of its pale grey tower, bathed in crimson, and that of its dark rude walls suffused in a bronzed umber, and with the red light gleaming inwards through its huge mullioned windows, and flickering on its stone roof, formed one of the most picturesque objects he had ever seen.[1]

I sometimes heard old Dr Colquhoun of Leith preach. There were fewer authors among the clergy in those days than now; and I felt a special interest in a living divine who had written so good a book, that my Uncle Sandy—no mean judge in such matters— had assigned to it a place in his little theological library, among the writings of the great divines of other ages. The old man's preaching days were, ere now, well-nigh done; he could scarce

---

[1] The extreme picturesqueness of these fires—in part a consequence of the great height and peculiar architecture of the buildings which they destroyed— caught the nice eye of Sir Walter Scott. "I can conceive," we find him saying, in one of his letters of the period, "no sight more grand or terrible than to see these lofty buildings on fire from top to bottom, vomiting out flames, like a volcano, from every aperture, and finally crashing down one after another, into an abyss of fire, which resembled nothing but hell; for there were vaults of wine and spirits which set up huge jets of flames whenever they were called into activity by the fall of these massive fragments. Between the corner of Parliament Square and the Tron Church, all is destroyed excepting some few buildings at the lower extremity." (Miller)

make himself heard over half the area of his large, hulking chapel, which was, however, always less than half-filled; but, though the feeble tones teasingly strained the ear, I liked to listen to his quaintly attired but usually very solid theology, and found, as I thought, more matter in his discourses than in those of men who spoke louder and in a flashier style. The worthy man, however, did me a mischief at this time. There had been a great Musical Festival held in Edinburgh about three weeks previous to the conflagration, at which oratorios were performed in the ordinary pagan style, in which amateurs play at devotion, without ever professing to feel it; and the Doctor, in his first sermon after the great fires, gave serious expression to the conviction, that they were judgments sent upon Edinburgh, to avenge the profanity of its Musical Festival. Edinburgh had sinned, he said, and Edinburgh was now punished; and it was according to the Divine economy he added, that judgments administered exactly after the manner of the infliction which we had just witnessed should fall upon cities and kingdoms. I liked the reasoning very ill. I knew only two ways in which God's judgments could be determined to be really such—either through direct revelation from God himself, or in those cases in which they take place so much in accordance with His fixed laws, and in such relation to the offence or crime visited in them by punishment, that man, simply by the exercise of his rational faculties, and reasoning from cause to effect, as is his nature, can determine them for himself. And the great Edinburgh fires had come under neither category. God did not reveal that He had punished the tradesmen and mechanics of the High Street for the musical sins of the lawyers and landowners of Abercromby Place and Charlotte Square; nor could any natural relation be established between the oratorios in the Parliament House or the concerts in the Theatre Royal, and the conflagrations opposite the Cross or at the top of the Tron Church steeple. All that could be proven in the case were the facts of the festival and of the fires; and the further fact, that, so far as could be ascertained, there was no visible connection between them, and that it was not the people who had joined in the one that had suffered from the others. And the Doctor's argument seemed to be the perilous, loose one, that as God had sometimes of old visited cities and nations with judgments which had no apparent connection with the sins punished, and which could not be recognised as judgments had not He himself told that such they were, the Edinburgh fires, of which He had told nothing, might be properly regarded—seeing that they had in the same way no connection with the oratorios, and had wrought no mischief to the people who had patronised the oratorios—as special judgments on the oratorios. The good old Papist had said, "I believe because it is impossible." What the Doctor in this instance seemed to say was, "I believe because it is not in the least likely." If, I argued, Dr Colquhoun's own house and library had been burnt, he would no doubt very properly have deemed the infliction a great trial to himself; but on what principle could he have further held that it was not only a trial to himself, but also a judgment on his neighbour? If we must not believe that the falling of the tower of Siloam was a special visitation on the sins of the poor men whom it crushed, how, or on what grounds, are we to believe that it was a special visitation on the sins of the men whom it did not in the least injure! I fear I remembered Dr Colquhoun's remarks on the fire better than aught else I ever heard from him; nay, I must add, that nothing had I ever found in the writings of the sceptics that had a worse effect on my mind; and I now mention the circumstance to show how sober in applications of the kind, in an age like the present, a theologian should be. It was some time ere I forgot the ill savour of that dead fly; and it was to beliefs of a serious and very important class that it served for a time to impart its own doubtful character.

But from the minister whose chapel I oftenest attended, I was little in danger of having my beliefs unsettled by reasonings of this stumbling cast. "Be sure," said both my uncles, as I was quitting Cromarty for the south, "be sure you go and hear Dr. M'Crie."[1]

---

[1] Thomas M'Crie (1772-1835), the most notable clergyman of the Original Seceders ("Auld Lichts") formed by the union of two of the smaller subdivisions

And so Dr M'Crie I did go and hear; and not once or twice, but often. The biographer of Knox—to employ the language in which Wordsworth describes the humble hero of the "Excursion"—

"was a man
Whom no one could have passed without remark."

And on first attending his church, I found that I had unwittingly seen him before, and that without remark I had *not* passed him. I had extended one of my usual evening walks, shortly after commencing work at Niddry, in the direction of the southern suburb of Edinburgh, and was sauntering through one of the green lanes of Liberton, when I met a gentleman whose appearance at once struck me. He was a singularly erect, spare, tall man, and bore about him an air which, neither wholly clerical nor wholly military, seemed to be a curious compound of both. The countenance was pale, and the expression, as I thought, somewhat melancholy; but an air of sedate power sat so palpably on every feature, that I stood arrested as he passed, and for half a minute or so remained looking after him. He wore, over a suit of black, a brown great-coat, with the neck a good deal whitened by powder, and the rim of the hat behind, which was slightly turned up, bore a similar stain. "There is mark about that old-fashioned man," I said to myself: "who or what can he be?" Curiously enough, the apparent combination of the military and the clerical in his gait and air suggested to me Sir Richard Steele's story, in the "Tatler," of the old officer, who, acting in the double capacity of major and chaplain to his regiment, challenged a young man for blasphemy, and, after disarming, would not take him to mercy until he had first begged pardon of God upon his knees on the duelling ground, for the irreverence with which he had treated His name. My curiosity regarding the stranger gentleman was soon gratified. Next Sabbath I attended the Doctor's chapel, and saw the tall, spare, clerico-military looking man in the pulpit. I have a good

of the Seceders, he wrote Lives of John Knox and Andrew Melville, and famously attacked Walter Scott for his portrayal of the Covenanters in *Old Mortality*.

deal of faith in the military air, when, in the character of a natural trait, I find it strongly marking men who never served in the army. I have not yet seen it borne by a civilian who had not in him at least the elements of the soldier; nor can I doubt that, had Dr M'Crie been a Scotch Covenanter of the times of Charles II., the insurgents at Bothwell would have had what they sadly wanted— a general. The shrewd sense of his discourses had great charms for me; and, though not a flashy, nor, in the ordinary sense of the term, even an eloquent preacher, there were none of the other Edinburgh clergy his contemporaries to whom I found I could listen with greater profit or satisfaction. A simple incident which occurred during my first morning attendance at his chapel, strongly impressed me with a sense of his sagacity. There was a great deal of coughing in the place, the effect of a recent change of weather; and the Doctor, whose voice was not a strong one, and who seemed somewhat annoyed by the ruthless interruptions, stopping suddenly short in the middle of his argument, made a dead pause. When people are taken greatly by surprise they cease to cough—a circumstance on which he had evidently calculated. Every eye now turned towards him, and for a full minute so dead was the silence that one might have heard a pin drop. "I see, my friends," said the Doctor, resuming speech, with a suppressed smile—"I see you can be all quiet enough when I am quiet." There was not a little genuine strategy in the rebuke; and as cough lies a good deal more under the influences of the will than most coughers suppose, such was its effect, that during the rest of the day there was not a tithe of the previous coughing.

The one-roomed cottage which I shared with its three other inmates, did not present all the possible conveniences for study; but it had a little table in a corner, at which I contrived to write a good deal; and my book-shelf already exhibited from twenty to thirty volumes, picked up on Saturday evenings at the book-stalls of the city, and which were all accessions to my little library. I, besides, got a few volumes to read from my friend William Ross, and a few more through my work-fellow Cha; and so my rate of acquirement in book-knowledge, if not equal to that of some former years, at least considerably exceeded what it had been in the previous season, which I had spent in the Highlands, and during which I had perused only three volumes—one of the three a slim volume of slim poems, by a lady, and the other, that rather curious than edifying work, "Presbyterian Eloquence Displayed." The cheap literature had not yet been called into existence; and, without in the least undervaluing its advantages, it was, I daresay, better on the whole as a mental exercise, and greatly better in the provision which it made for the future, that I should have to urge my way through the works of our best writers in prose and verse— works which always made an impression on the memory—than that I should have been engaged instead in picking up odds and ends of information from loose essays, the hasty productions of men too little vigorous, or too little at leisure, to impress upon their writings the stamp of their own individuality. In quiet moonlight nights I found it exceedingly pleasant to saunter all alone through the Niddry woods. Moonlight gives to even leafless groves the charms of full foliage, and conceals tameness of outline in a landscape. I found it singularly agreeable, too, to listen, from a solitude so profound as that which a short walk secured to me, to the distant bells of the city ringing out, as the clock struck eight, the old curfew peal; and to mark, from under the interlacing boughs of a long-arched vista, the intermittent gleam of the Inchkeith light, now brightening and now fading, as the lanthorn revolved. In short, the winter passed not unpleasantly away: I had now nothing to annoy me in the work-shed; and my only serious care arose from my unlucky house in Leith, for which I found myself summoned one morning, by an officer-looking man, to pay nearly three pounds—the last instalment which I owed, I was told, as one of the heritors of the place, for its fine new church. I must confess I was wicked enough to wish on this occasion that the property on the Coal-hill had been included in the judgment on the Musical Festival. But shortly after, not less to my astonishment than delight, I was informed by Mr Veitch that he had at length found a purchaser for my house; and, after getting myself served heir to my father before the Court of the Canongate, and paying a large arrear of feu-duty to that venerable corporation, in which I had to recognise my feudal superior, I got myself as surely dissevered from the Coal-hill as paper and parchment could do it, and pocketed, in virtue of the transaction, a balance of about fifty pounds. As nearly as I could calculate on what the property had cost us, from first to last, the *composition* which it paid was one of about five shillings in the pound. And such was the concluding passage in the history of a legacy which threatened for a time to be the ruin of the family. When I last passed along the Coal-hill, I saw my umquhile house existing as a bit of dingy wall, a single storey in height, and perforated by three narrow old-fashioned doors, jealously boarded up, and apparently, as in the days when it was mine, of no manner of use in the world. I trust, however, it is no longer the positive mischief to its proprietor that it was to me.

The busy season had now fairly commenced: wages were fast mounting up to the level of the former year, which they ultimately overtopped; and employment had become very abundant. I found, however, that it might be well for me to return home for a few months. The dust of the stone which I had been hewing for the last two years had begun to affect my lungs, as they had been affected in the last autumn of my apprenticeship, but much more severely; and I was too palpably sinking in flesh and strength to render it safe for me to encounter the consequences of another season of hard work as stone-cutter. From the stage of the malady at which I had already arrived, poor workmen, unable to do what I did, throw themselves loose from their employment, and sink in six or eight months into the grave—some at an earlier, some at a later period of life; but so general is the affection, that few of of our Edinburgh stone-cutters pass their fortieth year unscathed, and not one out of every fifty of their number ever reaches his forty-fifth year. I accordingly engaged my passage for the north in an Inverness sloop, and took leave of my few friends—of the excellent foreman of the Niddry squad, and of Cha and John Wilson, with both of whom, notwithstanding their opposite characters, I had become very intimate. Among the rest, too, I took leave of a paternal cousin settled in Leith, the wife of a genial-hearted sailor, master of a now wholly obsolete type of vessel, one of the old Leith and London smacks, with a huge single mast, massive and tall as that of a frigate, and a mainsail of a quarter of an acre. I had received much kindness from my cousin, who, besides her relationship to my father, had been a contemporary and early friend of my mother's; and my welcome from the master her husband—one of the best-natured men I ever knew—used always to be one of the heartiest. And after parting from Cousin Marshall, I mustered up resolution enough to call on yet another cousin.

Cousin William, the eldest son of my Sutherlandshire aunt, had been for some years settled in Edinburgh, first as an upper clerk and manager—for, after his failure as a merchant he had to begin the world anew; and now, in the speculation year, he had succeeded in establishing a business for himself, which bore about it a hopeful and promising air so long as the over-genial season lasted, but fell, with many a more deeply-rooted establishment, in the tempest which followed. On quitting the north, I had been charged with a letter for him by his father which I knew, however, to be wholly recommendatory of myself, and so I had failed to deliver it. Cousin William, like Uncle James, had fully expected that I was to make my way in life in some one of the learned professions; and as his position—though, as the result unfortunately showed, a not very secure one—was considerably in advance of mine, I kept aloof from him, in the character of a poor relation, who was quite as proud as he was poor, and in the belief that his new friends, of whom, I understood, he had now well-nigh as many as before, would hold that the cousinship of a mere working man did him little credit. He had learned from home, however, that I was in Edinburgh, and had made not a few ineffectual attempts to find me out, of which I had heard; and now, on forming my resolution to return to the north, I waited upon him at his rooms in Ambrose's Lodgings—at that time possessed of a sort of classical interest, as the famous Blackwood Club, with Christopher North at its head, used to meet in the hotel immediately below. Cousin William had a warm heart, and received me with great kindness, though I had, of course, to submit to the scold which I deserved; and as some young friends were to look in upon him in the evening, he said, I had to do what I would fain have avoided, perform penance by waiting, on his express invitation, to meet with them. They were, I ascertained, chiefly students of medicine and divinity, in attendance at the classes of the University, and not at all the formidable sort of persons I had feared to meet; and finding nothing very unattainable in their conversation, and as Cousin William made a dead set on me "to bring me out," I at length ventured to mingle in it, and found my reading stand me in some stead. There was a meeting, we were told, that evening, in the apartment below, of the Blackwood Club. The night I spent with my cousin was, if our information was correct, and the *Noctes* not a mere myth, one of the famous *Noctes Ambrosianæ;* and fain would I have seen, for but a moment, from some quiet corner, the men whose names fame had blown so widely; but I have ever been unlucky in the curiosity—though I have always strongly entertained it—which has the personal appearance of celebrated men for its object. I had ere now several times lingered in Castle Street of a Saturday evening, opposite the house of Sir Walter Scott, in the hope of catching a glimpse of that great writer and genial man, but had never been successful. I could fain, too, have seen Hogg (who at this time occasionally visited Edinburgh) with Jeffrey; old Dugald Stewart, who still lived; *Delta*, and Professor Wilson: but I quitted the place without seeing any of them; and ere I again returned to the capital, ten years after, death had been busy in the high places, and the greatest of their number was no longer to be seen. In short, Dr M'Crie was the only man whose name promises to live, of whose personal appearance I was able to carry away with me at this time a distinct image.

340

Addison makes his *Spectator* remark, rather in joke than earnest, that "a reader seldom peruses a book with pleasure till he knows whether the writer of it be a black or a fair man, of a mild or choleric disposition, married or a bachelor, with other particulars of the like nature, that conduce very much to the right understanding of an author." I am inclined to say nearly as much, without being in the least in joke. I think I understand an author all the better for knowing exactly how he looked. I would have to regard the massive vehemence of the style of Chalmers as considerably less characteristic of the man, had it been dissociated from the broad chest and mighty structure of bone; and the warlike spirit which breathes, in a subdued but still very palpable form, in the historical writings of the elder M'Crie, strikes me as singularly in harmony with the military air of this Presbyterian minister of the type of Knox and Melville. However theologians may settle the meaning of the text, it is one of the grand lessons of his writings, that such of the Churches of the Reformation as did *not* "take the sword, perished by the sword."

I was accompanied to the vessel by my friend William Ross, from whom I, alas! parted for the last time; and, when stepping aboard, Cousin William, whom I had scarce expected to see, but who had snatched an hour from business, and walked down all the way to Leith to bid me farewell, came forward to grasp me by the hand. I am not much disposed to quarrel with the pride of the working man, when, according to Johnson and Chalmers, it is a defensive, not an aggressive pride; but it does at times lead him to be somewhat less than just to the better feelings of the men who occupy places in the scale a little higher than his own. Cousin William, from whom I had kept so jealously aloof, had a heart of the finest water. His after course was rough and unprosperous. After the general crash of 1825-26, he struggled on in London for some six or eight years, in circumstances of great difficulty; and then, receiving some subordinate appointment in connection with the Stipendiary Magistracy of the West Indies, he sailed for Jamaica where—considerably turned of fifty at the time—he soon fell a victim to the climate.

In my voyage north I spent about half as many days on sea, between Leith Roads and the Sutors of Cromarty, as the Cunard steamers now spend in crossing the Atlantic. I had taken a cabin passage, not caring to subject my weakened lungs to the exposure of a steerage one; but during the seven days of thick, foggy mornings, clear moonlight nights, and almost unbroken calms, both night and morning, in which we tided our slow way north, I was much in the forecastle with the men, seeing how sailors lived, and ascertaining what they were thinking about, and how. We had rare narratives at nights—

> "Wonderful stories of battle and wreck,
> That were told by the men of the watch."

Some of the crew had been voyagers in their time to distant parts of the world; and though no existence can be more monotonous than the every-day life of the seaman, the profession has always its bits of striking incident, that, when strung together, impart to it an air of interest which its ordinary details sadly want, and which lures but to disappoint the young lads of a romantic cast, who are led to make choice of it in its presumed character as a continued series of stirring events and exciting adventures. What, however, struck me as curious in the narratives of my companions, was the large mixture of the supernatural which they almost always exhibited. The story of Jack Grant the mate, given in an early chapter, may be regarded as not inadequately representative of the sailor stories which were told on deck and forecastle, along at least the northern coasts of Scotland, nearly thirty years later. That life of peril which casts the seaman much at the mercy of every rough gale and lee-shore, and in which his calculations regarding ultimate results must be always very doubtful, has a strong tendency to render him superstitious. He is more removed, too, than the landsman of his education and standing, from the influence of general opinion, and the mayhap over-sceptical teaching of the Press; and, as a consequence of their position and circumstances, I found, at this period, seamen of the generation to which I myself belonged as firm believers in wraiths, ghosts, and death warnings, as the landward contemporaries of my grandfather had been sixty years before. A series of well-written nautical tales had appeared shortly previous to this time in one of the metropolitan monthlies—the *London Magazine*, if I rightly remember; and I was now interested to find in one of the sailors' stories, the original of decidedly the best of their number—"The Doomed Man." The author of the series—a Mr Hamilton, it was said, who afterwards became an Irvingite teacher, and grew too scrupulous to exercise in fiction a very pleasing pen, though he continued to employ, as a portrait-painter, a rather indifferent pencil—had evidently sought such opportunities of listening to sailors' stories as those on which I had at this time thrust myself. Very curious materials for fiction may be found in this way by the *litterateur*. It must be held that Sir Walter Scott was no incompetent judge of the capabilities, for the purposes of the novelist, of a piece of narrative; and yet we find him saying of the story told by a common sailor to his friend William Clerk, which he records in the "Letters on Demonology and Witchcraft," that "the tale, properly managed, might have made the fortune of a romancer."

At times by day—for the sailors' stories were stories of the night—I found interesting companionship in the society of a young student of divinity, one of the passengers, who, though a lad of parts and acquirements, did not deem it beneath him to converse on literary subjects with a working man in pale moleskin, and with whom I did not again meet until many years after, when we were both actively engaged in prosecuting the same quarrel— he as one of the majority of the Presbytery of Auchterarder, and I as editor of the leading newspaper of the Non-Intrusion party. Perhaps the respected Free Church minister of North Leith may be still able to call to memory—not, of course, the subjects, but the *fact*, of our discussions on literature and the belles-lettres at this time; and that, on asking me one morning whether I had not been, according to Burns, "crooning to mysel'," when on deck during the previous evening, what seemed from the cadence to be verse, I ventured to submit to him, as my night's work, a few descriptive stanzas. And, as forming in some sort a memorial of our voyage, and in order that my friendly critic may be enabled, after the lapse of considerably more than a quarter of a century, to review his judgment respecting them, I now submit them to the reader:—

STANZAS WRITTEN AT SEA

Joy of the poet's soul, I court thy aid;
.   .   .   .   .   .
Around our vessel heaves the midnight wave;
The cheerless moon sinks in the western sky;
Reigns breezeless silence!—in her ocean cave
The mermaid rests, while her fond lover nigh,
Marks the pale star-beams as they fall from high,
Gilding with tremulous light her couch of sleep.
Why smile incred'lous? the rapt Muse's eye
Through earth's dark caves, o'er heaven's fair plains, can sweep,
Can range its hidden cell, where toils th' unfathom'd deep.

On ocean's craggy floor, beneath the shade
Of bushy rock-weed, tangled, dusk, and brown,
She sees the wreck of founder'd vessel laid,
In slimy silence, many a fathom down
From where the star-beam trembles; o'er it thrown
And heap'd the treasures men have died to gain,
And in sad mockery of the parting groan,
That bubbled 'mid the wild unpitying main,
Quick gushing o'er the bones, the restless tides complain.

Gloomy and wide rolls the sepulchral sea,
Grave of my kindred, of my sire the grave!
Perchance, where now he sleeps, a space for me
Is mark'd by Fate beneath the deep green wave.
It well may be! Poor bosom, why dost heave
Thus wild? Oh, many a care, troublous and dark,
On earth attends thee still; the mermaid's cave
Grief haunts not; sure 'twere pleasant there to mark,
Serene, at noontide hour, the sailor's passing barque.

344

Sure it were pleasant through the vasty deep,
When on its bosom plays the golden beam,
With headlong speed by bower and cave to sweep;
When flame the waters round with emerald gleam—
When, borne from high by tides and gales, the scream
Of sea-mew softened falls—when bright and gay
The crimson weeds, proud ocean's pendants, stream
From trophied wrecks and rock-towers darkly grey—
Through scenes so strangely fair 'twere pleasant, sure, to stray!

Why this strange thought? If, in that ocean laid,
The ear would cease to hear, the eye to see,
Though sights and sounds like these circled my bed,
Wakeless and heavy would my slumbers be:
Though the mild soften'd sun-light beam'd on me
If a dull heap of bones retained my name,
(That bleach'd or blacken'd 'mid the wasteful sea),
Its radiance all unseen, its golden beam
In vain through coral groves or emerald roofs might stream.

Yet dwells a spirit in this earthly frame
Which Oceans cannot quench nor Time destroy;—
A deathless, fadeless ray, a heavenly flame,
That pure shall rise when fails each base alloy
That earth instils, dark grief, or baseless joy:
Then shall the ocean's secrets meet its sight;—
For I do hold that happy souls enjoy
A vast all-reaching range of angel-flight,
From the fair source of day, even to the gates of night.

Now night's dark veil is rent; on yonder land,
That blue and distant rises o'er the main,
I see the purple sky of morn expand,
Scattering the gloom. Then cease, my feeble strain:
When darkness reign'd, thy whisperings soothed my pain—
The pain by weariness and languor bred.
But now my eyes shall greet a lovelier scene
Than fancy pictured: from his dark green bed
Soon shall the orb of day exalt his glorious head.

I found my two uncles, Cousin George, and several other friends and relations, waiting for me on the Cromarty beach; and was soon as happy among them as a man suffering a good deal from debility, but not much from positive pain, could well be. When again, about ten years after this time, I visited the south of Scotland, it was to receive the instructions necessary to qualify me for a bank accountant; and when I revisited it at a still later period, it was to undertake the management of a metropolitan newspaper. In both these instances I mingled with a different sort of persons from those with whom I had come in contact in the years 1824-25. And, in now taking leave of the lower class, I may be permitted to make a few general remarks regarding them.

It is a curious change which has taken place in this country during the last hundred years. Up till the times of the Rebellion of 1745, and a little later, it was its remoter provinces that formed its dangerous portions; and the effective strongholds from which its advance-guards of civilisation and good order gradually gained upon old anarchy and barbarism, were its great towns. We are told by ecclesiastical historians, that in Rome, after the age of Constantine, the term villager (*Pagus*) came to be regarded as synonymous with heathen, from the circumstance that the worshippers of the gods were then chiefly to be found in remote country places; and we know that in Scotland the Reformation pursued a course exactly resembling that of Christianity itself in the old Roman world: it began in the larger and more influential towns; and it was in the remoter country districts that the displaced religion lingered longest, and found its most efficient champions and allies. Edinburgh, Glasgow, Perth, St. Andrews, Dundee, were all Protestant, and sent out their well-taught burghers to serve in the army of the Lords of the Congregation, when Huntly and Hamilton were arming their vassals to contend for the obsolete faith. In a later age the accessible Lowlands were imbued with an evangelistic Presbyterianism, when the more mountainous and inaccessible provinces of the country were still in a condition to furnish, in what was known as the Highland Host, a dire instrument of persecution. Even as late as the middle of the last century, "Sabbath," according to a popular writer, "never got aboon the Pass of Killiecrankie;" and the Stuarts, exiled for their adherence to Popery, continued to found almost their sole hopes of restoration on the swords of their co-religionists the Highlanders. During the last hundred years, however, this old condition of matters has been strangely reversed; and it is in the great towns that *Paganism* now chiefly prevails. In at least their lapsed classes—a rapidly increasing proportion of their population—it is those cities of our country which first caught the light of religion and learning, that have become pre-eminently its dark parts; just, if I may employ the comparison, as it is those portions of the moon which earliest receive the light when she is in her increscent state, and shine like a thread of silver in the deep blue of the heavens, that first become dark when she falls into the wane.

It is mainly during the elapsed half of the present century that this change for the worse has taken place in the large towns of Scotland. In the year 1824 it was greatly less than half accomplished; but it was fast going on; and I saw, partially at least, the processes in operation through which it has been effected. The cities of the country have increased their population during the past fifty years greatly beyond the proportion of its rural districts—a result in part of the revolutions which have taken place in the agricultural system of the Lowlands, and of the clearances of the Highlands; and in part also of that extraordinary development of the manufactures and trade of the kingdom which the last two generations have witnessed. Of the wilder Edinburgh mechanics with whom I formed at this time any acquaintance, less than one-fourth were natives of the place. The others were mere settlers in it, who had removed mostly from country districts and small towns, in which they had been known, each by his own circle of neighbourhood, and had lived, in consequence, under the wholesome influence of public opinion. In Edinburgh—grown too large at the time to permit men to know aught of their neighbours—they were set free from this wholesome influence, and, unless when under the guidance of higher principle, found themselves at liberty to do very much as they pleased. And—with no *general* opinion to control—cliques and parties of their wilder spirits soon formed in their sheds and workshops a standard of opinion of their own, and found only too effectual means of compelling their weaker comrades to conform to it. And hence a great deal of wild dissipation and profligacy, united, of course, to the inevitable improvidence. And though dissipation and improvidence are quite compatible with intelligence in the first generation, they are sure always to part company from it in the second. The family of the unsteady spendthrift workman is never a well-taught family. It is reared up in ignorance; and, with evil example set before and around it, it almost necessarily takes its place among the lapsed classes. In the third generation the descent is of course still greater and more hopeless than in the second. There is a type of even physical degradation already manifesting itself in some of our large towns, especially among degraded females, which is scarce less marked than that exhibited by the negro, and which both my Edinburgh and Glasgow readers must have often remarked on the respective High Streets of these cities. The features are generally bloated and overcharged, the profile lines usually concave, the complexion coarse and high, and the expression that of a dissipation and sensuality become chronic and inherent. And how this class—constitutionally degraded, and with the moral sense, in most instances, utterly undeveloped and blind—are ever to be reclaimed, it is difficult to see. The immigrant Irish form also a very appreciable element in the degradation of our large towns. They are, however, *pagans*, not of the new, but of the old type: and are chiefly formidable from the squalid wretchedness of a physical character which they have transferred from their mud cabins into our streets and lanes, and from the course of ruinous competition into which they have entered with the unskilled labourers of the country, and which has had the effect of reducing our lowlier countrymen to a humbler level than they perhaps ever occupied before. Meanwhile, this course of degradation is going on, in all our larger towns, in an ever-increasing ratio; and all that philanthropy and the Churches are doing to counteract it is but as the discharge of a few squirts on a conflagration. It is, I fear, preparing terrible convulsions for the future. When the dangerous classes of a country are located in its remote districts, as they were in Scotland in the early half of the last century, it is comparatively easy to deal with them: but the *sans culottes* of Paris in its First Revolution, placed side by side with its executive Government, proved very formidable indeed; nor is it, alas! very improbable that the ever-growing masses of our large towns, broken loose from the sanction of religion and morals, may yet terribly avenge on the upper classes and the Churches of the country the indifferency with which they have been suffered to sink.

I was informed by Cousin George, shortly after my arrival, that my old friend of the Doocot Cave, after keeping shop as a grocer for two years, had given up business, and gone to college to prepare himself for the Church. He had just returned home, added George, after completing his first session, and had expressed a strong desire to meet with me. His mother, too, had joined in the invitation— would I not take tea with them that evening?—and Cousin George had been asked to accompany me. I demurred; but at length set out with George, and, after an interruption in our intercourse of about five years, spent the evening with my old friend. And for years after we were inseparable companions, who, when living in the same neighbourhood, spent together almost every hour not given to private study or inevitable occupation, and who, when separated by distance, exchanged letters enough to fill volumes. We had parted boys, and had now grown men; and for the first few weeks we took stock of each other's acquirements and experiences, and the measure of each other's calibre, with some little curiosity. The mind of my friend had developed rather in a scientific than literary direction. He afterwards carried away the first mathematical prize of his year at college, and the second in natural philosophy; and he had, I now found, great acuteness as a metaphysician, and no inconsiderable acquaintance with the antagonistic positions of the schools of Hume and Reid. On the other hand, my opportunities of observation had been perhaps greater than his, and my acquaintance with men, and even with books, more extensive; and in the interchange of ideas which we carried on, both were gainers; he occasionally picked up in our conversations a fact of which he had been previously ignorant; and I, mayhap, learned to look more closely than before at an argument. I introduced him to the Eathie Lias, and assisted him in forming a small collection, which, ere he ultimately dissipated it, contained some curious fossils—among the others, the second specimen of *Pterichthys* ever found; and he, in turn, was able to give me a few geological notions, which, though quite crude enough—for natural science was not taught at the university which he attended—I found of use in the arrangement of my facts—now become considerable enough to stand in need of those threads of theory without which large accumulations of fact refuse to hang together in the memory. There was one special hypothesis which he had heard broached, and the utter improbability of which I was not yet geologist enough to detect, which for a time filled my whole imagination. It had been said, he told me, that the ancient world, in which my fossils, animal and vegetable, had flourished and decayed—a world greatly older than that before the Flood—had been tenanted by rational, responsible beings, for whom, as for the race to which we ourselves belong, a resurrection and a day of final judgment had awaited. But many thousands of years had elapsed since that day—emphatically the *last* to the Pre-Adamite race—had come and gone. Of all the accountable creatures that had been summoned to its bar, bone had been gathered to its bone, so that not a vestige of the framework of their bodies occurred in the rocks or soils in which they had been originally inhumed; and, in consequence, only the remains of their irresponsible contemporaries, the inferior animals, and of the vegetable productions of their fields and forests, were now to be found. The dream filled for a time my whole imagination; but though poetry might find ample footing on a hypothesis so suggestive and bold, I need scarce say that it has itself *no* foundation in science. Man had no responsible predecessor on earth. At the determined time, when his appointed habitation was completely fitted for him, he came and took possession of it; but the old geologic ages had been ages of immaturity—*days* whose work as a work of promise was "good," but not yet "very good," nor yet ripened for the appearance of a moral agent, whose nature it is to be a fellow-worker with the Creator in relation to even the physical and the material. The planet which we inhabit seems to have been prepared for man, and for man only.

Partly through my friend, but in part also from the circumstance that I retained a measure of intimacy with such of my schoolfellows as had subsequently prosecuted their education at college, I was acquainted, during the later years in which I wrought as a mason, with a good many university-taught lads; and I sometimes could not avoid comparing them in my mind with working men of, as nearly as I could guess, the same original calibre. I did not always find that general superiority on the side of the scholar which the scholar himself usually took for granted. What he had specially studied he knew, save in rare and exceptional cases, better than the working man; but while the student had been mastering his Greek and Latin, and expatiating in Natural Philosophy and the Mathematics, the working man, if of an inquiring mind, had been doing something else; and it is at least a fact, that all the great readers of my acquaintance at this time—the men most extensively acquainted with English literature—were not the men who had received the classical education. On the other hand, in framing an argument, the advantage lay with the scholars. In that common sense, however, which reasons but does not argue, and which enables men to pick their stepping prudently through the journey of life, I found that the classical education gave no superiority whatever; nor did it appear to form so fitting an introduction to the realities of business as that course of dealing with things tangible and actual in which the working man has to exercise his faculties, and from which he derives his experience. One cause of the over-low estimate which the classical scholar so often forms of the intelligence of that class of the people to which our skilled mechanics belong, arises very much from the forwardness of a set of blockheads who are always sure to obtrude themselves upon his notice, and who come to be regarded by him as average specimens of their order. I never yet knew a truly intelligent mechanic obtrusive. Men of the stamp of my two uncles, and of my friend William Ross, never press themselves on the notice of the classes above them. A minister newly settled in a charge, for instance, often finds that it is the dolts of his flock that first force themselves upon his acquaintance. I have heard the late Mr Stewart of Cromarty remark, that the humbler dunder-heads of the parish had all introduced themselves to his acquaintance long ere he found out its clever fellows. And hence often sad mistakes on the part of a clergyman in dealing with the people. It seems never to strike him that there may be among them men of his own calibre, and, in certain practical departments, even better taught than he; and that this superior class is always sure to lead the others. And in preaching down to the level of the men of humbler capacity, he fails often to preach to men of any capacity at all, and is of no use. Some of the clerical contemporaries of Mr Stewart used to allege that, in exercising his admirable faculties in the theological field, he sometimes forgot to lower himself to his people, and so preached over their heads. And at times, when they themselves came to occupy his pulpit, as occasionally happened, they addressed to the congregation sermons quite simple enough for even children to comprehend. I taught at the time a class of boys in the Cromarty Sabbath-School, and invariably found on these occasions, that while the memories of my pupils were charged to the full with the striking thoughts and graphic illustrations of the very elaborate discourses deemed too high for them, they remembered of the very simple ones, specially lowered to suit narrow capacities, not a single word or note. All the attempts at originating a cheap literature that have failed, have been attempts pitched too low; the higher toned efforts have usually succeeded. If the writer of these chapters has been in any degree successful in addressing himself as a journalist to the Presbyterian people of Scotland, it has always been, not by writing *down* to them, but by doing his best on all occasions to write *up* to them. He has ever thought of them as represented by his friend William, his uncles, and his Cousin George—by shrewd old John Fraser, and his reckless though very intelligent acquaintance Cha; and by addressing to them on every occasion as good sense and as solid information as he could possibly muster, he has at times succeeded in catching their ear, and perhaps, in some degree, in influencing their judgment.

CHAPTER XVII

"Beware, Lorenzo, a slow, sudden death."—YOUNG.

THERE was one special subject which my friend, in our quiet evening walks, used to urge seriously upon my attention. He had thrown up, under strong religious impressions, what promised to be so good a business, that in two years he had already saved money enough to meet the expenses of a college course of education. And assuredly, never did man determine on entering the ministry with views more thoroughly disinterested than his. Patronage ruled supreme in the Scottish Establishment at the time; and my friend had no influence and no patron; but he could not see his way clear to join with the Evangelical Dissenters or the Secession; and, believing that the most important work on earth is the work of saving souls, he had entered on his new course in the full conviction that, if God had work for him of this high character to do, He would find him an opportunity of doing it. And now, thoroughly in earnest, and as part of the special employment to which he had devoted himself, he set himself to press upon my attention the importance, in their personal bearing, of religious concerns.

I was not unacquainted with the standard theology of the Scottish Church. In the parish school, I had, indeed, acquired no ideas on the subject; and though I now hear a good deal said, chiefly with a controversial bearing, about the excellent religious influence of our parochial seminaries, I never knew any one who owed other than the merest smattering of theological knowledge to these institutions, and not a single individual who had ever derived from them any tincture, even the slightest, of religious feeling. In truth, during almost the whole of the last century, and for at least the first forty years of the present, the people of

354

Scotland were, with all their faults, considerably more Christian than the larger part of their schoolmasters. So far as I can remember, I carried in my memory from school only a single remark at all theological in its character, and it was of a kind suited rather to do harm than good. In reading in the class one Saturday morning a portion of the Hundred and Nineteenth Psalm, I was told by the master that that ethical poem was a sort of alphabetical acrostic—a circumstance, he added, that accounted for its broken and inconsecutive character as a composition. Chiefly, however, from the Sabbath-day catechizings to which I had been subjected during boyhood by my uncles, and latterly from the old divines, my Uncle Sandy's favourites, and from the teachings of the pulpit, I had acquired a considerable amount of religious knowledge. I had thought, too, a good deal about some of the peculiar doctrines of Calvinism, in their character as abstruse positions—such as the doctrine of the Divine decrees, and of man's inability to assume the initiative in the work of his own conversion. I had, besides, a great admiration of the Bible, especially of its narrative and poetical parts; and could scarce give strong enough expression to the contempt which I entertained for the vulgar and tasteless sceptics who, with Paine at their head, could speak of it as a weak or foolish book. Further, reared in a family circle, some of whose members were habitually devout, and all of whom respected and stood up for religion, and were imbued with the stirring ecclesiastical traditions of their country, I felt that the religious side in any quarrel had a sort of hereditary claim upon me. I believe I may venture to say, that previous to this time I had never seen a religious man badgered for his religion, and much in a minority, without openly taking part with him; nor is it impossible that, in a time of trouble, I might have almost deserved the character given by old John Howie[1] to a rather notable "gentleman sometimes called Burley," who, "although he was by some reckoned none of the most religious," joined himself to the suffering party, and was "always zealous and honest-hearted."

[1] Author of *Scots Worthies* (1775).

355

And yet my religion was a strangely incongruous thing. It took the form, in my mind, of a mass of indigested theology, with here and there a prominent point developed out of due proportion, from the circumstance that I had thought upon it for myself; and while, entangled, if I may so speak, amid the recesses and under cover of the general chaotic mass, there harboured no inconsiderable amount of superstition, there rested over it the clouds of a dreary scepticism. I have sometimes, in looking back on the doubts and questionings of this period, thought, and perhaps even spoken of myself as an infidel. But an infidel I assuredly was not: my belief was at least as real as my incredulity, and had, I am inclined to think, a much deeper seat in my mind. But, wavering between the two extremes—now a believer, and anon a sceptic; the belief usually exhibiting itself as a strongly-based instinct, the scepticism as the result of some intellectual process—I lived on for years in a sort of uneasy see-saw condition, without any middle ground between the two extremes, on which I could at once reason and believe.

That middle ground I now succeeded in finding. It is at once delicate and dangerous to speak of one's own spiritual condition, or of the emotional sentiments on which one's conclusions regarding it are often so doubtfully founded. Egotism in the religious form is perhaps more tolerated than in any other; but it is not on that account less perilous to the egotist himself. There need be, however, less delicacy in speaking of one's beliefs than of one's feelings; and I trust I need not hesitate to say, that I was led to see at this time, through the instrumentality of my friend, that my theologic system had previously wanted a central object, to which the heart, as certainly as the intellect, could attach itself; and that the true centre of an efficient *Christianity* is, as the name ought of itself to indicate, "the Word made Flesh". Around this central sun of the Christian system—appreciated, however, not as a *doctrine* which is a mere abstraction, but as a Divine Person— so truly Man that the affections of the human heart can lay hold upon Him, and so truly God that the mind, through faith, can at all times and in all places be brought into direct contact with Him—all that is really religious takes its place in a subsidiary and subordinate relation. I say subsidiary and subordinate. The Divine Man is the great attractive centre, the sole gravitating point of a system which owes to Him all its coherency, and which would be but a chaos were He away. It seems to be the existence of the human nature in this central and paramount object that imparts to Christianity, in its subjective character, its peculiar power of influencing and controlling the human mind. There may be men who, through a peculiar idiosyncrasy of constitution, are capable of loving, after a sort, a mere abstract God, unseen and inconceivable; though, as shown by the air of sickly sentimentality borne by almost all that has been said and written on the subject, the feeling in its true form must be a very rare and exceptional one. In all my experience of men, I never knew a genuine instance of it. The love of an abstract God seems to be as little natural to the ordinary human constitution as the love of an abstract sun or planet. And so it will be found, that in all the religions that have taken strong hold of the mind of man, the element of a vigorous humanity has mingled, in the character of its gods, with the theistic element. The gods of classic mythology were simply powerful men set loose from the tyranny of the physical laws; and, in their purely human character, as warm friends and deadly enemies, they were both feared and loved. And so the belief which bowed at their shrines ruled the old civilized world for many centuries. In the great ancient mythologies of the East— Buddhism and Brahmanism—both very influential forms of belief—we have the same elements, genuine humanity added to god-like power. In the faith of the Moslem, the human character of the man Mahommed, elevated to an all potential vicegerency in things sacred, gives great strength to what without it would be but a weak theism. Literally, it is Allah's supreme prophet that maintains for Allah himself a place in the Mahommedan mind. Again, in Popery we find an excess of humanity scarce less great than in the classical mythology itself, and with nearly corresponding results. Though the Virgin Mother takes, as queen of heaven, a first place in the scheme, and forms in that character a greatly more interesting goddess than any of the old ones who counselled Ulysses, or responded to the love of Anchises or of Endymion, she has to share her empire with the minor saints, and to recognise in them a host of rivals. But undoubtedly to this popular element Popery owes not a little of its indomitable strength. In, however, all these forms of religion, whether inherently false from the beginning, or so overlaid in some after stage by the fictitious and the untrue as to have their original substratum of truth covered up by error and fable, there is such a want of coherency between the theistic and human elements, that we always find them undergoing a process of separation. We see the human element ever laying hold on the popular mind, and there manifesting itself in the form of a vigorous superstition; and the theistic element, on the other hand, recognised by the cultivated intellect as the exclusive and only element, and elaborated into a sort of natural theology, usually rational enough in its propositions, but for any practical purpose always feeble and inefficient. Such a separation of the two elements took place of old in the ages of the classical mythology; and hence the very opposite characters of the wild but genial and popular fables so exquisitely adorned by the poets, and the rational but uninfluential doctrines received by a select few from the philosophers. Such a separation took place, too, in France in the latter half of the last century; and still on the European Continent generally do we find this separation represented by the asserters of a weak theism on the one hand, and of a superstitious saint-worship on the other. In the false or corrupted religions, the two indispensable elements of Divinity and Humanity appear as if blended together by a mere mechanical process; and it is their natural tendency to separate, through a sort of subsidence on the part of the human element from the theistic one, as if from some lack of the necessary affinities. In Christianity, on the other hand, when existing in its integrity as the religion of the New Testament, the union of the two elements is complete: it partakes of the nature, not of a mechanical, but of a chemical mixture; and its great central doctrine—the true Humanity and true Divinity of the Adorable Saviour—is a truth equally receivable by at once the humblest and the loftiest intellects. Poor dying children possessed of but a few simple ideas, and men of the most robust intellects, such as the Chalmerses, Fosters, and Halls of the Christian Church, find themselves equally able to rest their salvation on the *man* "Christ, who is over all, *God* blessed for ever." Of this fundamental truth of the two natures, that condensed enunciation of the gospel which forms the watchword of our faith, "Believe in the Lord Jesus Christ, and thou shalt be saved," is a direct and palpable embodiment; and Christianity is but a mere name without it.

I was impressed at this time by another very remarkable feature in the religion of Christ in its subjective character. Kames,[1] in his "Art of Thinking," illustrates, by a curious story, one of his observations on the "nature of man." "Nothing is more common," he says, "than love converted into hatred; and we have seen instances of hatred converted into love." And in exemplifying the remark, he relates his anecdote of "Unnion and Valentine." Two English soldiers, who fought in the wars of Queen Anne—the one a petty officer, the other a private sentinel—had been friends and comrades for years; but, quarrelling in some love affair, they became bitter enemies. The officer made an ungenerous use of his authority, and so annoyed and persecuted the sentinel as almost to fret him into madness; and he was frequently heard to say that he would die to be avenged of him. Whole months were spent in the infliction of injuries on the one side, and in the venting of complaints on the other; when, in the midst of their mutual rage, they were both selected, as men of tried courage, to share in some desperate attack, which was, however, unsuccessful; and the officer, in the retreat, was disabled, and struck down by a shot in the thigh. "Oh, Valentine! and will you leave me here to perish?"

---

[1] Lord Kames, Henry Home (1696-1782), Law Lord and essayist on matters moral, historical, agricultural and metaphysical, including *An Introduction to the Art of Thinking* published in 1761.

he exclaimed, as his old comrade rushed past him. The poor injured man immediately returned; and, in the midst of a thick fire, bore off his wounded enemy to what seemed a place of safety, when he was struck by a chance ball, and fell dead under his burden. The officer, immediately forgetting his wound, rose up, tearing his hair; and, throwing himself on the bleeding body, he cried, "Ah, Valentine! and was it for me, who have so barbarously used thee, that thou has died? I will not live after thee." He was not by any means to be forced from the corpse; but was removed with it bleeding in his arms, and attended with tears by all his comrades, who knew of his harshness to the deceased. When brought to a tent, his wounds were dressed by force; but the next day, still calling on Valentine, and lamenting his cruelties to him, he died in the pangs of remorse and despair.

This surely is a striking story; but the commonplace remark based upon it by the philosopher is greatly less so. Men who have loved *do* often learn to hate the object of their affections; and men who have hated sometimes learn to love: but the portion of the anecdote specially worthy of remark appears to be that which, dwelling on the o'ermastering remorse and sorrow of the rescued soldier, shows how effectually his poor dead comrade had, by dying for him "while he was yet his enemy," "heaped coals of fire upon his head." And such seems to be one of the leading principles on which, with a Divine adaptation to the heart of man, the scheme of Redemption has been framed. The Saviour approved His love, "in that, while we were yet sinners, He died for us." There is an inexpressibly great power in this principle; and many a deeply-stirred heart has felt it to its core. The theologians have perhaps too frequently dwelt on the Saviour's vicarious satisfaction for human sin in relation to the offended justice of the Father. How, or on what principle, the Father was satisfied, I know not, and may never know. The enunciation regarding vicarious satisfaction may be properly received in faith as a *fact*, but, I suspect, not properly reasoned upon until we shall be able to bring the moral sense of Deity, with its requirements, within the limits of a small and trivial logic. But the thorough adaptation of the scheme to man's nature is greatly more appreciable, and lies fully within the reach of observation and experience. And how thorough that adaptation is, all who have really looked at the matter ought to be competent to say. Does an earthly priesthood, vested with alleged powers to interpose between God and man, always originate an ecclesiastical tyranny, which has the effect, in the end, of shutting up the mass of men from their Maker?——here is there a High Priest passed into the heavens——the only Priest whom the evangelistic Protestant recognises as really such——to whom, in his character of Mediator between God and man, all may apply, and before whom there need be felt none of that abject prostration of the spirit and understanding which man always experiences when he bends before the merely human priest. Is self-righteousness the besetting infirmity of the religious man?—— in the scheme of vicarious righteousness it finds no footing. The self-approving Pharisee must be content to renounce his own merits, ere he can have part or lot in the fund of merit which alone avails; and yet without personal righteousness he can have no evidence whatever that he has an interest in the all-prevailing imputed righteousness. But it is in the closing scene of life, when man's boasted virtues become so intangible in his estimation that they elude his grasp, and sins and shortcomings, little noted before, start up around him like spectres, that the scheme of Redemption appears worthy of the infinite wisdom and goodness of God, and when what the Saviour did and suffered seems of efficacy enough to blot out the guilt of every offence. It is when the minor lights of comfort are extinguished that the Sun of Righteousness shines forth, and more than compensates for them all.

The opinions which I formed at this time on this matter of prime importance I found no after occasion to alter or modify. On the contrary, in passing from the subjective to the objective view, I have seen the doctrine of the union of the two natures greatly confirmed. The truths of geology appear destined to exercise in the future no inconsiderable influence on natural theology; and with this especial doctrine they seem very much in accordance. Of that long and stately march of creation with which the records of the stony science bring us acquainted, the distinguishing characteristic is progress. There appears to have been a time when there existed on our planet only dead matter unconnected with vitality; and then a time in which plants and animals of a low order began to be, but in which even fishes, the humblest of the vertebrata, were so rare and exceptional, that they occupied a scarce appreciable place in Nature. Then came an age of fishes huge of size, and that to the peculiar ichthyic organization added certain well-marked characteristics of the reptilian class immediately above them. And then, after a time, during which the reptile had occupied a place as inconspicuous as that occupied by the fish in the earlier periods of animal life, an age of reptiles of vast bulk and high standing was ushered in. And when, in the lapse of untold ages, *it* also had passed away, there succeeded an age of great mammals. Molluscs, fishes, reptiles, mammals, had each in succession their periods of vast extent; and then there came a period that differed even more, in the character of its master-existence, from any of these creations, than they, with their many vitalities, had differed from the previous inorganic period in which life had not yet begun to be. The human period began— the period of a fellow-worker with God, created in God's own image. The animal existences of the previous ages formed, if I may so express myself, mere figures in the landscapes of the great garden which they inhabited. Man, on the other hand, was placed in it to "keep and to dress it;" and such has been the effect of his labours, that they have altered and improved the face of whole continents. Our globe, even as it might be seen from the moon, testifies, over its surface, to that unique nature of man, unshared in by any of the inferior animals, which renders him, in things physical and natural, a fellow-worker with the Creator who first produced it. And of the identity of at least his intellect with that of his Maker, and, of consequence, of the integrity of the revelation which declares that he was created in God's own image, we have direct evidence in his ability of not only conceiving of God's contrivances, but even of reproducing them; and this, not as a mere imitator, but as an original thinker. He may occasionally borrow the principles of his contrivances from the works of the Original Designer, but much more frequently, in studying the works of the original Designer, does he discover in them the principles of his own contrivances. He has not been an imitator: he has merely been exercising, with resembling results, the resembling mind, *i.e.*, the mind made in the Divine image. But the existing scene of things is not destined to be the last. High as it is, it is too low and too imperfect to be regarded as God's finished work: it is merely one of the *progressive* dynasties; and Revelation and the implanted instincts of our nature alike teach us to anticipate a glorious *terminal* dynasty. In the first dawn of being, simple vitality was united to matter: the vitality thus united became, in each succeeding period, of a higher and yet higher order;—it was in succession the vitality of the mollusc, of the fish, of the reptile, of the sagacious mammal, and, finally, of responsible, immortal man, created in the image of God. What is to be the next advance? Is there to be merely a repetition of the past—an introduction a second time of "man made in the image of God?" No! The geologist, in the tables of stone which form his records, finds no example of dynasties once passed away again returning. There has been no repetition of the dynasty of the fish—of the reptile—of the mammal. The dynasty of the future is to have glorified man for its inhabitant; but it is to be the dynasty—the "*kingdom*"— not of glorified man made in the image of God, but of God himself in the form of man. In the doctrine of the two natures, and in the further doctrine that the terminal dynasty is to be peculiarly the dynasty of Him in whom the natures are united, we find that required progression beyond which progress cannot go. Creation and the Creator meet at one point, and in one person. The long ascending line from dead matter to man has been a progress Godwards—not an asymptotical progress, but destined from the beginning to furnish a point of union; and, occupying that point as true God and true man, as Creator and created, we recognise the adorable Monarch of all the Future. It is, as urged by the Apostle, the especial glory of our race, that it should have furnished that point of contact at which Godhead has united Himself, not to man only, but also, through man, to His own Universe—to the Universe of Matter and of Mind.

I remained for several months in delicate and somewhat precarious health. My lungs had received more serious injury than I had at first supposed; and it seemed at one time rather doubtful whether the severe mechanical irritation which had so fretted them that the air-passages seemed overcharged with matter and stone-dust, might not pass into the complaint which it stimulated, and become confirmed consumption. Curiously enough, my comrades had told me in sober earnest—among the rest, Cha, a man of sense and observation—that I would pay the forfeit of my sobriety by being sooner affected than they by the stone-cutter's malady: "a good *bouse*" gave, they said, a wholesome fillip to the constitution, and "cleared the sulphur off the lungs;" and mine would suffer for want of the medicine which kept theirs clean. I know not whether there was virtue in their remedy: it seems just possible that the shock given to the constitution by an overdose of strong drink may in certain cases be medicinal in its effects; but they were certainly not in error in their prediction. Among the hewers of the party I was the first affected by the malady. I still remember the rather pensive than sad feeling with which I used to contemplate, at this time, an early death, and the intense love of nature that drew me, day after day, to the beautiful scenery which surrounds my native town, and which I loved all the more from the consciousness that my eyes might so soon close upon it for ever. "It *is* a pleasant thing to behold the sun." Among my manuscripts—useless scraps of paper, to which, however, in their character as fossils of the past epochs of my life, I cannot help attaching an interest not at all in themselves—I find the mood represented by only a few almost infantile verses, addressed to a docile little girl of five years, my eldest sister by my mother's second marriage, and my frequent companion, during my illness, in my short walks.

TO JEANIE

Sister Jeanie, haste, we'll go
To whare the white-starred gowans grow,
Wi' the puddock flower o' gowden hue,
The snaw-drap white and the bonny vi'let blue.

Sister Jeanie, haste, we'll go
To whare the blossomed lilacs grow—
To whare the pine-tree, dark an' high,
Is pointing its tap at the cludless sky.

Jeanie, mony a merry lay
Is sung in the young-leaved woods today;
Flits on light wing the dragon-flee,
An' hums on the flowrie the big red-bee.

Down the burnie wirks its way
Aneath the bending birken spray,
An wimples roun' the green moss-stane,
An' mourns, I kenna why, wi' a ceaseless mane.

Jeanie, come; thy days o' play
Wi' autumn-tide shall pass away;
Sune shall these scenes, in darkness cast,
Be ravaged wild by the wild winter blast.

Though to thee a spring shall rise,
An' scenes as fair salute thine eyes;
An' though, through many a cludless day,
My winsome Jean shall be heartsome and gay.

He wha grasps thy little hand
Nae langer at thy side shall stand,
Nor o'er the flower-besprinkled brae
Lead thee the low'nest and the bonniest way.

Dost thou see yon yard sae green,
Spreckled wi' mony a mossy stane?
A few short weeks o' pain shall fly,
An' asleep in that *bed* shall thy puir brither lie.

Then thy mither's tears awhile
May chide thy joy an' damp thy smile;
But sune ilk grief shall wear awa',
And I'll be forgotten by ane an' by a'.

Dinna think the thought is sad;
Life vexed me aft, but this mak's glad:
When cauld my heart and closed my e'e,
Bonny shall the dreams o' my slumbers be.

At length, however, my constitution threw off the malady; though—as I still occasionally feel—the organ affected never quite regained its former vigour; and I began to experience the quiet but exquisite enjoyment of the convalescent. After long and depressing illness, youth itself appears to return with returning health; and it seems to be one of the compensating provisions, that while men of robust constitution and rigid organization get gradually old in their spirits and obtuse in their feelings, the class that have to endure being many times sick have the solace of being also many times young. The reduced and weakened frame becomes as susceptible of the emotional as in tender and delicate youth. I know not that I ever spent three happier months than the autumnal months of this year, when gradually picking up flesh and strength amid my old haunts, the woods and caves. My friend had left me early in July for Aberdeen, where he had gone to prosecute his studies under the eye of a tutor, one Mr Duncan, whom he described to me in his letters as perhaps the most deeply learned man he had ever seen. "You may ask him a common question," said my friend, "without getting an answer—for he has considerably more than the average absentness of the great scholar about him; but if you inquire of him the state of any one controversy ever agitated in the Church or the world, he will give it you at once, with, if you please, all the arguments on both sides."

The trait struck me at the time as one of some mark; and I thought of it many years after, when fame had blown the name of my friend's tutor pretty widely as Dr Duncan, Hebrew Professor in our Free Church College, and one of the most profoundly learned of Orientalists. Though separated, however, from my friend, I found a quiet pleasure in following up, in my solitary walks, the views which his conversations had suggested; and in a copy of verses, the production of this time, which, with all their poverty and stiffness, please me as true, and as representative of the convalescent feeling, I find direct reference to the beliefs which he had laboured to instil. My verses are written in a sort of metre which, in the hands of Collins became flexible and exquisitely poetic, and which in those of Kirke White is at least pleasing, but of which we find poor enough specimens in the "Anthologies" of Southey, and which perhaps no one so limited in his metrical vocabulary, and so defective in his musical ear, as the writer of these chapters, should ever have attempted.

SOLACE

No star of golden influence hailed the birth
Of him who, all unknown and lonely, pours,
    As fails the light of eve,
    His pensive, artless song;
Yea, those who mark out honour, ease, wealth, fame,
As man's sole joys, shall find no joy in him;
    Yet of far nobler kind
    His silent pleasures prove.
For not unmarked by him the ways of men;
Nor yet to him the ample page unknown,
    Where, traced by Nature's hand,
    Is many a pleasing line.
Oh! when the world's dull children bend the knee,
Meanly obsequious, to some mortal god,
    It yields no vulgar joy
    Alone to stand aloof;
Or when they jostle on wealth's crowded road,
And swells the tumult on the breeze, 'tis sweet,

Thoughtful, at length reclined,
To list the wrathful hum.
What though the weakly gay affect to scorn
The loitering dreamer of life's darkest shade,
Stingless the jeer, whose voice
Comes from the erroneous path.
Scorner, of all thy toils the end declare!
If pleasure, pleasure comes uncalled, to cheer
The haunts of him who spends
His hours in quiet thought.
And happier he who can repress desire,
Than they who seldom mourn a thwarted wish;
The vassals they of fate—
The unbending conqueror he.
And thou, blest Muse, though rudely strung thy lyre,
Its tones can guile the dark and lonesome day—
Can smooth the wrinkled brow,
And dry the sorrowing tear.
Thine many a bliss—oh, many a solace thine!
By thee upheld, the soul asserts her throne,
The chastened passions sleep,
And dove-eyed Peace prevails.
And thou, fair Hope! when other comforts fail—
When night's thick mists descend—thy beacon flames,
Till glow the dark clouds round
With beams of promised bliss.
Thou failest not when, mute the soothing lyre,
Lives thy unfading solace: sweet to raise
Thy eye, O quiet Hope.
And greet a friend in heaven!—
A friend, a brother, one whose awful throne
In holy fear heaven's mightiest sons approach;
Man's heart to feel for man—
To save him God's great power!
Conqueror of death, joy of the accepted soul,
Oh, wonders raise no doubt when told of thee!
Thy way past finding out,
Thy love, can tongue declare?
Cheered by thy smile, Peace dwells amid the storm;
Held by thy hand, the floods assail in vain;
With grief is blent a joy,
And beams the vault of death.

Passing, in one of my walks this autumn, the cave in which I used to spend in boyhood so many happy hours with Finlay, I found it smoking, as of old, with a huge fire, and occupied by a wilder and more careless party than even my truant school-fellows. It had been discovered and appropriated by a band of gipsies, who, attracted by the soot-stains on its roof and sides, and concluding that it had been inhabited by the gipsies of other days, had, without consulting factor or landlord, at once entered upon possession, as the proper successors of its former occupants. They were a savage party, with a good deal of the true gipsy blood in them, but not without mixture of a broken-down class of apparently British descent; and one of their women was purely Irish. From what I had previously heard about gipsies, I was not prepared for a mixture of this kind; but I found it pretty general, and ascertained that at least one of the ways in which it had taken place was exemplified by the case of the one Irish woman. Her gipsy husband had served as a soldier, and had married her when in the army. I have been always exceedingly curious to see man in his rude elements——to study him as the savage whether among the degraded classes of our own country, or, as exhibited in the writings of travellers and voyagers, in his aboriginal state; and I now did not hesitate to visit the gipsies, and to spend not unfrequently an hour or two in their company. They at first seemed jealous of me as a spy; but finding me inoffensive, and that I did not betray counsel, they came at length to recognise me as the "quiet, sickly lad," and to chatter as freely in my presence as in that of the other pitchers with ears, which they used to fabricate out of tin by the dozen and the score, and the manufacture of which, with the making of horn spoons, formed the main branch of business carried on in the cave. I saw in these visits curious glimpses of gipsy life. I could trust only to what I actually witnessed: what was told me could on no occasion be believed; for never were there lies more gross and monstrous than those of the gipsies; but even the lying formed of itself a peculiar trait. I have never heard lying elsewhere that set all probability so utterly at defiance—a consequence, in part, of their recklessly venturing, like unskilful authors, to expatiate in walks of invention over which their experience did not extend. On one occasion an old gipsy woman, after pronouncing my malady consumption, prescribed for me, as an infallible remedy, raw parsley minced small and made up into balls with fresh butter; but seeing, I suppose, from my manner, that I lacked the necessary belief in her specific, she went on to say, that she had derived her knowledge of such matters from her mother, one of the most "skeely women that ever lived." Her mother, she said, had once healed a lord's son of a grievous hurt in half a minute, after all the English doctors had shown they could do nothing for him. His eye had been struck out of its socket by a blow, and hung half-way down his cheek; and though the doctors could of course return it to its place, it refused to stick, always falling out again. Her mother, however, at once understood the case; and, making a little slit at the back of the young man's neck she got hold of the end of a sinew, and, pulling in the dislodged orb at a tug, she made all tight by running a knot on the controlling ligament, and so kept the eye in its place. And, save that the young lord continued to squint a little, he was well at once. The peculiar anatomy on which this invention was framed must have, of course, resembled that of a wax-doll with winking eyes; but it did well enough for the woman; and, having no character for truth to maintain, she did not hesitate to build on it. On asking her whether she ever attended church, she at once replied, "O yes, at one time very often. I am the daughter of a minister—a *natural* daughter, you know: my father was the most powerful preacher in all the south, and I always went to hear him." In about an hour after, however, forgetting her extemporary sally, and the reverend character with which she had invested her sire, she spoke of him, in another equally palpable invention, as the greatest "king of the gipsies" that the gipsies ever had. Even the children had caught this habit of monstrous mendacity. There was one of the boys of the band, considerably under twelve, who could extemporize lying narratives by the hour, and seemed

370

always delighted to get a listener; and a little girl, younger still, who "lisped in *fiction*, for the *fiction* came." There were two things that used to strike me as peculiar among these gipsies—a Hindu type of head, small of size, but with a considerable fulness of forehead, especially along the medial line, in the region, as the phrenologist would perhaps say, of *individuality* and *comparison*; and a singular posture assumed by the elderly females of the tribe in squatting before their fires, in which the elbow rested on the knees brought close together, the chin on the palms, and the entire figure (somewhat resembling in attitude a Mexican mummy) assumed an outlandish appearance, that reminded me of some of the more grotesque sculptures of Egypt and Hindustan. The peculiar type of head was derived, I doubt not, from an ancestry originally different from that of the settled races of the country; nor is it impossible that the peculiar position—unlike any I have ever seen Scottish females assume—was also of foreign origin.

I have witnessed scenes among these gipsies, of which the author of the "Jolly Beggars" might have made rare use, but which formed a sort of materials that I lacked the special ability rightly to employ. It was reported on one occasion that a marriage ceremony and wedding were to take place in the cave; and I sauntered the way, in the hope of ascertaining how its inmates contrived to do for themselves what of course no clergyman could venture to do for them—seeing that, of the parties to be united, the bridegroom might have already as many wives living as "Peter Bell," and the bride as many husbands. A gipsy marriage had taken place a few years previous in a cave near Rosemarkie. An old male gipsy, possessed of the rare accomplishment of reading, had half-read, half-spelled the English marriage-service to the young couple, and the ceremony was deemed complete at its close. And I now expected to witness something similar. In an opening in the wood above, I encountered two very drunk gipsies, and saw the firstfruits of the coming merriment. One of the two was an uncouth-looking monster, sallow-skinned, flat-faced, round-shouldered, long and thinly limbed, at least six feet two inches in height, and, from his strange misproportions, he might have passed for seven feet any day, were it not that his trousers, made for a much shorter man, and rising to the middle of his calfless leg, gave him much the appearance of a big boy walking on stilts. The boys of the place called him "Giant Grimbo;" while his companion, a tight dapper little fellow, who always showed off a compact, well-rounded leg in corduroy inexpressibles, they had learned to distinguish as "Billy Breeches." The giant, who carried a bagpipe, had broken down ere I came up with them; and now, sitting on the grass, he was droning out in fitful blasts a diabolical music, to which Billy Breeches was dancing; but, just as I passed, Billy also gave way, after wasting an infinity of exertion in keeping erect; and, falling over the prostrate musician, I could hear the bag groaning out its soul as he pressed against it, in a lengthened melancholious squeal. I found the cave bearing an aspect of more than ordinary picturesqueness. It had its two fires, and its double portion of smoke, that went rolling out in the calm like an inverted river; for it clung close to the roof, as if by a reversed gravitation, and turned its foaming surface downwards. At the one fire an old gipsy woman was engaged in baking oaten cakes; and a great pot, that dispensed through the cave the savoury odour of unlucky poultry cut short in the middle of their days, and of hapless hares destroyed without the game licence, depended over the other. An ass, the common property of the tribe, stood meditating in the foreground; two urchins, of about from ten to twelve years a-piece—wretchedly supplied in the article of clothing—for the one, provided with only a pair of tattered trousers, was naked from the waist upwards, and the other, furnished with only a dilapidated jacket, was naked from the waist downwards—were engaged in picking up fuel for the fire, still further in front; a few of the ordinary inmates of the place lounged under cover of the smoke, apparently in a mood not in the least busy; and on a couch of dried fern sat evidently the central figure of the group, a young, sparkling-eyed brunette, more than ordinarily marked by the Hindu peculiarities of head and feature, and attended by a savage-looking fellow of about twenty, dark as a mulatto, and with a profusion of long flexible hair black as jet, hanging down to his eyes, and clustering about his cheeks and neck. These were, I ascertained, the bride and bridegroom. The bride was engaged in sewing a cap—the bridegroom in watching the progress of the work. I observed that the party, who were less communicative than usual, seemed to regard me in the light of an intruder. An elderly tinker, the father of the bride, grey as a leafless thorn in winter, but still stalwart and strong, sat admiring a bit of spelter of about a pound weight. It was gold, he said, or, as he pronounced the word, "guild," which had been found in an old cairn, and was of immense value, "for it was peer guild, and that was the best o' guild;" but if I pleased, he would sell it to me, a very great bargain. I was engaged with some difficulty in declining the offer, when we were interrupted by the sounds of the bagpipe. Giant Grimbo and Billy Breeches had succeeded in regaining their feet, and were seen staggering towards the cave. "Where's the whisky, Billy?" inquired the proprietor of the gold, addressing himself to the man of the small clothes. "Whisky!" said Billy, "ask Grimbo." "Where's the whisky, Grimbo?" reiterated the tinker. "Whisky!" replied Grimbo, "Whisky!" and yet again, after a pause and a hiccup, "Whisky!" "Ye confounded blacks!" said the tinker, springing to his feet with an agility wonderful for an age so advanced as his, "Have you drunk it all? But take that, Grimbo," he added, planting a blow full on the side of the giant's head, which prostrated his vast length along the floor of the cave. "And take that, Billy," he iterated, dealing such another blow to the shorter man, which sent him right athwart his prostrate comrade. And then, turning to me, he remarked with perfect coolness, "That, master, I call smart hitting." "Honest lad," whispered one of the women immediately after, "it will be a *reugh* time wi' us here the nicht: you had just better be stepping your ways." I had already begun to think so without prompting; and so, taking my leave of the gipsies, I failed being, as I had proposed, one of the witnesses of the wedding.

There is a sort of grotesque humour in scenes of the kind described, that has charms for artists and authors of a particular class—some of them men of broad sympathies and great genius; and hence, through their representations, literary and pictorial, the ludicrous point of view has come to be the conventional and ordinary one. And yet it is a sad enough merriment, after all, that has for its subject a degradation so extreme. I never knew a gipsy that seemed to possess a moral sense—a degree of *Pariahism* which has been reached by only one other class in the country, and that a small one—the descendants of degraded females in our large towns. An education in Scotland, however secular in its character, always casts a certain amount of enlightenment on the conscience; a home, however humble, whose inmates win their bread by honest industry, has a similar effect; but in the peculiar walks in which for generations there has been no education of any kind, or in which bread has been the wages of infamy, the moral sense seems so wholly obliterated, that there appears to survive nothing in the mind to which the missionary or the moralist can appeal. It seems scarce possible for a man to know even a very little of these classes, without learning, in consequence, to respect honest labour, and even secular knowledge, as at least the *second-best* things, in their moral bearing and influence, that can exist among a people.

CHAPTER XVIII

"For such is the flaw or the depth of the plan
In the make of that wonderful creature called man,
No two virtues, whatever relation they claim,
Nor even two different shades of the same,
Though like as was ever twin-brother to brother,
Possessing the one shall imply you've the other."—BURNS.

DURING my period of convalescence, I amused myself in hewing for my uncles, from an original design, an ornate dial-stone; and the dial-stone still exists, to show that my skill as a stone-cutter rose somewhat above the average of the profession in those parts of the country in which it ranks highest. Gradually, as I recovered health and strength, little jobs came dropping in. I executed sculptured tablets in a style not common in the north of Scotland; introduced into the churchyards of the locality a better type of tombstone than had obtained in them before, save, mayhap, at a very early period; distanced all my competitors in the art of inscription-cutting; and at length found that, without exposing my weakened lungs to the rough tear and wear to which the ordinary stone-cutter must subject himself, I could live. I deemed it an advantage, too, rather than the reverse, that my new branch of employment brought me not unfrequently for a few days into country districts sufficiently distant from home to present me with new fields of observation, and to open up new tracts of inquiry. Sometimes I spent half a week in a farm-house in the neighbourhood of some country churchyard—sometimes I lodged in a village—oftener than once I sheltered beside some gentleman's seat, where the august shadow of lairdship lay heavy on society; and in this way I came to see and know a good deal of the Scottish people, in their many-coloured aspects, of which otherwise I might have remained ignorant. At times, too, on some dusty cottage shelf

I succeeded in picking up a rare book, or, what was not less welcome, got a curious tradition from the cottager; or there lay within the reach of an evening walk some interesting piece of antiquity, or some rock-section, which I found it profitable to visit. A solitary burying-ground, too, situated, as country burying-grounds usually are, in some pleasant spot, and surrounded by its groups of ancient trees, formed a much more delightful scene of labour than a dusty work-shed, or some open area in a busy town; and altogether I found my new mode of life a quiet and happy one. Nor, with all its tranquillity, was it a sort of life in which the intellect was in any great danger of falling asleep. There was scarce a locality in which new game might not be started, that, in running down, kept the faculties in full play. Let me exemplify by describing the courses of inquiry, physical and metaphysical, which opened up to me, when spending a few days, first in the burying-ground of Kirkmichael, and next in the churchyard of Nigg.

I have elsewhere somewhat fancifully described the ruinous chapel and solitary graveyard of Kirkmichael as lying on the sweep of a gentle declivity, within a few yards of a flat sea-beach, so little exposed to the winds, that it would seem as if "ocean muffled its waves in approaching this field of the dead." And so the two vegetations—that of the land and of the sea—undisturbed by the surf, which on opener coasts prevents the growth of either along the upper littoral line, where the waves beat heaviest, here meet and mingle, each encroaching for a little way on the province of the other. And at meal-times, and when returning homewards in the evening along the shore, it furnished me with amusement enough to mark the character of the several plants of both floras that thus meet and cross each other, and the appearances which they assume when inhabiting each other's province. On the side of the land, beds of thrift, with its gay flowers the sea-pinks, occupied great prominent cushions, that stood up like little islets amid the flowing sea, and were covered over by salt water during stream-tides to the depth of from eighteen inches to two feet. With these there occasionally mingled spikes of the sea-lavender; and now and then, though more rarely, a *sea-aster*, that might be seen raising above the calm surface its composite flowers, with their bright yellow staminal pods, and their pale purple petals. Far beyond, however, even the cushions of thrift, I could trace the fleshy, jointed stems of the glass-wort, rising out of the mud, but becoming diminutive and branchless as I followed them downwards, till, at depths where they must have been frequently swum over by the young coal-fish and the flounder, they appeared as mere fleshy spikes, scarce an inch in height, and then ceased. On the side of the sea it was the various fucoids that rose highest along the beach; the serrated fucus barely met the salt-wort; but the bladder-bearing fucus (*fucus nodosus*[1]) mingled its brown fronds not unfrequently with the crimson flowers of the thrift,[2] and the vesicular fucus (*fucus vesiculosus*) rose higher still, to enter into strange companionship with the sea-side plantains and the common scurvy-grass. Green enteromorpha[3] of two species—*E. compressa* and *E. intestinalis*—I also found abundant along the edges of the thrift-beds; and it struck me as curious at the time, that while most of the land-plants which had thus descended beyond the sea-level were of the high dicotyledonous division, the sea-weeds with which they mingled their leaves and seed-vessels were low in their standing—fuci and enteromorpha—plants at least not higher than their kindred cryptogamia, the lichens and mosses of the land. Far beyond, in the outer reaches of the bay, where land-plants never approached, there were meadows of a sub-marine vegetation, of (for the sea) a comparatively high character. Their numerous plants (*zostera marina*) had true roots, and true leaves, and true flowers; and their spikes ripened amid the salt waters towards the close of autumn, round white seeds, that, like many of the seeds of the land, had their sugar and starch. But these plants kept far aloof, in their green depths, from their

[1] The Knotted Wrack is distinguished from *fucus vesiculosus*, the Bladder Wrack or Black Tang, by having the bladders or air-cells arranged singly along the centre of a frond which has no mid-rib.
[2] The Sea-Pink.
[3] Ribbon-like seaweed with hollow fronds.

cogeners the monocotyledons of the terrestrial flora. It was merely the low *Fucaceæ*[1] and *Conferveæ*[2] of the sea that I found meeting and mixing with the descending dicotyledons of the land. I felt a good deal of interest in marking, about this time, how certain belts of marine vegetation occurred on a vast boulder situated in the neighbourhood of Cromarty, on the extreme line of the ebb of spring-tides. I detected the various species ranged in zones, just as on lofty hills the botanist finds his agricultural moorland, and alpine zones rising in succession the one over the other. At the base of the huge mass, at a level to which the tide rarely falls, the characteristic vegetable is the rough-stemmed tangle—*Laminaria digitata*. In the zone immediately above the lowest, the prevailing vegetable is the smooth-stemmed tangle—*Laminaria saccharina*. Higher still there occurs a zone of the serrated fucus—*F. serratus*—blent with another familiar fucus—*F. nodosus*. Then comes a yet higher zone of *Fucus vesiculosus*; and higher still, a few scattered tufts of *Fucus canaliculatus* ;[5] and then, as on lofty mountains that rise above the line of perpetual snow, vegetation ceases, and the boulder presents a round bald head, that rises over the surface after the first few hours of ebb have passed. But far beyond its base, where the sea never falls, green meadows of *zostera* flourish in the depths of the water, where they unfold their colourless flowers, unfurnished with petals, and ripen their farinaceous seeds, that, wherever they rise to the surface, seem very susceptible of frost. I have seen the shores strewed with a line of green *zostera*, with its spikes charged with seed, after a smart October frost, that had been coincident with the ebb of a low spring-tide, had nipt its rectilinear fronds and flexible stems.

But what, it may be asked, was the bearing of all this observation? I by no means saw its entire bearing at the time: I simply observed and recorded, because I found it pleasant to

---

[1] A genus of olive-brown seaweed.

[2] Properly a low order of fresh-water algæ, that forms a green lime on stagnant pools.

[5] The Channelled Wrack, distinguished from other species by having no air-bladder.

observe and record. And yet one of the wild dreams of Maillet[1] in his "*Telliamed*" had given a certain degree of unity, and a certain definite direction, to my gleanings of fact on the subject, which they would not have otherwise possessed. It was held by this fanciful writer, that the vegetation of the land had been derived originally from that of the ocean. "In a word," we find him saying, "do not herbs, plants, roots, grain and all of this kind that the earth produces and nourishes, come from the sea? Is it not at least natural to think so, since we are certain that all our habitable lands came originally from the sea? Besides, in small islands far from the continent which have appeared a few ages ago at most, and where it is manifest that never any men had been, we find shrubs, herbs and roots. Now, you must be forced to own that either the productions owed their origin to the sea, *or to a new creation, which is absurd.*" And then Maillet goes on to show, after a manner which—now that algæology has become a science—must be regarded as at least curious, that the plants of the sea, though not so well developed as those of the land, are really very much of the same nature. "The fishermen of Marseilles find daily," he says, "in their nets, and among their fish, plants of a hundred kinds, with their fruits still upon them; and though these fruits are not so large nor so well nourished as those of our earth, yet their species is in no other respects dubious. There they find clusters of white and black grapes, peach-trees, pear-trees, prune-trees, apple-trees, and all sorts of flowers." Such was the sort of wild fable invented in a tract of natural science in which I found it of interest to acquaint myself with the truth. I have since seen the extraordinary vision of Maillet revived, first by Oken, and then by the author of the "Vestiges of Creation;"[2] and when, in grappling with some

[1] Benoit de Maillet (1656-1738), an early champion of Development or Evolution, who derived birds from the flying-fish.

[2] Written and published anonymously in 1844, *The Vestiges of Creation*'s pro-evolution argument caused a huge literary and scientific controversy fifteen years prior to Darwin's *Origin of Species*. The author, the Edinburgh publisher Robert Chambers (1802-71), was a personal acquaintance of Miller, and, given the fierceness with which Miller attacked the book in his own reply *Footprints of the Creator* (1849), it was probably as well for Chambers that his authorship remained a secret.

of the views and statements of the latter writer, I set myself to write the chapter of my little work which deals with this special hypothesis, I found that I had in some sort studied in the school in which the education necessary to its production was most thoroughly to be acquired. Had the ingenious author of the "Vestiges" taken lessons for but a short time at the same form, he would scarce have thought of reviving in those latter ages the dream of Oken and Maillet. A knowledge of the facts would to a certainty have protected him against the reproduction of the hypothesis.

The lesson at Nigg was of a more curious kind, though, mayhap, less certainly conclusive in its bearings. The house of the proprietor of Nigg bordered on the burying-ground. I was engaged in cutting an inscription on the tombstone of his wife, recently dead; and a poor idiot, who found his living in the kitchen, and to whom the deceased had shown kindness, used to come every day to the churchyard, to sit beside me, and jabber in broken expressions his grief. I was struck with the extremeness of his idiocy; he manifested even more than the ordinary inability of his class to deal with figures, for he could scarce tell whether nature had furnished him with one head or with two; and no power of education could have taught him to count his fingers. He was equally defective, too, in the mechanical. Angus could not be got into trousers; and the contrivance of the button remained a mystery which he was never able to comprehend. And so he wore a large blue gown, like that of a beadsman, which slipped over his head, and was bound by a belt round his middle, with a stout woollen shirt underneath. But, though unacquainted with the mystery of the button, there were mysteries of another kind with which he seemed to have a most perfect acquaintance: Angus— always a faithful attendant at church—was a great critic of sermons; nor was it every preacher that satisfied him; and such was his imitative turn, that he himself could preach by the hour, in the manner—so far at least as voice and gesture went—of all the popular ministers of the district. There was, however, rather a paucity of idea in his discourses: in his more energetic passages, when he struck the book and stamped with his foot, he usually iterated, in sonorous Gaelic—"The wicked, the wicked, O wretches the wicked!" while a passage of a less depreciatory character served him for setting off his middle tones and his pathos. But that for which his character was chiefly remarkable was an instinctive, foxlike cunning, that seemed to lie at its very basis—a cunning which co-existed, however, with perfect honesty, and a devoted attachment to his patron the proprietor.

The town of Cromarty had its poor imbecile man of quite a different stamp. Jock Gordon had been, it was said, "like other people" till his fourteenth year, when a severe attack of illness left him bankrupt in both mind and body. He rose from his bed lame of a foot and hand, his one side shrunken and nerveless, the one lobe of his brain apparently inoperative, and with less than half his former energy and intellect; not all an idiot, however, though somewhat more helpless—the poor mutilated fragment of a reasoning man. Among his other failings, he stuttered lamentably. He became an inmate of the kitchen of Cromarty House; and learned to run, or, I should rather say, to *limp*, errands—for he had risen from the fever that ruined him to run no more—with great fidelity and success. He was fond of church-going, of reading good little books, and, notwithstanding his sad stutter, of singing. During the day he might be heard, as he hobbled along the streets on business, "*singing in into himself,*" as the children used to say, in a low unvaried undertone, somewhat resembling the humming of a bee; but when night fell, the whole town heard him. He was no patronizer of modern poets or composers. "There a ship, and a ship of fame," and "Death and the Fair Lady," were his especial favourites; and he could repeat the "Gosport Tragedy," and the "Babes in the Wood," from beginning to end. Sometimes he stuttered in the notes, and then they lengthened on and on into a never-ending quaver that our first-rate singers might have envied. Sometimes there was a sudden break—Jock had been consulting the pocket in which he stored his bread; but no sooner was his mouth half-cleared than he began again. In middle-life, however, a great calamity overtook Jock. His patron, the occupant of Cromarty House, quitted the country for France: Jock was left without occupation or aliment; and the streets heard no more of his songs. He grew lank and thin, and stuttered and limped more painfully than before, and was in the last stage of privation and distress, when the benevolent proprietor of Nigg, who resided half the year in a town house in Cromarty, took pity upon him, and introduced him to his kitchen. And in a few days Jock was singing and limping errands with as much energy as ever. But the time at length came when his new benefactor had to quit his house in town for his seat in the country; and it behoved Jock to take temporary leave of Cromarty, and follow him. And then the poor imbecile man of the town-kitchen had, of course, to measure himself against his formidable rival the vigorous idiot of the country one.

On Jock's advent at Nigg—which had taken place a few weeks previous to my engagement in the burying-ground of the parish— the character of Angus seemed to dilate in energy and power. He repaired to the churchyard with spade and pickaxe, and began digging a grave. It was a grave, he said, for wicked Jock Gordon; and Jock, whether he thought it or no, had come to Nigg, he added, only to be buried. Jock, however, was not to be dislodged so; and Angus, professing sudden friendship for him, gave expression to the magnanimous resolution, that he would not only tolerate Jock, but also be very kind to him, and show him the place where he kept all his money. He had lots of money, he said, which he had hidden in a dike; but he would show the place to Jock Gordon— to poor cripple Jock Gordon: he would show him the very hole, and Jock would get it all. And so he brought Jock to the hole— a cavity, in a turf-wall in the neighbouring wood—and, taking care that his own way of retreat was clear, he bade him insinuate his hand. No sooner had he done so, however, than there issued forth from between his fingers a cloud of wasps, of the variety so abundant in the north country, that build their nests in earthy banks and old mole-hills; and poor Jock, ill fitted for retreat in any sudden emergency, was stung within an inch of his life. Angus returned in high glee, preaching about "wicked Jock Gordon, whom the very wasps wouldn't let alone;" but though he pretended no further friendship for a few days after, he again drew to him in apparent kindness; and on the following Saturday, on Jock being despatched to a neighbouring smithy with a sheep's head to singe, Angus volunteered his services to show him the way.

Angus went trotting before; Jock came limping behind: the fields were open and bare; the dwellings few and far between; and after having passed, in about an hour's walking, half a dozen little hamlets, Jock began to marvel exceedingly that there should be no sign of the smith's shop. "Poor foolish Jock Gordon!" ejaculated Angus, quickening his trot into a canter; "what does he know about carrying sheep's heads to the smithy?" Jock laboured hard to keep up with his guide, quavering and semi-quavering, as his breath served—for Jock always began to sing, when in solitary places, after nightfall, as a protection against ghosts. At length the daylight died entirely away, and he could only learn from Angus that the smithy was further off than ever; and, to add to his trouble and perplexity, the roughness of the ground showed him that they were wandering from the road. First they went toiling athwart what seemed an endless range of fields, separated from one another by deep ditches and fences of stone; then they crossed over a dreary moor, bristling with furze and sloe-thorn; then over a waste of bogs and quagmires; then across a track of newly ploughed land; and then they entered a second wood. At length, after a miserable night's wandering, day broke upon the two forlorn satyrs; and Jock found himself in a strange country, with a long narrow lake in front and a wood behind. He had wandered after his guide into the remote parish of Tarbet.

Tarbet abounded at that time in little muddy lakes, edged with water-flags and reeds, and swarming with frogs and eels; and it was one of the largest and deepest of these that now lay before Jock and his guide. Angus tucked up his blue gown, as if to wade across. Jock would have as soon thought of fording the German ocean. "Oh, wicked Jock Gordon!" exclaimed the fool, when he saw him hesitate; "the colonel's waiting, poor man, for his head, and Jock will no' take it to the smithy." He stepped into the water. Jock followed in sheer desperation; and, after clearing the belt of reeds, both sank to the middle in the mingled water and mud. Angus had at length accomplished the object of his journey. Extricating himself in a moment—for he was lithe and active— he snatched the sheep's head and trotters from Jock, and, leaping ashore, left the poor man sticking fast. It was church-time ere he reached, on his way back, the old Abbey of Fearn, still employed as a Protestant place of worship; and as the sight of the gathering people awakened his church-going propensity, he went in. He was in high spirits—seemed, by the mouths he made, very much to admire the sermon, and paraded the sheep's head and trotters through the passages and gallery a score of times at least, like a monk of the order of St. Francis exhibiting the relics of some favourite saint. In the evening he found his way home, but learned, to his grief and astonishment, that "wicked Jock Gordon" had got there shortly before him in a cart. The poor man had remained sticking in the mud for three long hours after Angus had left him, until at length the very frogs began to cultivate his acquaintance, as they had done that of King Log of old; and in the mud he would have been sticking still, had he not been extricated by a farmer of Fearn, who, in coming to church, had taken the lake in his way. He left Nigg, however, for Cromarty on the following day, convinced that he was no match for his rival, and dubious how the next adventure might terminate.

Such was the story which I found current in Nigg, when working in its churchyard, with the hero of the adventure often beside me. It led me to take special note of his class, and to collect facts respecting them, on which I erected a sort of semi-metaphysical theory of human character, which, though it would not now be regarded as by any means a novel one, I had thought out for myself, and which possessed for me, in consequence, the charm of originality. In these poor creatures, I thus argued, we find, amid much general dilapidation and brokenness of mind, certain instincts and peculiarities remaining entire. Here, in Angus, for instance, there is that instinctive cunning which some of the lower animals, such as the fox, possess, existing in a wonderful degree of perfection. Pope himself, who "could not drink tea without a stratagem," could scarce have possessed a larger share of it. And yet how distinct must not this sort of ingenuity be from the mechanical ingenuity! Angus cannot fix a button in its hole. I even see him baffled by a tall snuff-box, with a small quantity of snuff at its bottom, that lies beyond the reach of his finger. He has not ingenuity enough to lay it on its side, or to empty its snuff on his palm; but stretches and ever stretches towards it the unavailing digit, and then gets angry to find it elude his touch. There are other idiots, however, who have none of Angus's cunning, in whom this mechanical ability is decidedly developed. Many of the *crétins* of the Alps are said to be remarkable for their skill as artisans; and it is told of a Scotch idiot, who lived in a cottage on the Maolbuie Common, in the upper part of the Black Isle, and in whom a similar mechanical ability existed, abstracted from ability of almost every other kind, that, among other things, he fabricated, out of a piece of rude metal, a large sacking needle. Angus is attached to his patron, and mourns for the deceased lady; but he seems to have little general regard for the species—simply courting for the time those from whom he expects snuff. The Cromarty idiot, on the contrary, is obliging and kindly to all, and bears a peculiar love to children; and, though more an imbecile in some respects than even Angus, he has a turn for dress, and can attire himself very neatly. In this last respect, however, the Cromarty fool was excelled by an idiot of the last age, known to the children of many a village and hamlet as Fool Charloch, who used to go wandering about the country, adorned, somewhat in the style of an Indian chief, with half a peacock's tail stuck in his cap. Yet another idiot, a fierce and dangerous creature, seemed as invariably malignant in his dispositions as the Cromarty one is benevolent, and died in a prison, to which he was committed for killing a poor half-witted associate. Yet another idiot of the north of Scotland had a strange turn for the supernatural. He was a mutterer of charms, and a watcher of omens, and possessed, it was said, the second sight. I collected not a few other facts of a similar kind, and thus reasoned regarding them:—

These idiots are imperfect men, from whose minds certain faculties have been effaced, and other faculties left to exhibit themselves, all the more prominently from the circumstances of their standing so much alone. They resemble men who have lost their hands, but retain their feet, or who have lost their sight or smell, but retain their taste and hearing. But as the limbs and the senses, if they did not exist as separate parts of the frame, could not be separately lost, so in the mind itself, or in at least the organization through which the mind manifests itself, there must also be separate parts, or they would not be thus found isolated by Nature in her mutilated and abortive specimens. Those metaphysicans who deal by the mind as if it were simply a general power existing in *states*, must be scarce less in error than if they were to regard the *senses* as merely a general power existing in states, instead of recognising them as distinct, independent powers, so various often in their degree of development, that, from the full perfection of any one of them, the perfection, or even the existence, of any of the others cannot be predicated. If, for instance, it were—as some physicians hold—the same general warmth of emotive power that glows in benevolence and burns in resentment, the fierce, dangerous idiot that killed his companion, and the kindly-dispositioned Cromarty one who takes home pailfuls of water to the poor old women of the place, and parts with his own toys to its children, would, instead of thus exhibiting the opposite poles of character, at least so far resemble one another, that the vindictive fool would at times be kindly and obliging, and the benevolent one at times violent and resentful. But such is not the case: the one is never madly savage—the other never genial and kind; and so it seems legitimate to infer, that it is not a general power or energy that acts through them in different states, but two particular powers or energies, as unlike in their natures, and as capable of acting apart, as seeing and hearing. Even powers which seem to have so much in common, that the same words are sometimes made use of in reference to both, may be as distinct as smelling and tasting. We speak of the *cunning* workman, and we speak of the *cunning* man; and refer to a certain faculty of contrivance manifested in dealing with characters and affairs on the part of the one, and in dealing with certain modifications of matter on the part of the other; but so entirely different are the two faculties, and, further, so little dependent are they, in at least their first elements, on intellect, that we may find the cunning which manifests itself in affairs existing, as in Angus, totally dissociated from mechanical skill; and, on the other hand, the cunning of the artisan, existing as in the idiot of the Maolbuie, totally dissociated from that of the diplomatist. In short, regarding idiots as persons of fragmentary mind, in whom certain primary mental elements may be found standing out in a state of great entireness, and all the more striking in their relief from the isolation, I came to view them as *bits of analysis*, if I may so express myself, made to my hand by Nature, and from the study of which I could conceive of the structure of minds of a more complete, and therefore more complex, character. As children learn the alphabet from cards, each of which contains only a letter or two a-piece, printed large, I held at this time, and, with a few modifications, hold still, that those primary sentiments and propensities which form the basis of character may be found separately stamped in the same way on the comparatively blank minds of the imbecile; and that the student of mental philosophy might learn from them what may be regarded as the alphabet of his science, much more truthfully than from those metaphysicians who represent mind as a power not manifested in contemporaneous and separable faculties, but as existing in consecutive states.

Cromarty had been fortunate in its parish ministers. From the death of its last curate, shortly after the Revolution, and the consequent return of its old "outed minister," who had resigned his living for conscience' sake twenty-eight years before, and now came to spend his evening of life with his people, it had enjoyed the services of a series of devout and popular men; and so the cause of the Establishment was particularly strong in both town and parish. At the beginning of the present century Cromarty had not its single Dissenter; and though a few of what were known as "Haldane's people"[1] might be found in it, some eight or ten years later, they failed in effecting a lodgment, and ultimately quitted it for a neighbouring town. Almost all the Dissent that has arisen in Scotland since the Revolution has been an effect of Moderatism[2] and forced settlements; and as the place had known neither, its people continued to harbour within the Church of their fathers, nor wished to change. A vacancy had occurred in the incumbency, during my sojourn in the south, through the death of the incumbent, the respected minister of my childhood and youth; and I found, on my return, a new face in the pulpit. It was that of a remarkable man—the late Mr Stewart of Cromarty—one of at once the most original thinkers and profound theologians I ever knew; though he has, alas! left as little mark of his exquisite talent behind him, as those sweet singers of former ages, the memory of whose enchanting notes has died, save as a doubtful echo, with the generation that heard them. I sat, with few interruptions, for sixteen years under his ministry and for nearly twelve of these enjoyed his confidence and friendship.

I never could press myself on the notice of superior men, however desirous of forming their acquaintance; and have, in consequence, missed opportunities innumerable of coming in friendly contact with persons whom it would be at once a pleasure and an honour to know. And so, for the first two years or rather more, I was content to listen with profound attention to the pulpit addresses of my new minister, and to appear as a catechumen,

[1] Followers of the brothers R and J A Haldane, rich lay preachers of a strong evangelical type early in the nineteenth century.
[2] The Broad Church party in the Church of Scotland, "moderate" in its creed, and submissive to the Law Courts in the Intrusion Controversy. Its opponents, the Evangelicals, afterwards formed the Free Church.

when my turn came, at his diets of catechising. He had been struck, however, as he afterwards told me, by my sustained attention when at church; and, on making inquiry regarding me among his friends, he was informed that I was a great reader, and, it was believed, a writer of verse. And coming unwittingly out upon him one day as he was passing, when quitting my work-place for the street, he addressed me. "Well, lad," he said, "it is your dinner hour: I hear I have a poet among my people?" "I doubt it much," I replied. "Well," he rejoined, "one may fall short of being a poet, and yet gain by exercising one's tastes and talents in the poetic walk. The accomplishment of verse is at least not a vulgar one." The conversation went on as we passed together along the street; and he stood for a time opposite the manse door. "I am forming," he said, "a small library for our Sabbath-school scholars and teachers: most of the books are simple enough little things; but it contains a few works of the intellectual class. Call upon me this evening that we may look over them, and you may perhaps find among them some volumes you would wish to read." I accordingly waited upon him in the evening; and we had a long conversation together. He was, I saw, curiously sounding me, and taking my measure in all directions; or, as he himself afterwards used to express it in his characteristic way, he was like a traveller who, having come unexpectedly on a dark pool in a ford, dips down his staff, to ascertain the depth of the water and the nature of the bottom. He inquired regarding my reading, and found that in the belles-lettres, especially in English literature, it was about as extensive as his own. He next inquired respecting my acquaintance with the metaphysicians. "Had I read Reid?" "Yes." "Brown?" "Yes." "*Hume?*" "Yes." "Ah! ha! Hume!! By the way, has he not something very ingenious about miracles? Do you remember his argument?" I stated the argument. "Ah, very ingenious—most ingenious. And how would you answer that?" I said, "I thought I could give an abstract of the reply of Campbell," and sketched in outline the reverend Doctor's argument. "And do you deem that satisfactory?" said the minister. "No, not at all,"

I replied. "No! no! *that's* not satisfactory." "But perfectly satisfactory," I rejoined, "that such is the general partiality for the better side, that the worse argument has been received as perfectly adequate for the last sixty years." The minister's face gleamed with the broad fun that entered so largely into his composition, and the conversation shifted into other channels.

From that night forward I enjoyed perhaps more of his confidence and conversation than any other man in his parish. Many an hour did he spend beside me in the churchyard, and many a quiet tea did I enjoy in the manse; and I learned to know how much solid worth and true wisdom lay under the somewhat eccentric exterior of a man who sacrificed scarce anything to the conventionalities. This, with the exception of Chalmers, sublimest of Scottish preachers—for, little as he was known, I will challenge for him that place—was a genial man who, for the sake of a joke, would sacrifice anything save principle; but, though marvellously careless of maintaining intact the "gloss of the clerical enamel," never was there sincerity more genuine than his, or a more thorough honesty. Content to be in the right, he never thought of simulating it, and sacrificed even less than he ought to appearances. I may mention, that on coming to Edinburgh, I found the peculiar taste formed under the ministrations of Mr Stewart most thoroughly gratified under those of Dr Guthrie;[1] and that in looking round the congregation, I saw, with pleasure rather than surprise, that all Mr Stewart's people resident in Edinburgh had come to the same conclusion; for there—sitting in the Doctor's pews—they all were. Certainly in fertility of illustration, in soul-stirring evangelistic doctrine, and in a general basis of rich humour, the resemblance between the deceased and the living minister seems complete; but genius is always unique; and while in breadth of popular power Dr Guthrie stands alone among living

[1] Dr Thomas Guthrie (1803-73), originally from Brechin, was ordained at Greyfriars Church in Edinburgh in 1837 after seven years at Arbirlot near Arbroath. His sermons were famous and drew large congregations wherever he preached. A leading non-Intrusionist, Guthrie was, with Chalmers, one of the best-known figures of the Disruption of 1843.

preachers, I have never either heard or read argument in the analogical field that in ingenuity or originality equalled that of Mr Stewart.

That in which he especially excelled all the men I ever knew was the power of detecting and establishing occult resemblances. He seemed able to read off, as if by intuition—not by snatches and fragments, but as a consecutive whole—that old revelation of type and symbol which God first gave to man; and, when privileged to listen to him, I have been constrained to recognise, in the evident integrity of the reading, and the profound and consistent theological system which the pictorial record conveyed, a demonstration of the divinity of its origin, not less powerful and convincing than the demonstrations of the other and more familiar departments of the Christian evidences. Compared with other theologians in this province, I have felt under his ministry as if, when admitted to the company of some party of modern *savans* employed in deciphering a hieroglyphic-covered obelisk of the desert, and here successful in discovering the meaning of an insulated sign, and there of a detached symbol, we had been suddenly joined by some sage of the olden time, to whom the mysterious inscription was but a piece of common language written in a familiar alphabet, and who could read off fluently, and as a whole, what the others could but darkly guess at in detached and broken parts. To this singular power of tracing analogies there was added in Mr Stewart an ability of originating the most vivid illustrations. In some instances a sudden stroke produced a figure that at once illumined the subject-matter of his discourse, like the light of a lanthorn flashed hastily upon a painted wall; in others he dwelt upon an illustrative picture, finishing it with stroke after stroke, until it filled the whole imagination, and sank deep into the memory. I remember hearing him preach, on one occasion, on the return of the Jews as a people to HIM whom they had rejected, and the effect which their sudden conversion could not fail to have on the unbelieving and Gentile world. Suddenly his language, from its high level of eloquent simplicity, became that of metaphor; " When JOSEPH," he said, " shall reveal himself to his *brethren*, the *whole house of Pharaoh shall hear the weeping*." On another occasion I heard him dwell on that vast profundity, characteristic of the Scriptural revelation of God, which ever deepens and broadens the longer and more thoroughly it is explored, until at length the student— struck at first by its expansiveness, but conceiving of it as if it were a mere *measured* expansiveness—finds that it partakes of the unlimited infinity of the Divine nature itself. Naturally and simply, as if growing out of the subject, like a berry-covered mistletoe out of the massy trunk of an oak, there sprung up one of his more lengthened illustrations. A child bred up in the interior of the country has been brought for the first time to the sea-shore, and carried out into the middle of one of the noble firths that indent so deeply our line of coast. And, on his return, he describes to his father, with all a child's eagerness, the wonderful expansiveness of the *ocean* which he had seen. He went out, he tells him, far amid the great waves and the rushing tides, until at length the hills seemed diminished into mere hummocks, and the wide land itself appeared along the waters but as a slim strip of blue. And then, when in mid-sea, the sailors heaved the lead; and it went down, and down, and down, and the long line slipped swiftly away, coil after coil, till, ere the plummet rested on the ooze below, all was well-nigh expended. And was it not the great sea, asks the boy, that was so vastly broad, and so profoundly deep ? Ah ! my child, exclaims the father, you have not seen aught of its greatness: you have sailed over merely one of its little arms. Had it been out into the wide ocean that the seamen had carried you, "you would have *seen* no shore, and you would have *found* no bottom." In one rare quality of the orator Mr Stewart stood alone among his contemporaries. Pope refers to a strange power of creating love and admiration by "just touching the brink of all we hate." And Burke, in some of his nobler passages, happily exemplified the thing. He intensified the effect of his burning eloquence by the employment of figures so homely—nay, almost so repulsive—that the man of lower powers who ventured on their use would find them effective in but lowering his subject, and ruining his cause. I need but refer, in illustration, to the well-known figure of the disembowelled bird, which occurs in the indignant denial that the character of the revolutionary French in aught resembled that of the English. " We have not," says the orator, " been drawn and trussed, in order that we may be filled, like stuffed birds in a museum, with chaff, and rags, and paltry blurred shreds of paper about the rights of man." Into this perilous but singularly effective department closed against even superior men, Mr Stewart could enter safely and at will. One of the last sermons I heard him preach—a discourse of singular power—was on the "Sin-offering" of the Jewish economy, as minutely described in Leviticus. He drew a picture of the slaughtered animal, foul with dust and blood, and streaming, in its impurity, to the sun, as it awaited the consuming fire amid the uncleanness of ashes outside the camp—its throat gashed across—its entrails laid open; a vile and horrid thing, which no one could see without experiencing emotions of disgust, nor touch without contracting defilement. The description appeared too painfully vivid—its introduction too little in accordance with the rules of a just taste. But the master in this difficult walk knew what he was doing. "And that," he said, pointing to the strongly-coloured picture he had just completed—"And THAT IS SIN." By one stroke the intended effect was produced, and the rising disgust and horror transferred from the revolting material image to the great moral evil.

How could such a man pass from earth, and leave no trace behind him? Mainly, I believe, from two several causes. As the minister of an attached provincial congregation, a sense of duty, and the promptings of a highly intellectual nature, to which exertion was enjoyment, led him to study much and deeply; and he poured forth *viva voce* his full-volumed and ever-sparkling tide of eloquent idea, as freely and richly as the nightingale, unconscious of a listener, pours forth her melody in the shade. But, strangely diffident of his own powers, he could not be made to believe that what so much impressed and delighted the privileged few who surrounded him, was equally suited to impress and delight the intellectual many outside; or that he was fitted to speak through the press in tones which would compel the attention, not merely of the religious, but also of the literary world. Further, practising but little the art of elaborate composition, and master of a spoken style more effective for the purposes of the pulpit than almost any written one, save that of Chalmers, he failed, in all his attempts in writing, to satisfy a fastidious taste, which he had suffered greatly to outgrow his ability of production. And so he failed to leave any adequate mark behind him. I find that for my stock of theological idea not directly derived from Scripture, I stand more indebted to two Scotch theologians than to all other men of their profession and class. The one of these was Thomas Chalmers—the other, Alexander Stewart: the one a name known wherever the English language is spoken; while of the other it is only remembered, and by comparatively a few, that the impression did exist at the time of his death, that

> "A mighty spirit was eclipsed—a power
> Had passed from day to darkness, to whose hour
> Of light no likeness was bequeathed—no name."

CHAPTER XIX

"See yonder poor o'er-labour'd wight,
So abject, mean, and vile,
Who begs a brother of the earth
To give him leave to toil;
And see his lordly *fellow-worm*
The poor petition spurn."—BURNS.

WORK failed me about the end of June 1828; and, acting on the advice of a friend who believed that my style of cutting inscriptions could not fail to secure for me a good many little jobs in the churchyards of Inverness, I visited that place, and inserted a brief advertisement in one of the newspapers, soliciting employment. I ventured to characterize my style of engraving as neat and *correct*; laying especial emphasis on the correctness, as a quality not very common among the stone-cutters of the north. It was not a Scotch, but an English mason, who, when engaged, at the instance of a bereaved widower, in recording on his wife's tombstone that a "virtuous woman is a *crown* to her husband," corrupted the text, in his simplicity, by substituting "5s." for the "*crown.*" But even Scotch masons do make odd enough mistakes at times, especially in the provinces; and I felt it would be something gained could I but get an opportunity of showing the Inverness public that I had at least English enough to avoid the commoner errors. My verses, thought I, are at least tolerably correct: could I not get some one or two copies introduced into the poet's corner of the *Inverness Courier* or *Journal*, and thus show that I have literature enough to be trusted with the cutting of an epitaph on a gravestone? I had a letter of introduction from a friend in Cromarty to one of the ministers of the place, himself an author, and a person of influence with the proprietors of the *Courier*; and, calculating on some amount of literary sympathy from a man accustomed to court the public through the medium of the press, I thought I might just venture on stating the case to him. I first, however, wrote a brief address, in octo-syllabic quatrains, to the river which flows through the town, and gives to it its name:—a composition which has, I find, more of the advertisement in it than is quite seemly, but which would have perhaps expressed less confidence had it been written less under the influence of a shrinking timidity, that tried to reassure itself by words of comfort and encouragement.

I was informed that the minister's hour for receiving visitors of the humbler class was between eleven and twelve at noon; and, with the letter of introduction and my copy of verses in my pocket, I called at the manse, and was shown into a little narrow ante-room, furnished with two seats of deal that ran along the opposite walls. I found the place occupied by some six or seven individuals—more than half their number old withered women, in very shabby habiliments, who, as I soon learned from a conversation which they kept up in a grave undertone, about weekly allowances, and the partialities of the session, were paupers. The others were young men, who had apparently serious requests to prefer anent marriage and baptism; for I saw that one of them was ever and anon drawing from his breast-pocket a tattered copy of the Shorter Catechism, and running over the questions; and I overheard another asking his neighbour, "who drew up the contract lines for him," and "where he had got the whisky." The minister entered; and, as he passed into the inner room, we all rose. He stood for a moment in the doorway, and, beckoning on one of the young men—him of the Catechism—they went in together, and the door closed. They remained closeted together for about twenty minutes or half an hour, and then the young man went out; and another young man—he who had procured the contract lines and the whisky—took his place. The interview in this second case, however, was much shorter than the first; and a very few minutes served to despatch the business of the third young man; and then the minister, coming to the doorway, looked first at the old women and then at me, as if mentally determining our respective claims to priority; and, mine at length prevailing—I know not on what occult principle—I was beckoned in. I presented my letter of introduction, which was graciously read; and though the nature of the business did strike me as ludicrously out of keeping with the place, and it did cost me some little trouble to suppress at one time a burst of laughter, that would, of course, have been prodigiously improper in the circumstances, I detailed to him in a few words my little plan, and handed him my copy of verses. He read them aloud with slow deliberation.

ODE TO THE NESS

Child of the lake! whose silvery gleam
Cheers the rough desert, dark and lone,[1]
A brown, deep, sullen, restless stream,
With ceaseless speed thou hurriest on.
And yet thy banks with flowers are gay;
The sun laughs on thy troubled breast;
And o'er thy tides the zephyrs play,
Though nought be thine of quiet rest.[2]

Stream of the lake! to him who strays,
Lonely, thy winding marge along,
Not fraught with lore of other days,
And yet not all unblest in song—
To him thou tell'st of busy men,
Who madly waste their present day,
Pursuing hopes, baseless as vain,
While life, untasted, glides away.

---

[1] Loch Ness (Miller)

[2] This portrait of the Ness is, I fear, scarce true to the ordinary character of the river. I had visited it during the previous winter, and walked a few miles along its sides, when the tract of country through which it flows lay bleached and verdureless, and steeped in the soaking rain of weeks, and the stream itself, big in flood, roared from bank to brae in its shallower reaches, or boiled sullen and turbid in many a circling eddy in its darker pools. And my description somewhat incongruously unites a sunlit summer landscape, rich in flower and foliage, with the brown wintry river (Miller).

Stream of the lake! why hasten on?
A boist'rous ocean spreads before,
Where dash dark tides, and wild winds moan,
And foam-wreaths skirt a cheerless shore.
Nor bending flowers, nor waving fields,
Nor aught of rest is there for thee;
But rest to thee no pleasure yields;
Then haste and join the stormy sea!

Stream of the lake! of bloody men,
Who thirst the guilty fight to try—
Who seek for joy in mortal pain,
Music in misery's thrilling cry—
Thou tell'st: peace yields no joy to them,
Nor harmless Pleasure's golden smile;
Of evil deed the cheerless fame
Is all the meed that crowns their toil.

Not such would prove if Pleasure shone—
Stream of the deep and peaceful lake!—
His course, whom Hardship urges on,
Through cheerless waste and thorny brake.
For, ah! each pleasing scene he loves,
And peace is all his heart's desire;
And, ah! of scenes where Pleasure roves,
And Peace, could gentle minstrel tire?

Stream of the lake! for thee await
The tempests of an angry main;
A brighter hope, a happier fate,
He boasts, whose present course is pain.
Yes, even for him may death prepare
A home of pleasure, peace, and love;
Thus blessed by hope, little his care,
Though rough his present course may prove.

The minister paused as he concluded, and looked puzzled.
"Pretty well, I daresay," he said; "but I do not now read poetry.
You, however, use a word that is not English—'Thy winding
marge along.' Marge!—What is marge?" "You will find it in
Johnson," I said. " Ah, but we must not use all the words we find

in Johnson." "But the poets make frequent use of it." "What poets?" "Spenser." "Too old—too old; no authority now," said the minister. "But the Wartons also use it." "I don't know the Wartons." "It occurs also," I iterated, "in one of the most finished sonnets of Henry Kirke White." "What sonnet?" "That to the river Trent.

> 'Once more, O Trent! along thy pebbly *marge*,
> A pensive invalid, reduced and pale,
> From the close sick-room newly set at large,
> Woos to his woe-worn cheek the pleasant gale.'

It is, in short, one of the common English words of the poetic vocabulary." Could a man in quest of a patronage, and actually at the time soliciting a favour, possibly contrive to say anything more imprudent? And this, too, to a gentleman so much accustomed to be deferred to when he took up his ground on the *Standards*, as sometimes to forget, through the sheer force of habit, that he was not a standard himself! He coloured to the eyes; and his condescending humility, which seemed, I thought, rather too great for the occasion, and was of a kind which my friend Mr Stewart never used to exhibit, appeared somewhat ruffled. "I have no acquaintance," he said, "with the editor of the *Courier*; we take opposite sides on very important questions; and I cannot recommend your verses to him; but call on Mr— he is one of the proprietors; and, with *my compliments*, state your case to him; he will be perhaps able to assist you. Meanwhile, I wish you all success." The minister hurried me out, and one of the withered old women was called in. "This," I said to myself, as I stepped into the street, "is the sort of patronage which letters of introduction procure for one. I don't think I'll seek any more of it."

Meeting on the street, however, with two Cromarty friends, one of whom was just going to call on the gentleman named by the minister, he induced me to accompany him. The other said, as he took his separate way, that, having come to visit an old townsman settled in Inverness, a man of some influence in the burgh, he would state my case to him; and he was sure he would exert himself to procure me employment. I have already referred to the remark of Burns. It is recorded by his brother Gilbert, that the poet used often to say, "That he could not well conceive a more mortifying picture of human life, than a man seeking work;" and that the exquisite dirge, "Man was made to mourn," owes its existence to the sentiment. The feeling is certainly a very depressing one; and as on most other occasions work rather sought me than I the work, I experienced more of it at this time than at any other period of my life. I of course could hardly expect that people should die off and require epitaphs merely to accommodate me. That demand of employment as a right in all cases and circumstances, which the more extreme "claims-of-labour men" do not scruple to urge, is the result of a sort of indignant reaction on this feeling—a feeling which became poetry in Burns and nonsense in the Communists; but which I experienced neither as nonsense nor poetry, but simply as a depressing conviction that I was one man too many in the world. The gentleman on whom I now called with my friend was a person both of business habits and literary tastes; but I saw that my poetic scheme rather damaged me in his estimation. The English verse produced at this time in the far north was of a kind ill fitted for the literary market, and usually published, or rather printed—for published it never was—by that teasing subscription scheme which so often robs men of good money, and gives them bad books in exchange; and he seemed to set me down as one of the annoying semi-beggar class;—rather a mistake, I should hope. He, however, obligingly introduced me to a gentleman of literature and science, the secretary of a society of the place, antiquarian and scientific in its character, termed the "Northern Institution," and the honorary conservator of its museum—an interesting miscellaneous collection which I had previously seen, and in connection with which I had formed my only other scheme of getting into employment.

I wrote that old English hand which has been revived of late by the general rage for the medieval, but which at that time was one of the lost arts, with much neatness; and could produce imitations of the illuminated manuscripts that preceded our printed books, which even an antiquary would have pronounced respectable. And, addressing the members of the Northern Institution on the character and tendency of their pursuits, in a somewhat lengthy piece of verse, written in what I at least intended to be the manner of Dryden, as exemplified in his middle-style poems, such as the "Religio Laici," I engrossed it in the old hand, and now called on the Secretary, to request that he would present it at the first meeting of the Society, which was to be held, I understood, in a few days. The Secretary was busy at his desk; but he received me politely, spoke approvingly of my work as an imitation of the old manuscript, and obligingly charged himself with its delivery at the meeting: and so we parted for the time, not in the least aware that there was a science which dealt with characters greatly more ancient than those of the old manuscripts, and laden with profounder meanings, in which we both took a deep interest, and regarding which we could have exchanged facts and ideas with mutual pleasure and profit. The Secretary of the Northern Institution at this time was Mr George Anderson, the well-known geologist, and joint author with his brother of the admirable "Guide-Book to the Highlands," which bears their name. I never heard how my address fared. It would, of course, have been tabled—looked at, I suppose, for a few seconds by a member or two—and then set aside; and it is probably still in the archives of the Institution awaiting the light of future ages, when its simulated antiquity shall have become real. It was not written in a character to be read, nor, I fear, very readable in any character; and so the members of the Institution must have remained ignorant of all the wisdom I had found in their pursuits, antiquarian and ethnological. The following forms an average specimen of the production:—

> " 'Tis yours to trace
> Each deep-fixed trait that marks the human race;
> And as the Egyptian priests, with mystery fraught,
> By signs, not words, of Sphynx, and Horus taught,

So, 'mid your stores, by *things*, not books, ye scan
The powers, scope, history, of the mind of man.
Yon chequered wall displays the arms of war
Of times remote, and nations distant far;
Alas! the club and brand but serve to show
How wide extends the reign of wrong and woe;
And torcs uncouth, and feathery circlets, tell
In human hearts what gewgaw follies dwell.
Yes! all that man has framed his image bears;
And much of hate, and much of pride, appears.
    "Pleasant it is each diverse step to scan,
By which the savage first assumes the man;
To mark what feelings sway his softening breast,
Or what strong passion triumphs o'er the rest.
Narrow of heart, or free, or brave, or base,
Ev'n in the infant we the man may trace;
And from the rude ungainly sires may know
Each striking trait the polished sons shall show.
Dependent on what moods assume the reign,
Science shall smile, or spread her stores in vain:
As coward fears, or generous passions sway,
Shall freedom reign, or heartless slaves obey.
    "Not unto chance must aught of power be given,—
A country's genius is the gift of Heaven.
What warms the poet's lays with generous fire,
To which no toil can reach, no art aspire?
Who taught the sage, with deepest wisdom fraught,
While scarce one pupil grasps the ponderous thought?
Nay, wherefore ask?—as Heaven the mind bestows,
A Napier calculates and a Thomson glows.
Now turn to where, beneath the city wall,
The sun's fierce rays in unbroke splendour fall;
Vacant and weak, there sits the idiot boy,
Of pain scarce conscious, scarce alive to joy;
A thousand busy sounds around him roar;
Trade wields the tool, and Commerce plies the oar;
But, all unheeding of the restless scene,
Of toil he nothing knows, and nought of gain:
The thoughts of common minds were strange to him,
Ev'n as to such a Napier's thoughts would seem.
Thus, as in men, in peopled states, we find
Unequal powers, and varied tones of mind:

Timid or dauntless, high of thought or low,
O'erwhelmed with phlegm, or fraught with fire they glow.
And as the sculptor's art is better shown
In Parian marble than in porous stone,
Wreaths fresh or sear'd repay refinement's toil,
As genius owns or dulness stamps the soil.
Where isles of coral stud the southern main,
And painted kings and cinctured warriors reign,
Nations there are who native worth possess,
Whom every art shall court, each science bless;
And tribes there are, heavy of heart and slow,
On whom no coming age a change shall know."

There was, I suspect, a waste of effort in all this planning; but some men seem destined to do things clumsily and ill, at many times the expense which serves to secure success to the more adroit. I despatched my Ode to the newspaper, accompanied by a letter of explanation; but it fared as ill as my Address to the Institution; and a single line in italics in the next number intimated that it was not to appear. And thus both my schemes were, as they ought to be, knocked on the head. I have not schemed any since. Strategy, is, I fear, not my *forte*; and it is idle to attempt doing in spite of nature what one has not been born to do well. Besides, I began to be seriously dissatisfied with myself; there seemed to be nothing absolutely wrong in a man who wanted honest employment taking this way of showing he was capable of it; but I felt the spirit within rise against it; and so I resolved to ask no more favours of any one, even should poets' corners remain shut against me for ever, or however little Institutions, literary or scientific, might favour me with their notice. I strode along the streets, half an inch taller on the strength of the resolution; and straightway, as if to reward me for my magnanimity, an offer of employment came my way unsolicited. I was addressed by the recruiting serjeant of a Highland regiment, who asked me if I did not belong to the Aird? "No, not to the Aird, to Cromarty," I replied. "Ah, to Cromarty—very fine place! But would you not better bid adieu to Cromarty, and come along with me? We have a capital grenadier company; and in our regiment a stout and steady man is always sure to get on." I thanked him, but declined his invitation; and, with an apology on his part, which was not in the least needed or expected, we parted.

Though verse and old English failed me, the simple statement made by my Cromarty friend to my townsman located in Inverness, that I was a good workman, and wanted work, procured me at once the cutting of an inscription, and two little jobs in Cromarty besides, which I was to execute on my return home. The Inverness job was soon completed; but I had the near prospect of another; and as the little bit of the public that came my way approved of my cutting, I trusted employment would flow in apace. I lodged with a worthy old widow, conscientious and devout, and ever doing her humble work consciously in the eye of the Great Taskmaster—one of a class of persons not at all so numerous in the world as might be desirable, but sufficiently common to render it rather a marvel that some of our modern masters of fiction should never have chanced—judging from their writings—to come in contact with any of them. She had an only son, a working cabinetmaker, who used occasionally to annoy her by his silly jokes at serious things, and who was courting at this time a sweetheart who had five hundred pounds in the bank— an immensely large sum to a man in his circumstances. He had urged his suit with such apparent success, that the marriage day was fixed and at hand, and the house which he had engaged as his future residence fully furnished. And it was his prospective brother-in-law who was to be my new employer, so soon as the wedding should leave him leisure enough to furnish epitaphs for two tombstones recently placed in the family burying-ground. The wedding-day arrived; and, to be out of the way of the bustle and the pageant, I retired to the house of a neighbour, a carpenter, whom I had obliged by a few lessons in practical geometry and architectural drawing. The carpenter was at the wedding; and, with the whole house to myself, I was engaged in writing, when up flew the door, and in rushed my pupil the carpenter. "What

has happened?" I asked. "Happened!" said the carpenter,—
"Happened!! The bride's away with another man!! The bridegroom has taken to his bed, and raves like a madman; and his poor
old mother—good honest woman—is crying like a child. Do come
and see what can be done." I accompanied him to my landlady's,
where I found the bridegroom in a paroxysm of mingled grief and
rage, congratulating himself on his escape, and bemoaning his
unhappy disappointment, by turns. He lay athwart the bed, which
he told me in the morning he had quitted for the last time; but
as I entered, he half rose, and, seizing on a pair of new shoes which
had been prepared for the bride, and lay on a table beside him,
he hurled them against the wall, first the one and then the other,
until they came rebounding back across the room; and then, with
an exclamation that need not be repeated, he dashed himself down
again. I did my best to comfort his poor mother, who seemed to
feel very keenly the slight done to her son, and to anticipate with
dread the scandal and gossip of which it would render her humble
household the subject. She seemed sensible, however, that he had
made an escape, and at once acquiesced in my suggestion, that all
that should now be done would be to get every expense her son
had been at in his preparations for housekeeping and the wedding
transferred to the shoulders of the other party. And such an
arrangement could, I thought, be easily effected through the
bride's brother, who seemed to be a reasonable man, and who
would be aware also that a suit at law could be instituted in the
case against his sister; though in any such suit I held it might be
best for both parties not to engage. And at the old woman's request,
I set out with the carpenter to wait on the bride's brother, in order
to see whether he was not prepared for some such arrangement
as I suggested, and, besides, able to furnish us with some
explanation of the extraordinary step taken by the bride.

We were overtaken, as we passed along the street, by a person
who was, he said, in search of us, and who now requested us to
accompany him; and, threading our way, under his guidance,
through a few narrow lanes that traverse the assemblage of houses

on the west bank of the Ness, we stopped at the door of an obscure alehouse. This, said our conductor, we have found to be the retreat of the bride. He ushered us into a room occupied by some eight or ten persons, drawn up on the opposite sides, with a blank space between. On the one side sat the bride, a high-coloured, buxom young girl, serene and erect as Britannia on the halfpennies, and guarded by two stout fellows, masons or slaters apparently, in their working dresses. They looked hard at the carpenter and me as we entered, of course regarding us as the assailants against whom they would have to maintain their prize. On the other side sat a group of the bride's relatives—among the rest her brother—silent, and all apparently very much grieved; while in the space between them there stumped up and down a lame, sallow-complexioned oddity, in shabby black, who seemed to be making a set oration, to which no one replied, about the sacred claims of love, and the cruelty of interfering with the affections of young people. Neither the carpenter nor myself felt any inclination to debate with the orator, or fight with the guards, or yet to interfere with the affections of the young lady; and so, calling out the brother into another room, and expressing our regret at what had happened, we stated our case, and found him, as we had expected, very reasonable. We could not, however, treat for the absent bride-groom, nor could he engage for his sister; and so we had to part without coming to any agreement. There were points about the case which at first I could not understand. My jilted acquaintance the cabinetmaker had not only enjoyed the countenance of all his mistress's relatives, but he had been also as well received by herself as lovers usually are: she had written him kind letters, and accepted of his presents; and then, just as her friends were sitting down to the marriage breakfast she had eloped with another man. The other man, however—a handsome fellow, but great scamp— had a prior claim to her regards: he had been the lover of her choice, though detested by her brother and all her friends, who were sufficiently well acquainted with his character to know that he would land her in ruin; and, during his absence in the country, where he was working as a slater, they had lent their influence and countenance to my acquaintance the cabinetmaker, in order to get her married to a comparatively safe man, out of the slater's reach. And, not very strong of will, she had acquiesced in the arrangement. On the eve of the marriage, however, the slater had come into town; and, exchanging clothes with an acquaintance, a Highland soldier, he had walked unsuspected opposite her door, until, finding an opportunity of conversing with her on the morning of the wedding-day, he had represented her new lover as a silly, ill-shaped fellow, who had just head enough to be mercenary, and himself as one of the most devoted and discon-solate of lovers. And, his soft tongue and fine leg gaining the day, she had left the marriage guests to enjoy their tea and toast without her, and set off with him to the change-house. Ultimately the affair ended ill for all parties. I lost my job, for I saw no more of the bride's brother; the wrong-headed cabinetmaker, contrary to the advice of his mother and her lodger, entered into a law-suit, in which he got small damages and much vexation; and the slater and his mistress broke out into such a course of dissipation after becoming man and wife, that they and the five hundred pounds came to an end almost together. Shortly after, my landlady and her son quitted the country for the United States. So favourably had the poor woman impressed me as one of the truly excellent, that I took a journey from Cromarty to Inverness—a distance of nineteen miles—to bid her farewell; but I found, on my arrival, her house shut up, and learned that she had left the place for some sailing port on the west coast two days before. She was a humble washerwoman; but I am convinced that in the other world, which she must have entered long ere now, she ranks considerably higher!

I waited on in Inverness, in the hope that, according to Burns, "my brothers of the earth would give me leave to toil;" but the hope was a vain one, as I succeeded in procuring no second job. There was no lack, however, of the sort of employment which I could cut out for myself; but the remuneration—only now in the process of being realized, and that very slowly—had to be deferred to a distant day. I had to give more than twelve years' *credit* to the pursuits that engaged me: and as my capital was small, it was rather a trying matter to be "kept so long out of my wages." There is a wonderful group of what are now termed *osars*,[1] in the immediate neighbourhood of Inverness—a group to which that Queen of Scottish tomhans, the picturesque Tomnahuirich, belongs, and to the examination of which I devoted several days. But I learned only to state the difficulty which they form—not to solve it; and now that Agassiz has promulgated his glacial theory, and that traces of the great ice agencies have been detected all over Scotland, the mystery of the *osars* remains a mystery still. I succeeded, however, in determining at this time, that they belong to a later period than the boulder clay, which I found underlying the great gravel formation of which they form a part, in a section near Loch Ness that had been laid open shortly before, in excavating for the great Caledonian Canal. And as all, or almost all, the shells of the boulder clay are of species that still live, we may infer that the mysterious *osars* were formed not very long ere the introduction upon our planet of the inquisitive little creature that has been puzzling himself—hitherto at least with no satisfactory result—in attempting to account for their origin. I examined, too, with some care, the old coast-line, so well developed in this neighbourhood as to form one of the features of its striking scenery, and which must be regarded as the geological memorial and representative of those latter ages of the world in which the human epoch impinged on the old Pre-Adamite periods. The magistrates of the place were engaged at the time in doing their duty, like sensible men, as they were, in what I could not help thinking a somewhat barbarous instance. The neat, well proportioned, very uninteresting jail-spire of the burgh, about which, in its integrity, no one cares anything, had been shaken by an earthquake, which took place in the year 1816, into one of the greatest curiosities in the kingdom. The earthquake, which, for a

[1] A Swedish name for what are called *kames* in Scotland, or as here, *tomhans*, ridges of gravel and sand sometimes extending for miles; relics of the Ice Age.

Scotch one, had been unprecedentedly severe, especially in the line
of the great Caledonian Valley, had, by a strange vorticose motion,
twisted round the spire, so that, at the transverse line of
displacement, the *panes* and corners of the octagonal broach which
its top formed overshot their proper positions fully seven inches.
The corners were carried into nearly the middle of the *panes*, as
if some gigantic hand, in attempting to twirl round the building
by the spire, as one twirls round a spinning-top by the stalk or bole,
had, from some failure in the coherency of the masonry, succeeded
in turning round only the part of which it had laid hold. Sir
Charles Lyell figures, in his "Principles," similar shifts in stones
of two obelisks in a Calabrian convent, and subjoins the ingenious
suggestion on the subject of Messrs Darwin and Millet. And here
was there a Scotch example of the same sort of mysterious
phenomena, not less curious than the Calabrian one, and certainly
unique in its character *as Scotch*, which, though the injured
building had already stood twelve years in its displaced condition,
and might stand for as many more as the hanging tower of Pisa,
the magistrates were laboriously effacing at the expense of the
burgh. They were completely successful too; and the jail-spire was
duly restored to its state of original insignificance, as a fifth-rate
piece of ornamental masonry. But how very absurd, save, mayhap,
here and there, to a geologist, must not these remarks appear!

But my criticisms on the magistracy, however foolish, were
silent criticisms, and did harm to no one. About the time, however,
in which I was indulging in them, I imprudently exposed myself,
by one of those impulsive acts of which men repent at their leisure,
to criticisms not silent, and of a kind that occasionally *do* harm.
I had been piqued by the rejection of my verses on the Ness. True,
I had no high opinion of their merit, deeming them little more
than equal to the average verses of provincial prints; but then I
had intimated my scheme of getting them printed to a few
Cromarty friends, and was now weak enough to be annoyed at the
thought that my townsfolk would regard me as an incompetent
blockhead, who could not write rhymes good enough for a

newspaper. And so I rashly determined on appealing to the public in a small volume. Had I known as much as in an after period about newspaper affairs, and the mode in which copies of verses are often dealt with by editors and their assistants—fatigued with nonsense, and at once hopeless of finding grain in the enormous heaps of chaff submitted to them, and too much occupied to seek for it, even should they believe in its occurrence in the form of single seeds sparsely scattered—I would have thought less of the matter. As the case was, however, I hastily collected from among my piles of manuscripts, some fifteen or twenty pieces in verse, written chiefly during the preceding six years, and put them into the hands of the printer of the *Inverness Courier*. It would have been a greatly wiser act, as I soon came to see, had I put them into the fire instead; but my choice of a printing-office secured to me at least one advantage—it brought me acquainted with one of the ablest and most accomplished of Scotch editors—the gentleman who now owns and still conducts the *Courier*; and, besides, having once crossed the Rubicon, I felt all my native obstinacy stirred up to make good a position for myself, despite of failures and reverses on the farther side. It is an advantage in some cases to be committed. The clear large type of the *Courier* office did, however, show me many a blemish in my verse that had escaped me before, and broke off associations which—curiously linked with the manuscripts—had given to the stanzas and passages which they contained charms of tone and colour not their own. I began to find, too, that my humble accomplishment of verse was too narrow to contain my thinking;—the thinking ability had been growing, but not the ability of poetic expression; nay, much of the thinking seemed to be of a kind not suited for poetic purposes at all;—and though it was of course far better that I should come to know this in time, than that, like some, even superior men, I should persist in wasting, in inefficient verse, the hours in which vigorous prose might be produced, it was at least quite mortifying enough to make the discovery with half a volume of metre committed to type, and in the hands of the printer. Resolving, however, that my humble name should not appear in the title-page, I went on with my volume. My new friend the editor kindly inserted, from time to time, copies of its verses in the columns of his paper, and strove to excite some degree of interest and expectation regarding it; but my recent discovery had thoroughly sobered me, and I awaited the publication of my volume not much elated by the honour done me, and as little sanguine respecting its ultimate success as well might be. And ere I quitted Inverness, a sad bereavement, which greatly narrowed the circle of my best-beloved friends, threw very much into the background all my thoughts regarding it.

On quitting Cromarty, I had left my Uncle James labouring under an attack of rheumatic fever; but though he had just entered his grand climacteric, he was still a vigorous and active man, and I could not doubt that he had strength of constitution enough to throw it off. He had failed to rally, however; and after returning one evening from a long exploratory walk, I found in my lodgings a note awaiting me, intimating his death. The blow fell with stunning effect. Ever since the death of my father, my two uncles had faithfully occupied his place; and James, of a franker and less reserved temper than Alexander, and more tolerant of my boyish follies, had, though I sincerely loved the other, laid stronger hold on my affections. He was of a genial disposition, too, that always remained sanguine in the cast of its hopes and anticipations; and he had unwittingly flattered my vanity by taking me pretty much at my own estimate—overweeningly high, of course, like that of almost all young men, but mayhap necessary, in the character of a force, to make headway in the face of obstruction and difficulty. Uncle James, like *Le Balafré* in the novel, would have "ventured his nephew against the wight Wallace." I immediately set out for Cromarty; and, curious as it may seem, found grief so companionable, that the four hours which I spent by the way seemed hardly equal to one. I retained, however, only a confused recollection of my journey, remembering little more than that, when passing at midnight along the dreary Maolbuie, I saw the moon in her wane, rising red and lightless out of the distant sea; and that, lying, as it were, prostrate on the horizon, she reminded me of some o'ermatched wrestler thrown helpless on the ground.

On reaching home, I found my mother, late as the hour was, still up, and engaged in making a dead-dress for the body. "There is a letter from the south, with a black seal, awaiting you," she said; "I fear you have also lost your friend William Ross." I opened the letter, and found her surmise too well founded. It was a farewell letter, written in feeble characters but in no feeble spirit; and a brief postscript, added by a comrade, intimated the death of the writer. "This," wrote the dying man, with a hand fast forgetting its cunning, "is, to all human probability, my last letter; but the thought gives me little trouble; for my hope of salvation is in the blood of Jesus. Farewell, my sincerest friend!" There is a provision through which nature sets limits to both physical and mental suffering. A man partially stunned by a violent blow is sometimes conscious that it is followed by other blows, rather from seeing than from feeling them; his capacity of suffering has been exhausted by the first; and the others that fall upon him, though they may injure, fail to pain. And so also it is with strokes that fall on the affections. In other circumstances, I would have grieved for the death of my friend, but my mind was already occupied to the full by the death of my uncle; and though I *saw* the new stroke, several days elapsed ere I could *feel* it. My friend, after half a lifetime of decline, had sunk suddenly. A comrade who lived with him—a stout, florid lad—had been seized by the same insidious malady as his own, about a twelvemonth before; and, previously unacquainted with sickness, in him the progress of the disease had been rapid, and his sufferings were so great, that he was incapacitated for work several months ere his death. But my poor friend, though sinking at the time, wrought for both: he was able to prosecute his employments—which, according to Bacon, "required rather the finger than the arm"—in even the latter stages of his complaint; and after supporting and tending his dying comrade till he sank, he himself suddenly broke down and died. And thus perished unknown, and in the prime of his days, a man of sterling principle and fine genius. I found employment enough for the few weeks which still remained of the working season of this year, in hewing a tombstone for my uncle James, on which I inscribed an epitaph of a few lines, that had the merit of being true. It characterized the deceased—"James Wright"—as "an honest, warm-hearted man, who had the happiness of living without reproach, and of dying without fear."

CHAPTER XX

"This while my notion's ta'en a sklent,
To try my fate in guid black prent;
But still the mair I'm that way bent,
Something cries, Hoolie!
I red you, honest man, tak tent;
Ye'll shaw your folly."—BURNS.

MY volume of verse[1] passed but slowly through the press; as I had begun to look rather ruefully forward to its appearance there was no anxiety evinced on my part to urge it on. However, all the pieces were thrown into type; and I followed them up by a tail-piece in prose, formed somewhat on the model of the preface of Pope—for I was a great admirer, at the time, of the English written by the "wits of Queen Anne"—in which I gave serious expression to the suspicion that, as a writer of verse, I had mistaken my vocation.

"It is more than possible," I said, "that I have completely failed in poetry. It may appear that, while grasping at originality of description and sentiment, and striving to attain propriety of expression, I have only been depicting common images, and embodying obvious thoughts, and this, too, in inelegant language. Yet even in this case, though disappointed, I shall not be without my sources of comfort. The pleasure which I enjoy in composing verses is quite independent of other men's opinions of them; and I expect to feel as happy as ever in this amusement, even though assured that others could find no pleasure in reading what I had found so much in writing. It is no small solace to reflect, that the fable of the dog and shadow cannot apply to me, since my predilection for poetry has not prevented me from acquiring the skill of at least the common mechanic. I am not more ignorant of masonry and architecture than many professors of these arts who never measured a stanza. There is also some satisfaction in reflecting that, unlike some would-be satirists, I have not assailed private character; and that, though men may deride me as an unskilful poet, they cannot justly detest me as a bad or ill-natured man. Nay, I shall possibly have the pleasure of repaying those who may be merry at my expense, in their own coin.

[1] *Poems Written in the Leisure Hours of a Journeyman Mason* (Inverness 1829).

414

An ill-conditioned critic is always a more pitiable sort of person than an unsuccessful versifier; and the desire of showing one's own discernment at the expense of one's neighbour, a greatly worse thing than the simple wish, however divorced from the ability, of affording him harmless pleasure. Further, it would, I think, not be difficult to show that my mistake in supposing myself a poet is not a whit more ridiculous, and infinitely less mischievous, than many of those into which myriads of my fellow-men are falling every day. I have seen the vicious attempting to teach morals, and the weak to unfold the mysteries. I have seen men set up for freethinkers who were born not to think at all. To conclude, there will surely be cause for self-congratulation in reflecting that, by becoming an author, I have only lost a few pounds, not gained the reputation of being a mean fellow, who had teased all his acquaintance until they had subscribed for a worthless book; and that the severest remark of the severest critic can only be, 'a certain anonymous rhymer is no poet.'"

As, notwithstanding the blank in the title-page, the authorship of my volume would be known in Cromarty and its neighbourhood, I set myself to see whether I could not, meanwhile, prepare for the press something better suited to make an impression in my favour. In tossing the bar or throwing the stone, the competitor who begins with a rather indifferent cast is never very unfavourably judged if he immediately mend it by giving a better; and I resolved on mending my cast, if I could, by writing for the *Inverness Courier*—which was now open to me, through the kindness of the editor—a series of carefully prepared letters on some popular subject. In the days of Goldsmith, the herring-fishing employed, as he tells us in one of his essays, "all Grub Street." In the north of Scotland this fishery was a popular theme little more than twenty years ago. The welfare of whole communities depended in no slight degree on its success: it formed the basis of many a calculation, and the subject of many an investment; and it was all the more suitable for my purpose from the circumstance that there was no Grub Street in that part of the world to employ itself about it. It was, in at least all its better aspects, a fresh subject; and I deemed myself more thoroughly acquainted with it than at least most of the men who were skilful enough, as *litterateurs*, to communicate their knowledge in writing. I knew the peculiarities of fishermen as a class, and the effects of this special branch of their profession on their character: I had seen them pursuing their employments amid the sublime of nature, and had occasionally taken a share in their work; and, further, I was acquainted with not a few antique traditions of the fishermen of other ages, in which, as in the narratives of most seafaring men, there mingled with a certain amount of real incident, curious snatches of the supernatural. In short, the subject was one on which, as I knew a good deal regarding it that was not generally known, I was in some degree qualified to write; and so I occupied my leisure in casting my facts respecting it into a series of letters, of which the first appeared in the *Courier* a fortnight after my volume of verse was laid on the tables of the north-country booksellers.

I had first gone out to sea to assist in catching herrings about ten years before; and I now described, in one of my letters, as truthfully as I could, those features of the scene to which I had been introduced on that occasion, which had struck me as novel and peculiar. And what had been strange to me proved equally so, I found, to the readers of the *Courier*. My letters attracted attention, and were republished in my behalf by the proprietors of the paper, "in consequence," said my friend the editor, in a note which he kindly attached to the pamphlet which they formed, "of the interest they had excited in the northern counties."[1] Their modicum of success, lowly as was their subject, compared with that of some of my more ambitious verses, taught me my proper course. Let it be my business, I said, to know what is not generally known;—let me qualify myself to stand as an interpreter between nature and the public: while I strive to narrate as pleasingly and describe as vividly as I can, let truth, not fiction, be my walk; and if I succeed in uniting the novel to the true, in provinces of more

---

[1] I am reminded by the editor of the *Courier*, in a very kind critique on the present volume, of a passage in the history of my little work which had escaped my memory. "It had come," he states, "to the knowledge of Sir Walter Scott, who endeavoured to procure a copy after the limited impression was exhausted." (Miller).

general interest than the very humble one in which I have now partially succeeded, I shall succeed also in establishing myself in a position which, if not lofty, will yield me at least more solid footing than that to which I might attain as a mere *litterateur* who, mayhap, pleased for a little, but added nothing to the general fund. The resolution was, I think, a good one; would that it had been better kept! The following extracts may serve to show that, humble as my new subject may be deemed, it gave considerable scope for description of a kind not often associated with herrings, even when they employed all Grub Street:

"As the night gradually darkened, the sky assumed a dead and leaden hue: the sea, roughened by the rising breeze, reflected its deeper hues with an intensity approaching to black, and seemed a dark uneven pavement, that absorbed every ray of the remaining light. A calm silvery patch, some fifteen or twenty yards in extent, came moving slowly through the black. It seemed merely a patch of water coated with oil; but, obedient to some other moving power than that of either tide or wind, it sailed aslant our line of buoys, a stone-cast from our bows— lengthened itself along the line to thrice its former extent—paused as if for a moment—and then three of the buoys, after erecting themselves on their narrower base, with a sudden jerk slowly sunk. 'One—two—three buoys!' exclaimed one of the fishermen, reckoning them as they disappeared—'*there* are ten barrels for us secure.' A few moments were suffered to elapse: and then, unfixing the haulser from the stem, and bringing it aft to the stern, we commenced hauling. The nets approached the gunwale. The first three appeared, from the phosphoric light of the water, as if bursting into flames of a pale green colour. Here and there a herring glittered bright in the meshes, or went darting away through the pitchy darkness, visible for a moment by its own light. The fourth net was brighter than any of the others, and glittered through the waves while it was yet several fathoms away: the pale green seemed as if mingled with broken sheets of snow, that—flickering amid the mass of light—appeared, with every tug given by the fishermen, to shift, dissipate, and again form; and there streamed from it into the surrounding gloom myriads of green rays, an instant seen and then lost—the retreating fish that had avoided the meshes, but had lingered, until disturbed, beside their entangled companions. It contained a considerable body of herrings. As we raised them over the gunwale, they felt warm to the hand, for in the middle of a large shoal even the temperature of the water is raised—a fact well known to every herring fisherman; and in shaking them out of the meshes, the ear became sensible of a shrill, chirping sound, like that of the mouse, but much fainter—a ceaseless cheep, cheep, occasioned apparently—for no true fish is furnished with organs of sound—by a sudden

417

escape from the air-bladder. The shoal, a small one, had spread over only three of the nets—the three whose buoys had so suddenly disappeared; and most of the others had but their mere sprinkling of fish, some dozen or two in a net; but so thickly had they lain in the fortunate three, that the entire haul consisted of rather more than twelve barrels.

We started up about midnight, and saw an open sea, as before; but the scene had considerably changed since we had lain down. The breeze had died into a calm; the heavens, no longer dark and grey, were glowing with stars; and the sea, from the smoothness of the surface, appeared a second sky, as bright and starry as the other; with this difference, however, that all its stars seemed to be comets!—the slightly tremulous motion of the surface elongated the reflected images, and gave to each its tail. There was no visible line of division at the horizon. Where the hills rose high along the coast, and appeared as if doubled by their undulating strip of shadow, what might be deemed a dense bank of cloud lay sleeping in the heavens, just where the upper and nether firmaments met; but its presence rendered the illusion none the less complete: the outline of the boat lay dark around us, like the fragment of some broken planet suspended in middle space, far from the earth and every star; and all around we saw extended the complete sphere—unhidden above from Orion to the Pole, and visible beneath from the Pole to Orion. Certainly sublime scenery possesses in itself no virtue potent enough to develop the faculties, or the mind of the fisherman would not have so long lain asleep. There is no profession whose recollections should rise into purer poetry than his; but if the mirror bear not its previous amalgam of taste and genius, what does it matter though the scene which sheds upon it its many-coloured light should be rich in grandeur and beauty? There is no corresponding image produced: the susceptibility of reflecting the landscape is never imparted by the landscape itself, whether to the mind or to the glass. There is no class of recollections more illusory than those which associate—as if they existed in the relation of cause and effect—some piece of striking scenery with some sudden development of the intellect or imagination. The eyes open, and there is an external beauty seen; but it is not the external beauty that has opened the eyes.

It was still a dead calm—calm to blackness; when, in about an hour after sunrise, what seemed light fitful airs began to play on the surface, imparting to it, in irregular patches, a tint of grey. First one patch would form, then a second beside it, then a third, and then for miles around, the surface, else so silvery, would seem frosted over with grey; the apparent breeze appeared as if propagating itself from one central point. In a few seconds after, all would be calm as at first; and then from some other centre the patches of grey would again form and widen, till the whole Firth seemed covered by them. A peculiar poppling noise, as if a thunder-shower was beating the surface with its multitudinous drops, rose around our boat; the water seemed sprinkled with an infinity of points of silver, that for an instant glittered to the sun, and then resigned their places to other quick glancing points, that in turn were succeeded by yet others. The herrings by millions, and thousands of millions, were at play around us, leaping a few inches into the air, and then falling and disappearing, to rise and leap again. Shoal rose beyond shoal, till the whole bank of Gulliam seemed beaten into foam, and the low poppling sounds were multiplied into a roar, like that of the wind through some tall wood, that might be heard in the calm for miles. And again, the shoals extending around us seemed to cover, for hundreds of square miles, the vast Moray Firth. But though they played beside our buoys by thousands, not a herring swam so low as the upper baulk of our drift. One of the fishermen took up a stone, and, flinging it right over our second buoy into the middle of the shoal, the fish disappeared from the surface for several fathoms around. 'Ah, there they go,' he exclaimed, 'if they go but low enough. Four years ago I startled thirty barrels of light fish into my drift just by throwing a stone among them.' I know not what effect the stone might have had on this occasion; but on hauling our nets for the third and last time, we found we had captured about eight barrels of fish; and then hoisting sail—for a light breeze from the east had sprung up—we made for the shore with a cargo of twenty barrels."

Meanwhile the newspaper critics of the south were giving expression to all sorts of judgments on my verses. It was intimated in the title of the volume that they had been "written in the leisure hours of a journeyman mason;" and the intimation seemed to furnish most of my reviewers with the proper cue for dealing with them. "The time has gone by," said one, "when a literary mechanic used to be regarded as a phenomenon: were a second Burns to spring up now, he would not be entitled to so much praise as the first." "It is our duty to tell this writer," said another, "that he will make more in a week by his trowel than in half a century by his pen." "We are glad to understand," said a third—very judiciously, however—"that our author has the good sense to rely more on his chisel than on the Muses." The lessons taught were of a sufficiently varied, but, on the whole, rather contradictory character. By one writer I was told that I was a dull, correct fellow, who had written a book in which there was nothing amusing and nothing absurd. Another, however, cheered my forlorn spirits by assuring me that I was a "man of genius, whose poems, with much that was faulty, contained also much that was interesting." A third was sure I had "no chance whatever of being known beyond the limits of my native place," and that my "book exhibited none, or next to none, of those indications which sanction the expectation of better things to come;" while a fourth, of a more sanguine vein, found in my work the evidence of "gifts of Nature, which the stimulus of encouragement, and the tempering lights of experience, might hereafter develop, and direct to the achievement of something truly wonderful." There were two names in particular that my little volume used to suggest to the newspaper reviewers. The Tam o' Shanter and Souter Johnnie of the ingenious Thom[1] were in course of being exhibited at the time; and it was known that Thom had wrought as a journeyman mason; and there was a rather slim poet called Sillery,[2] the author of several forgotten volumes of verse, one of which had issued from the press contemporaneously with mine, who, as he had a little money, and was said to treat his literary friends very luxuriously, was praised beyond measure by the newspaper critics, especially by those of the Scottish capital. And Thom as a mason, and Sillery as a poet, were placed repeatedly before me. One critic, who was sure I would never come to anything, magnanimously remarked, however, that as he bore me no ill will, he would be glad to find himself mistaken; nay, that it would give him "unfeigned pleasure to learn I had attained to the well-merited fame of even Mr Thom himself." And another, after deprecating the undue severity so often shown by the bred writer to the working man, and asserting that the "journeyman mason" was in this instance, notwithstanding his treatment, a man of fair parts, ended by remarking, that it was of course not every man of merit who could expect to attain to the "high poetic elegance and celebrity of a Charles Doyne Sillery."

All this, however, was criticism at a distance, and disturbed me

[1] William Thom (1788-1848) author of "The Mitherless Bairn".
[2] C. D. Sillery, author of "Vallery, or, The Citadel of the Lake." 2 Vols, Edinburgh, 1829.

but little when engaged in toiling in the churchyard, or in enjoying my quiet evening walks. But it became more formidable when, on one occasion, it came to beard me in my den.

The place was visited by an itinerant lecturer on elocution—one Walsh, who, as his art was not in great request among the quiet ladies and busy gentlemen of Cromarty, failed to draw houses; till at length there appeared one morning, placarded on post and pillar, an intimation to the effect that Mr Walsh would that evening deliver an elaborate criticism on the lately-published volume of "Poems written in the leisure hours of a Journeyman Mason," and select from it a portion of his evening readings. The intimation drew a good house; and, curious to know what was awaiting me, I paid my shilling, with the others, and got into a corner. First in the entertainment there came a wearisome dissertation on harmonic inflections, double emphasis, the echoing words, and the monotones. But, to borrow from Meg Dods,[1] "Oh, what a style of language!" The elocutionist, evidently an untaught and grossly ignorant man, had not an idea of composition. Syntax, grammar, and good sense, were set at nought in every sentence; but then, on the other hand, the inflections were carefully maintained, and went rising and falling over the nonsense beneath, like the wave of some shallow bay over a bottom of mud and comminuted sea-weed. After the dissertation we were gratified by a few recitations. "Lord Ullin's Daughter," "The Razor Seller," and "My Name is Norval," were given in great force. And then came the critique. "Ladies and gentleman," said the reviewer, "we cannot expect much from a journeyman mason in the poetry line. Right poetry needs teaching. No man can be a proper poet unless he be an elocutionist; for, unless he be an elocutionist, how can he make his verses emphatic in the right places, or manage the harmonic inflexes, or deal with the rhetorical pauses? And now, ladies and gentlemen, I'll show you, from various passages in this book, that the untaught journeyman mason who made it never took lessons in elocution. I'll first read

[1] In Scott's *St Ronan's Well.*

421

you a passage from a piece of verse called the 'Death of Gardiner'—the person meant being the late Colonel Gardiner, I suppose. The beginning of the piece is about the running away of Johnnie Cope's men:

"Yet in that craven, dread-struck host,
　　One val'rous heart beat keen and high;
In that dark hour of shameful flight,
　　One stayed behind to die!
Deep gash'd by many a felon blow,
　　He sleeps where fought the vanquish'd van—
Of silver'd locks and furrow'd brow,
　　A venerable man.
E'en when his thousand warriors fled—
　　Their low-born valour quail'd and gone—
He—the meek leader of that band—
　　Remained, and fought alone.
He stood; fierce foemen throng'd around;
　　The hollow death-groans of despair,
The clashing sword, the cleaving axe,
　　The murd'rous dirk were there.
Valour more stark, or hands more strong,
　　Ne'er urged the brand or launch'd the spear;
But what were these to that old man!
　　God was his only fear.
He stood where adverse thousands throng'd,
　　And long that warrior fought, and well;—
Bravely he fought, firmly he stood,
　　Till where he stood he fell.
He fell—he breathed one patriot prayer,
　　Then to his God his soul resign'd:
Not leaving of earth's many sons
　　A better man behind.
His valour, his high scorn of death,
　　To fame's proud meed no impulse owed;
His was a pure, unsullied zeal,
　　For Britain and for God.
He fell—he died;—the savage foe
　　Trod careless o'er the noble clay;
Yet not in vain that champion fought,
　　In that disastrous fray.

On bigot creeds and felon swords
　　Partial success may fondly smile,
Till bleeds the patriot's honest heart,
　　And flames the martyr's pile.
Yet not in vain the patriot bleeds;
　　Yet not in vain the martyr dies;
From ashes mute, and voiceless blood,
　　What stirring memories rise!
The scoffer owns the bigot's creed,
　　Though keen the secret gibe may be;
The sceptic seeks the tyrant's dome,
　　And bends the ready knee.
But oh! in dark oppression's day,
　　When flares the torch, when flames the sword,
Who are the brave in freedom's cause?
　　The men who fear the Lord."[1]

---

[1] The following are the opening stanzas of the piece—quite as obnoxious to criticism, I fear, as those selected by Walsh:—

"Have ye not seen, on winter's eve,
　　When snow-rack dimm'd the welkin's face,
Borne wave-like by the fitful breeze,
　　The snow-wreath shifting place?
Silent and slow as drifting wreath,
　　Ere day, the clans from Preston Hill
Moved downward to the vale beneath:—
　　Dark was the scene and still!
In stormy autumn day, when sad
　　The boding peasant frets forlorn,
Have ye not seen the mountain stream
　　Bear down the standing corn?
At dawn, when Preston bog was cross'd,
　　Like mountain stream that bursts its banks,
Charged wild those Celtic hearts of fire,
　　On Cope's devoted ranks.
Have ye not seen, from lonesome waste,
　　The smoke-tower rising tall and slow,
O'erlooking, like a stately tree,
　　The russet plain below?
And have ye mark'd that pillar'd wreath,
　　When sudden struck by northern blast,
Amid the low and stunted heath
　　In broken volumes cast?
At sunrise, as by northern blast
　　The pillar'd smoke is roll'd away,
Fled all that cloud of Saxon war,
　　In headlong disarray."

"Now, ladies and gentlemen," continued the critic, "this is very bad poetry. I defy any elocutionist to read it satisfactorily with the inflexes. And, besides, only see how full it is of tautology. Let us take but one of the verses:—'He fell—he died!' To fall in battle means, as we all know, to die in battle;—to die in battle is exactly the same thing as to fall in battle. To say 'he fell—he died,' is therefore just tantamount to saying that he fell, he fell, or that he died, he died, and is bad poetry, and tautology. And this is one of the effects of ignorance, and a want of right education." Here, however, a low grumbling sound, gradually shaping itself into words, interrupted the lecturer. There was a worthy old captain among the audience, who had not given himself very much to the study of elocution or the belles-lettres; he had been too much occupied in his younger days in dealing at close quarters with the French under Howe and Nelson, to leave him much time for the niceties of recitation or criticism. But the brave old man bore a genial, generous heart; and the strictures of the elocutionist emitted, as all saw, in the presence of the assailed author, jarred on his feelings. "It was not gentlemanly," he said, "to attack in that way an inoffensive man: it was wrong. The poems were, he was told, very good poems. He knew good judges that thought so; and unprovoked remarks on them, such as those of the lecturer, ought not to be permitted." The lecturer replied, and in glibness and fluency would have been greatly an overmatch for the worthy captain; but a storm of hisses backed the old veteran, and the critic gave way. As his remarks were, he said, not to the taste of the audience—though he was taking only the ordinary critical liberty—he would go on to the readings. And with a few extracts, read without note or comment, the entertainment of the evening concluded. There was nothing very formidable in the critique of Walsh; but, having no great powers of face, I felt it rather unpleasant to be stared at in my quiet corner by every one in the room, and looked, I daresay, very much put out; and the sympathy and condolence of such of my townsfolk as comforted me in the state of supposed annihilation and nothingness to which his criticism had reduced me, were just a little annoying. **Poor Walsh** however, had he but known what threatened him, would have been considerably less at ease than his victim.

The cousin Walter introduced to the reader in an early chapter as the companion of one of my Highland journeys, had grown up into a handsome and very powerful young man. One might have guessed his stature at about five feet ten or so, but it in reality somewhat exceeded six feet: he had amazing length and strength of arm; and such was his structure of bone, that, as he tucked up his sleeve to send the bowl along the town links, or to fling the hammer or throw the stone, the knobbed protuberances of the wrist, with the sinews rising sharp over them, reminded one rather of the framework of a horse's leg, than of that of a human arm. And Walter, though a fine, sweet-tempered fellow, had shown, oftener than once or twice, that he could make a very formidable use of his great strength. Some of the later instances had been rather interesting in their kind. There had been a large Dutch transport, laden with troops, forced by stress of weather into the bay shortly before, and a handsome young soldier of the party— a native of Northern Germany, named Wolf—had, I know not how, scraped acquaintance with Walter. Wolf, who, like many of his country-folk, was a great reader, and intimately acquainted, through German translations, with the Waverley Novels, had taken all his ideas of Scotland and its people from the descriptions of Scott; and in Walter, as handsome as he was robust, he found the *beau-idéal* of a Scottish hero. He was a man cast in exactly the model of the Harry Bertrams, Halbert Glendinnings, and Quentin Durwards of the novelist. For the short time the vessel lay in the harbour, Wolf and Walter were inseparable. Walter knew a little, mainly at second hand, through his cousin, about the heroes of Scott; and Wolf delighted to converse with him in his broken English about Balfour of Burley, Rob Roy, and Vich Ian Vohr: and ever and anon would he urge him to exhibit before him some feat of strength or agility—a call to which Walter was never slow to respond. There was a serjeant among the troops—a Dutchman, regarded as their strongest man, who used to pride himself much on his prowess; and who, on hearing Wolf's description of Walter, expressed a wish to be introduced to him. Wolf soon found the means of gratifying the serjeant. The strong Dutchman stretched out his hand, and, on getting hold of Walter's, grasped it very hard. Walter saw his design, and returned the grasp with such overmastering firmness, that the hand became powerless within his. "Ah!" exclaimed the Dutchman, in his broken English, shaking his fingers, and blowing upon them, "me no try squeeze hand with you again; you very *very* strong man." Wolf for a minute after stood laughing and clapping his hands, as if the victory were his, not Walter's. When at length the day arrived on which the transport was to sail, the two friends seemed as unwilling to part as if they had been attached for years. Walter presented Wolf with a favourite snuff-box; Wolf gave Walter his fine German pipe.

Before I had risen on the morning of the day succeeding that in which I had been demolished by the elocutionist, Cousin Walter made his way to my bedside, with a storm on his brow dark as midnight. "Is it true, Hugh," he inquired, "that the lecturer Walsh ridiculed you and your poems in the Council House last night?" "Oh, and what of that?" I said; "who cares anything for the ridicule of a blockhead?" "Ay," said Walter, "that's always your way; but *I* care for it! Had I been there last night, I would have sent the puppy through the window, to criticize among the nettles in the yard. But there's no time lost: I shall wait on him when it grows dark this evening, and give him a lesson in good manners." "Not for your life, Walter!" I exclaimed. "Oh," said Walter, "I shall give Walsh all manner of fair play." "Fair play!" I rejoined; "you cannot give Walsh fair play; you are an overmatch for five Walshes. If you meddle with him at all, you will kill the poor slim man at a blow, and then not only will you be apprehended for manslaughter—mayhap for murder—but it will also be said that I was mean enough to set you on to do what I had not courage enough to do myself. You *must* give up all thoughts of meddling with Walsh." In short, I at length partially succeeded in convincing Walter that he might do me a great mischief by assaulting my critic; but so little confident was I of his seeing the matter in its proper light, that when the lecturer, unable to get audiences, quitted the place, and Walter had no longer opportunity of avenging my cause, I felt a load of anxiety taken off my mind.

There reached Cromarty shortly after, a criticism that differed considerably from that of Walsh, and restored the shaken confidence of some of my acquaintance. The other criticisms which had appeared in newspapers, critical journals, and literary gazettes, had been evidently the work of small men; and, feeble and commonplace in their style and thinking, they carried with them no weight—for who cares anything for the judgment, on one's writings, of men who themselves cannot write? But here, at length, was there a critique eloquently and powerfully written. It was, however, at least as extravagant in its praise as the others in their censure. The friendly critic knew nothing of the author he commended; but he had, I suppose, first seen the deprecatory criticisms, and then glanced his eye over the volume which they condemned; and finding it considerably better than it was said to be, he had rushed into generous praise, and described it as really a great deal better than it was. After an extravagantly high estimate of the powers of its author, he went on to say—"Nor, in making these observations, do we speak relatively, or desire to be understood as merely saying that the poems before us are remarkable productions to emanate from a 'journeyman mason.' That this is indeed the case, no one who reads them can doubt; but in characterizing the poetical talent they display, our observations are meant to be quite absolute; and we aver, without fear of contradiction, that the pieces contained in the humble volume before us bear the stamp and impress of no ordinary genius; that they are bespangled with gems of genuine poetry; and that their unpretending author well deserves—what he will doubtless obtain—the countenance and support of a discerning public. Nature is not an aristocrat. To the plough-boy following his team a-field—to the shepherd tending his flocks in the wilderness—or to the rude cutter of stone, cramped over his rough occupation in the wooden shed—she sometimes dispenses her richest and rarest gifts as liberally as to the proud patrician, or the titled representative of a long, line of illustrious ancestry. She is no respecter of persons; and all other distinctions yield to the title which her favours confer. The names, be they ever so humble, which she illustrates, need no other decoration to recommend them; and hence, even that of our 'journeyman mason' may yet be destined to take its place with those of men who, like him, first poured their 'wood notes wild' in the humblest and lowliest sphere of life, but, raised into deathless song, have become familiar as household words to all who love and admire the unsophisticated productions of native genius." The late Dr James Browne of Edinburgh, author of the "History of the Highlands," and working editor of the "Encyclopaedia Britannica," was, as I afterwards learned, the writer of this over-eulogistic, but certainly, in the circumstances, generous critique.

Ultimately I found my circle of friends very considerably enlarged by the publication of my Verses and Letters. Mr Isaac Forsyth of Elgin, the brother and biographer of the well-known Joseph Forsyth, whose classical volume on Italy still holds its place as perhaps the best work to which the traveller of taste in that country can commit himself, exerted himself, as the most influential of the north-country booksellers, with disinterested kindness in my behalf. The late Sir Thomas Dick Lauder, too, resident at that time at his seat of Relugas in Moray, lent me, unsolicited, his influence; and, distinguished by his fine taste and literary ability, he ventured to pledge both in my favour. I also received much kindness from the late Miss Dunbar of Boath—a literary lady of the high type of the last age, and acquainted in the best literary circles, who, now late in life, admitted amid her select friends one friend more, and cheered me with many a kind letter, and invited my frequent visits to her hospitable mansion.

If, in my course as a working man, I never incurred pecuniary obligation, and never spent a shilling for which I had not previously laboured, it was certainly not from want of opportunity afforded me. Miss Dunbar meant what she said, and oftener than once did she press her purse on my acceptance. I received much kindness, too, from the late Principal Baird.[1] The venerable Principal, when on one of his Highland journeys—benevolently undertaken in behalf of an educational scheme of the General Assembly, in the service of which he travelled, after he was turned of seventy, more than eight thousand miles—had perused my Verses and Letters; and, expressing a strong desire to know their author, my friend the editor of the *Courier* despatched one of his apprentices to Cromarty, to say that he thought the opportunity of meeting with such a man ought not to be neglected. I accordingly went up to Inverness, and had an interview with Dr Baird. I had known him previously by name as one of the correspondents of Burns, and the editor of the best edition of the poems of Michael Bruce; and, though aware at the time that his estimate of what I had done was by much too high, I yet felt flattered by his notice. He urged me to quit the north for Edinburgh. The capital furnished, he said, the proper field for a literary man in Scotland. What between the employment furnished by the newspapers and the magazines, he was sure I would effect a lodgment, and work my way up; and until I gave the thing a fair trial, I would, of course, come and live with him. I felt sincerely grateful for his kindness, but declined the invitation. I did think it possible, that in some subordinate capacity—as a concocter of paragraphs, or an abridger of Parliamentary debates, or even as a writer of occasional articles—I might find more remunerative employment than as a stonemason. But though I might acquaint myself in a large town, when occupied in this way, with the world of books, I questioned whether I could enjoy equal opportunities of acquainting myself with the occult and the new in natural science, as when plying my labours in the provinces as

[1] George Baird (1761-1840), Principal of Edinburgh University.

a mechanic. And so I determined that, instead of casting myself on an exhausting literary occupation, in which I would have to draw incessantly on the stock of fact and reflection which I had already accumulated, I should continue for at least several years more to purchase independence by my labours as a mason, and employ my leisure hours in adding to my fund, gleaned from original observation, and in walks not previously trodden.

The venerable Principal set me upon a piece of literary task-work, which, save for his advice, I would never have thought of producing, and of which these autobiographic chapters are the late but legitimate offspring. "Literary men," he said, "are sometimes spoken of as consisting of two classes—the educated and the uneducated; but they must all alike have an education before they can become literary men; and the less ordinary the mode in which the education has been acquired, the more interesting always is the story of it. I wish you to write for me an account of yours." I accordingly wrote an autobiographic sketch for the Principal, which brought up my story till my return, in 1825, from the south country to my home in the north; and which, though greatly overladen with reflection and remark, has preserved for me both the thoughts and incidents of an early time more freshly than if they had been suffered to exist till now, as mere recollections in the memory. I next set myself to record, in a somewhat elaborate form, the traditions of my native place and the surrounding district; and, taking the work very leisurely, not as labour, but as amusement—for my labours, as at an earlier period, continued to be those of the stone-cutter—a bulky volume grew up under my hands. I had laid down for myself two rules. There is no more fatal error into which a working man of a literary turn can fall, than the mistake of deeming himself too good for his humble employments; and yet it is a mistake as common as it is fatal. I had already seen several poor wretched mechanics, who, believing themselves to be poets, and regarding the manual occupation by which they could alone live in independence as beneath them, had become in consequence little better than mendicants—too good to work for their bread, but not too good virtually to beg it; and, looking upon them as beacons of warning, I determined that, with God's help, I should give their error a wide offing, and never associate the ideas of meanness with an honest calling, or deem myself too good to be independent. And, in the second place, as I saw that the notice, and more especially the hospitalities, of persons in the upper walks, seemed to exercise a deteriorating effect on even strong-minded men in circumstances such as mine, I resolved rather to avoid than court the attentions from this class which were now beginning to come my way. Johnson describes his "Ortogrul of Basra" as a thoughtful and meditative man; and yet he tells us, that after he had seen the palace of the Vizier, and "admired the walls hung with golden tapestry, and the floors covered with silken carpets, he despised the simple neatness of his own little habitation." And the lesson of the fiction is, I fear, too obviously exemplified in the real history of one of the strongest-minded men of the last age—Robert Burns. The poet seems to have left much of his early complacency in his humble home behind him, in the splendid mansions of the men who, while they failed worthily to patronize him, injured him by their hospitalities. I found it more difficult, however, to hold by this second resolution than by the first. As I was not large enough to be made a lion of, the invitations which came my way were usually those of real kindness; and the advances of kindness I found it impossible always to repel; and so it happened that I did at times find myself in company in which the working man might be deemed misplaced and in danger. On two several occasions, for instance, after declining previous invitations not a few, I had to spend a week at a time as the guest of my respected friend Miss Dunbar of Boath; and my native place was visited by few superior men that I had not to meet at some hospitable board. But I trust I may say, that the temptation failed to injure me; and that on such occasions I returned to my obscure employments and lowly home, grateful for the kindness I had received, but in no degree discontented with my lot.

Miss Dunbar belonged, as I have said, to a type of literary lady now well-nigh passed away, but of which we find frequent trace in the epistolary literature of the last century. The class comes before us in elegant and tasteful letters, indicative of minds imbued with literature, though mayhap not ambitious of authorship, and that show what ornaments their writers must have proved of the society to which they belonged, and what delight they must have given to the circles in which they more immediately moved. The Lady Russel, the Lady Luxborough, the Countess of Pomfret, Mrs Elizabeth Montague, &c. &c.,—names well fixed in the epistolary literature of England, though unknown in the walks of ordinary authorship—may be regarded as specimens of the class. Even in the cases in which its members did become authoresses, and produced songs and ballads instinct with genius, they seem to have had but little of the author's ambition in them; and their songs, cast carelessly upon the waters, have been found, after many days, preserved rather by accident than design. The Lady Wardlaw, who produced the noble ballad of "Hardyknute"—the Lady Ann Lindsay, who wrote "Auld Robin Gray"—the Miss Blamire, whose "Nabob" is so charming a composition, notwithstanding its unfortunately prosaic name—and the late Lady Nairne, authoress of the "Land o' the Leal," "John Tod," and the "Laird o' Cockpen"—are specimens of the class that fixed their names among the poets with apparently as little effort or design as singing birds pour forth their melodies.

The north had, in the last age, its interesting group of ladies of this type, of whom the central figure might be regarded as the late Mrs Elizabeth Rose of Kilravock, the correspondent of Burns, and the cousin and associate of Henry Mackenzie, the "Man of Feeling." Mrs Rose seems to have been a lady of a singularly fine mind—though a little touched, mayhap, by the prevailing sentimentalism of the age. The Mistress of Harley, Miss Walton, might have kept exactly such journals as hers; but the talent which they exhibited was certainly of a high order; and the feeling, though cast in a somewhat artificial mould, was, I doubt not, sincere. Portions of these journals I had an opportunity of perusing when on my visit to my friend Miss Dunbar; and there is a copy of one of them now in my possession. Another member of this group was the late Mrs Grant of Laggan—at the time when it existed unbroken, the mistress of a remote Highland manse, and known but to her personal friends, by those earlier letters which form the first half of her "Letters from the Mountains," and which, in ease and freshness, greatly surpass aught which she produced after she began her career of authorship. Not a few of her letters, and several of her poems, were addressed to my friend Miss Dunbar. Some of the other members of the group were greatly younger than Mrs Grant and the Lady of Kilravock. And of these, one of the most accomplished was the late Lady Gordon Cumming of Altyre, known to scientific men by her geologic labours among the ichthyolitic formations of Moray, and mother of the famous lion-hunter, Mr Gordon Cumming. My friend Miss Dunbar was at this time considerably advanced in life, and her health far from good. She possessed, however, a singular buoyancy of spirits, which years and frequent illness had failed to depress; and her interest and enjoyment in nature and in books remained as high as when, long before, her friend Mrs Grant had addressed her as

"Helen, by every sympathy allied,
  By love of virtue and by love of song,
Compassionate in youth and beauty's pride."

Her mind was imbued with literature, and stored with literary anecdote: she conversed with elegance, giving interest to whatever she touched; and, though she seemed never to have thought of authorship in her own behalf, she wrote pleasingly, and with great facility, in both prose and verse. Her verses, usually of a humorous cast, ran trippingly off the tongue, as if the words had dropped by some happy accident—for the arrangement bore no mark of effort—into exactly the places where they at once best brought out the writer's meaning, and addressed themselves most pleasingly to the ear. The opening stanzas of a light *jeu d'esprit* on a young naval officer engaged in a lady-killing expedition in Cromarty, dwell in my memory; and—first premising, by way of explanation, that Miss Dunbar's brother, the late Baronet of Boath, was a captain in the navy, and that the ladykiller was his first lieutenant—I shall take the liberty of giving all I remember of the piece, as a specimen of her easy style:—

"In Cromarty Bay,
As the '*Driver*' snug lay,
The Lieutenant would venture ashore;
And, a figure to cut,
From the head to the foot
He was fashion and finery all o'er.

A hat richly laced,
To the left side was placed,
Which made him look martial and bold;
His coat of true blue
Was spick and span new,
And the buttons were burnished with gold.

His neckcloth well puffed,
Which six handkerchiefs stuffed,
And in colour with snow might have vied,
Was put on with great care,
As a bait for the fair,
And the ends in a love-knot were tied." &c &c.

I greatly enjoyed my visits to this genial-hearted and accomplished lady. No chilling condescensions on her part measured out to me my distance: Miss Dunbar took at once the common ground of literary tastes and pursuits; and if I did not feel my inferiority there, she took care that I should feel it nowhere else. There was but one point on which we differed. While hospitably extending to me every facility for visiting the objects of scientific interest in her neighbourhood—such as those sand-wastes of Culbin in which an ancient barony finds burial, and the geologic sections presented by the banks of the Findhorn—she was yet desirous to fix me down to literature as my proper walk; and I, on the other hand, was equally desirous of escaping into science.

CHAPTER XXI

"He who, with pocket hammer, smites the edge
Of luckless rock or prominent stone, disguised
In weather stains, or crusted o'er by nature
With her first growths—detaching by the stroke
A chip or splinter, to resolve his doubts;
And, with that ready answer satisfied,
The substance classes by some barbarous name,
And hurries on."—WORDSWORTH.

IN the course of my two visits to Miss Dunbar, I had several opportunities of examining the sand-wastes of Culbin, and of registering some of the peculiarities which distinguish the arenaceous sub-aerial formation from the arenaceous sub-aqueous one. Of the present surface of the earth, considerably more than six millions of square miles are occupied in Africa and Asia alone by sandy deserts. With but the interruption of the narrow valley of the Nile, an enormous zone of arid sand, full nine hundred miles across, stretches from the eastern coast of Africa to within a few days' journey of the Chinese frontier: it is a belt that girdles nearly half the globe;—a vast "ocean," according to the Moors, "without water." The sandy deserts of the rainless districts of Chile are also of great extent: and there are few countries in even the higher latitudes that have not their tracts of arenaceous waste. These sandy tracts, so common in the present scene of things, could not, I argued, be restricted to the recent geologic periods. They must have existed, like all the commoner phenomena of nature, under every succeeding system in which the sun shone, and the winds blew, and ocean-beds were upheaved to the air and the light, and the waves threw upon the shore, from arenaceous sea-bottoms, their accumulations of light sand. And I was now employed in acquainting myself with the marks by which I might be able to distinguish sub-aerial from sub-aqueous formations, among the ever-recurring sandstone beds of the geologic deposits. I have spent, when thus engaged, very delightful hours amid the waste. In pursuing one's education, it is always very pleasant to get into those *forms* that are not yet introduced into any school.

One of the peculiarities of the sub-aerial formation which I at this time detected struck me as curious. On approaching, among the sand-hills, an open level space, covered thickly over with water-rolled pebbles and gravel, I was surprised to see that, dry and hot as the day was elsewhere, the little open space seemed to have been subjected to a weighty dew or smart shower. The pebbles glistened bright in the sun, and bore the darkened hue of recent wet. On examination, however, I found that the rays were reflected, not from wetted, but from polished surfaces. The light grains of sand, dashed against the pebbles by the winds during a long series of years—grain after grain repeating its minute blow, where, mayhap, millions of grains had struck before—had at length given a resinous-looking, uneven polish to all their exposed portions, while the portions covered up retained the dull unglossy coat given them of old by the agencies of friction and water. I have not heard the peculiarity described as a characteristic of the arenaceous deserts; but though it seems to have escaped notice, it will, I doubt not, be found to obtain wherever there are sands for the winds to waft along, and hard pebbles against which the grains may be propelled. In examining, many years after, a few specimens of silicified wood brought from the Egyptian desert, I at once recognised on their flinty surfaces the resinous-like gloss of the pebbles of Culbin; nor can I doubt that, if geology has its sub-aerial formations of consolidated sand, they will be found characterized by their polished pebbles. I marked several other peculiarities of the formation. In some of the abrupter sections laid open by the winds, tufts of the bent-grass (*Arundo arenaria*— common here, as in all sandy wastes) that had been buried up where they grew, might be distinctly traced, each upright in itself, but rising tuft above tuft in the steep angle of the hillock which they had originally covered. And though, from their dark colour, relieved against the lighter hue of the sand, they reminded me of the carbonaceous markings of sandstone of the Coal Measures, I recognised at least *their arrangement* as unique. It seems to be such an arrangement—sloping in the general line, but upright in each of the tufts—as could take place in only a sub-aerial formation. I observed further, that in frequent instances there occurred on the surface of the sand, around decaying tufts of the bent-grass, deeply-marked circles, as if drawn by a pair of compasses or a trainer—effects apparently of eddy winds whirling round, as on a pivot, the decayed plants; and yet further, that footprints, especially those of rabbits and birds, were not unfrequent in the waste. And as lines of stratification were, I found, distinctly preserved in the formation, I deemed it not improbable that, in cases in which high winds had arisen immediately after tracts of wet weather, and covered with sand, rapidly dried on the heights, the damp beds in the hollows, both the circular markings and the footprints might remain fixed in the strata, to tell of their origin. I found in several places, in chasms scooped out by a recent gale, pieces of the ancient soil laid bare, which had been covered up by the sand-flood nearly two centuries before. In one of the openings the marks of the ancient furrows were still discernible; in another, the thin stratum of ferruginous soil had apparently never been brought under the plough; and I found it charged with roots of the common brake (*Pteris aquilina*), in a perfect state of keeping, but black and brittle as coal. Beneath this layer of soil lay a thin deposit of the stratified gravel of what is now known as the later glacial period—the age of *osars* and moraines; and beneath all— for the underlying Old Red Sandstone of the district is not exposed amid the level wastes of Culbin—rested the boulder clay, the memorial of a time of submergence, when Scotland sat low in the sea as a wintry archipelago of islands, brushed by frequent icebergs, and when sub-arctic molluscs lived in her sounds and bays. A section of a few feet in vertical extent presented me with four distinct periods. There was, first, the period of the sand-flood, represented by the bar of pale sand; then, secondly, the period of cultivation and human occupancy, represented by the dark plough-furrowed belt of hardened soil; thirdly, there was the gravel; and, fourthly, the clay. And that shallow section exhausted the historic ages, and more; for the double band of gravel and clay belonged palpably to the geologic ages, ere man had appeared on our planet. There had been found in the locality, only a few years previous to this time, a considerable number of stone arrow-heads—some of them only partially finished, and some of them marred in the making, as if some fletcher[1] of the stone age had carried on his work on the spot; and all these memorials of a time long anterior to the first beginnings of history in the island were restricted to the stratum of hardened mould.

I carried on my researches in this—what I may term the chronological—direction, in connection with the old coast-line, which, as I have already said, is finely developed in the neighbourhood of Cromarty on both sides of the Firth, and represented along the precipices of the Sutors by its line of deep caves, into which the sea never now enters. And it, too, pressed upon me the fact of the amazing antiquity of the globe. I found that the caves hollowed by the surf—when the sea stood from fifteen to five-and-twenty feet above its present level, or, as I should perhaps rather say, when the land sat that much lower—were deeper, on the average, by about one-third, than those caves of the present coast-line that are still in the course of being hollowed by the waves. And yet the waves have been breaking against the present coast-line during the whole of the historic period. The ancient wall of Antoninus, which stretched between the Firths of Forth and Clyde, was built at its terminations with reference to the existing levels; and ere Cæsar landed in Britain, St Michael's Mount was connected with the mainland, as now, by a narrow neck of beach laid bare by the ebb, across which, according to Diodorus Siculus,[2] the Cornish miners used to drive,

[1] Arrow-maker.
[2] Diodorus calls it "A certain island lying in front of Britain called Ictis." Its identity is matter of dispute, but the weight of opinion seems to be in favour of one of the Kentish islands, such as Thanet, whose relation to the land at the time would suit the description, while that of St Michael's Mount probably would not.

at low water, their carts laden with tin. If the sea has stood for two thousand six hundred years against the present coast-line— and no geologist would fix his estimate of the term lower—then must it have stood against the old line, ere it could have excavated caves one-third deeper than the modern ones, three thousand nine hundred years. And both sums united more than exhaust the Hebrew chronology. Yet what a mere beginning of geologic history does not the epoch of the old coast-line form! It is but a starting-point from the recent period. Not a single shell seems to have become extinct during the last six thousand years. The organisms which I found deeply embedded in the soil beneath the old coast-line were exactly those which still live in our seas; and I have been since told by Mr Smith of Jordanhill, one of our highest authorities on the subject, that he detected only three shells of the period with which he was not familiar as existing forms, and that he subsequently met with all three, in his dredging expeditions, still alive. The six thousand years of human history form but a portion of the geologic day that is passing over us: they do not extend into the *yesterday* of the globe, far less touch the myriads of ages spread out beyond. Dr Chalmers had taught, more than a quarter of a century previous to this time, that the Scriptures do not fix the antiquity of the earth. "If they fix anything," he said, "it is only the antiquity of the human species." The Doctor, though not practically a geologist at the time, had shrewdly weighed both the evidence adduced and the scientific character of the men who adduced it, and arrived at a conclusion, in consequence, which may now be safely regarded as the final one. I, on the other hand, who knew comparatively little about the standing of the geologists, or the weight which ought to attach to their testimony, based my findings regarding the vast antiquity of the earth on exactly the data on which they had founded theirs; and the more my acquaintance with the geologic deposits has since extended, the firmer have my convictions on the subject become, and the more pressing and inevitable have I felt the ever-growing demand for longer and yet longer periods for their formation. As certainly as the sun is the centre of our system, must our earth have revolved around it for millions of years. An American theologian, the author of a little book entitled the "Epoch of Creation," in doing me the honour of referring to my convictions on this subject, states, that I "betray indubitable tokens of being spell-bound to the extent of infatuation, by the foregone conclusion of" my "theory concerning the high antiquity of the earth, and the succession of animal and vegetable creations." He adds further, in an eloquent sentence, a page and a half long, that had I first studied and credited my Bible, I would have failed to believe in successive creations and the geologic chronology. I trust, however, I may say I did first study and believe my Bible. But such is the structure of the human mind, that, save when blinded by passion or warped by prejudice, it must yield an involuntary consent to the force of evidence; and I can now no more refuse believing, in opposition to respectable theologians such as Mr Granville Penn, Professor Moses Stuart, and Mr Eleazar Lord, that the earth is of an antiquity incalculably vast, than I can refuse believing, in opposition to still more respectable theologians, such as St Augustine, Lactantius, and Turretine, that it has antipodes, and moves round the sun. And further, of this, men such as the Messrs Penn, Stuart, and Lord may rest assured, that what I believe in this matter now, all theologians, even the weakest, will be content to believe fifty years hence.

Sometimes a chance incident taught me an interesting geological lesson. At the close of the year 1830, a tremendous hurricane from the south and west, unequalled in the north of Scotland, from at least the time of the great hurricane of Christmas 1806, blew down in a single hour four thousand full-grown trees on the Hill of Cromarty. The vast gaps and avenues which it opened in the wood above could be seen from the town; and no sooner had it begun to take off than I set out for the scene of its ravages. I had previously witnessed, from a sheltered hollow of the old coast-line, the extraordinary appearance of the sea. It would seem as if the very violence of the wind had kept down the waves. It brushed off their tops as they were rising, and swept along the spray in one dense cloud, white as driving snow, that rose high into the air as it receded from the shore, and blotted out along the horizon the line between sky and water. As I approached the wood, I met two poor little girls of from eight to ten years, coming running and crying along the road in a paroxysm of consternation; but, gathering heart on seeing me, they stood to tell that when the storm was at its worst they were in the midst of the falling trees. Setting out for the Hill on the first rising of the wind, in the expectation of a rich harvest of withered boughs, they had reached one of its most exposed ridges just as the gale had attained to its extreme height, and the trees began to crash down around them. Their little tear-bestained countenances still continued to show how extreme the agony of their terror had been. They would run, they said, for a few paces in one direction, until some huge pine would come roaring down, and block up their path; when, turning with a shriek, they would run for a few paces in another; and then, terrified by a similar interruption, again strike off in a third. At length, after passing nearly an hour in the extremest peril, and in at least all the fear which the circumstances justified, they succeeded in making their way unhurt to the outer skirts of the wood. Bewick[1] would have found in the incident the subject of a vignette that would have told its own story. In getting into the thick of the trees, I was struck by the extraordinary character of the scene presented. In some places, greatly more than half their number lay stretched upon the ground. On the more exposed prominences of the Hill, scarce a tree was left standing for acres together: they covered the slopes; tree stretched over tree like tiles on a roof, with here and there some shattered trunk whose top had been blown off, and carried by the hurricane some fifteen or twenty yards away, leaning in sad ruin over its fallen comrades. What, however, formed the most striking, because less expected, parts of the scene, were the tall walls of turf that stood up everywhere among the fallen trees, like the ruins of dismantled

[1] The famous engraver on wood of natural subjects (died 1828).

cottages. The granitic gneiss of the Hill is covered by a thick deposit of the red boulder clay of the district, and the clay, in turn, by a thin layer of vegetable mould, interlaced in every direction by the tree roots, which, arrested in their downward progress by the stiff clay, are restricted to the upper layer. And, save where here and there I found some tree snapped across in the midst, or divested of its top, all the others had yielded at the line between the boulder clay and the soil, and had torn up, as they fell, vast walls of the felted turf, from fifteen to twenty feet in length, by from ten to twelve feet in height. There were quite enough of these walls standing up among the prostrate trees, to have formed a score of the eastern Sultan's ruined villages; and they imparted to the scene one of its strangest features. I have mentioned in an early chapter that the Hill had its dense thickets, which, from the gloom that brooded in their recesses even at mid-day, were known to the boys of the neighbouring town as the "dungeons." They had now fared, however, in this terrible overturn, like dungeons elsewhere in times of revolution, and were all swept away; and piles of prostrate trees—in some instances ten or twelve in a single heap—marked where they had stood. In several localities, where they fell over swampy hollows, or where deep-seated springs came gushing to the light, I found the water partially dammed up, and saw that were they to be left to cumber the ground as the debris of forests destroyed by hurricanes in the earlier ages of Scottish history would certainly have been left, the deep shade and the moisture could not have failed to induce a total change in the vegetation. I marked, too, the fallen trees all lying one way, in the direction of the wind; and the thought at once struck me, that in this recent scene of devastation I had the origin of full one-half of our Scottish mosses exemplified. Some of the mosses of the south date from the times of Roman invasion. Their lower tiers of trunks bear the mark of the Roman axe; and in some instances, the sorely wasted axe itself—a narrow, oblong tool, somewhat resembling that of the American backwoodsman—has been found sticking in the buried stump. Some of our other mosses are of still more modern origin: there exist Scottish mosses that seem to have been formed when Robert the Bruce felled the woods and wasted the country of John of Lorn. But of the others, not a few have palpably owed their origin to violent hurricanes, such as the one which on this occasion ravaged the Hill of Cromarty. The trees which form their lower stratum are broken across, or torn up by the roots, *and their trunks all lie one way*. Much of the interest of a science such as geology must consist in the ability of making dead deposits represent living scenes; and from this hurricane I was enabled to conceive, pictorially, if I may so express myself, of the origin of those comparatively recent deposits of Scotland which, formed almost exclusively of vegetable matter, contain, with rude works of art, and occasionally remains of the early human inhabitants of the country, skeletons of the wolf, the bear, and the beaver, with horns of the *bos primigenius*[1] and *bos longifrons*,[2] and of a gigantic variety of red deer, unequalled in size by animals of the same species in these latter ages.

Occasionally I was enabled to vivify in this way even the ancient deposits of the Lias, with their vast abundance of cephalopodous mollusca—belemnites, ammonites, and nautili. My friend of the Cave had become parish schoolmaster of Nigg: and his hospitable dwelling furnished me with an excellent centre for exploring the geology of the parish, especially its Liassic deposits at Shandwick, with their huge gryphites and their numerous belemnites, of at least two species, comparatively rare at Eathie—the *belemnite abreviatus* and *belemnite elongatus*. I had learned that these curious shells once formed part of the internal framework of a mollusc more nearly akin to the cuttle-fishes of the present day than aught else that now exists; and the cuttle-fishes—not rare in at least one of their species (*loligo vulgare*) in the Firth of Cromarty—I embraced every opportunity of examining. I have seen from eighteen to twenty individuals of this species enclosed at once in the inner chamber of one of our salmon-

[1] The ancient European wild ox or Urus or Aurochs described by Cæsar; considerably larger than modern cattle: now extinct.
[2] The "Celtic" shorthorn, probably the original of the domesticated breeds.

wears. The greater number of these shoals I have ordinarily found dead, and tinged with various shades of green, blue, and yellow—for it is one of the characteristics of the creature to assume, when passing into a state of decomposition, a succession of brilliant colours; but I have seen from six to eight individuals of their number still alive in a little pool beside the nets, and still retaining their original pink tint, freckled with red. And these I have observed, as my shadow fell across their little patch of water, darting from side to side in panic terror within the narrow confines, emitting ink at almost every dart, until the whole pool had become a deep solution of sepia. Some of my most interesting recollections of the cuttle-fish are associated, however, with the capture and dissection of a single specimen. The creature, in swimming, darts through the water much in the manner that a boy slides down an ice-crusted declivity, feet foremost;—the lower or nether extremities go first, and the head behind; it follows its tail, instead of being followed by it: and this curious peculiarity in its mode of progression, though, of course, on the whole, the mode best adapted to its conformation and instincts, sometimes proves fatal to it in calm weather, when not a ripple breaks upon the pebbles, to warn that the shore is near. An enemy appears: the creature ejects its cloud of ink, like a sharp-shooter discharging his rifle ere he retreats; and then, darting away, tail foremost, under cover of the cloud, it grounds itself high upon the beach, and perishes there. I was walking, one very calm day, along the Cromarty shore, a little to the west of the town, when I heard a peculiar sound—a *squelch*, if I may employ such a word—and saw that a large loligo, fully a foot and a half in length, had thrown itself high and dry upon the beach. I laid hold of it by its sheath or sack; and the loligo, in turn, laid hold of the pebbles, apparently to render its abduction as difficult as possible, just as I have seen a boy, when borne off against his will by one stronger than himself, grasping fast to door-posts and furniture. The pebbles were hard and smooth, but the creature raised them very readily with his suckers. I subjected one of my hands to its grasp, and it seized fast hold; but though the suckers were still employed, it made use of them on a different principle. Around the circular rim of each there is a fringe of minute thorns, hooked somewhat like those of the wild rose. In clinging to the hard polished pebbles, these were overlapped by a fleshy membrane, much in the manner that the cushions of a cat's paw overlap its claws when the animal is in a state of tranquillity; and by means of the projecting membrane, the hollow interior was rendered air-tight, and the vacuum completed: but in dealing with the hand—a soft substance—the thorns were laid bare, like the claws of a cat when stretched out in anger, and at least a thousand minute prickles were fixed in the skin at once. They failed to penetrate it, for they were short, and individually not strong; but, acting together by hundreds, they took at least a very firm hold.

What follows may be deemed barbarous; but the men who gulp down at a sitting half-a-hundred live oysters to gratify their taste, may surely forgive me the destruction of a single mollusc to gratify my curiosity! I cut open the sack of the creature with a sharp penknife, and laid bare the viscera. What a sight for Harvey, when prosecuting, in the earlier stages, his grand discovery of the circulation! *There*, in the centre, was the yellow muscular heart, propelling into the transparent, tubular arteries, the *yellow* blood. Beat—beat—beat:—I could see the whole as in a glass model; and all I lacked were powers of vision nice enough to enable me to detect the fluid passing through the minuter arterial branches, and then returning by the veins to the *two* other hearts of the creature; for, strange to say, it is furnished with three. There in the midst I saw the yellow heart, and, lying altogether detached from it, two other deep-coloured hearts at the sides. I cut a little deeper. *There* was the gizzard-like stomach, filled with fragments of minute mussel and crab shells; and *there*, inserted in the spongy, conical, yellowish-coloured liver, and somewhat resembling in form a Florence flask, was the ink-bag distended, with its deep dark sepia—the identical pigment sold under that name in our colour-shops, and so extensively used in landscape drawing by the limner.

I then dissected and laid open the circular or ring-like brain that surrounds the creature's parrot-like beak, as if its *thinking* part had no other vocation than simply to take care of the mouth and its pertinents—almost the sole employment, however, of not a few brains of a considerably higher order. I next laid open the huge eyes. They were curious organs, more simple in their structure than those of the true fishes, but admirably adapted, I doubt not, for the purposes of seeing. A camera obscura may be described as consisting of two parts—a lens in front, and a darkened chamber behind; but in the eyes of fishes, as in the brute and human eye, we find a third part added; there is a lens in the middle, a darkened chamber behind, and a lighted chamber, or rather vestibule, in front. Now, this lighted vestibule—the cornea—is wanting in the eye of the cuttle-fish. The lens is placed in front, and the darkened chamber behind. The construction of the organ is that of a common camera obscura. I found something worthy of remark, too, in the peculiar style in which the chamber is darkened. In the higher animals it may be described as a chamber hung with black velvet—the *pigmentum nigrum* which covers it is of the deepest black; but in the cuttle-fish it is a chamber hung with velvet, not of a black, but of a dark purple hue—the *pigmentum nigrum* is of a purplish red colour. There is something interesting in marking this first departure from an invariable condition of eyes of the more perfect structure, and in then tracing the peculiarity downwards through almost every shade of colour, to the emerald-like eye-specks of the pecten, and the still more rudimentary red eye-specks of the star-fish. After examining the eyes, I next laid open, in all its length, from the neck to the point of the sack, the dorsal bone of the creature—its internal shell, I should rather say, for bone it has none. The form of the shell in this species is that of a feather equally developed in the web on both sides. It gives rigidity to the body, and furnishes the muscles with a fulcrum; and we find it composed like all other *shells*, of a mixture of animal matter and carbonate of lime. Such was the lesson taught me in a single walk; and I have recorded it at some length. The subject

446

of it, the loligo, has been described by some of our more distinguished naturalists, such as Kirby in his Bridgewater Treatise, as "one of the most wonderful works of the creator"; and the reader will perhaps remember how fraught with importance to natural science an incident similar to the one related proved in the life of the youthful Cuvier. It was when passing his twenty-second year on the sea-coast, near Fiquainville, that this greatest of modern naturalists was led, by finding a cuttle-fish stranded on the beach, which he afterwards dissected, to study the anatomy and character of the mollusca. To me, however, the lesson served merely to vivify the dead deposits of the Oolitic system, as represented by the Lias of Cromarty and Ross. The middle and later ages of the great secondary division were peculiarly ages of the cephalopodous molluscs: their belemnites, ammonites, nautili,[1] baculites, hamites, turrilites, and scaphites, belonged to the great natural class—singularly rich in its extinct orders and genera, though comparatively poor in its existing ones—which we find represented by the cuttle-fish; and when engaged in disinterring the remains of the earlier-born members of the family— ammonites, belemnites, and nautili—from amid the shales of Eathie or the mud-stones of Shandwick, the incident of the loligo has enabled me to conceive of them, not as mere dead remains, but as the living inhabitants of primeval seas, stirred by the diurnal tides, and lighted up by the sun.

When pursuing my researches amid the deposits of the Lias, I was conducted to an interesting discovery. There are two great systems[2] of hills in the north of Scotland—an older and a newer— that bisect each other like the furrows of a field that had first been ploughed across and then diagonally. The diagonal furrows, as the last drawn, are still very entire. The great Caledonian Valley, open

[1] A family of cuttle-fish. The rest are varieties of ammonites having the shell straight (*baculites*), or bent in a crook at both ends (*hamites*) or turret-like (*turrilites*), or bent into boat-shape (*scaphites*).

[2] The idea underlying this explanation of the mountain system of the Highlands has long been discarded. That system has been carved by streams and weathering influences out of a plateau representing the base of an ancient true mountain range, and is not the result of any vertical uplifts.

from sea to sea, is the most remarkable of these; but the parallel valleys of the Nairn, of the Findhorn, and of the Spey, are all well-defined furrows; nor are the mountain ridges which separate them less definitely ranged in continuous lines. The ridges and furrows of the earlier ploughing are, on the contrary, as might be anticipated, broken and interrupted: the effacing plough has passed over them: and yet there are certain localities in which we find the fragments of this earlier system sufficiently entire to form one of the main features of the landscape. In passing through the upper reaches of the Moray Firth, and along the Caledonian Valley, the cross furrows may be seen branching off to the west, and existing as the valleys of Loch Fleet, of the Dornoch Firth, of the Firth of Cromarty, of the Bay of Munlochy, of the Firth of Beauly, and, as we enter the Highlands proper, as Glen Urquhart, Glen Morrison, Glen Garry, Loch Arkaig, and Loch Eil. The diagonal system—represented by the great valley itself, and known as the system of Ben Nevis and the Ord of Caithness in our own country and, according, to De Beamount, as that of Mount Pilate and Coté d'Or on the Continent—was upheaved after the close of the Oolitic ages. It was not until at least the period of the Weald that its "hills had been formed and its mountains brought forth;" and in the line of the Moray Firth the Lias and Oolite lie uptilted, at steep angles, against the sides of its long ranges of precipice. It is not so easy determining the age of the older system. No formation occurs in the north of Scotland between the Lias and the Old Red Sandstone; the vast Carboniferous, Permian, and Triassic deposits are represented by a wide gap; and all that can be said regarding the older hills is, that they disturbed and bore up with them the Old Red Sandstone; but that as there lay at their bases, at the time of their upheaval, no more modern rock to be disturbed, it seems impossible definitely to fix their era. Neither does there appear among their estuaries or valleys any trace of the Oolitic deposits. Existing, in all probability, during even the times of the Lias, as the sub-aerial framework of Oolitic Scotland—as the framework on which the Oolitic vegetables grew—no deposit of the system could of course have taken place over them. I had not yet, however, formed any very definite idea regarding the two systems, or ascertained that they belonged apparently to a different time; and finding the Lias upheaved against the steeper sides of the Moray Firth—one of the huge furrows of the more modern system—I repeatedly sought to find it uptilted also against the shores of the Cromarty Firth—one of the furrows of the greatly more ancient one. I had, however, prosecuted the search in a somewhat desultory manner; and as in the autumn of 1830 a pause of a few days took place in my professional labours between the completing of one piece of work and the commencement of another, I resolved on devoting the time to a thorough survey of the Cromarty Firth, in the hope of detecting the Lias. I began my search at the granitic gneiss of the Hill, and, proceeding westwards, passed in succession, in the ascending order, over the uptilted beds of the lower Old Red Sandstone, from the Great Conglomerate base of the system, till I reached the middle member of the deposit, which consists, in this locality, of alternate beds of limestone, sandstone, and stratified clay, and which we find represented in Caithness by the extensively developed flag-stones. And then, the rock disappearing, I passed over a pebbly beach mottled with boulders; and in a little bay not half a mile distant from the town, I again found the rock laid bare.

I had long before observed that the rock rose to the surface in this little bay; I had even employed, when a boy, pieces of its stratified clay as slate-pencil; but I had yet failed minutely to examine it. I was now, however, struck by its resemblance, in all save colour, to the Lias. The strata lay at a low angle: they were composed of an argillaceous shale, and abounded in limestone nodules; and, save that both shale and nodules bore, instead of the deep Liassic grey, an olivaceous tint, I might have almost supposed I had fallen on a continuation of some of the Eathie beds. I laid open a nodule with a blow of the hammer, and my heart leaped up when I saw that it enclosed an organism. A dark, ill-defined, bituminous mass occupied the centre; but I could distinguish what seemed to be spines and small ichthyic bones projecting from its edges; and when I subjected them to the scrutiny of the glass, unlike those mere chance resemblances which sometimes deceive for a moment the eye, the more distinct and unequivocal did their forms become. I laid open a second nodule. It contained a group of glittering rhomboidal scales, with a few cerebral plates, and a jaw bristling with teeth. A third nodule also supplied its organism, in a well-defined ichthyolite, covered with minute, finely-striated scales, and furnished with a sharp spine on the anterior edge of every fin. I eagerly wrought on, and disinterred, in the course of a single tide, specimens enough to cover a museum table; and it was with intense delight that, as the ripple of the advancing tide was rising against the pebbles, and covering up the ichthyolitic beds, I carried them to the higher slopes of the beach, and, seated on a boulder, began carefully to examine them in detail with a common botanist's microscope. But not a plate, spine, or scale, could I detect among their organisms, identical with the ichthyic remains of the Lias. I had got amid the remains of an entirely different and incalculably more ancient creation. My new-found organisms represented, not the first, but merely the second age of vertebrate existence on our planet; but as the remains of the earlier age exist as the mere detached teeth and spines of placoids,[1] which, though they give full evidence of the *existence* of the fishes to which they belong, throw scarce any light on their structure, it is from the ganoids of this second age that the palaeontologist can with certainty know under what peculiarities of form, and associated with what varieties of mechanism, vertebral life existed in the earlier ages of the world. In my new-found deposit—to which I soon added, however, within the limits of the parish, some six or eight deposits more, all charged with the same ichthyic remains—I found I had work enough before me for the patient study of years.

[1] Fish having long tubercles or detached plates bearing spines, e.g. Sharks.

CHAPTER XXII

"They lay aside their private cares,
To mend the Kirk and State affairs;
They'll talk o' patronage and priests,
Wi' kindling fury in their breasts;
Or tell what new taxation's comin',
An' ferlie at the folk in *Lon'on*."—BURNS.

WE had, as I have already stated, no Dissenters in the parish of Cromarty. What were known as the Haldanes' people had tried to effect a lodgment among us in the town, but without success: in the course of several years they failed to acquire more than six or eight members; and these were not of the more solid people, but marked as an eccentric class, fond of argument, and possessed by a rage for the novel and the extreme. The leading teachers of the party were a retired English merchant, and an ex-blacksmith, who, quitting the forge in middle life, had pursued the ordinary studies to no very great effect, and become a preacher. And both were, I believe, good men, but by no means prudent missionaries. They said very strong things against the Church of Scotland, in a place where the Church of Scotland was much respected; and it was observed, that while they did not do a great deal to convert the irreligious to Christianity, they were exceedingly zealous in their endeavours to make the religious Baptists. Much to my annoyance in my younger days, they used to waylay Uncle Sandy on his return from the Hill, on evenings when I had gone to get some lessons from him regarding sand-worms, or razor-fish, or the sea-hare, and engage him in long controversies about infant baptism and Church Establishments. The matters which they discussed were greatly too high for me, nor was I by any means an attentive listener; but I picked up enough to know that Uncle Sandy, though a man of slow speech, held stiffly to the Establishment scheme of Knox, and the defence of Presbyterian-

451

ism; and it did not require any particularly nice perceptive powers to observe that both his antagonists and himself used at times to get pretty warm, and to talk tolerably loud—louder, at least, than was at all necessary in the quiet evening woods. I remember, too, that in urging him to quit the National Church for theirs, they usually employed language borrowed from the Revelations; and that, calling his Church *Babylon*, they bade him come out of her, that he might not be a partaker of her plagues. Uncle Sandy had seen too much of the world, and read and heard too much of controversy, to be out of measure shocked by the phrase; but with a decent farmer of the parish the hard words of the proselytizers did them a mischief. The retired merchant had urged him to quit the Establishment; and the farmer had replied by asking, in his simplicity, whether he thought he ought to leave his Church to sink in that way? "Yes," exclaimed the merchant, with great emphasis; "leave her to sink to her place—the lowest hell!" This was terrible: the decent farmer opened his huge eyes at hearing what he deemed a bold blasphemy. The Church of which the Baptist spoke was, in Cromarty at least, the Church of the *outed*[1] Mr Hugh Anderson, who gave up his all in the time of the persecution, for conscience' sake; it was the Church of Mr Gordon, whose ministry had been so signally countenanced during the period of the great revival;[2] it was the Church of devout Mr Monro, and of worthy Mr Smith, and of many a godly elder and God-fearing member who had held by Christ the Head; and yet here was it denounced as a Church whose true place was hell. The farmer turned away, sick of the controversy; and the imprudent speech of the retired merchant flew like wildfire over the parish. "Surely," says Bacon, "princes have need, in tender matters and ticklish times, to beware what they say, especially in those short speeches which fly about like darts, and are thought to be shot out of their secret intentions." Princes are, however, not the only men

[1] Deprived of his benefice in the seventeenth century for not accepting the jurisdiction of bishops instituted by Charles II.

[2] Roughly covering the years 1740-1746, but attaining its height at different years in different parishes.

who would do well to beware of short speeches. The short speech of the merchant ruined the Baptist cause in Cromarty; and the two missionaries might, on its delivery, have just done, if they but knew the position to which it reduced them, what they were content to do a few years after—pack up their movables and quit the place.

Having for years no antagonists to contend with outside the pale of the Establishment, it was of course natural that we should find opponents within. But during the incumbency of Mr Smith—the minister of the parish for the first one-and-twenty years of my life—even these were wanting; and we passed a very quiet time, undisturbed by controversy of any kind, political or ecclesiastical. Nor were the first few years of Mr Stewart's incumbency less quiet. The Catholic Relief Bill was a pebble cast into the pool, but a very minute one; and the ripple which it raised caused scarce any agitation. Mr Stewart did not see his way clearly through all the difficulties of the measure; but, influenced in part by some of his brethren in the neighbourhood, he at length made up his mind to petition against it; and to his petition, praying that no concessions should be made to the Papists, greatly more than nineteen-twentieths of the male parishioners affixed their names. The few individuals who kept aloof were chiefly lads of an extra-liberal turn, devoid, like most extreme politicians, of the ordinary ecclesiastical sympathies of their country-folk; and as I cultivated no acquaintance with them, and was more ecclesiastical than political in my leanings, I had the satisfaction of finding myself standing, in opposition to all my friends, on the Catholic Relief measure, in a respectable minority of one. Even Uncle Sandy, after some little demur, and an explosion against the Irish Establishment, set off and signed the petition. I failed, however, to see that I was in the wrong. With the two great facts of the Irish Union and the Irish Church before me, I could not petition against Roman Catholic Emancipation. I felt, too, that were I myself a Roman Catholic, I would listen to no Protestant argument until what I held to be justice had first been done me. I would have at once inferred that a religion associated with what I deemed injustice was a false, not a true, religion; and, on the strength of the inference, would have rejected it without further inquiry; and could I fail to believe that what I myself would have done in the circumstances, many Roman Catholics were actually doing? And believing I could defend my position, which was certainly not an obtrusive one, and was at times assailed in conversation by my friends, in a way that showed, as I thought, they did not understand it, I sat down and wrote an elaborate letter on the subject, addressed to the editor of the *Inverness Courier*, in which, as I afterwards found, I was happy enough to anticipate in some points the line taken up, in his famous emancipation speech, by a man whom I had early learned to recognise as the greatest and wisest of Scottish ministers—the late Dr Chalmers. On glancing over my letter, however, and then looking around me on the good men among my townsfolk—including my uncle and my minister—with whom it would have the effect of placing me in a more decided antagonism than any mere refusal to sign their petition, I resolved, instead of dropping it into the post office, to drop it into the fire, which I accordingly did; and so the matter took end; and what I had to say in my own defence, and in that of emancipation, was in consequence never said.

This, however, was but the mere shadow of a controversy; it was merely a possible controversy, strangled in the birth. But some three years after, the parish was agitated by a dire ecclesiastical dispute, which set us all together by the ears. The place had not only its parish church, but also its Gaelic chapel, which, though on the ordinary foundation of a chapel of ease, was endowed, and under the patronage of the crown. It had been built about sixty years previous, by a benevolent proprietor of the lands of Cromarty—"George Ross, the Scotch agent"—whom Junius ironically described as the "trusted friend and worthy confidant of Lord Mansfield;" and who, whatever the satirist may have thought of either, was in reality a man worthy the friendship of the accomplished and philosophic lawyer. Cromarty, originally a

Lowland settlement, had had from the Reformation down till the latter quarter of the last century no Gaelic place of worship. On the breaking-up of the feudal system, however, the Highlanders began to drop into the place in quest of employment; and George Ross, affected by their uncared-for religious condition, built for them, at his own expense, a chapel, and had influence enough to get an endowment for its minister from the Government. Government retained the patronage in its own hands; and as the Highlanders consisted of but labourers and farm servants, and the workers in a hempen manufactory, and had no manner of influence, their wishes were not always consulted in the choice of a minister. About the time of Mr Stewart's appointment, through the late Sir Robert Peel, who had courteously yielded to the wishes of the English congregation, the Gaelic people had got a minister presented to them whom they would scarcely have chosen for themselves, but who had, notwithstanding, popular points about him. Though not of high talent, he was frank and genial, and visited often, and conversed much; and at length the Highlanders came to regard him as the very *beau-idéal* of a minister. He and Mr Stewart belonged to the antagonist parties in the Church. Mr Stewart took his place in the old Presbyterian section, under Chalmers and Thomson; while the Gaelic minister held by Drs Inglis and Cook: and so thoroughly were their respective congregations influenced by their views, that at the Disruption in 1843, while considerably more than nine-tenths of the English-speaking parishioners closed their connection with the State, and became Free Church men, at least an equal proportion of the chapel Highlanders clung to the Establishment. Curiously enough, however, there arose a controversy between the congregations at this time, in which each seemed, in relation to the general question at issue, to take the part proper to the other.

I do not think the English congregation were in any degree jealous of the Gaelic one. The English contained the *élite* of the place—all its men of property and influence, from its merchants and heritors, down to the humblest of the class that afterwards became its ten-pound franchise-holders; whereas the Gaelic people were, as I have said, simply poor labourers and weavers: and if the sense of superiority did at times show itself on the more potent side, it was only among the lowlier people of the English congregation. When, on a certain occasion, a stranger fell asleep in the middle of one of Mr Stewart's best sermons, and snored louder than was seemly, an individual beside him was heard muttering, in a low whisper that the man ought to be sent up to "*the Gaelic*," for he was not fit to be among them; and there might be a few other similar manifestations; but the parties were not on a sufficiently equal level to enact the part of those rival congregations that are for ever bemoaning the shortcomings each of the other, and that in their days of fasting and humiliation have the sins of their neighbours at least as strongly before them as their own. But if the English congregation were not jealous of the Gaelic one, the Gaelic one, as was perhaps natural in their circumstances, were, I am afraid, jealous of the English: they were poor people, they used sometimes to say, but their souls were as precious as those of richer folk, and they were surely as well entitled to have their just rights as the English people—axioms which, I believe, no one in the other congregation disputed, or even canvassed at all. We were, however, all roused one morning to consider the case, by learning that on the previous day the minister of the Gaelic chapel had petitioned the Presbytery of the district, either to be assigned a parish within the bounds of the parish of Cromarty, or to have the charge erected into a collegiate one, and his half of it, of course, rendered co-ordinate with Mr Stewart's.

The English people were at once very angry, and very much alarmed. As the two congregations were scattered all over the same piece of territory, it would be impossible to cut it up into two parishes, without separating between a portion of Mr Stewart's people and their minister, and making them the parishioners of a man whom they had not yet learned to like; and, on the other hand, by erecting the charge into a collegiate one, the minister whom they had not yet learned to like would acquire as real a jurisdiction over them as that possessed by the minister of their choice. Or—as the case was somewhat quaintly stated by one of themselves—by the one alternative "the Gaelic man would become whole minister to the half of them, and by the other, half minister to the whole of them." And so they determined on making a vigorous resistance. Mr Stewart himself, too, liked the move of his neighbour the Gaelic minister exceedingly ill. He was not desirous, he said, to have a colleague thrust upon him in his charge, to keep him right on Moderate principles—a benefit for which he had not bargained when he accepted the presentation; nor yet, as the other alternative, did he wish to see his living child, the parish, divided into two, and the half of it given to the strange claimant that was not its parent. There was another account, too, on which he disliked the movement: the two great parties in the Church were equally represented at this time in the Presbytery;— they had their three members a-piece; and he, of course, saw that the introduction of the Gaelic minister into it would have the effect of casting the balance in favour of Moderatism. And so, as both minister and people were equally in earnest, counter petitions were soon got up, praying the Presbytery, as a first step in the process, that copies of the Gaelic minister's document should be served upon them. The Presbytery decided, in terms of their prayer, that copies should be served; and the Gaelic minister, on the somewhat extreme ground that the people had no right to appear in the business at all, appealed to the General Assembly. And so the people had next to petition that venerable court in behalf of what they deemed their imperilled rights; while the Gaelic congregation, under the full impression that their over-bearing English neighbours were treating them "as if they had no souls," got up a counter petition, virtually to the effect that the parish might be either cut in two, and the half of it given to their minister, or that he might be at least made second minister to every man in it. The minister, however, finding at the General Assembly that the ecclesiastical party on whose support he had relied were opposed *in toto* to the erection of chapels of ease into regular charges, and that the peculiarities of the case were such as to cut off all chance of his being supported by their opponents, fell from his appeal, and the case was never called in Court. Some of our Cromarty fisher-folk, who were staunch on the English side, though they could not quite see the merits, had rather a different version of the business. "The Gaelic man had no sooner entered the Kirk o' the General Assembly," they said, "than the maister of the Assembly rose, and, speaking very rough, said, 'Ye contrarious rascal, what tak's you here? What are ye aye troubling that decent lad Mr Stewart for? I'm sure he's no meddling wi' you! Get about your business, ye contrarious rascal!'"

I took an active part in this controversy; wrote petitions and statements for my brother parishioners, with paragraphs for the local newspapers, and a long letter for the *Caledonian Mercury*, in reply to a tissue of misrepresentation which appeared in that print, from the pen of one of the Gaelic minister's legal agents; and, finally, I replied to a pamphlet by the same hand, which, though miserable as a piece of writing—for it resembled no other composition ever produced, save, mayhap, a very badly-written law paper—contained statements which I deemed it necessary to meet. And such were my first attempts in the rough field of ecclesiastical controversy—a field into which inclination would never have led me, but which has certainly lain very much in my way, and in which I have spent many a laborious hour. My first pieces were rather stiffly written, somewhat on the perilous model of Junius; but as it was hardly possible to write so ill as my opponent, I could appeal to even his friends whether it was quite right of him to call me illiterate and untaught, in prose so much worse than my own. Chiefly by getting the laughers now and then on my side, I succeeded in making him angry; and he replied to my jokes by *calling names*—a phrase, by the way, which, forgetting his Watts' Hymns, and failing to consult his Johnson, he characterized as not English. I was, he said, a "shallow, pretending ninny;" an "impudent, illiterate lad;" "a fanatic" and a "frantic person;" the "low underling of a faction," and "Peter

458

the Hermit;" and, finally, as the sum-total of the whole, he assured me that I stood in *his* "estimation the most ignoble and despised in the whole range of the human species." This was frightful! but I not only outlived it all, but learned, I fear, after in this way first tasting blood, to experience a rather too keen delight in the anger of an antagonist. I may add, that when, some two or three years after the period of this controversy, the General Assembly admitted what were known as the Parliamentary ministers, and the ministers of chapels of ease, to a seat in the church courts, neither my townsmen nor myself saw aught to challenge in the arrangement. It contained none of the elements which had provoked our hostility in the Cromarty chapel case: it did not make over the people of one minister to the charge of another, whom they would never have chosen for themselves; but, without encroaching on popular rights, equalized, on the Presbyterian scheme, the standing of ministers and the claims of congregations.

The next matter which engaged my townsfolk was a considerably more serious one. When, in 1831, cholera first threatened the shores of Britain, the Bay of Cromarty was appointed by Government one of the quarantine ports; and we became familiar with the sight, at first deemed sufficiently startling, of fleets of vessels lying in the upper roadstead, with the yellow flag waving from their mast-tops. The disease, however, failed to find its way ashore; and, when, in the summer of the following year, it was introduced into the north of Scotland, it went stalking around the town and parish for several months, without visiting either. It greatly more than decimated the villages of Portmahomak and Inver, and bore heavily on the parishes of Nigg and Urquhart, with the towns of Inverness, Nairn, Avoch, Dingwall, and Rosemarkie; in fine, the quarantine seaport town that seemed at first to be most in danger from the disease, appeared latterly to be almost the only place of any size in the locality exempted from its ravages. It approached, however, alarmingly near. The opening of the Cromarty Firth is little more than a mile across; a glass of the ordinary power enables one to count every pane in the windows of the dwellings that mottle its northern shore, and to distinguish their inhabitants; and yet among these dwellings cholera was raging; and we could see, in at least one instance, a dead body borne forth by two persons on a hand-barrow, and buried in a neighbouring sand-bank. Stories, too, of the sad fate of individuals with whom the townsfolk were acquainted, and who had resided in well-known localities, told among them with powerful effect. Such was the general panic in the infected places, that the bodies of the dead were no longer carried to the churchyard, but huddled up in solitary holes and corners; and the pictures suggested to the fancy, of familiar faces lying uncoffined in the ground beside some lonely wood, or in some dark morass or heathy moor, were fraught to many with a terror stronger than that of death. We knew that the corpse of a young robust fisherman, who used occasionally to act as one of the Cromarty ferrymen, and with whose appearance, in consequence, every one was familiar, lay festering in a sand-bank; that the iron frame of a brawny blacksmith was decomposing in a mossy hole beside a thorn-bush; that half the inhabitants of the little fishing village of Inver were strewn in shallow furrows along the arid waste which surrounded their dwellings; that houses divested of their tenants, and become foul dens of contagion, had been set on fire and burnt to the ground; and that around the infected fishing-hamlets of Hilton and Balintore the country-people had drawn a sort of *barrière sanitaire*, and cooped up within the limits of their respective villages the wretched inhabitants. And in the general consternation—a consternation much more extreme than that evinced when the disease actually visited the place—it was asked by the townsfolk whether *they* ought not, so long as the place remained uninfected, to draw a similar *cordon* round themselves. A public meeting was accordingly held, to deliberate on the best means of shutting themselves in; and at the meeting almost all the adult male inhabitants attended, with the exception of the gentlemen in the commission of the peace, and the town officials, who, though quite prepared to wink hard at our irregularities, failed to see that, on any grounds tenable in the eye of the law, they themselves could take a share in them.

Our meeting at first threatened to be stormy. The extra Liberals, who, in the previous ecclesiastical struggle, had taken part to a man with the Gaelic people, as they did, in the subsequent church controversy, with the Court of Session, began by an attack on the Town Justices. We might all see now, said a Liberal writer lad who addressed us, how little these people were our friends. Now, when the place was threatened by the pestilence, they would do nothing for us; they would not even so much as countenance our meeting; we saw there was not one of them present; in short, they cared nothing at all about us, or whether we died or lived. But he and his friends would stand by us to the last; nay, while the magistrates were evidently afraid, with all their wealth, to move in the matter, terrified, no doubt, by the prosecutions for damages which might be instituted against them were they to stop the highways, and turn back travellers, he himself, though far from rich, would be our security against all legal processes whatever. This, of course, was very noble; all the more noble from the circumstance that the speaker could not, as the *Gazette* informed us, meet his own actual liabilities at the time, and was yet fully prepared, notwithstanding, to meet all our possible ones. Up started, however, almost ere he had done speaking, a friend of the Justices, and made so angry a speech in their defence, that the meeting threatened to fall into two parties, and explode in a squabble. I rose in the extremity, and, though unhappily no orator, addressed my townsfolk in a few homely sentences. Cholera, I reminded them, was too evidently of neither party; and the magistrates were, I was sure, nearly as much frightened as we are. But they really could do nothing for us. In matters of life and death, however, when laws and magistrates failed to protect quiet people, the people were justified in asserting the natural right to protect themselves; and, whatever laws and lawyers might urge to the contrary, that right was now ours. In a neighbouring county, the inhabitants of certain infected villages were already fairly shut up amid their dwellings by the countryfolk around, who could themselves show a clean bill of health; and we, if in the circumstances of these villagers, would very possibly be treated after the same manner. And what remained to us in our actual circumstances was just to anticipate the process of being ourselves bottled in, by bottling the country out. The town, situated on a promontory, and approachable at only a few points, could easily be guarded; and instead of squabbling about the merits of Justices of the Peace—very likely somewhat Conservative in their leanings—or of spirited Reformers who would like very well to be Justices of the Peace also, and would doubtless make very excellent ones, I thought it would be far better for us immediately to form ourselves into a Defence Association, and proceed to regulate our watches and set our guards. My short speech was remarkably well received. There was a poor man immediately beside me, who was in great dread of cholera, and who actually proved one of its first victims in the place—for in little more than a week after he was in his grave—who backed me by an especially vigorous Hear, hear!—and the answering Hear, hears, of the meeting bore down all reply. We accordingly at once formed our Defence Association; and ere midnight our rounds and stations were marked out, and our watches set. All power passed at once out of the hands of the magistrates; but the worthy men themselves said very little about it; and we had the satisfaction of knowing that their families—especially their wives and daughters—were very friendly indeed both to the Association and the temporary suspension of the law, and that, on both their own account and ours, they wished us all manner of success.

We kept guard for several days. All vagabonds and trampers were turned back without remorse; but there was a respectable class of travellers from whom there was less danger to be apprehended; and with these we found it somewhat difficult to deal. I would have admitted them at once; but the majority of the Association demurred;—to do that would be, according to Corporal Trim, to "set one man greatly over the head of another;"

and it was ultimately agreed that, instead of at once admitting them, they should be first brought into a wooden building fitted up for the purpose, and thoroughly fumigated with sulphur and chloride of lime. I know not with whom the expedient first originated: it was said to have been suggested by some medical man who knew a great deal about cholera. And though, for my own part, I could not see how the demon of the disease was to be expelled by the steam of a little sulphur and chloride, as the evil spirit in Tobit was expelled by the smoke of the fish's liver, it seemed to satisfy the Association wonderfully well; and a stranger well smoked came to be regarded as safe. There was a day at hand which promised an unusual amount of smoking. The agitation of the Reform Bill had commenced—a great court of appeal was on that day to hold at Cromarty; and it was known that both a Whig and Tory party from Inverness, in which cholera was raging at the time, would to a certainty attend it. What, it was asked, were we to do with the politicians—the formidable bankers, factors, and lawyers—who would form, we knew, the Inverness cavalcade? Individually, the question seemed to be asked under a sort of foreboding terror, that calculated consequences; but when the Association came to ask it collectively, and to answer it in a body, it was in a bold tone, that set fear at defiance. And so it was resolved, *nem. con.*, that the Inverness politicians should be smoked like the others. My turn to mount guard had come round on the previous night at twelve o'clock; but I had calculated on being off the station ere the Inverness people came up. Unluckily, however, instead of being appointed a simple sentry, I was made officer for the night. It was the duty assigned to me to walk round the several posts, and see that the various sentinels were keeping a smart outlook, which I did very faithfully; but when the term of my watch had expired, I found no relieving officer coming up to take my place. The prudent man appointed on the occasion was, I feared, tiding over the coming difficulty in some quiet corner; but I continued my rounds, maugre the suspicion, in the hope of his appearance. And as I approached one of the most important stations—that on the great highway which connects the town of Cromarty with Kessock Ferry—*there* was the Whig portion of the Inverness cavalcade just coming up. The newly-appointed sentinel stood aside, to let his officer deal with the Whig gentlemen, as, of course, best became both their quality and *his* official standing. I would rather have been elsewhere; but I at once brought the procession to a stand. A man of high spirit and influence—a banker, and very much a Whig—at once addressed me with a stern—"By what authority, Sir?" "By the authority," I replied, "of five hundred able-bodied men in the neighbouring town, associated for the protection of themselves and their families." "Protection against what?" "Protection against the pestilence;— you come from an infected place." "Do you know what you are doing, Sir?" said the banker fiercely. "Yes; doing what the law cannot do for us, but what we have determined to do for ourselves." The banker grew pale with anger; and he was afterwards heard to say, that had he had a pistol at the time, he would have shot upon the spot the man who stopped him; but not having a pistol, he could not shoot me; and so I sent him and his party away under an escort, to be smoked. And as they were somewhat obstreperous by the way, and knocked the hat of one of the guards over his nose, they got, in the fumigating process, as I was sorry to learn, a double portion of the sulphur and the chloride; and came into court, to contend with the Tories, gasping for breath. I was aware I acted on this occasion a very foolish part; I ought to a certainty to have run away on the approach of the Inverness cavalcade; but the running away would have involved, according to Rochester, an amount of moral courage which I did not possess. I fear, too, I must admit, that the rough tones of the banker's address stirred up what had long lain quietly enough in my veins—some of the wild buccaneering blood of John Feddes and the old seafaring Millers; and so I weakly remained at my post, and did what the Association deemed my duty. I trust the banker did not recognise me, and that now, after the lapse of more than twenty years, he will be inclined to extend to me his forgiveness.

I take this late opportunity of humbly begging his pardon, and of assuring him, that at the very time I brought him to bay I was heartily at one with him in his politics. But then my townsfolk, being much frightened, were perfectly impartial in smoking Whigs and Tories all alike; and I could bethink me of no eligible mode of exempting my friends from a process of fumigation which was, I daresay, very unpleasant, and in whose virtues my faith was assuredly not strong.

When engaged, however, in keeping up our *cordon* with apparent success, cholera entered the place in a way on which it was impossible we could have calculated. A Cromarty fisherman had died of the disease at Wick rather more than a month previous, and the clothes known to have been in contact with the body were burnt by the Wick authorities in the open air. He had, however, a brother on the spot, who had stealthily appropriated some of the better pieces of dress; and these he brought home with him in a chest; though such was the dread with which he regarded them that for more than four weeks he suffered the chest to lie beside him unopened. At length, in an evil hour, the pieces of dress were taken out, and, like the "goodly Babylonish garment" which wrought the destruction of Achan and the discomfiture of the camp, they led, in the first instance, to the death of the poor imprudent fisherman, and to that of not a few of his townfolk immediately after. He himself was seized by cholera on the following day; in less than two days more he was dead and buried; and the disease went creeping about the streets and lanes for weeks after—here striking down a strong man in the full vigour of middle life—there shortening, apparently by but a few months, the span of some worn-out creature, already on the verge of the grave. The visitation had its wildly picturesque accompaniments. Pitch and tar were kept burning during the night in the openings of the infected lanes; and the unsteady light flickered with ghastly effect on house and wall, and tall chimney-top, and on the flitting figures of the watchers. By day, the frequent coffins, borne to the grave by but a few bearers, and the frequent smoke that rose outside the place from fires kindled to consume the clothes of the infected, had their sad and startling effect; a migration, too, of a considerable portion of the fisher population to the caves of the hill, in which they continued to reside till the disease left the town, formed a striking accompaniment of the visitation; and yet, curiously enough, as the danger seemed to increase the consternation lessened, and there was much less fear among the people when the disease was actually ravaging the place, than when it was merely stalking within sight around it. We soon became familiar, too, with its direst horrors, and even learned to regard them as comparatively ordinary and commonplace. I had read, about two years before, the passage in Southey's "Colloquies," in which Sir Thomas More is made to remark that modern Englishmen have no guarantee whatever, in these latter times, that their shores shall not be visited, as of old, by devastating plagues. "As touching the pestilence," says Sir Thomas (or rather the poet in his name), "you fancy yourselves secure because the plague has not appeared among you for the last hundred and fifty years—a portion of time which, long as it may seem, compared with the brief term of mortal existence, is as nothing in the physical history of the globe. The importation of that scourge is as possible now as it was in former times; and were it once imported, do you suppose it would rage with less violence among the crowded population of your metropolis than it did before the fire? What," he adds, "if the sweating sickness, emphatically called the English disease, were to show itself again? Can any cause be assigned why it is not as likely to break out in the nineteenth century as in the fifteenth?" And, striking as the passage is, I remembered perusing it with that incredulous feeling, natural to men in a quiet time, which leads them to draw so broad a line between the experience of history, if of a comparatively remote age, or of a distant place, and their own personal experience. In the loose sense of the sophist, it was contrary to my experience that Britain should become the seat of any such fatal and widely devastating disease as used to ravage it of old. And yet, now that

466

I saw as terrible and unwonted an infliction as either the plague or the sweating sickness decimating our towns and villages, and the terrible scenes described by De Foe and Patrick Walker fully rivalled, the feeling with which I came to regard it was one, not of strangeness, but of familiarity.

When thus unsuccessfully employed in keeping watch and ward against our insidious enemy, the Reform Bill for Scotland passed the House of Lords, and became the law of the land. I had watched with interest the growth of the popular element in the country—had seen it gradually strengthening, from the despotic times of Liverpool and Castlereagh, through the middle period of Canning and Goderich, down, till even Wellington and Peel, men of iron as they were, had to yield to the pressure from without, and to repeal first the Test and Corporation Acts, and next to carry, against their own convictions, the great Roman Catholic Emancipation measure. The people, during a season of undisturbed peace, favourable to the growth of opinion, were becoming more decidedly a power in the country than they had ever been before; and of course, as one of the people, and in the belief, too, that the influence of the many would be less selfishly exerted than that of the few, I was pleased that it should be so, and looked forward to better days. For myself personally I expected nothing. I had early come to see that toil, physical or intellectual, was to be my portion throughout life, and that through no possible improvement in the government of the country could I be exempted from labouring for my bread. From State patronage I never expected anything, and I have received from it about as much as I ever expected.

I was employed in labouring pretty hard for my bread one fine evening in the summer of 1830—engaged in hewing with bare breast and arms, in the neighbourhood of the harbour of Cromarty, a large tombstone, which, on the following day, was to be carried across the ferry to a churchyard on the opposite side of the Firth. A group of French fishermen, who had gathered round me, were looking curiously at my mode of working, and, as I thought, somewhat curiously at myself, as if speculating on the physical powers of a man with whom there was at least a possibility of their having one day to deal. They formed part of the crew of one of those powerfully-manned French luggers which visit our northern coasts every year, ostensibly with the design of prosecuting the herring fishery, but which, supported mainly by large Government bounties, and in but small part by their fishing speculations, are in reality kept up by the State as a means of rearing sailors for the French navy. Their lugger—an uncouth-looking vessel, representative rather of the navigation of three centuries ago than of that of the present-day—lay stranded in the harbour beside us; and, their work over for the day, they seemed as quiet and silent as the calm evening whose stillness they were enjoying; when the letter-carrier of the place came up to where I was working, and handed me, all damp from the press, a copy of the *Inverness Courier*, which I owed to the kindness of its editor. I was at once attracted by the heading, in capitals, of its leading article— "Revolution in France—Flight of Charles X"—and pointed it out to the Frenchmen. None of them understood English; but they could here and there catch the meaning of the more important words, and, exclaiming *"Révolution en France!!—Fuite de Charles X!!"*—they clustered round it in a state of the extremest excitement, gabbling faster and louder than thrice as many Englishmen could have done in any circumstances. At length, however, their resolution seemed taken: curiously enough, their lugger bore the name of "Charles X;" and one of them, laying hold of a large lump of chalk, repaired to the vessel's stern, and by covering over the white-lead letters with the chalk, effaced the royal name. Charles was virtually declared by the little bit of France that sailed in the lugger, to be no longer king; and the incident struck me, trivial as it may seem, as significantly illustrative of the extreme slightness of that hold which the rulers of modern France possess on the affections of their people. I returned to my home as the evening darkened, more moved by this unexpected revolution than by any other political event of my time—brimful of hope for the cause of freedom all over the civilized world, and, in especial—misled by a sort of *analogical experience*—sanguine in my expectations for France. It had had, like our own country, its first stormy revolution, in which its monarch had lost his head; and then its Cromwell, and then its Restoration, and its easy, luxurious king, who, like Charles II., had died in possession of the throne, and who had been succeeded by a weak bigot brother, the very counterpart of James VII. And now, after a comparatively orderly revolution like that of 1688, the bigot had been dethroned, and the head of another branch of the royal family called in to enact the part of William III. The historical parallel seemed complete; and could I doubt that what would next follow would be a long period of progressive improvement, in which the French people would come to enjoy, as entirely as those of Britain, a well-regulated freedom, under which revolutions would be unnecessary, mayhap impossible? Was it not evident, too, that the success of the French in their noble struggle would immediately act with beneficial effect on the popular cause in our own country and everywhere else, and greatly quicken the progress of reform?

And so I continued to watch with interest the course of the Reform Bill, and was delighted to see it, after a passage singularly stormy and precarious, at length safely moored in port. In some of the measures, too, to which it subsequently led, I greatly delighted, especially in the emancipation of our negro slaves in the colonies. Nor could I join many of my personal friends in their denunciation of that appropriation measure, as it was termed—also an effect of the altered constituency—which suppressed the Irish bishoprics. As I ventured to tell my minister, who took the other side—if a Protestant Church failed, after enjoying for three hundred years the benefits of a large endowment, and every advantage of position which the statute-book could confer, to erect herself into the Church of the many, it was high time to commence dealing with her in her true character—as the Church of the few. At home, however, within the narrow precincts of my native town, there were effects of the measure which, though comparatively trifling, I liked considerably worse than the suppression of the bishoprics. It broke up the townsfolk into two portions—the one consisting of elderly or middle-aged men, who had been in the commission of the peace ere the passing of the bill, and who now, as it erected the town into a parliamentary burgh, became our magistrates, in virtue of the support of a majority of the voters; and a younger and weaker, but clever and very active party, few of whom were yet in the commission of the peace, and who, after standing unsuccessfully for the magistracy, became the leaders of a patriotic opposition, which succeeded in rendering the seat of justice a rather uneasy one in Cromarty. The younger men were staunch Liberals, but great Moderates—the elder, sound Evangelicals, but decidedly Conservative in their leanings; and as I held ecclesiastically by the one party, and secularly by the other, I found my position, on the whole, a rather anomalous one. Both parties got involved in law-suits. When the Whig Members of Parliament for the county and burgh came the way, they might be seen going about the streets arm-in-arm with the young Whigs, which was, of course, a signal honour; and during the heat of a contested election, young Whiggism, to show itself grateful, succeeded in running off with a Conservative voter, whom it had caught in his cups, and got itself involved in a law-suit in consequence, which cost it several hundred pounds. The Conservatives, on the other hand, also got entangled in an expensive law-suit. The town had its annual fair, at which from fifty to a hundred children used to buy gingerbread, and which had been held for many years at the eastern end of the town links. Through, however, some unexplained piece of strategy on the part of the young Liberals, a market-day came round, on which the gingerbread women took their stand on a green a little above the harbour; and, of course, where the gingerbread was, there the children were gathered together; and the magistrates, astonished, visited the spot in order to ascertain, if possible, the philosophy of the change. They found the ground occupied by a talkative

470

pedlar, who stood up strongly for the young Liberals and the new side. The magistrates straightway demanded the production of his license. The pedlar had none. And so he was apprehended and summarily tried, on a charge of contravening the statute 55 Geo. III., cap. 71; and, being found guilty of hawking without a license, he was committed to prison. The pedlar, backed, it was understood, by the young Liberals, raised an action for wrongous imprisonment; and, on the ground that the day on which he had sold his goods was a fair or market-day, on which anybody might sell anything, the magistrates were cast in damages. I liked the lawsuits very ill, and held that the young Liberals would have been more wisely employed in making money by their shops and professions—secure that the coveted honours would ultimately get into the wake of the good bank-accounts—than that they should be engaged either in scattering their own means in courts of law, or in impinging on the means of their neighbours. And ultimately I found my proper political position as a supporter in all ecclesiastical and municipal matters of my Conservative townsmen, and a supporter in almost all the national ones of the Whigs; whom, however, I always liked better, and deemed more virtuous, when they were out of office than when they were in.

On one occasion I even became political enough to stand for a councillorship. My friends, chiefly through the death of elderly voters and the rise of younger men, few of whom were Conservative, felt themselves getting weak in the place; and fearing that they could not otherwise secure a majority at the Council board, they urged me to stand for one of the vacancies, which I accordingly did, and carried my election by a swimming majority. And in duly attending the first meeting of Council, I heard an eloquent speech from a gentleman in the opposition, directed against the individuals who, as he finely expressed it, "were wielding the destinies of his native town;" and saw, as the only serious piece of business before the meeting, the Councillors clubbing pennies a-piece, in order to defray, in the utter lack of town funds, the expense of a ninepenny postage. And then, with,

I fear, a very inadequate sense of the responsibilities of my new office, I stayed away from the Council board, and did nothing whatever in its behalf, with astonishing perseverance and success, for three years together. And thus began and terminated my municipal career—a career which, I must confess, failed to secure for me the thanks of my constituency; but then, on the other hand, I am not aware that the worthy people ever seriously complained. There was absolutely nothing to do in the councilship; and, unlike some of my brother office-bearers, the requisite nothing I did, quietly and considerately, and very much at my leisure, without any unnecessary display of stump-oratory, or of anything else.

CHAPTER XXIII

"Days passed; an' now my patient steps
That maiden's walks attend;
My vows had reach'd that maiden's ear,
Ay, an' she ca'd me friend.
An' I was bless'd as bless'd can be;
The fond, daft dreamer Hope
Ne'er dreamed o' happier days than mine,
Or joys o' ampler scope."—HENRISON'S SANG.

I USED, as I have said, to have occasional visitors when working in the churchyard. My minister has stood beside me for hours together, discussing every sort of subject, from the misdeeds of the Moderate divines—whom he liked all the worse for being brethren of his own cloth—to the views of Isaac Taylor on the corruptions of Christianity or the possibilities of the future state. Strangers, too, occasionally came the way, desirous of being introduced to the natural curiosities of the district, more especially to its geology; and I remember first meeting in the churchyard in this way, the late Sir Thomas Dick Lauder; and of having the opportunity afforded me of questioning, mallet in hand, the present distinguished Professor of Humanity in the Edinburgh University,[1] respecting the nature of the cohesive agent in the non-calcareous sandstone which I was engaged in hewing. I had sometimes a different, but not less interesting, class of visitors. The town had its small but very choice circle of accomplished intellectual ladies, who, earlier in the century, would have been perhaps described as members of the bluestocking sisterhood; but the advancing intelligence of the age had rendered the phrase obsolete; and they simply took their place as well-informed, sensible women, whose acquaintance with the best authors was regarded as in no degree disqualifying them from their proper

[1] Professor Pillans (Miller).

473

duties as wives or daughters. And my circle of acquaintance included the entire class. I used to meet them at delightful tea-parties, and sometimes borrowed a day from my work to conduct them through the picturesque burn of Eathie, or the wild scenes of Cromarty Hill, or to introduce them to the fossiliferous deposits of the Lias or the Old Red Sandstone. And not unfrequently their evening walks used to terminate where I wrought, in the old chapel of St Regulus, or in the parish burying-ground, beside a sweet wooded dell known as the "Ladies' Walk;" and my labours for the day closed in what I always very much relished—a conversation on the last good book, or on some new organism, recently disinterred, of the Secondary or Palæozoic period.

I had been hewing, about this time, in the upper part of my uncle's garden, and had just closed my work for the evening, when I was visited by one of my lady friends, accompanied by a stranger lady, who had come to see a curious old dial-stone which I had dug out of the earth long before, when a boy, and which had originally belonged to the ancient Castle-garden of Cromarty. I was standing with them beside the dial, which I had placed in my uncle's garden, and remarking, that as it exhibited in its structure no little mathematical skill, it had probably been cut under the eye of the eccentric but accomplished Sir Thomas Urquhart; when a third lady, greatly younger than the others, and whom I had never seen before, came hurriedly tripping down the garden-walk, and, addressing the other two apparently quite in a flurry—"Oh, come, come away," she said, "I have been seeking you ever so long." "Is this you, L——?"[1] was the staid reply: "Why, what now?—you have run yourself out of breath." The young lady was, I saw, very pretty; and though in her nineteenth year at the time, her light and somewhat *petite* figure, and the waxen clearness of her complexion, which resembled rather that of a fair child than of a grown woman, made her look from three to four years younger. And as if in some degree still a child her two lady friends

[1] Lydia Fraser, whom Miller eventually married, after a five-years courtship, in 1837.

seemed to regard her. She stayed with them scarce a minute ere she tripped off again; nor did I observe that she favoured me with a single glance. But what else could be expected by an ungainly, dust-besprinkled mechanic in his shirt sleeves, and with a leathern apron before him? Nor *did* the mechanic expect aught else; and when informed long after, by one whose testimony was conclusive on the point, that he had been pointed out to the young lady by some such distinguished name as "the Cromarty Poet," and that she had come up to her friends somewhat in a flurry, simply that she might have a nearer look of him, he received the intelligence somewhat with surprise. All the first interviews in all the novels I ever read are of a more romantic and less homely cast than the special interview just related; but I know not a more curious one.

Only a few evenings after, I met the same young lady, in circumstances of which the writer of a tale might have made a little more. I was sauntering, just as the sun was sinking, along one of my favourite walks on the Hill—a tree-skirted glade—now looking out through the openings on the ever fresh beauties of the Cromarty Firth, with its promontories, and bays, and long lines of winding shore, and anon marking how redly the slant light fell through intersticial gaps on pale lichened trunks and huge boughs, in the deeper recesses of the wood—when I found myself unexpectedly in the presence of the young lady of the previous evening. She was sauntering through the wood as leisurely as myself—now and then dipping into a rather bulky volume which she carried, that had not in the least the look of a novel, and which, as I subsequently ascertained, was an elaborate essay on Causation. We, of course, passed each other on our several ways without sign of recognition. Quickening her pace, however, she was soon out of sight; and I just thought, on one or two occasions afterwards, of the apparition that had been presented as she passed, as much in keeping with the adjuncts—the picturesque forest and the gorgeous sunset. It would not be easy, I thought, were the large book but away, to furnish a very lovely scene with a more suitable figure. Shortly after, I began to meet the young lady at the charming tea-parties of the place. Her father, a worthy man, who, from unfortunate speculations in business, had met with severe losses, was at this time several years dead; and his widow had come to reside in Cromarty, on a somewhat limited income, derived from property of her own. Liberally assisted, however, by relations in England, she had been enabled to send her daughter to Edinburgh, where the young lady received all the advantages which a first-rate education could confer. By some lucky chance, she was there boarded, with a few other ladies, in early womanhood, in the family of Mr George Thomson, the well-known correspondent of Burns; and passed under his roof some of her happiest years. Mr Thomson—himself an enthusiast in art—strove to inoculate the youthful inmates of his house with the same fervour, and to develop whatever seeds of taste or genius might be found in them; and, characterized till the close of a life extended far beyond the ordinary term by the fine chivalrous manners of the thorough gentleman of the old school, his influence over his young friends was very great, and his endeavours, in at least some of the instances, very successful. And in none, perhaps, was he more so than in the case of the young lady of my narrative. From Edinburgh she went to reside with the friends in England to whose kindness she had been so largely indebted; and with them she might have permanently remained, to enjoy the advantages of superior position. She was at an age, however, which rarely occupies itself in adjusting the balance of temporal advantage; and her only brother having been admitted, through the interest of her friends, as a pupil into Christ's Hospital, she preferred returning to her widowed mother, left solitary in consequence, though with the prospect of being obliged to add to her resources by taking a few of the children of the town as day-pupils.

Her claim to take her place in the intellectual circle of the burgh was soon recognised. I found that, misled by the extreme youthfulness of her appearance, and a marked juvenility of manner, I had greatly mistaken the young lady. That she should be accomplished in the ordinary sense of the term—that she should draw, play, and sing well—would be what I should have expected; but I was not prepared to find that, mere girl as she seemed, she should have a decided turn, not for the lighter, but for the severer walks of literature, and should have already acquired the ability of giving expression to her thoughts in a style formed on the best English models, and not in the least like that of a young lady. The original shyness wore away, and we became great friends. I was nearly ten years her senior, and had read a great many more books than she; and, finding me a sort of dictionary of fact, ready of access, and with explanatory notes attached, that became long or short just as she pleased to draw them out by her queries, she had, in the course of her amateur studies, frequent occasion to consult me. There were, she saw, several ladies of her acquaintance who used occasionally to converse with me in the churchyard; but in order to make assurance doubly sure respecting the perfect propriety of such a proceeding on her part, she took the laudable precaution of stating the case to her mother's landlord, a thoroughly sensible man, one of the magistrates of the burgh, and an elder of the kirk; and he at once certified that there was no lady of the place who might not converse, without remark, as often and as long as she pleased with me. And so, fully justified, both by the example of her friends—all very judicious women, some of them only a few years older than herself—and by the deliberate judgment of a very sensible man, the magistrate and elder, my young lady friend learned to visit me in the churchyard, just like the other ladies; and, latterly at least, considerably oftener than any of them. We used to converse on all manner of subjects connected with the belles-lettres and the philosophy of mind, with, so far as I can at present remember, only one marked exception. On that mysterious affection which sometimes springs up between persons of the opposite sexes when thrown much together—though occasionally discussed by the metaphysicians and much sung by the poets— we by no chance ever touched. Love formed the one solitary subject which, from some curious contingency, invariably escaped us.

And yet, latterly at least, I had begun to think about it a good deal. Nature had not fashioned me one of the sort of people who fall in love at first sight. I had even made up my mind to live a bachelor life, without being very much impressed by the magnitude of the sacrifice; but I daresay it did mean something, that in my solitary walks for the preceding fourteen or fifteen years, a female companion often walked in fancy by my side, with whom I exchanged many a thought, and gave expression to many a feeling, and to whom I pointed out many a beauty in the landscape, and communicated many a curious fact, and whose understanding was as vigorous as her taste was faultless and her feelings exquisite. One of the English essayists—the elder Moore—has drawn a very perfect personage of this airy character (not, however, of the softer, but of the masculine sex), under the name of the "maid's husband;" and described him as one of the most formidable rivals that the ordinary lover of flesh and blood can possibly encounter. My day-dream lady—a person that may be termed with equal propriety the "bachelor's wife,"—has not been so distinctly recognised; but she occupies a large place in our literature, as the mistress of all the poets who ever wrote on love without actually experiencing it, from the days of Cowley down to those of Henry Kirke White; and her presence serves always to intimate a heart capable of occupation, but still unoccupied. I find the bachelor's wife delicately drawn in one of the posthumous poems of poor Alexander Bethune,[1] as a "fair being"—the frequent subject of his day-dreams—

> "Whose soft voice
> Should be the sweetest music to his ear,
> Awakening all the chords of harmony;
> Whose eye should speak a language to his soul,
> More eloquent than aught which Greece or Rome
> Could boast of in its best and happiest days;

---

[1] Alexander Bethune (1804-43), a poet and farm labourer from Fife. His brother John (1812-39) was also a poet—together they were known as the Fifeshire Foresters.

Whose smile should be his rich reward for toil;
Whose pure transparent cheek, when press'd to his,
Should calm the fever of his troubled thoughts,
And woo his spirit to those fields Elysian—
The paradise which strong affection guards."

It may be always predicated of these bachelor's wives, that they never closely resemble in their lineaments any living woman: poor Bethune's would not have exhibited a single feature of any of his fair neighbours, the lasses of Upper Rankeillour or Newburgh. Were the case otherwise, the dream maiden would be greatly in danger of being displaced by the real one whom she resembled; and it was a most significant event, which, notwithstanding my inexperience, I learned by and by to understand, that about this time my old companion, the "bachelor's wife," utterly forsook me, and that a vision of my young friend took her place. I can honestly aver, that I entertained not a single hope that the feeling should be mutual. On whatever other head my vanity may have flattered me, it certainly never did so on the score of personal appearance. My personal strength was, I knew, considerably above the average of that of my fellows, and at this time my activity also; but I was perfectly conscious that, on the other hand, my good looks rather fell below than rose above the medial line. And so, while I suspected, as I well might, that, as in the famous fairy story, "Beauty" had made a conquest of the "Beast," I had not the most distant expectation that the "Beast" would, in turn, make a conquest of "Beauty." My young friend had, I knew, several admirers—men who were younger and dressed better, and who, as they had all chosen the liberal professions, had fairer prospects than I; and as for the item of good looks, had she set her affections on even the least likely of them, I could have addressed him, with perfect sincerity, in the words of the old ballad:—

"Nae wonder, nae wonder, Gil Morrice,
    My lady lo'es ye weel:
The fairest part o' my body
    Is blacker than thy heel."

Strange to say, however, much about the time that I made my discovery, my young friend succeeded in making a discovery also;—the maid's husband shared on her part the same fate as the bachelor's wife did on mine; and her visits to the churchyard suddenly ceased.

A twelvemonth had passed ere we succeeded in finding all this out; but the young lady's mother had seen the danger somewhat earlier; and deeming, as was quite right and proper, an operative mason no very fitting mate for her daughter, my opportunities of meeting my friend at *conversazione* or tea-party had become few. I, however, took my usual evening walk through the woods of the Hill; and as my friend's avocations set her free at the same delightful hour, and as she also was a walker on the Hill, we did sometimes meet, and witness together, from amid the deeper solitudes of its bosky slopes, the sun sinking behind the distant Ben Wyvis. These were very happy evenings; the hour we passed together always seemed exceedingly short; but, to make amends for its briefness, there were at length few working days in the milder season of which it did not form the terminal one;—from the circumstance, of course, that the similarity of our tastes for natural scenery led us always into the same lonely walks about the same delicious sunset hour. For months together, even during this second stage of our friendship, there was one interesting subject on which we never talked. At length, however, we came to a mutual understanding. It was settled that we should remain for three years more in Scotland on the existing terms; and if during that time there should open to me no suitable field of exertion at home, we should then quit the country for America, and share together in a strange land whatever fate might be in store for us. My young friend was considerably more sanguine than I. I had laid faithfully before her those defects of character which rendered me a rather inefficient man-at-arms for contending in my own behalf in the battle of life. Inured to labour, and to the hardships of the bothy and the barrack, I believed that in the backwoods, where I would have to lift my axe on great trees, I might get on with my clearing and my crops like most of my neighbours; but then the backwoods would, I feared, be no place for her; and as for effectually pushing my way in the long-peopled portions of the United States, among one of the most vigorous and energetic races in the world, I could not see that I was in the least fitted for that. She, however, thought otherwise. The tender passion is always a strangely exaggerative one. Lodged in the male mind, it gives to the object on which it rests all that is excellent in woman, and in the female mind imparts to its object all that is noble in man; and my friend had come to regard me as fitted by nature either to head an army or lead a college, and to deem it one of the weaknesses of my character, that I myself could not take an equally favourable view. There was, however, one profession of which, measuring myself as carefully as I could, I deemed myself capable: I saw men whom I regarded as not my superiors in natural talent, and even possessed of no greater command of the pen, occupying respectable places in the periodical literature of the day, as the editors of Scotch newspapers, provincial, and even metropolitan, and deriving from their labours incomes of from one to three hundred pounds per annum; and were my abilities, such as they were, to be fairly set by sample before the public, and so brought into the literary market, they might, I thought, possibly lead to my engagement as a newspaper editor. And so, as a first step in the process, I resolved on publishing my volume of traditional history—a work on which I had bestowed considerable care, and which, regarded as a specimen of what I could do as a *litterateur*, would, I believed, show not inadequately my ability of treating at least those lighter subjects with which newspaper editors are occasionally called on to deal.

Nearly two of the three twelvemonths passed by, however, and I was still an operative mason. With all my solicitude, I could not give myself heartily to seek work of the kind which I saw newspaper editors had at that time to do. It might be quite well enough, I thought, for the lawyer to be a special pleader. With special pleadings equally extreme on the opposite sides of a case, and a qualified judge to hold the balance between, the cause of truth and justice might be even more thoroughly served than if the antagonist agents were to set themselves to be as impartial and equal-handed as the magistrate himself. But I could not extend the same tolerance to the special pleading of the newspaper editor. I saw that, to many of the readers of his paper, the editor did not hold the place of a law-agent, but of a judge: it was his part to submit to them, therefore, not ingenious pleadings, but, to the best of his judgment, honest decisions. And not only did no place present itself for me in the editorial field, but I really could see no place in it that, with the views which I entertained on this head, I would not scruple to occupy. I saw no party cause for which I could honestly plead. My ecclesiastical friends had, with a few exceptions, cast themselves into the Conservative ranks; and there I could not follow them. The Liberals, on the other hand, being in office at the time, had become at least as like their old opponents as their former selves, and I could by no means defend all that *they* were doing. In Radicalism I had no faith; and Chartism—with my recollection of the kind of treatment which I had received from the workmen of the south still strongly impressed on my mind— I thoroughly detested. And so I began seriously to think of the backwoods of America. But there was another destiny in store for me. My native town, up till this time, though a place of considerable trade, was unfurnished with a branch bank; but on the representation of some of its more extensive traders, and of the proprietors of the neighbouring lands, the Commercial Bank of Scotland had agreed to make it the scene of one of its agencies, and arranged with a sagacious and successful merchant and shipowner of the place to act as its agent. It had fixed, too, on a young man as its accountant, at the suggestion of a neighbouring proprietor; and I heard of the projected bank simply as a piece of news of interest to the town and its neighbourhood, but, of course, without special bearing on any concern of mine. Receiving, however, one winter morning, an invitation to breakfast with the future agent—Mr Ross—I was not a little surprised, after we had taken a quiet cup of tea together, and beaten over half-a-dozen several subjects, to be offered by him the accountantship of the branch bank. After a pause of a full half-minute, I said that the walk was one in which I had no experience whatever—that even the little knowledge of figures which I had acquired at school had been suffered to fade and get dim in my mind from want of practice—and that I feared I would make but a very indifferent accountant. "I shall undertake for you," said Mr Ross, "and do my best to assist you. All you have to do at present is just to signify your acceptance of the offer made." I referred to the young man who, I understood, had been already nominated accountant. Mr Ross stated that, being wholly a stranger to him, and as the office was one of great trust, he had, as the responsible party, sought the security of a guarantee, which the gentleman who had recommended the young man declined to give; and so his recommendation had fallen to the ground. "But *I* can give you no guarantee," I said. "From you," rejoined Mr Ross, "none shall ever be asked." And such was one of the more special *Providences* of my life; for why should I give it a humbler name?

In a few days after, I had taken leave of my young friend in good hope, and was tossing in an old and somewhat crazy coasting vessel, on my way to the parent bank at Edinburgh, to receive there the instructions necessary to the branch accountant. I had wrought as an operative mason, including my term of apprenticeship, for fifteen years—no inconsiderable portion of the more active part of a man's life; but the time was not altogether lost. I enjoyed in these years fully the average amount of happiness, and learned to know more of the Scottish people than is generally known. Let me add—for it seems to be very much the fashion of the time to draw dolorous pictures of the condition of the labouring classes—that from the close of the first year in which I wrought as a journeyman, up till I took final leave of the mallet and chisel, I never knew what it was to want a shilling; that my two uncles, my grandfather, and the mason with whom I served my apprenticeship—all working men—had had a similar experience; and that it was the experience of my father also. I cannot doubt that deserving mechanics may, in exceptional cases, be exposed to want; but I can as little doubt that the cases *are* exceptional, and that much of the suffering of the class is a consequence either of improvidence on the part of the competently skilled, or of a course of trifling during the term of apprenticeship—quite as common as trifling at school—that always lands those who indulge in it in the hapless position of the inferior workman. I trust I may further add, that I was an honest mechanic. It was one of the maxims of Uncle James, that as the Jews, restricted by law to their forty stripes, always fell short of the legal number by one, lest they should by any accident exceed it, so a working man, in order to balance any disturbing element of selfishness in his disposition, should bring his charges for work done, slightly but sensibly within what he deemed the proper mark, and so give, as he used to express himself, his "customers the cast of the baulk." I do think I acted up to the maxim; and that, without injuring my brother workmen by lowering their prices, I never yet charged an employer for a piece of work that, fairly measured and valued, would not be rated at a slightly higher sum than that at which it stood in my account.

I had quitted Cromarty for the south late in November, and landed at Leith on a bleak December morning, just in time to escape a tremendous storm of wind and rain from the west, which, had it caught the smack in which I sailed on the Firth, would have driven us all back to Fraserburgh, and, as the vessel was hardly sea-worthy at the time, perhaps a great deal further. The passage had been stormy; and a very noble, but rather unsocial fellow-passenger—a fine specimen of the golden eagle—had been sea-sick, and evidently very uncomfortable, for the greater part of the way. The eagle must have been accustomed to motion a great deal more rapid than that of the vessel, but it was motion of a different kind; and so he fared as persons do who never feel a qualm when hurried along a railway at the rate of forty miles an hour, but who yet get very squeamish in a tossing boat, that creeps through a rough sea at a speed not exceeding, in the same period of time, from four to five knots. The day preceding the storm was leaden-hued and sombre, and so calm, that though the little wind there was blew the right way, it carried us on, from the first light of morning, when we found ourselves abreast of the Bass, to only near Inchkeith; for when night fell, we saw the May light twinkling dimly far astern, and that of the Inch rising bright and high right ahead. I spent the greater part of the day on deck, marking, as they came into view, the various objects—hill, and island, and seaport town—of which I had lost sight nearly ten years before; feeling the while, not without some craven shrinkings, that having got to the end, in the journey of life, of one very definite stage, with its peculiar scenery and sets of objects, I was just on the eve of entering upon another stage, in which the scenery and objects would be all unfamiliar and new. I was now two years turned of thirty; and though I could not hold that any very great amount of natural endowment was essentially neces-sary to the bank accountant, I knew that most men turned of thirty might in vain attempt acquiring the ability even of heading a pin with the necessary adroitness, and that I might fail, on the same principle, to pass muster as an accountant. I determined, however, obstinately to set myself to acquire, whatever might be the result; and entered Edinburgh in something like spirits on the strength of the resolution. I had transmitted the manuscript of my legendary work, several months before, to Sir Thomas Dick Lauder; and as he was now on terms, in its behalf, with Mr Adam Black, the well-known publisher, I took the liberty of waiting on him, to see how the negotiation was speeding. He received me with great kindness; hospitably urged that I should live with him, so long as I resided in Edinburgh, in his noble mansion, the Grange House; and, as an inducement, introduced me to his library, full charged with the best editions of the best authors, and enriched with many a rare volume and curious manuscript. "Here," he said, "Robertson the historian penned his last work—the 'Disquisition'; and here," opening the door of an adjoining room, "he died." I, of course, declined the invitation. The Grange House, with its books, and its pictures, and its hospitable master, so rich in anecdote, and so full of the literary sympathies, would have been no place for a poor pupil-accountant, too sure that he was to be stupid, but not the less determined on being busy. Besides, on calling immediately after at the bank, I found that I would have to quit Edinburgh on the morrow for some country agency, in which I might be initiated into the system of book-keeping proper to a branch bank, and where the business transacted would be of a kind similar to what might be expected in Cromarty. Sir Thomas, however, kindly got Mr Black to meet me at dinner; and, in the course of the evening, that enterprising bookseller agreed to undertake the publication of my work, on terms which the nameless author of a volume somewhat local in its character, and very local in its name, might well regard as liberal.

Linlithgow was the place fixed on by the parent bank as the scene of my initiation into the mysteries of branch banking; and, taking my passage in one of the track-boats which at that time plied on the Canal between Edinburgh and Glasgow, I reached the fine old burgh as the brief winter day was coming to a close, and was seated next morning at my desk, not a hundred yards from the spot on which Hamilton of Bothwellhaugh had taken his stand when he shot the good Regent. I was, as I had anticipated, very stupid; and must have looked, I suppose, even more obtuse than I actually was: for my temporary superior the agent, having gone to Edinburgh a few days after my arrival, gave expression, in the head bank, to the conviction that it would be in vain attempting making "yon man" an accountant. Altogether deficient in the cleverness that can promptly master isolated details when in ignorance of their bearing on the general scheme to which they belong, I could literally do nothing until I had got a hold of the system; which, locked up in the ponderous tomes of the agency, for some little time eluded my grasp. At length, however, it gradually unrolled itself before me in all its nice proportions, as one of perhaps the completest forms of "book-keeping" which the wit of man has yet devised; and I then found that the details which, when I had approached them as if from the outside, had repulsed and beaten me back, could, like the outworks of a fortress, be commanded from the centre with the utmost ease. Just as I had reached this stage, the regular accountant of the branch was called away to an appointment in one of the joint-stock banks of England; and the agent, again going into Edinburgh on business, left me for the greater part of a day in direction of the agency. Little more than a fortnight had elapsed since he had given his unfavourable verdict; and he was now asked how, in the absence of the accountant, he could have got away from his charge. He had left *me* in the office, he said. "What! the *Incompetent?*" "Oh, that," he replied, "is all a mistake; the Incompetent has already mastered our system." The mechanical ability, however, came but slowly; and I never acquired the facility, in running up columns of summations, of the early-taught accountant; though, making up by diligence what I wanted in speed, I found, after my first few weeks of labour in Linlithgow, that I could give as of old an occasional hour to literature and geology. The proof-sheets of my book began to drop in upon me, demanding revision; and to a quarry in the neighbourhood of the town, rich in the organisms of the Mountain Limestone, and overflown by a bed of basalt[1] so regularly columnar that one of the legends of the district attributed its formation to the "ancient Pechts,"[2] I was able to devote, not without profit, the evenings of several Saturdays. I formed at this time, my first acquaintance with the Palæozoic[3] shells, as they occur in the rock—an acquaintance which has since been extended in some measure through the Silurian deposits, Upper and Lower; and these shells, though marked, in the

[1] Lava.

[2] i.e. Picts. The name given to the northern inhabitants of Scotland in late Roman times and down to the eighth century. Later ignorance regarding them resulted in their being made the subjects of a mythology.

[3] The group of rocks containing the oldest evidences of organic life. These rocks are otherwise known as *Primary*, and the subsequent great divisions of geologic time as *Secondary* and *Tertiary*.

immensely extended ages of the division to which they belong, by specific, and even generic variety, I have found exhibiting throughout a unique family type or pattern, as entirely different from the family type of the Secondary shells as both are different from the family types of the Tertiary and the existing ones. Each of the three great periods of creation had its own peculiar fashion; and after having acquainted myself with the fashions of the second and third periods, I was now peculiarly interested in the acquaintance which I was enabled to commence with that of the first and earliest also. I found, too, in a bed of trap beside the Edinburgh road, scarce half a mile to the east of the town, numerous pieces of carbonized lignite, which still retained the woody structure—probably the broken remains of some forest of the Carboniferous period, enveloped in some ancient lava bed, that had rolled over its shrubs and trees, annihilating all save the fragments of charcoal, which, locked up in its viscid recesses, had resisted the agency that dissipated the more exposed embers into gas. I had found, in like manner, when residing at Conon-side and Inverness, fragments of charcoal locked up in the glassy vesicular stone of the old vitrified forts of Craig Phadrig and Knock Farril, and existing as the sole representatives of the vast masses of fuel which must have been employed in fusing the ponderous walls of these unique fortalices. And I was now interested to find exactly the same phenomena among the *vitrified* rocks of the Coal Measures. Brief as the days were, I had always a twilight hour to myself in Linlithgow; and as the evenings were fine for the season, the old Royal Park of the place, with its noble church, its massive palace, and its sweet lake, still mottled by the hereditary swans whose progenitors had sailed over its waters in the days when James IV worshipped in the spectred aisle, formed a delightful place of retreat, little frequented by the inhabitants of the town, but only all the more my own in consequence; and in which I used to feel the fatigue of the day's figuring and calculation drop away into the cool breezy air, like cobwebs from an unfolded banner, as I climbed among the ruins, or sauntered along the grassy shores of the loch. My stay at Linlithgow was somewhat prolonged, by the removal, first of the accountant of the branch, and then of its agent, who was called south to undertake the management of a newly erected English bank; but I lost nothing by the delay. An admirable man of business, one of the officials of the parent bank in Edinburgh (now its agent in Kirkcaldy, and recently provost of the place), was sent temporarily to conduct the business of the agency; and I saw, under him, how a comparative stranger arrived at his conclusions respecting the standing and solvency of the various customers with whom, in behalf of the parent institute, he was called on to deal. And, finally, my brief term of apprenticeship expired—about two months in all—I returned to Cromarty; and, as the opening of the agency there waited only my arrival, straightway commenced my new course as an accountant. My minister, when he first saw me seated at the desk, pronounced me "at length fairly caught;" and I must confess I did feel as if my latter days were destined to differ from my earlier ones, well nigh as much as those of Peter of old, who, when he was "young, girded himself, and walked whither he would, but who, when old, was girded by others, and carried whither he would not."

Two long years had to pass from this time ere my young friend and I could be united—for such were the terms on which we had to secure the consent of her mother; but, with our union in the vista, we could meet more freely than before; and the time passed not unpleasantly away. For the first six months of my new employment, I found myself unable to make my old use of the leisure hours which, I found, I could still command. There was nothing very intellectual, in the higher sense of the term, in recording the bank's transactions, or in summing up columns of figures, or in doing business over the counter; and yet the fatigue induced was a fatigue not of sinew and muscle, but of nerve and brain, which, if it did not quite disqualify me for my former intellectual amusements, at least greatly disinclined me towards them, and rendered me a considerably more indolent sort of person than either before or since. It is asserted by artists of discriminating eye, that the human hand bears an expression stamped upon it by the general character, as surely as the human face; and I certainly used to be struck, during this transition period, by the relaxed and idle expression that had on the sudden been assumed by mine. And the slackened hands represented, I too surely felt, a slackened mind. The unintellectual toils of the labouring man have been occasionally represented as less favourable to mental cultivation than the semi-intellectual employments of that class immediately above him, to which our clerks, shopmen, and humbler accountants belong; but it will be found that exactly the reverse is the case, and that, though a certain conventional gentility of manner and appearance on the side of the somewhat higher class may serve to conceal the fact, it is on the part of the labouring man that the real advantage lies. The mercantile accountant or law-clerk bent over his desk, his faculties concentrated on his columns of figures, or on the pages which he has been carefully engrossing, and unable to proceed one step in his work without devoting to it all his attention, is in greatly less favourable circumstances than the ploughman or operative mechanic, whose mind is free though his body labours, and who thus finds, in the very rudeness of his employments, a compensation for their humble and laborious character. And it will be found that the humbler of the two classes is much more largely represented in our literature than the class by one degree less humble. Ranged against the poor clerk of Nottingham, Henry Kirke White, and the still more hapless Edinburgh engrossing clerk, Robert Fergusson, with a very few others, we find in our literature a numerous and vigorous phalanx, composed of men such as the Ayrshire Ploughman, the Ettrick Shepherd, the Fifeshire Foresters, the sailors Dampier and Falconer, Bunyan, Bloomfield, Ramsay, Tannahill, Alexander Wilson, John Clare, Allan Cunningham, and Ebenezer Elliot. And I was taught at this time to recognise the simple principle on which the greater advantages lie on the side of the humbler class. Gradually, however, as I became more inured to sedentary life, my mind recovered its spring, and my old ability returned of employing my leisure hours, as before, in intellectual exertion. Meanwhile my legendary volume[1] issued from the press, and was, with a few exceptions, very favourably received by the critics. Leigh Hunt gave it a kind and genial notice in his Journal; it was characterized by Robert Chambers not less favourably in *his*; and Dr Hetherington, the future historian of the Church of Scotland and of the Westminister Assembly of Divines—at that time a licentiate of the Church—made it the subject of an elaborate and very friendly critique in the *Presbyterian Review*. Nor was I less gratified by the terms in which it was spoken of by the late Baron Hume, the nephew and residuary legatee of the historian—himself very much a critic of the old school—in a note to a north-country friend. He described it as a work "written in an English style which" he "had begun to regard as one of the lost arts." But it attained to no great popularity. For being popular, its subjects were too local, and its treatment of them perhaps too quiet. My publishers tell me, however, that it not only continues to sell, but moves off considerably better in its later editions that it did on its first appearance.

The branch bank furnished me with an entirely new and curious field of observation, and formed a very admirable school. For the cultivation of a shrewd common sense, a bank office is one of perhaps the best schools in the world. Mere cleverness serves often only to befool its possessor. He gets entangled among his own ingenuities, and is caught as in a net. But ingenuities, plausibilities, special pleadings, all that make the stump-orator great, must be brushed aside by the banker. The question with him comes always to be a sternly naked one:—Is, or is not, Mr— a person fit to be trusted with the bank's money? Is his sense of monetary obligations nice, or obtuse? Is his judgment good, or the contrary? Are his speculations sound, or precarious? What are his resources?—what his liabilities? Is he facile in lending the use of his name? Does he float on wind-bills, as boys swim on bladders? or

---

[1] *Scenes and Legends of the North of Scotland; or the Traditional History of Cromarty* (1835).

is his paper representative of only real business transactions? Such are the topics which, in the recesses of his own mind, the banker is called on to discuss; and he must discuss them, not merely plausibly or ingeniously, but solidly and truly; seeing that error, however illustrated or adorned, or however capable of being brilliantly defended in speech or pamphlet, is sure always with him to take the form of pecuniary loss. My superior in the agency—Mr Ross, a good and honourable-minded man, of sense and experience—was admirably fitted for calculations of this kind; and I learned, both in his behalf, and from the pleasure which I derived from the exercise, to take no little interest in them also. It was agreeable to mark the moral effects of a well-conducted agency such as his. However humbly honesty and good sense may be rated in the great world generally, they always, when united, bear premium in a judiciously managed bank office. It was interesting enough, too, to see quiet, silent men, like "honest Farmer Flamburgh," getting wealthy, mainly because, though void of display, they were not wanting in integrity and judgment; and clever, unscrupulous fellows, like "Ephraim Jenkinson," who "spoke to good purpose," becoming poor, very much because, with all their smartness, they lacked sense and principle. It was worthy of being noted, too, that in looking around from my peculiar point of view on the agricultural classes, I found the farmers, on really good farms, usually thriving, if not themselves in fault, however high their rents; and that, on the other hand, farmers on sterile farms were *not* thriving, however moderate the demands of the landlord. It was more melancholy, but not less instructive, to learn, from authorities whose evidence could not be questioned—bills paid by small instalments, or lying under protest—that the small-farm system, so excellent in a past age, was getting rather unsuited for the energetic competition of the present one; and that the *small* farmers—a comparatively comfortable class some sixty or eighty years before, who used to give dowries to their daughters, and leave well-stocked farms to their sons—were falling into strait-ened circumstances, and becoming, however respectable elsewhere, not very good men in the bank. It was interesting, too, to mark the character and capabilities of the various branches of trade carried on in the place—how the business of its shopkeepers fell always into a very few hands, leaving to the greater number, possessed, apparently, of the same advantages as their thriving compeers, only a mere show of custom—how precarious in its nature the fishing trade always is, especially the herring fishery, not more from the uncertainty of the fishings themselves, than from the fluctuations of the markets—and how in the pork trade of the place a judicious use of the bank's money enabled the curers to trade virtually on a doubled capital, and to realize, with the deduction of the bank discounts, doubled profits. In a few months my acquaintance with the character and circumstances of the business men of the district became tolerably extensive, and essentially correct; and on two several occasions, when my superior left me for a time to conduct the entire business of the agency, I was fortunate enough not to discount for him a single bad bill. The implicit confidence reposed in me by so good and sagacious a man was certainly quite enough of itself to set me on my metal. There was, however, at least one item in my calculations in which I almost always found myself incorrect: I found I could predict every bankruptcy in the district; but I usually fell short from ten to eighteen months of the period in which the event actually took place. I could pretty nearly determine the time when the difficulties and entanglements which I saw *ought* to have produced their proper effects, and landed in failure; but I missed taking into account the desperate efforts which men of energetic temperament make in such circumstances, and which, to the signal injury of their friends and the loss of their creditors, succeed usually in staving off the catastrophe for a season. In short, the school of the branch bank was a very admirable school; and I profited so much by its teachings, that when questions connected with banking are forced on the notice of the public, and my brother editors have to apply for articles on the subject to literary bankers, I find I can write my banking articles for myself.

The seasons passed by; the two years of probation came to a close, like all that had gone before; and after a long, and, in its earlier stages, anxious courtship of in all five years, I received from the hand of Mr Ross that of my young friend, in her mother's house, and was united to her by my minister, Mr Stewart. And then, setting out, immediately after the ceremony, for the southern side of the Moray Firth, we spent two happy days together in Elgin; and, under the guidance of one of the most respected citizens of the place, my kind friend Mr Isaac Forsyth, visited the more interesting objects connected with the town or its neighbourhood. He introduced us to the Elgin Cathedral; to the veritable John Shanks, the eccentric keeper of the building, who could never hear of the Wolf of Badenoch, who had burnt it four hundred years before, without flying into a rage, and becoming what the dead man would have deemed libellous;—to the font, too, under a dripping vault of ribbed stone, in which an insane mother used to sing to sleep the poor infant, who, afterwards becoming Lieutenant-General Anderson, built for poor paupers like his mother, and poor children such as he himself had once been, the princely institution which bears his name. And then, after passing from the stone font to the institution itself, with its happy children, and its very unhappy old men and women, Mr Forsyth conveyed us to the pastoral, semi-Highland valley of Pluscardine, with its beautiful wood-embosomed priory—one of perhaps the finest and most symmetrical specimens of the unornamented Gothic of the times of Alexander II to be seen anywhere in Scotland. Finally, after passing a delightful evening at his hospitable board, and meeting, among other guests, my friend Mr Patrick Duff—the author of the "Geology of Moray"— I returned with my young wife to Cromarty, and found her mother, Mr Ross, Mr Stewart, and a party of friends, waiting for us in the house which my father had built for himself forty years before, but which it had been his destiny never to inhabit. It formed our home for the three following years. The subjoined verses—prose, I suspect, rather than poetry, for the mood in which they were written was too earnest a one to be imaginative—I introduce, as representative of my feelings at this time: they were written previous to my marriage, on one of the blank pages of a pocket-Bible, with which I presented my future wife:—

TO LYDIA

LYDIA, since ill by sordid gift
    Were love like mine express'd,
Take Heaven's best boon, this Sacred Book,
    From him who loves thee best.
Love strong as that I bear to thee
    Were sure unaptly told
By dying flowers, or lifeless gems,
    Or soul-ensnaring gold.

I know 'twas He who formed this heart
    Who seeks this heart to guide;
For why?—He bids me love thee more
    Than all on earth beside.[1]
Yes, Lydia, bids me cleave to thee,
    As long this heart has cleaved:
Would, dearest, that His other laws
    Were half so well received!

Full many a change, my only love,
    On human life attends;
And at the cold sepulchral stone
    Th' uncertain vista ends.
How best to bear each various change,
    Should weal or woe befall,
To love, live, die, this Sacred Book,
    Lydia, it tells us all.

Oh, much-beloved, our coming day
    To us is all unknown,
But sure we stand a broader mark
    Than they who stand alone.

---

[1] "For this cause shall a man leave father and mother, and shall cleave to his wife, and they twain shall be one flesh." (Miller).

One knows it all: not His an eye,
    Like ours, obscured and dim;
And knowing us, He gives this Book,
    That we may know of Him.

His words, my love, are gracious words,
    And gracious thoughts express:
He cares e'en for each little bird
    That wings the blue abyss.
Of coming wants and woes He thought,
    Ere want or woe began;
And took to Him a human heart,
    That He might feel for man.

Then oh! my first, my only love,
    The kindliest, dearest, best!
On Him may all our hopes repose,—
    On Him our wishes rest.
His be the future's doubtful day,
    Let joy or grief befall:
In life or death, in weal or woe,
    Our God, our guide, our all.

CHAPTER XXIV

"Life is a drama of a few brief acts;
The actors shift, the scene is often changed,
Pauses and revolutions intervene,
The mind is set to many a varied tune,
And jars and plays in harmony by turns."
—ALEXANDER BETHUNE.

THOUGH my wife continued, after our marriage, to teach a few pupils, the united earnings of the household did not much exceed a hundred pounds per annum—not quite so large a sum as I had used to think it a few years before; and so I set myself to try whether I could not turn my leisure hours to some account, by writing for the periodicals. My old inability of pressing for work continued to be as embarrassing as ever, and, save for a chance engagement of no very promising kind, which presented itself to me unsolicited about this time, I might have failed in procuring the employment which I sought. An ingenious self-taught mechanic—the late Mr John Mackay Wilson of Berwick-on-Tweed—after making good his upward way from his original place at the compositor's frame, to the editorship of a provincial paper, started, in the beginning of 1835, a weekly periodical, consisting of "Border Tales," which, as he possessed the story-telling ability, met with considerable success. He did not live, however, to complete the first yearly volume; the forty-ninth weekly number intimated his death; but as the publication had been a not unprofitable one, the publisher resolved on carrying it on; and it was stated in a brief notice, which embodied a few particulars of Mr Wilson's biography, that, his materials being unexhausted, "tales yet untold lay in reserve to keep alive his memory." And in the name of Wilson the publication was kept up for, I believe, five years. It reckoned among its contributors the two Bethunes, John and Alexander, and the late Professor

Gillespie of St Andrews, with several other writers, none of whom seem to have been indebted to any original matter collected by its first editor; and I, who, at the publisher's request, wrote for it, during the first year of my marriage, tales enough to fill an ordinary volume, had certainly to provide all my materials for myself. The whole brought me about twenty-five pounds—a considerable addition to the previous hundred and odds of the household, but, for the work done, as inadequate a remuneration as ever poor writer got in the days of Grub Street. My tales, however, though an English critic did me the honour of selecting one of them as the best in the monthly part in which it appeared, were not of the highest order: it took a great deal of writing to earn the three guineas, which were the stipulated wages for filling a weekly number; and though poor Wilson may have been a fine enough fellow in his way, one had no great encouragement to do one's very best, in order to "keep alive his memory." In all such matters, according to Sir Walter Scott and the old proverb, "Every herring should hang by its own head."

I can show, however, that at least one of my contributions *did* gain Wilson some little credit. In the perilous attempt to bring out, in the dramatic form, the characters of two of our national poets— Burns and Fergusson—I wrote for the "Tales" a series of "Recollections," drawn ostensibly from the memory of one who had been personally acquainted with them both, but in reality based on my own conceptions of the men, as exhibited in their lives and writings. And in an elaborate life of Fergusson lately published, I find a borrowed extract from my contribution and an approving reference to the whole, coupled with a piece of information entirely new to me. "These Recollections," says the biographer, "are truly interesting and touching, *and were the result of various communications made to Mr Wilson*, whose painstaking researches I have had frequent occasion to verify in the course of my own." Alas, no! Poor Wilson was more than a twelvemonth in his grave ere the idea of producing these "Recollections" first struck the writer—a person to whom no communications on the subject were ever made by any one, and who, unassisted save by one of the biographies of the poet—that in Chambers's "Lives of Illustrious Scotsmen"—wrote full two hundred miles from the scene of his sad and brief career. The same individual who, in Mr Wilson's behalf, is so complimentary to my "painstaking research," is, I find, very severe on one of Fergusson's previous biographers—the scholarly Dr Irving, author of the "Life of Buchanan", and the "Lives of the older Scottish Poets"—a gentleman who, whatever his estimate of the poor poet may have been, would have spared no labour in elucidating the various incidents which composed his history. The man of research is roughly treated, and a compliment awarded to the diligence of the man of none. But it is always thus with Fame:

> "Some she disgraced, and some with honours crown'd;
> Unlike successes equal merits found:
> So her blind sister, fickle Fortune, reigns,
> And, undiscerning, scatters crowns and chains."

In the memoir of John Bethune by his brother Alexander, the reader is told that he was much depressed and disappointed, about a twelvemonth or so previous to his decease, by the rejection of several of his stories in succession, which were returned to him, "with an editor's sentence of death passed upon them." I know not whether it was by the editor of the "Tales of the Borders" that sentence in the case was passed; but I know he sentenced some of mine, which were, I daresay, not very good, though well-nigh equal, I thought, to most of his own. Instead, however, of yielding to depression, like poor Bethune, I simply resolved to write for him no more; and straightway made an offer of my services to Mr Robert Chambers, by whom they were accepted; and during the two following years I occasionally contributed to his Journal, on greatly more liberal terms than those on which I had laboured for the other periodical, and with my name attached to my several articles. I must be permitted to avail myself of the present opportunity of acknowledging the kindness of Mr Chambers.

There is perhaps no other writer of the present day who has done so much to encourage struggling talent as this gentleman. I have for many years observed that publications, however obscure, in which he finds aught really praiseworthy, are secure always of getting, in his widely-circulated periodical, a kind approving word—that his criticisms invariably bear the stamp of a benevolent nature, which experiences more of pleasure in the recognition of merit than in the detection of defect—that his kindness does not stop with these cheering notices, for he finds time, in the course of a very busy life, to write many a note of encouragement and advice to obscure men in whom he recognises a spirit superior to their condition—and that the compositions of writers of this meritorious class, when submitted to him editorially, rarely fail, if really suitable for his Journal, to find a place in it, or to be remunerated on a scale that invariably bears reference to the value of the communications, not to the circumstances of their authors.

I can scarce speak of my contributions to the periodicals at this time as forming any part of my education. I acquired, in their composition, a somewhat readier command of the pen than before; but they, of course, tended rather to the dissipation of previous stores than to the accumulation of new ones; nor did they give exercise to those higher faculties of mind which I deemed it most my interest to cultivate. My real education at the time was that in which I was gradually becoming initiated behind the bank-counter, as my experience of the business of the district extended; and that which I contrived to pick up in my leisure evenings along the shores. A rich ichthyolitic deposit of the Old Red Sandstone lies, as I have already said, within less than half a mile of the town of Cromarty; and, when fatigued with my calculations in the bank, I used to find it delightful relaxation to lay open its fish by scores, and to study their peculiarities as exhibited in their various states of keeping, until I at length became able to determine their several genera and species from even the minutest fragments. The number of ichthyolites which that deposit of itself furnished—a patch little more than forty yards square—seemed altogether astonishing: it supplied me with specimens at almost every visit, for ten years together; nor, though, after I left Cromarty for Edinburgh, it was often explored by geologic tourists, and by a few cultivators of science in the place, was it wholly exhausted for ten years more. The ganoids of the second age of vertebrate existence must have congregated as thickly upon that spot in the times of the Lower Old Red Sandstone, as herrings ever do now, in their season, on the best fishing-banks of Caithness or the Moray Firth. I was for some time greatly puzzled in my attempts to restore these ancient fishes, by the peculiarities of their organization. It was in vain I examined every species of fish caught by the fishermen of the place, from the dogfish and the skate to the herring and the mackerel. I could find in our recent fishes no such scales of enamelled bone as those which had covered the *Dipterans*[1] and the *Celacanths*;[2] and no such plate-encased animals as the various species of *Coccosteus*[3] or *Pterichthys*.[4] On the other hand, with the exception of a double line of vertebral processes in the *Coccosteus*, I could find in the ancient fishes no internal skeleton: they had apparently worn all their bones outside, where the crustaceans wear their shells, and were furnished inside with but frameworks of perishable cartilage. It seemed somewhat strange, too, that the geologists who occasionally came my way—some of them men of eminence—seemed to know even less about my Old Red fishes and their peculiarities of structure, than I did myself. I had represented the various species of the deposit simply by numerals, which not a few of the specimens of my collection still retain on

[1] Ancient lung-fishes (Dipnoi) with bony head-coverings and rounded enamelled scales.

[2] A family of "Ganoids" having "hollow fill-spines."

[3] Armour-plated fish very common in the Orcadian O. R., but there is really only one species. Whether related to the "lung-fishes" or to the sharks is a disputed point.

[4] The genus of "Ganoids" encased in enamelled plates and, as to the tail, in small, rounded, bony scales, first discovered by Miller (1831). One species, probably the only one, is named after him. The generic name (winged-fish) is due to its hollow wing-like appendages placed behind the head. The type is now extinct, but it is believed to have been a true fish with a cartilaginous skeleton, like the shark, which lived at the bottom of a river or a great lake. It was small, not exeeding a foot in length.

their faded labels; and waited on until someone should come the way learned enough to substitute for my provisional figures words by which to designate them; but the necessary learning seemed wanting, and I at length came to find that I had got into a *terra incognita* in the geological field, the greater portion of whose organisms were still unconnected with human language. They had no representatives among the vocables.

I formed my first imperfect acquaintance with the recent ganoidal fishes in 1836, from a perusal of the late Dr Hibbert's paper on the deposit of Burdiehouse, which I owed to the kindness of Mr George Anderson. Dr Hibbert, in illustrating the fishes of the Coal Measures, figured and briefly described the Lepidosteus of the American rivers as a still surviving fish of the early type; but his description of the animal, though supplemented shortly after by that of Dr Buckland in his Bridgewater Treatise, carried me but a little way. I saw that two of the Old Red genera— *Osteolepis*[1] and *Diplopterus*[2]—resembled the American fish externally. It will be seen that the first-mentioned of these ancient ichthyolites bears a name compounded, though, in the reverse order, of exactly the same words. But while I found the skeleton of the Lepidosteus described as remarkably hard and solid, I could detect in the *Osteolepis* and its kindred genus no trace of internal skeleton at all. The Cephalaspean[3] genera, too, *Coccosteus* and *Pterichthys*—greatly puzzled me: I could find no living analogues for them; and so, in my often-repeated attempts at restoration, I had to build them up plate by plate, as a child sets up its dissected map or picture bit by bit—every new specimen that turned up furnishing a key for some part previously unknown—until at length, after many an abortive effort, the creatures rose up before me in their strange, unwonted proportions, as they had lived, untold ages before, in the primaeval seas. The extraordinary form

[1] A fringe-finned fish very common in the Orcadian Old Red; allied to the still living Polypterus of the Nile.

[2] A fringe-finned fish. These are of the ordinary fish type.

[3] A family of extinct fishes whose "heads" (cephalai) were covered with "buckler-like" plates.

of *Pterichthys* filled me with astonishment; and with its arched carapace and flat plastron restored before me, I leaped to the conclusion, that as the recent Lepidosteus,[1] with its ancient representatives of the Old Red Sandstone, were sauroid fishes—strange connecting links between fishes and alligators—so the *Pterichthys* was a Chelonian fish—a connecting link between the fish and the tortoise. A gurnard—insinuated so far through the shell of a small tortoise as to suffer its head to protrude from the anterior opening, furnished with oar-like paddles instead of pectoral fins, and with its caudal fin clipped to a point—would, I found, form no inadequate representative of this strangest of fishes. And when, some years after, I had the pleasure of introducing it to the notice of Agassiz, I found that, with all his world-wide experience of its class, it was as much an object of wonder to him as it had been to myself. "It is impossible," we find him saying, in his great work, "to see aught more bizarre in all creation than the *Pterichthyan* genus: the same astonishment that Cuvier felt in examining the Plesiosaurus, I myself experienced, when Mr H. Miller, the first discoverer of these fossils, showed me the specimens which he had detected in the Old Red Sandstone of Cromarty." And there were peculiarities about the *Coccosteus* that scarce less excited my wonder than the general form of the *Pterichthys*, and which, when I first ventured to describe them, were regarded by the higher authorities in Palaeontology as mere blunders on the part of the observer. I have, however, since succeeded in demonstrating that, if blunders at all—which I greatly doubt, for Nature makes very few—it was Nature herself that was in error, not the observer. In this strange *Coccostean* genus, Nature *did* place a group of opposing teeth in each ramus of the lower jaw, just in the line of the symphysis—an arrangement unique, so far as is yet known, in the vertebrate division of creation, and which must have rendered the mouth of these creatures an extraordinary combination of the horizontal

[1] The bony-pike or gar-pike, a fresh water fish of North America, clad, like *Polypterus*, in close fitting enamelled scales.

503

mouth proper to the vertebrata, and of the vertical mouth proper to the crustaceans. It was favourable to the integrity of my work of restoration, that the press was not waiting for me, and that when portions of the creatures on which I wrought were wanting, or plates turned up whose places I was unable to determine, I could lay aside my self-imposed task for the time, and only resume it when some new-found specimen supplied me with the materials requisite for carrying it on. And so the restorations which I completed in 1840, and published in 1841,[1] were found, by our highest authorities in 1848, after they had been set aside for nearly six years, to be essentially the true ones after all. I see, however, that one of the most fanciful and monstrous of all the interim restorations of *Pterichthys* given to the world—that made by Mr Joseph Dinkel in 1844 for the late Dr Mantell, and published in the "Medals of Creation," has been reproduced in the recent illustrated edition of the "Vestiges of Creation." But the ingenious author of that work could scarce act prudently were he to stake the soundness of his hypothesis on the integrity of the restoration. For my own part, I consent, if it can be shown that the *Pterichthys* which once lived and moved on this ancient globe of ours ever either rose or sunk into the *Pterichthys* of Mr Dinkel, freely and fully to confess, not only the possibility, but also the *actuality* of the transmutation of both species and genera. I am first, however, prepared to demonstrate, before any competent jury of Palaeontologists in the world, that not a single plate or scale of Mr Dinkel's restoration represents those of the fish which he professed to restore; that the same judgment applies equally to his restoration of *Coccosteus*; and that, instead of reproducing in his figures the true forms or ancient Cephalaspeans, he has merely given, instead, the likeness of things that never were "in the heaven above, or in the earth beneath, or in the waters under the earth."

The place in the geologic scale, as certainly as the forms and characters, of these ancient fishes, had to be determined. Mr George Anderson had informed me, as early as 1834, that some

[1] *The Old Red Sandstone.*

of them were identical with the ichthyolites of the Gamrie deposit; but then the place of the Gamrie deposit was still to fix. It had been recently referred to the same geological horizon as the Carboniferous Limestone, and was regarded as lying unconformable to the Old Red Sandstone of the district in which it occurs; but, wholly dissatisfied with the evidence adduced, I continued my search, and, though the process was a slow one, saw the position of the Cromarty beds gradually approximating towards determination. It was not, however, until the autumn of 1837 that I got them fairly fixed down to the Old Red Sandstone, and not until the winter of 1839 that I was able conclusively to demonstrate their place in the base of the system, little more than a hundred feet, and in one part not more than eighty feet, above the upper strata of the Great Conglomerate. I had often wished, during my explorations, to be able to extend my field of observation into the neighbouring counties, in order to determine whether I could not possess myself, at a distance, of the evidence which, for a time at least, I failed to find at home; but my daily engagements in the bank fixed me down to Cromarty and its neighbourhood; and I found myself somewhat in the circumstances of a tolerably lively beetle stuck on a pin, that, though able, with a little exertion, to spin round its centre, is yet wholly unable to quit it. I acquired, however, at the close of 1837, in the late Dr John Malcolmson of Madras, a noble auxiliary, who could expatiate freely over the regions virtually barred against me. He had been led to visit Cromarty by a brief description of its geology, rather picturesque than scientific, which had appeared in my legendary volume; and after I had introduced him to its ichthyolitic beds on both sides of the Hill and at Eathie, and acquainted him with their character and organisms, he set himself to trace out the resembling deposits of the neighbouring shires of Banff, Moray, and Nairn. And in little more than a fortnight he had detected the ichthyolites in numerous localities all over an Old Red Sandstone tract, which extends from the primary districts of Banff to near the field of Culloden. The Old Red Sandstone of the north, hitherto deemed so poor in fossils, he found—with the Cromarty deposits as his key—teeming with organic remains. In the spring of 1838, Dr Malcolmson visited England and the Continent, and introduced some of my Cephalaspean fossils to the notice of Agassiz, and some of the evidence which I had laid before him regarding their place in the scale, to Mr (now Sir Roderick) Murchison. And I had the honour, in consequence, of corresponding with both these distinguished men; and the satisfaction of knowing, that by both, the fruit of my labours was deemed important. I observe that Humboldt, in his "Cosmos," specially refers to the judgment of Agassiz on the extraordinary character of the new zoological link with which I had furnished him; and I find Murchison, in his great work on the Silurian System, published in 1839, laying no little emphasis on the stratigraphical fact. After referring to the previously formed opinion that the Gamrie deposit, with its ichthyolites, was not an Old Red one, he goes on to say—"On the other hand, I have recently been informed by Dr Malcolmson, that Mr Miller of Cromarty (who has made some highly interesting discoveries near that place) pointed out to him nodules resembling those of Gamrie, and containing similar fishes, in highly-inclined strata, which are interpolated in, and completely subordinate to, the great mass of Old Red Sandstone of Ross and Cromarty. This important observation will, I trust, be soon communicated to the Geological Society, for it strengthens the inference of M. Agassiz respecting the epoch during which the *Cheiracanthus*[1] and *Cheirolepis*[2] lived." All this will, I am afraid, appear tolerably weak to the reader, and somewhat more than tolerably tedious. Let him remember, however, that the only merit to which I lay claim in the case is that of patient research—a merit in which whoever wills may rival or surpass me; and that this humble faculty of patience, when rightly directed, may lead to more extraordinary developments of idea than even genius itself. What I had been slowly deciphering were the *ideas* of God as developed in the mechanism and framework of His creatures, during the

[1] One of the *Acanthodii*; the "spiny ones," small fish of the shark type.
[2] A genus of fossil fish remotely related to the sturgeon.

second age of vertebrate existence; and one portion of my inquiries determined the date of these ideas, and another their character.

Many of the best sections of the Sutors and the adjacent hills, with their associated deposits, cannot be examined without boat; and so I purchased for a few pounds a light little yawl, furnished with mast and sail, and that rowed four oars, to enable me to carry out my explorations. It made me free of the Cromarty and Moray Firths for some six or eight miles from the town, and afforded me many a pleasant evening's excursion to the deep-sea caves and skerries, and the picturesque surf-wasted stacks of the granitic wall of rock which runs in the Ben Nevis line of elevation, from Shandwick on the east to the Scarfs Crag on the west. I know not a richer tract for the geologist. Independently of the interest that attaches to its sorely-contorted granitic gneiss—which seems, as Murchison shrewdly remarks, to have been protruded through the sedimentary deposits in a solid state, as a fractured bone is sometimes protruded through the integuments—there occurs along the range three several deposits of the Old Red ichthyolites, and three several deposits of the Lias, besides the sub-aqueous ones, with two insulated skerries, which I am inclined to regard as outliers of the Oolite. These last occur in the form of half-tide rocks, very dangerous to the mariner, which lie a full half-mile from the shore, and can be visited with safety only at low water during dead calms, when no ground swell comes rolling in from the sea. I have set out as early as two o'clock in a fine summer morning for these skerries, and, after spending several hours upon them, have been seated at the bank desk before ten; but these were mornings of very hard work. It was the long Saturday afternoons that were my favourite seasons of explorations; and when the weather was fine, my wife would often accompany me in these excursions; and we not unfrequently anchored our skiff in some rocky bay, or over some fishing bank, and, provided with rods and lines, caught, ere our return, a basket of rock-cod or coal-fish for supper, that always seemed of finer flavour than the fish supplied us in the market. These were happy holidays. Shelley predicates of a day of exquisite beauty, that it would continue to "live like joy in memory." I do retain recollections of these evenings spent in my little skiff—recollections mingled with a well-remembered imagery of blue seas and purple hills, and a sun-lit town in the distance, and tall wood-crested precipices near at hand, which flung lengthened shadows across shore and sea—that not merely represent enjoyments which have been, but that, in certain moods of the mind, take the form of enjoyment still. They are favoured spots in the chequered retrospect of the past, on which the sunshine of memory falls more brightly than on most of the others.

When thus employed, there broke out very unexpectedly, a second war with the Liberal Moderates of the town, in which, unwillingly rather than otherwise, I had ultimately to engage. The sacrament of the Supper is celebrated in most of the parish churches of the north of Scotland only once a year; and, as many of the congregations worship at that time in the open air, the summer and autumn seasons are usually selected for the "occasion," as best fitted for open-air meetings. As, however, the celebration is preceded and followed by week-day preachings, and as on one of these week-days—the Thursday preceding the Sacramental Sabbath—no work is done, kirk-sessions usually avoid fixing their sacrament in a busy time, such as the time of harvest in the rural districts, or of the herring-fishing in the seaport towns; and as the parish of Cromarty has both its rural population and its fishing one, the kirk-session of the place have to avoid both periods. And so the early part of July, ere the herring-fishing or the harvest comes on, is the time usually fixed upon for the Cromarty sacrament. In this year, however (1838), it so chanced that the day appointed for the Queen's coronation proved coincident with the sacramental Thursday, and the Liberal Moderate party urged upon the Session that the preparations for the sacrament should give way to the rejoicings for the coronation. We had not been much accustomed to rejoicings of the kind in the north since the good old times when respectable Tory gentlemen used to show themselves drunk in public on the King's

508

birthday, in order to demonstrate their loyalty: the coronation days of both George IV. and William IV. had passed off as quietly as Sabbaths; and the Session, holding that it might be quite as well for people to pray for their young Queen at church, and then quietly drink her health when they got home, as to grow glorious in her behalf in taverns and tap-rooms, refused to alter their day. Believing that, though essentially in the right, they were yet politically in the wrong, and that a plausible case might be made out against them by the newspaper press, I waited on my minister, and urged him to give way to the Liberals, and have his preparation-day changed from Thursday to Friday. He seemed quite willing enough to act on the suggestion; nay, he had made a similar one, he told me, to his Session; but the devout eldership, strong in the precedents of centuries, had declined to subordinate the religious services of the Kirk to the wassail and merriment sanctioned by the State. And so they determined on keeping their day of sacramental preparation on the Thursday, as their fathers had done. Meanwhile, the Liberals held what was very properly termed a public meeting, seeing that, though the public had failed to attend it, the public had been quite at liberty to do so, nay, had even been specially invited; and there appeared in the provincial newspapers a long report of its proceedings, including five speeches—all written by a legal gentleman—in which it was designated a meeting of the inhabitants of the town and parish of Cromarty. The resolutions were, of course, of the most enthusiastically loyal character. There was not a member of the meeting who was not prepared to spend upon himself the last drop of his bottle of port in Her Majesty's behalf. Thursday came—the Thursday of the sacrament and of the coronation; and, with ninety-nine hundredths of the churchgoing portion of my townsfolk, I went to church as usual. The parochial resolutioners, amounting in all to ten, were, I can honestly avouch, scarce at all missed in a congregation of nearly as many hundreds. About mid-day, however, we could hear the muffled report of their carronades; and, shortly after the service was over, and we had

509

returned to our homes, there passed through the streets a forlorn little group of individuals, that looked exceedingly like a press-gang, but was in reality intended for a procession. Though joined by a proprietor from a neighbouring parish, a lawyer from a neighbouring burgh, a small coast-guard party, with its commanding officer, and two half-pay Episcopalian officers besides, the number who walked, including boys, did not exceed twenty-five persons; and of these, as I have said, only ten were parishioners. The processionists had a noble dinner in the head inn of the place—merrier than even dinners of celebration usually are, as it was, of course, loyalty and public spirit to ignore the special claim upon the day asserted by the Church; and the darkening evening saw a splendid bonfire blazing from the brae-head. And the Liberal newspapers south and north taking part with the processionists, in many a paragraph and short leader, represented their frolic—for such it was, and a very foolish one—as a splendid triumph of the people of Cromarty over Presbyterial bigotry and clerical domination. Nay, so bad did the case of my minister and his Session appear, thus placed in opposition to at once the people and the Queen, that the papers on the other side failed to take it up. A well-written letter on the subject by my wife, which fairly stated the facts, was refused admission into even the ecclesiastico-Conservative journal, specially patronized, at the time, by the Scottish Church; and my minister's friends and brethren in the south could do little else than marvel at what they deemed his wondrous imprudence.

I had anticipated, from the first, that his position was to be a bad one; but I ill liked to see him with his back to the wall. And though I had determined, on the rejection of my counsel, to take no part in the quarrel, I now resolved to try whether I could not render it evident that he was really not at issue with his people, but with merely a very inconsiderable clique among them, who had never liked him; and that it was much a joke to describe him as disaffected to his sovereign, simply because he had held his preparation services on the day of her coronation. In order to make good my first point, I took the unpardonable liberty of giving the names in full, in a letter which appeared in our northern newspapers, of every individual who walked in the procession, and represented themselves as the people; and challenged the addition of even a single name to a list ludicrously brief. And in making good the second, I fairly succeeded, as, there were not a few comical circumstances in the transaction, in getting the laughers on my side. The clique was amazingly angry, and wrote not very bright letters, which appeared as advertisements in the newspapers, and paid duty to make evident the fact. There was a shallow and very ignorant young shoemaker in the place, named Chaucer, a native of the south of Scotland, who represented himself as the grandson of the old poet of the days of Edward III., and wrote particularly wretched doggerel to make good his claim. And, having a quarrel with the kirk-session, in a certain delicate department, he had joined the processionists, and celebrated their achievements in a ballad entirely worthy of them. And it was perhaps the severest cut of all, that the recognised leader of the band pronounced Chaucer the younger a greatly better poet than me. There were representations, too, made to my superiors in the banking department at Edinburgh, which procured me a reprimand, though a gentle one; but my superior in Cromarty—Mr Ross—as wise and good a man as any in the direction, and thoroughly acquainted with the merits of the case, was wholly on my side. I am afraid the reader may deem all this very foolish, and hold that I would have been better employed among the rocks, in determining the true relations of their various beds, and the character of their organisms, than in bickering in a petty village quarrel, and making myself enemies. And yet, man being what he is, I fear an ability of efficient squabbling is a greatly more marketable one than any ability whatever of extending the boundaries of natural science. At least so it was, that while my geological researches did nothing for me at this time, my letter in the procession controversy procured for me the offer of a newspaper editorship. But though, in a pecuniary point of view,

I should have considerably bettered my circumstances by closing with it, I found I could not do so without assuming the character of the special pleader, and giving myself to the advocacy of views and principles which I really did not hold; and so I at once declined the office, as one for which I did not deem myself suited, and could not in conscience undertake.

I found about this time more congenial employment, though, of course, it occupied only my leisure hours, in writing the memoir of a townsman—the late Mr William Forsyth, of Cromarty—at the request of his relation and son-in-law, my friend Mr Isaac Forsyth of Elgin. William Forsyth had been a grown man ere the abolition of the hereditary jurisdictions; and from the massiveness and excellence of his character, and his high standing as a merchant, in a part of the country in which merchants at the time were few, he had succeeded, within the precincts of the town, to not a little of the power of the hereditary Sheriff of the district; and after acting for more than half a century as a laborious Justice of the Peace, and succeeding in making up more quarrels than most country lawyers have an opportunity of fomenting—for the age was a rude and combative one, and the merchant ever a peacemaker—he lived long enough to see Liberty-and-Equality Clubs and Processions, and died about the close of the first war of the French Revolution. It was an important half-century in Scotland—though it exhibits but a narrow, inconspicuous front in the history of the country—that intervened between the times of the hereditary jurisdictions and the Liberty-and-Equality Clubs. It was specially the period during which popular opinion began to assume its potency, and in which the Scotland of the past merged, in consequence, into the very dissimilar Scotland of the present. And I derived much pleasure in tracing some of the more striking features of this transition age in the biography of Mr Forsyth. My little work was printed, but not published, and distributed by Mr Forsyth of Elgin among the friends of the family, as perhaps a better and more adequate memorial of a worthy and able man than could be placed over his grave. It was on the occasion of the death of his last-surviving child, the late Mrs Mackenzie of Cromarty—a lady from whom I had received much kindness, and under whose hospitable roof I had the opportunity afforded me of meeting not a few superior men—that my memoir was undertaken; and I regarded it as a fitting tribute to a worthy family just passed away, at once deserving of being remembered for its own sake, and to which I owed a debt of gratitude.

In the spring of 1839, a sad bereavement darkened my household, and for a time left me little heart to pursue my wonted amusements, literary or scientific. We had been visited, ten months after our marriage, by a little girl, whose presence had added not a little to our happiness; home became more emphatically such from the presence of the child, that in a few months had learned so well to know its mother, and in a few more to take its stand in the nurse's arms, at an upper window that commanded the street, and to recognise and make signs to its father as he approached the house. Its few little words, too, had a fascinating interest to our ears;—our own names, lisped in a language of its own, every time we approached; and the simple Scotch vocable "awa, awa," which it knew how to employ in such plaintive tones as we retired, and that used to come back upon us in recollection, like an echo from the grave, when, its brief visit over, it had left us for ever, and its fair face and silken hair lay in darkness amid the clods of the churchyard. In how short a time had it laid hold of our affections! Two brief years before, and we knew it not; and now it seemed as if the void which it left in our hearts the whole world could not fill. We buried it beside the old chapel of St Regulus, with the deep rich woods all around, save where an opening in front commands the distant land and the blue sea; and where the daisies which it had learned to love, mottled, starlike, the mossy mounds; and where birds, whose songs its ear had become skilful enough to distinguish, pour their notes over its little grave. The following simple but truthful stanzas, which I found among its mother's papers, seem to have been written in this place—sweetest of burying grounds—a few weeks after its burial, when a chill and backward spring, that had scowled upon its lingering illness, broke out at once into genial summer:—

Thou art "awa, awa," from thy mother's side,
　　And "awa, awa," from thy father's knee;
Thou'rt "awa" from our blessing, our care, our caressing,
　　But "awa" from our hearts thou'lt never be.

All things, dear child, that were wont to please thee
　　Are round thee here in beauty bright,—
There's music rare in the cloudless air,
　　And the earth is teeming with living delight.

Thou'rt "awa, awa," from the bursting spring time,
　　Tho' o'er thy head its green boughs wave;
The lambs are leaving their little footprints
　　Upon the turf of thy new-made grave.

And art thou "awa," and "awa" for ever,—
　　That little face,—that tender frame,—
That voice which first, in sweetest accents,
　　Call'd me the mother's thrilling name,—

That head of nature's finest moulding,—
　　Those eyes, the deep night ether's blue,
Where sensibility its shadows
　　Of ever-changing meaning threw?

Thy sweetness, patience under suffering,
　　All promised us an opening day
Most fair, and told that to subdue thee
　　Would need but love's most gentle sway.

Ah me! 'twas here I thought to lead thee,
　　And tell thee what are life and death,
And raise thy serious thoughts' first waking
　　To Him who holds our every breath.

And does my selfish heart then grudge thee
　　That angels are thy teachers now,—
That glory from thy Saviour's presence
　　Kindles the crown upon thy brow?

O no! to me earth must be lonelier,
    Wanting thy voice, thy hand, thy love;
Yet dost thou dawn a star of promise,
    Mild beacon to the world above.

CHAPTER XXV

"All for the Church, and a little less for the State."—BELHAVEN.

I HAD taken no very deep interest in the Voluntary controversy.[1] There was, I thought, a good deal of over-statement and exaggeration on both sides. On the one hand, the Voluntaries failed to convince me that a State endowment for ecclesiastical purposes is in itself in any degree a bad thing. I had direct experience to the contrary. I had evidence the most unequivocal that in various parts of the country it was a very excellent thing indeed. It had been a very excellent thing, for instance, in the parish of Cromarty, ever since the Revolution, down to the death of Mr Smith—in reality a valuable patrimony of the people there; for it had supplied the parish, free of cost, with a series of popular and excellent ministers, whom otherwise the parishioners would have had to pay for themselves. And it had now given us my friend Mr Stewart, one of the ablest and honestest ministers in Scotland, or elsewhere, whether Established or Dissenting. And these facts, which were but specimens of a numerous class, had a tangibility and solidity about them which influenced me more than all the theoretic reasonings pressed on my attention about the mischief done to the Church by the over-kindness of Constantine, or the corrupting effects of State favour. But then I could as little agree with some of my friends on the endowment side, that the Establishment, even in Scotland, was everywhere of value, as with some of the Voluntaries that it was nowhere of any. I had resided for months together in various parts of the country, where it would have mattered not a farthing to any one save the minister and his family, though the Establishment had been struck down at a

---

[1] Between the leading divines of the established Church and the Secession (1829-34), concerning the Scriptural propriety and the utility of Church Establishments.

516

blow. Religion and morals would have no more suffered by the annihilation of the minister's stipend, than by the suppression of the pension of some retired supervisor or superannuated officer of customs. Nor could I forget, that the only religion, or appearance of religion, that existed in parties of workmen among which I had been employed (as in the south of Scotland, for instance), was to be found among their Dissenters—most of them, at the time, asserters of the Voluntary principle. If the other workmen were reckoned, statistically at least, adherents of the Establishment, it was not because they either benefited by it or cared for it, but only somewhat in the way that, according to the popular English belief, persons born at sea are held to belong to the parish of Stepney. Further, I did not in the least like the sort of company into which the Voluntary controversy had introduced the good men on both sides; it gave a common cause to the Voluntary and the Infidel, and drew them cordially together; and, on the other hand, placed side by side, on terms pretentiously friendly, the pious asserter of endowments and the irreligious old Tory. There was religion on both sides of the controversy, but a religious controversy it was not.

The position of my grandmother's family, including of course Uncles James and Sandy, was a sort of midway one between the Secession and the Establishment. My grandmother had quitted the family of Donald Roy long ere he had been compelled, very unwillingly, to leave the Church; and as no forced settlements had taken place in the parish into which she had removed, and as its ministers had been all men of the right stamp, she had done what Donald himself had been so desirous to do—remained an attached member of the Establishment. One of her sisters had, however, married in Nigg; and she and her husband, following Donald into the ranks of the Secession, had reared one of their boys to the ministry, who became, in course of time, the respected minister of the congregation which his great-grandfather had founded. And, as the contemporary and first cousin of my uncles, the minister used to call upon them every time he came to town; and my Uncle James, in turn (Uncle Sandy very rarely went to the country), never missed, when in Nigg, or its neighbourhood, to repay his visits. There was thus a good deal of intercourse kept up between the families, not without effect. Most of the books of modern theology which my uncles read were Secession books, recommended by their cousin; and the religious magazine for which they subscribed was a Secession magazine. The latter bore, I remember, the name of the *Christian Magazine, or Evangelical Repository*. It was not one of the brightest of periodicals, but a sound and solid one, with, as my uncles held, a good deal of the old unction about it; and there was, in especial, one of the contributors whose papers they used to pick out as of peculiar excellence, and not unfrequently read a second time. They bore the somewhat Greek-looking signature of *Leumas*, as if the writer had been a brother or cousin-german of some of the old Christians to whom Paul used to notify kind regards and good wishes at the end of his epistles; but it was soon discovered that *Leumas* was merely the proper name Samuel reversed, though who the special Samuel was who turned his signature to the right about, placing the wrong end foremost, and wrote with all the concise weight and gravity of the old divines, my uncles never knew. They had both passed away ere, in perusing the "Second Gallery of Literary Portraits," I found myself introduced to worthy old *Leumas*, also a denizen of the unseen world at the time, as the father of the writer of that brilliant work—the Rev. George Gilfillan of Dundee. This kind of writing had, of course, its proper effect on my uncles, and, through them, on the family; it kept up our respect for the Secession. The Established Church, too, was in those days a tolerably faulty institution. My uncles took an interest in missions: and the Church had none; nay, its deliberate decision against them—that of 1796—remained still unreversed. It had had, besides, its forced settlements in our immediate neighbour-hood; and Moderatism, wise and politic in its generation, had perpetrated them by the hands of some of the better ministers of the district, who had learned to do what they themselves believed to be very wicked things, when their Church bade them—a sort of professional license which my uncles could not in the least understand. In short, the Secession better pleased them, in the main, than the Establishment, though to the Establishment they continued to adhere, and failed to see on what Seceder principle their old friends were becoming Voluntaries. On the breaking out of the controversy, I remembered all this; and, when told by good men of the Established Church that well-nigh all the vital religion of the country was on our side, and that it had left the Voluntary Seceders, though the good men themselves honestly believed what they said, I could not. Further, the heads of a conversation which I had overheard in my cousin the Seceder minister's house when I was a very young boy, and to which it could have been little suspected that I was listening—for I was playing at the time on the floor—had taken a strong hold of my memory, and often returned upon me at this period. My cousin and some of his elders were mourning—very sincerely, I cannot doubt—over the decay of religion among them: they were falling far short, they said, of the attainments of their fathers; there were no Donald Roys among them now; and yet they felt it to be a satisfaction, though a sad one, that the little religion which there was in the district seemed to be all among themselves. And now here was there exactly the same sort of conviction, equally strong, on the other side. But with all that liberally-expressed charity which forms one of the distinctive features of the present time, and is in reality one of its best things, there is still a vast amount of appreciation of this partial kind. Friends are seen in the Christian aspect; opponents in the polemic one; and it is too often forgotten that the friends have a polemic aspect to their opponents, and the opponents a Christian aspect to their friends. And not only in the present, but at all former periods, the case seems to have been the same. I am sometimes half disposed to think, that either the Prophet Elijah, or the seven thousand honest men who had not bowed the knee to Baal, must have been dissenters. Had the Prophet been entirely at one in his views with the seven thousand, it is not easy to conceive how he could have been wholly ignorant of their existence.

With all these latitudinarian convictions, however, I was thoroughly an Establishment man. The revenues of the Scottish Church I regarded as I have said, as the patrimony of the Scottish people; and I looked forward to a time when that unwarrantable appropriation of them, through which the aristocracy had sought to extend its influence, but which had served only greatly to reduce its power in the country, would come to an end. What I specially wanted, in short, was, not the confiscation of the people's patrimony, but simply its restoration from the Moderates and the lairds. And in the enactment of the Veto Law I saw the process of restoration fairly begun. I would have much preferred seeing a good broad anti-patronage agitation raised on the part of the Church. As shrewdly shown at the time by the late Dr M'Crie, such a course would have been at once wiser and safer. But for such an agitation even the Church's better ministers were not in the least prepared. From 1712 to 1784—a period of seventy-two years—the General Assembly had yearly raised its voice against the enactment of the patronage law of Queen Anne, as an unconstitutional encroachment on those privileges of the Church and those rights of the Scottish people which the Treaty of Union had been framed to secure. But the half-century which had passed since, through the act of a Moderate majority, the protest had been dropped, had produced the natural effect. By much the greater part of even the better ministers of the Church had been admitted into their offices through the law of patronage; and, naturally grateful to the patrons who had befriended them, they hesitated to make open war on the powers that had been exerted in their own behalf. According to Solomon, the "gift" had to a certain extent "destroyed the heart;" and so they were prepared to take up merely a half-way position, which their predecessors, the old popular divines, would have liked exceedingly ill. I could not avoid seeing that, fixed in a sort of overtopped hollow, if I may so speak, between the claims of patronage on the one hand, and the rights of the people on the other, it was a most perilous position, singularly open to misconception and misrepresentation on both sides; and as it virtually stripped the patrons of half their power, and extended to the people only half their rights, I was not a little afraid that the patrons might be greatly more indignant than the people grateful, and that the Church might, in consequence, find herself exposed to the wrath of very potent enemies, and backed by the support of only lukewarm friends. But however perilous and difficult as a post of occupation, it was, I could not avoid believing, a position conscientiously taken up; nor could I doubt that its grounds were strictly constitutional. The Church, in a case of disputed settlement, might, I believed, have to forfeit the temporalities if her decision differed from that of the law courts, but only the temporalities connected with the case at issue; and these I deemed worth risking in the popular behalf, seeing that they might be regarded as already lost to the country in every case in which a parish was assigned to a minister whom the parishioners refused to hear. It rejoiced me, too, to see the revival of the old spirit in the Church; and so I looked with an interest on the earlier stages of her struggle with the law courts, greatly more intense than that with which any mere political contest had ever inspired me. I saw with great anxiety decision after decision go against her; first that of the Court of Session in March 1838, and next that of the House of Lords in May 1839; and then, with the original Auchterarder case[1] of collision, I saw that of Lethendy and Marnoch mixed up; and, as one entanglement succeeded another, confusion becoming worse confounded. It was only when the Church's hour of peril came that I learned to know how much

[1] The call to the presentee to the parish of Auchterarder, Perth, was signed by only two persons out of a population of 3000; the large majority of the congregation protesting against his settlement. Thereupon the Church refused ordination. Patron and presentee took the case to the Court of Session which decided in their favour, enjoining the ordination of the presentee. The Church appealed to the House of Lords, and there the judgment of the Scottish Court was sustained (2nd May 1839). Lord Brougham, in particular, maintained that the protest of the congregation was of no avail to prevent the ordination than the kicking of the "champion's" horse would be to stop a Coronation. Sentiments expressed in this spirit marked him out specially for attack.

I really valued her, and how strong and numerous the associations were that bound her to my affections. I had experienced at least the average amount of interest in political measures whose tendency and principles I deemed good in the main—such as the Reform Bill, the Catholic Emancipation Act, and the Emancipation of the Negroes; but they had never cost me an hour's sleep. Now, however, I felt more deeply; and for at least one night, after reading the speech of Lord Brougham, and the decision of the House of Lords in the Auchterarder case, I slept none.

In truth, the position of the Church at this time seemed critical in the extreme. Offended by the usage which she had received at the hands of the Whigs, in her claims for endowments to her new chapels, and startled by their general treatment of the Irish Establishment, and the suppression of the ten bishoprics, she had thrown her influence into the Tory scale, and had done much to produce that reaction against the Liberal party in Scotland which took place during the Ministry of Lord Melbourne. In the representation of at least one county in which he was all-potent— Ross-shire—she had succeeded in substituting a Tory for a Whig; and there were few districts in the kingdom in which she had not very considerably increased the votes on the Tory, or, as it was termed, Conservative side. The people, however, though they might, and did, become quite indifferent enough to the Whigs, could not follow her into the Tory ranks. They stood aloof—very suspicious, not without reason, of her new political friends—no admirers of the newspapers which she patronized, and not in the least able to perceive the nature of the interest which she had begun to take in supernumerary bishops and the Irish Establishment. And now, when once more in a position worthy of her old character, and when her Tory friends—converted at once into the bitterest and most ungenerous of enemies—were turning upon her to rend her, she had at once to encounter the hostility of the Whigs, and the indifferency of the people. Further, with but one, or at most two exceptions, all the newspapers which she had patronised declared against her, and were throughout the struggle the bitterest and most abusive of her opponents. The Voluntaries, too, joined with redoubled vehemence in the cry raised to drown her voice, and misinterpret and misrepresent her claims. The general current of opinion ran strongly against her. My minister, warmly interested in the success of the Non-Intrusion principle, has told me, that for many months past I was the only man in his parish that seemed thoroughly to sympathize with him; and I have no doubt that the late Dr George Cook was perfectly correct and truthful when he about this time remarked, in one of his public addresses, that he could scarce enter an inn or a stage-coach without finding respectable men inveighing against the utter folly of the Non-Intrusionists, and the worse than madness of the Church Courts.

Could I do nothing for my church in her hour of peril? There was, I believed, no other institution in the country half so valuable, or in which the people had so large a stake. The Church was of right theirs—a patrimony won for them by the blood of their fathers, during the struggles and sufferings of more than a hundred years; and now that her better ministers were trying, at least partially, to rescue that patrimony for them from the hands of an aristocracy who, as a body at least, had no spiritual interest in the Church—belonging, as most of its members did, to a different communion—they were in danger of being put down, unbacked by the popular support which in such a cause they deserved. Could I not do something to bring up the people to their assistance? I tossed wakefully throughout a long night, in which I formed my plan of taking up the purely popular side of the question; and in the morning I sat down to state my views to the people, in the form of a letter addressed to Lord Brougham. I devoted to my new employment every moment not imperatively demanded by my duties in the bank office, and, in about a week after, was able to despatch the manuscript of my pamphlet to the respected manager of the Commercial Bank—Mr Robert Paul— a gentleman from whom I had received much kindness when in Edinburgh, and who, in the great ecclesiastical struggle, took decided part with the Church. Mr Paul brought it to his minister, the Rev Mr Candlish of St George's (now Dr Candlish), who, recognising its popular character, urged its immediate publication; and the manuscript was accordingly put into the hands of Mr Johnstone, the well-known Church bookseller. Dr Candlish had been one of a party of ministers and elders of the Evangelical majority who had met in Edinburgh shortly before, to take measures for the establishment of a newspaper. All the Edinburgh press, with the exception of one newspaper, had declared against the ecclesiastical party; and even that one rather received articles and paragraphs in their behalf through the friendship of the proprietor, than was itself on their side. There had been a larger infusion of Whiggism among the Edinburgh Churchmen than in any other part of the kingdom. They had seen very much, in consequence, that the line taken by the Conservative portion of their friends, in addressing the people through the press, had not been an efficient one;—their friends had set themselves to make the people both good Conservatives and good Churchmen, and of course had never got over the first point, and never would; and what they now proposed was, to establish a paper that, without supporting any of the old parties in the State, should be as Liberal in its politics as in its Churchmanship. But there was a preliminary point which they also could not get over. All the ready-made editors of the kingdom, if I may so speak, had declared against them; and for want of an editor, their meeting had succeeded in originating not the intended newspaper, but merely a formal recognition, in a few resolutions, of its desirableness and importance. On reading my pamphlet in manuscript, however, Dr Candlish at once concluded that the desiderated want was to be supplied by its writer. Here, he said, is the editor we have been looking for. Meanwhile, my little work issued from the press, and was successful. It ran rapidly through four editions of a thousand copies each—the number, as I subsequently ascertained, of a popular non-intrusion pamphlet that would fairly *sell*—and was read pretty extensively by men who were not Non-Intrusionists.

Among these there were several members of the Ministry of the time, including the late Lord Melbourne, who at first regarded it, as I have been informed, as the composition, under a popular form and a *nom de guerre*, of some of the Non-Intrusion leaders in Edinburgh; and by the late Mr O'Connell, who had no such suspicions, and who, though he lacked sympathy, as he said, with the ecclesiastical views which it advocated, enjoyed what he termed its "racy English," and the position in which it placed the Noble Lord to whom it was addressed. It was favourably noticed, too, by Mr Gladstone, in his elaborate work on Church Principles; and was, in short, both in the extent of its circulation, and the circles into which it found its way, a very successful pamphlet.

So filled was my mind with our ecclesiastical controversy, that, while yet unacquainted with the fate of my first *brochure*, I was busily engaged with a second. A remarkable case of intrusion had occurred in the district rather more than twenty years before; and, after closing my week's labours in the bank, I set out for the house of a friend in a neighbouring parish on a Saturday evening, that I might attend the deserted church on the following Sabbath, and glean from actual observation the materials of a truthful description, which would, I trusted, tell in the controversy. And as the case was one of those in which truth proves stronger than fiction, what I had to describe was really very curious; and my description received an extensive circulation. I insert the passage entire, as properly a part of my story.

"There were associations of a peculiarly high character connected with this northern parish. For more than a thousand years it had formed part of the patrimony of a truly noble family, celebrated by Philip Doddridge for its great moral worth, and by Sir Walter Scott for its high military genius; and through whose influence the light of the Reformation had been introduced into this remote corner, at a period when the neighbouring districts were enveloped in the original darkness. In a later age it had been honoured by the fines and proscriptions of Charles II.; and its minister—one of those men of God whose names still live in the memory of the country, and whose biography occupies no small space in the recorded history of her 'worthies'—had rendered himself so obnoxious to the tyranny and irreligion of the time, that he was ejected from his charge more than a year before any of the other non-conforming clergymen of the Church.[1] I approached the parish from the east. The day was warm and pleasant; the scenery through which I passed, some of the finest in Scotland. The mountains rose on the right, in huge Titanic masses, that seemed to soften their purple and blue in the clear sunshine, to the delicate tone of the deep sky beyond; and I could see the yet unwasted snows of winter glittering, in little detached masses, along their summits. The hills of the middle region were feathered with wood; a forest of mingled oaks and larches, which still blended the tender softness of spring with the full foliage of summer, swept down to the path; the wide undulating plain below was laid out into fields, mottled with cottages, and waving with the yet unshot corn; and a noble arm of the sea winded along the lower edge for nearly twenty miles, losing itself to the west among blue hills and jutting headlands, and opening in the east to the main ocean, through a magnificent gateway of rock. But the little groups which I encountered at every turning of the path, as they journeyed, with all the sober, well-marked decency of a Scottish Sabbath morning, towards the church of a neighbouring parish, interested me more than even the scenery. The clan which inhabited this part of the country had borne a well-marked character in Scottish story. Buchanan had described it as one of the most fearless and warlike in the north. It served under the Bruce at Bannockburn. It was the first to rise in arms to protect Queen Mary, on her visit to Inverness, from the intended violence of Huntly. It fought the battles of Protestantism in Germany, under Gustavus Adolphus. It covered the retreat of the English at Fontenoy; and presented an unbroken front to the enemy, after all the other troops had quitted the field. And it was the descendants of those very men who were now passing me on the road. The rugged, robust form, half bone, half muscle—the springy firmness of the tread—the grave, manly countenance—all gave indication that the original characteristics survived in their full strength; and it was a strength that inspired confidence, not fear. There were grey-haired, patriarchal-looking men among the groups, whose very air seemed impressed by a sense of the duties of the day; nor was there aught that did not agree with the object of the journey, in the appearance of even the youngest and least thoughtful.

"As I proceeded, I came up with a few people who were travelling in a contrary direction. A Secession meeting-house has lately sprung up in the parish, and these formed part of the congregation. A path, nearly obscured by grass and weeds, leads from the main road to the parish church. It was with difficulty I could trace it, and there were none to direct me, for I was now walking alone. The parish burying-ground, thickly sprinkled with graves and tombstones, surrounds the church. It is a quiet, solitary spot, of great beauty, lying beside the sea-shore, and as service had not yet commenced, I whiled away half an hour in sauntering among the stones, and deciphering the inscriptions. I could trace in the rude monuments of this retired little spot, a brief but interesting history

[1] Thomas Hog of Kiltearn. See "Scots Worthies;" or the cheap publication volumes of the Free Church for 1846 (Miller).

of the district. The older tablets, grey and shaggy with the mosses and lichens of three centuries, bear, in their uncouth semblances of the unwieldy battle-axe and double-handed sword of ancient warfare, the meet and appropriate symbols of the earlier time. But the more modern testify to the introduction of a humanizing influence. They speak of a life after death, in the "holy texts" described by the poet; or certify, in a quiet humility of style which almost vouches for their truth, that the sleepers below were "honest men, of blameless character, and who feared God." There is one tombstone, however, more remarkable than all the others. It lies beside the church-door, and testifies, in an antique inscription, that it covers the remains of the "GREAT MAN OF GOD AND FAITHFUL MINISTER OF JESUS CHRIST," who had endured persecution for the truth in the dark days of Charles and his brother. He had outlived the tyranny of the Stuarts; and, though worn by years and sufferings, had returned to his parish on the Revolution, to end his course as it had begun. He saw, ere his death, the law of patronage abolished, and the popular right virtually secured; and, fearing lest his people might be led to abuse the important privilege conferred upon them, and calculating aright on the abiding influence of his own character among them, he gave charge on his death-bed to dig his grave in the threshold of the church that they might regard him as a sentinel placed at the door, and that his tombstone might speak to them as they passed out and in. The inscription, which, after the lapse of nearly a century and a half, is still perfectly legible, concludes with the following remarkable words:—"THIS STONE SHALL BEAR WITNESS AGAINST THE PARISHIONERS OF KILTEARN IF THEY BRING ANE UNGODLY MINISTER IN HERE." Could the imagination of a poet have originated a more striking conception in connection with a church deserted by all its better people, and whose minister fattens on his hire, useless and contented?

"I entered the church, for the clergyman had just gone in. There were from eight to ten persons scattered over the pews below, and seven in the galleries above; and these, as there were no more '*Peter Clarks*' or '*Michael Tods*'[1] in the parish, composed the entire congregation. I wrapped myself up in my plaid, and sat down; and the service went on in the usual course; but it sounded in my ears like a miserable mockery. The precentor sung almost alone; and ere the clergyman had reached the middle of his discourse, which he read in an impassioned monotonous tone, nearly one half his skeleton congregation had fallen asleep; and the drowsy, listless expression of the others showed that, for every good purpose, they might have been asleep too. And Sabbath after Sabbath has this unfortunate man gone the same tiresome round, and with exactly the same effects, for the last twenty-three years;—at no time regarded by the better clergymen of the district as really their brother;—on no occasion recognised by

[1] Peter Clark and Michael Tod were the only individuals who in a population of three thousand souls, attached their signature to the *call* of the obnoxious presentee, Mr Young, in the famous Auchterarder case (Miller).

the parish as virtually its minister;—with a dreary vacancy and a few indifferent hearts inside his church, and the stone of the Covenanter at the door. Against whom does the inscription testify? for the people have escaped. Against the patron, the intruder, and the law of Bolingbroke—the Dr Robertsons of the last age, and the Dr Cooks of the present. It is well to learn from this hapless parish the exact sense in which, in a different state of matters, the Rev. Mr Young would have been constituted minister of Auchterarder. It is well, too, to learn, that there may be vacancies in the Church where no blank appears in the Almanac.

On my return home from this journey, early on the following Monday, I found a letter from Edinburgh awaiting me, requesting me to meet there with the leading Non-Intrusionists. And so, after describing, in the given extract, the scene which I had just witnessed, and completing my second pamphlet, I set out for Edinburgh, and saw for the first time men with whose names I had been familiar during the course of the Voluntary and Non-Intrusion controversies. And entering into their plans, though with no little shrinking of heart, lest I should be found unequal to the demands of a twice-a-week paper, that would have to stand, in Ishmael's position, against almost the whole newspaper press of the kingdom, I agreed to undertake the editorship of their projected newspaper, the *Witness*. Save for the intense interest with which I regarded the struggle, and the stake possessed in it, as I believed, by the Scottish people, no consideration whatever would have induced me to take a step so fraught, as I thought at the time, with peril and discomfort. For full twenty years I had never been engaged in a quarrel on my own account; all my quarrels, either directly or indirectly, were ecclesiastical ones;— I had fought for my minister, or for my brother parishioners; and fain now would I have lived at peace with all men; but the editorship of a Non-Intrusion newspaper involved, as a portion of its duties, war with all the world. I held, besides—not aware how very much the spur of necessity quickens production—that its twice-a-week demands would fully occupy all my time, and that I would have to resign, in consequence, my favourite pursuit— geology. I had once hoped, too—though of late years the hope had been becoming faint—to leave some little mark behind me in the literature of my country; but the last remains of the expectation had now to be resigned. The newspaper editor writes in sand when the flood is coming in. If he but succeed in influencing opinion for the present, he must be content to be forgotten in the future. But believing the cause to be a good one, I prepared for a life of strife, toil, and comparative obscurity. In counting the cost, I very considerably exaggerated it; but I trust I may say that, in all honesty, and with no sinister aim, or prospect of worldly advantage, I *did* count it, and fairly undertook to make the full sacrifice which the cause demanded.

It was arranged that our new paper should start with the new twelvemonth (1840); and I meanwhile returned to Cromarty, to fulfil my engagements with the bank till the close of its financial year, which in the Commercial Bank offices takes place at the end of autumn. Shortly after my return, Dr Chalmers visited the place on the last of his Church Extension journeys; and I heard, for the first time, that most impressive of modern orators address a public meeting, and had a curious illustration of the power which his *"deep mouth"* could communicate to passages little suited, one might suppose, to call forth the vehemency of his eloquence. In illustrating one of his points, he quoted from my "Memoir of William Forsyth" a brief anecdote, set in description of a kind which most men would have read quietly enough, but which, coming from him, seemed instinct with the Homeric vigour and force. The extraordinary impressiveness which he communicated to the passage served to show me, better than aught else, how imperfectly great orators may be represented by their written speeches. Admirable as the published sermons and addresses of Dr Chalmers are, they impart no adequate idea of that wonderful power and impressiveness in which he excelled all other British preachers.[1]

---

[1] The following is the passage which was honoured on this occasion by Chalmers, and which told, in his hands, with all the effects of the most powerful acting:—"Saunders Macivor, the mate of the 'Elizabeth', was a grave and somewhat hard-favoured man, powerful in bone and muscle, even after he had considerably turned his sixtieth year, and much respected for his inflexible integrity and the depth of his religious feelings. Both the mate and his devout

I had been introduced to the Doctor in Edinburgh a few weeks before; but on this occasion I saw rather more of him. He examined with curious interest my collection of geological specimens, which already contained not a few valuable fossils that could be seen nowhere else; and I had the pleasure of spending the greater part of a day in visiting in his company, by boat, some of the more striking scenes of the Cromarty Sutors. I had long looked up to Chalmers as, on the whole, the man of largest mind which the Church of Scotland had ever produced;—not more intense or practical than Knox, but broader of faculty; nor yet fitted by nature or accomplishment to make himself a more enduring name in literature than Robertson, but greatly nobler in sentiment, and of a larger grasp of general intellect. With any of our other Scottish ministers it might be invidious to compare him; seeing that some of the ablest of them are, like Henderson, little more than mere historic portraits drawn by their contemporaries,

wife were especial favourites with Mr Porteous of Kilmuir—a minister of the same class as the Pedens, Renwicks, and Cargills of a former age; and on one occasion when the sacrament was dispensed in his parish, and Saunders was absent on one of his Continental voyages, Mrs Macivor was an inmate of the manse. A tremendous storm burst out in the night-time, and the poor woman lay awake, listening in utter terror to the fearful roarings of the wind, as it howled in the chimneys, and shook the casements and the doors. At length, when she could lie still no longer, she arose, and crept along the passage to the door of the minister's chamber. "O, Mr Porteous," she said, "Mr Porteous, do ye no hear that?—and poor Saunders on his way back frae Holland! O, rise, rise, and ask the strong help o' your Master!" The minister accordingly rose, and entered his closet. The 'Elizabeth' at this critical moment was driving onwards through spray and darkness, along the northern shores of the Moray Firth. The fearful skerries of Shandwick, where so many gallant vessels have perished, were close at hand: and the increasing roll of the sea showed the gradual shallowing of the water. Macivor and his old townsman, Robert Hossack, stood together at the binnacle. An immense wave came rolling behind, and they had but barely time to clutch to the nearest hold, when it broke over them half-mast high, sweeping spars, bulwarks, cordage, all before it, in its course. It passed, but the vessel rose not. Her deck remained buried in a sheet of foam, and she seemed settling down by the head. There was a frightful pause. First, however, the bowsprit and the butts of the windlass began to emerge—next the forecastle—the vessel seemed as if shaking herself from the load; and then the whole deck appeared, as she went tilting over the next wave. 'There are still more mercies in store for us,' said Macivor, addressing his companion: 'she floats still.' 'O, Saunders, Saunders!' exclaimed Robert, 'there was surely some God's soul at work for us, or she would never have *cowed* yon'." (Miller).

but whose true intellectual measure cannot, from the lack of the necessary materials on which to form a judgment, be now taken anew; and that many of the others employed fine faculties in work, literary and ministerial, which, though important in its consequences, was scarce less ephemeral in its character than even the labours of the newspaper editor. The mind of Chalmers was emphatically a many-sided one. Few men ever came into friendly contact with him, who did not find in it, if they had really anything good in them, moral or intellectual, a side that suited themselves; and I had been long struck by that union which his intellect exhibited of a comprehensive philosophy with a true poetic faculty, very exquisite in quality, though dissociated from what Wordsworth terms the "accomplishment of verse." I had not a little pleasure in contemplating him on this occasion as the *poet* Chalmers. The day was calm and clear; but there was a considerable swell rolling in from the German Ocean, on which our little vessel rose and fell, and which sent the surf high against the rocks. The sunshine played amid the broken crags a-top, and amid the foliage of an overhanging wood; or caught, half-way down, some projecting tuft of ivy; but the faces of the steeper precipices were brown in the shade, and where the wave roared in deep caves beneath, all was dark and chill. There were several members of the party who attempted engaging the Doctor in conversation; but he was in no conversational mood. It would seem as if the words addressed to his ear failed at first to catch his attention, and that, with a painful courtesy, he had to gather up their meaning from the remaining echoes, and to reply to them doubtfully and monosyllabically, at the least possible expense of mind. His face wore, meanwhile, an air of dreamy enjoyment. He was busy, evidently, among the crags and bosky hollows, and would have enjoyed himself more had he been alone. In the middle of one noble precipice, that reared its tall pine-crested brow more than a hundred yards overhead, there was a bush-covered shelf of considerable size, but wholly inaccessible; for the rock dropped sheer into it from above, and then sank perpendicularly from its outer edge to the beach below; and the insulated shelf, in its green unapproachable solitude, had evidently caught his eye. *It* was the scene, I said,—taking the direction of his eye, as the antecedent for the *it*—it was the scene, says tradition, of a sad tragedy during the times of the persecution of Charles. A renegade chaplain, rather weak than wicked, threw himself, in a state of wild despair, over the precipice above; and his body, intercepted in its fall by that shelf, lay unburied among the bushes for years after, until it had bleached into a dry and whitened skeleton. Even as late as the last age, the shelf continued to retain the name of the "Chaplain's Lair." I found that my communication, chiming in with his train of cogitation at the time, caught both his ear and mind; and his reply, though brief, was expressive of the gratification which its snatch of incident had conveyed. As our skiff sped on a few oar-lengths more, we disturbed a flock of sea-gulls, that had been sporting in the sunshine over a shoal of sillocks; and a few of them winged their way to a jutting crag that rose immediately beside the shelf. I saw Chalmers' eye gleam as it followed them. "Would you not like, Sir," he said, addressing himself to my minister, who sat beside him—"Would you not like to be a sea-gull. I think *I* would. Sea-gulls are free of the three elements—earth, air, and water. These birds were sailing but half a minute since without boat, at once angling and dining, and now they are already rusticating in the Chaplain's Lair. I think I could enjoy being a sea-gull." I saw the Doctor once afterwards in a similar mood. When on a visit to him in Burntisland, in the following year, I marked, on approaching the shore by boat, a solitary figure stationed on the sward-crested trap-rock which juts into the sea immediately below the town; and after the time spent in hiking and walking round to the spot, there was the solitary figure still, standing motionless as when first seen. It was Chalmers—the same expression of dreamy enjoyment impressed on his features as I had witnessed in the little skiff, and with his eyes turned on the sea and the opposite land. It was a lovely morning. A faint breeze had just begun to wrinkle in detached belts and patches the mirror-like blackness of the previous calm, in which the broad Firth had lain sleeping since day-break; and the sunlight danced on the new-raised wavelets; while a thin long wreath of blue mist, which seemed coiling its tail like a snake round the distant Inchkeith, was slowly raising the folds of its dragon-like neck and head from off the Scottish capital, dim in the distance, and unveiling fortalice, and tower, and spire, and the noble curtain of blue hills behind. And there was Chalmers, evidently enjoying the exquisiteness of the scene, as only by the true poet scenery can be enjoyed. Those striking metaphors which so abound in his writings, and which so often, without apparent effort, lay the material world before the reader, show how thoroughly he must have drunk in the beauties of nature; the images retained in his mind became, like words to the ordinary man, the signs by which he thought, and, as such, formed an important element in the power of his thinking. I have seen his "Astronomical Discourses" disparagingly dealt with by a slim and meagre critic, as if they had been but the chapters of a mere treatise on astronomy—a thing which, of course, any ordinary man could write—mayhap even the critic himself. The "Astronomical Discourses", on the other hand, no one could have written save Chalmers. Nominally a series of sermons, they in reality represent, and in the present century form perhaps the only worthy representatives of, that school of philosophic poetry to which, in ancient literature, the work of Lucretius belonged, and of which, in the literature of our own country, the "Seasons" of Thomson, and Akenside's "Pleasures of the Imagination," furnish adequate examples. He would, I suspect, be no discriminating critic who would deal with the "Seasons" as if they formed merely the journal of a naturalist, or by the poem of Akenside as if it were simply a metaphysical treatise.

The autumn of this year brought me an unexpected but very welcome visitor, in my old Marcus' Cave friend Finlay; and when I visited all my former haunts, to take leave of them ere I quitted the place for the scene of my future labours, I had him to accompany me. Though for many years a planter in Jamaica, his affections were still warm, and his literary tastes unchanged. He was a writer, as of old, of sweet simple verses, and as sedulous a reader as ever; and, had time permitted, we found we could have kindled fires together in the caves, as we had done more than twenty years before, and have ranged the shores for shell-fish and crabs. He had had, however, in passing through life, his full share of its cares and sorrows. A young lady to whom he had been engaged in early youth had perished at sea, and he had remained single for her sake. He had to struggle, too, in his business relations, with the embarrassments incident to a sinking colony; and though a West Indian climate was beginning to tell on his constitution, his circumstances, though tolerably easy, were not such as to permit his permanent residence in Scotland. He returned in the following year to Jamaica; and I saw some time after, in a Kingston paper, an intimation of his election to the Colonial House of Representatives, and the outline of a well-toned sensible address to his constituents, in which he urged that the sole hope of the colony lay in the education and mental elevation of its negro population to the standard of the people at home. I have been informed that the latter part of his life was, like that of many of the Jamaica planters in their altered circumstances, pretty much a struggle; and his health at length breaking down, in a climate little favourable to Europeans, he died about three years ago— with the exception of my friend of the Doocot Cave, now Free Church minister of Nigg, the last of my Marcus' Cave companions. Their remains lie scattered over half the globe.

I closed my connection with the bank at the termination of its financial year; gave a few weeks very sedulously to geology, during which I was fortunate enough to find specimens on which Agassiz has founded two of his fossil species; got, at parting, an elegant breakfast service of plate from a kind and numerous circle of friends, of all shades of politics and both sides of the Church; and was entertained at a public dinner, at which I attempted a speech, that got on but indifferently, though it looked quite well enough in my friend Mr Carruthers' report, and which was, I suppose, in some sort apologized for by the fiddlers, who struck up at its close, "A man's a man for a' that." It was, I felt, not the least gratifying part of the entertainment, that old Uncle Sandy was present, and that his health was cordially drunk by the company in the recognised character of my best and earliest friend. And then, taking leave of my mother and uncle, of my respected minister, and my honoured superior in the bank, Mr Ross, I set out for Edinburgh, and in a few days after was seated at the editorial desk—a point at which, for the present, the story of my education must terminate. I wrote for my paper during the first twelvemonth a series of geological chapters, which were fortunate enough to attract the notice of the geologists of the British Association, assembled that year at Glasgow, and which, in the collected form, compose my little work on the Old Red Sandstone. The paper itself rose rapidly in circulation, till it ultimately attained to its place among what are known as our first-class Scottish newspapers; and of its subscribers, perhaps a more considerable proportion of the whole are men who have received a university education, than can be reckoned by any other Scotch journal of the same number of readers. And during the course of the first three years, my employers doubled my salary. I am sensible, however, that these are but small achievements. In looking back upon my youth, I see, methinks, a wild fruit tree, rich in leaf and blossom; and it is mortifying enough to mark how very few blossoms have set, and how diminutive and imperfectly formed the fruit is into which even the productive few have been developed. A right use of the opportunities of instruction afforded me in early youth would have made me a scholar ere my twenty-fifth year, and have saved to me at least ten of the best years of life —years which were spent in obscure and humble occupations. But while my story must serve to show the evils which result from truant carelessness in boyhood, and that what was sport to the young lad may assume the form of serious misfortune to the man, it may also serve to show, that much may be done by after diligence to retrieve an early error of this kind—that life itself is a school, and Nature always a fresh study—and that the man who keeps his eyes and his mind open will always find fitting, though, it may be, hard schoolmasters, to speed him on in his lifelong education.